THE NEW SYSTEMATICS

EDITED BY

JULIAN HUXLEY

OXFORD UNIVERSITY PRESS

OXFORD UNIVERSITY PRESS
AMEN HOUSE, E. C. 4
London Edinburgh Glasgow New York
Toronto Melbourne Cápetown Bombay
Calcutta Madras
HUMPHREY MILFORD
PUBLISHER TO THE UNIVERSITY

FIRST EDITION 1940

Reprinted photographically in Great Britain in 1941,
1915 by LOWE & BRYDONE, PRINTERS, LTD., LONDON,
from sheets of the first edition

FOREWORD

THIS volume is sponsored by the Association for the Study of Systematics in relation to General Biology. The Association's Committee on Publications felt that some statement of the problems which beset the systematist on the one hand, and on the other the general biologist interested in the rich harvest of systematic data, would be of value and might aid the evolution of taxonomy which is now in progress. British authors have in the main been approached; this, it was felt, would facilitate co-ordination of the different articles. Here and there, however, where this country could not supply a suitable authority on some subject, authors of other nationalities have been invited to write a chapter.

The Committee is fully conscious of the somewhat presumptuous sound of the title it chose for the book. It would have been more accurate to call it *Modern Problems in Systematics*, or *Towards the New Systematics*. For the new systematics is not yet in being: before it is born, the mass of new facts and ideas which the last two or three decades have hurled at us must be digested, correlated, and synthesized. However, it was felt that a good title goes a long way, and should be its own excuse. At least it will draw attention to the fact that a 'new systematics', or at least a new attack on systematic problems, is an important need for biology.

I am well aware of my anomalous position in this enterprise—a non-systematist as editor of a book on systematics. All that I can plead is first that it was only at the express request of the Committee that I undertook the work; and secondly that I am deeply interested in the subject, and that an outsider may sometimes be able to hold the balance between divergent views more easily than one who is himself in the thick of the fray.

I have to thank various members of the Association, whose constant help and advice have considerably lightened my editorial task.

J. H.

CONTENTS

viii   **CONTENTS**

INTRODUCTORY

TOWARDS THE NEW SYSTEMATICS

By J. S. HUXLEY

The New Approach to Systematics

TO hope for the new systematics is to imply no disrespect for the old. It has been largely the rapid progress made by classical taxonomy itself that has necessitated the introduction of new methods of analysis, new approaches to synthesis. The very success of taxonomists in collecting material from all parts of an organism's range, in separating and naming groups, and of drawing ever finer distinctions has thrown up a number of general questions which must be answered if taxonomy is to find principles which will enable it to cope with the vast burden of its own data, and to advance to the status of a fully fledged sub-science in which observation and theory, deduction and experiment, all contribute to progress.[1]

Meanwhile the rise of other branches of biology has been exerting a profound effect on the outlook of taxonomists. Genetics, cytology, ecology, selection theory, field natural history, palaeontology, even developmental physiology—they all are proving to be relevant to this or that aspect of taxonomy. In addition the intensive pursuit of practical aims by such branches of science as mycology and medical and agricultural entomology has revealed taxonomic facts which inevitably were hidden from the museum workers by whom classical taxonomy was built up.

The result has been that the outlook for taxonomy has altogether changed. Even a quarter of a century ago it was possible to think of systematics as a specialized, rather narrow branch of biology, on the whole empirical and lacking in unifying principles, indispensable as a basis for all biological workers, but without much general interest or application to other branches of their science. To-day, on the other hand, systematics has become one of the focal points of biology. Here we can check

---

[1] See Turrill (1938) for a discussion of the future of taxonomy from a botanical standpoint.

B

our theories concerning selection and gene-spread against concrete instances, find material for innumerable experiments, build up new inductions: the world is our laboratory, evolution itself our guinea-pig.

In this domain of small-scale evolution, or micro-evolution as Timofeeff-Ressovsky (1939)[1] calls it, systematics poses the majority of the problems. And it is certainly destined to play a prominent part in their solution, even if it must call in the aid of other branches of biology to do so, and if it must make considerable adjustments in the process.

Fundamentally, the problem of systematics, regarded as a branch of general biology, is that of detecting evolution at work. Specifically, its chief question is how discontinuity of groups is introduced into the biological continuum. There is another important question often neglected by taxonomy, but inevitably confronting the systematic worker in palaeontology—namely, how continuous change is effected in a group even when new discontinuity is not arising.

Broadly speaking, the answer to both questions combined is a threefold one. Small-scale evolution, including both mere change and discontinuous differentiation, depends first on selection, secondly on isolation, and thirdly on intrinsic factors, including hybridization. None of these is more important than the others: all are equally necessary.

There still is a widespread reluctance, especially among some of the younger experimental biologists, to recognize the prevalence of adaptation and the power of selection. This is doubtless in large part a natural reaction against the facile arm-chair reasoning of a certain school of earlier evolutionists. It is also, however, due to a failure to come to grips with the general principles of the subject. Men like Fisher (1930), Haldane (1932), and Sewall Wright (1931, 1939) have recently done great service by pointing out that selection may take many different forms and achieve very different results according to the conditions under which it operates. Selection in small isolated groups will be different in its results from selection in large continuous groups. Sexual (inter-male), intra-familial, and other forms of intra-specific selection will produce special results, which may be useless or even deleterious to the species

[1] The majority of references under date 1939 are to other chapters in this volume.

as a whole. Huxley (1938), Worthington (1939), Elton (1930), and others have raised the question of the varying intensity of selection in different conditions. Isolation may reduce the intensity of selection; ecological peculiarities of the environment may increase it; selection will act quite differently at different points in the cycle of abundance of species with periodic fluctuations in numbers. Experimental work has shown how quite small changes in population-density or in environmental conditions may reverse selective balance (see examples in Haldane, 1932). Fisher (1930 b, and see Ford, 1939) has shown how the study of dimorphism makes it possible to evaluate the strength of selection actually operating in nature. The use of mathematical methods has given a firm deductive basis for selection theory (though it is clear that the postulates of this new branch of biology are as yet over-simplified, and we must be careful of generalizing its deductions prematurely).

One of the most striking features of recent evolutionary theory has been the swing-back to a selectionist interpretation, after the anti-selectionist interlude initiated by Bateson, de Vries, and Morgan. It should be further emphasized that this has been most marked among those who have been in closest genetic contact with the problem—men like Muller, Sturtevant, Timofeeff-Ressovsky, or Ford, as well as among the mathematical group of deductive selectionists. We may safely prophesy that the anti-selectionist views of those not so directly concerned with the machinery of evolution, notably among the experimental biologists and the palaeontologists, will be dissipated as the implications of modern genetics become more widely realized.[1]

In passing, there is also to be noted a rather similar reluctance among general biologists to accept the fact that species have a greater reality in nature, or, if we dislike the philosophical implications of this term, a greater degree of objectivity, than higher taxonomic categories. According to such objectors, all taxonomic units are equally artificial and are merely useful fictions. Here again, it must be said that those who have actually come into close contact with the problems, not only the museum

---

[1] It is worth pointing out that, as Timofeeff-Ressovsky (1939) stresses, palaeontology, owing to the nature of its data, can only give us information concerning the course of evolution, and not concerning its mechanism.

workers but also the experimental taxonomists who are applying genetic and ecological analysis to the study of groups in
nature, come to quite other conclusions. By them, species are
seen in the majority of cases to be definable as distinct self-perpetuating units with an objective existence in nature, and therefore on a different theoretical footing from genera or families
or other higher categories, which are not definable in this concrete way (see Diver, 1939; Timofeeff-Ressovsky, 1939).

The Origins of Species

In any case, the problem of species, in its dual aspect of their
differentiation and their maintenance as separate groups, is
at the heart of both the theory and the practice of taxonomy.

Let us look at some of the aspects of the species problem and
of taxonomy in its function of representing evolution in action.
In the first place, it is clear that isolation is the essential factor
in bringing about taxonomic divergence. Whereas, however,
classical systematics had concentrated mainly on geographical
isolation and its results, it is now clear that ecological, physiological, and genetic isolation can be equally effective.

We know relatively few cases of ecological species *in statu
nascendi*. However, Dice (1931) records two subspecies of Peromyscus in the same geographical area, but separated by their
ecological preferences for woodland and open country respectively; Worthington (1939) cites cases among fish; Dementiev
(1938) gives examples of bird subspecies separated by altitude;
and Salisbury (1939) adduces instances of ecological species as
well as subspecies in plants.

In any case, that such isolation must have played a part in
evolution is shown by crucial cases where a type is, in one region
only, represented by a number of different species (or even
genera) filling different ecological niches. Thus the extraordinary array of Gammarids found in Lake Baikal can only
have evolved by ecological isolation, *in situ*. (Korotneff, 1905–
12).

Physiological isolation is seen most diagrammatically in the
physiological races of various parasites and phytophagous insects,
which, as we learn from Thorpe (1939), may remain markedly
distinct and yet show a bare minimum of morphological difference. In some cases they will refuse to cross, or will yield

infertile offspring, so that they deserve the title of species. If the systematists have been reluctant to raise them to this status, this is partly for reasons of convenience, since it is discouraging to have morphologically indistinguishable or barely distinguishable types assignable to different species; but largely because in the past morphological difference has in general been decisive or at least of major importance as a criterion of species-difference. This, however, has been a historical accident, due to the fact that systematists naturally began by paying attention to groups which could be readily distinguished morphologically without the laborious business of experiment, breeding tests, or cytological examination (just as geneticists began by focusing attention on clear-cut character-differences, and only later discovered the existence and the importance of small mutations and alleles with slight effects).

That this is so is further shown by the study of genetic isolation and its effects, of which Muller (1939) gives examples. *Drosophila simulans* is a good species: but it was only discovered as a result of its breeding behaviour, and it is doubtful if it would ever have been recognized by the museum taxonomist. The two 'races' of *Drosophila pseudo-obscura* are intersterile: they thus have a good claim to be raised to the status of species.[1]

Perhaps the greatest interest of the genetic approach has been the proof that many kinds of genetic isolation exist; and that these may produce biological discontinuities of all degrees of completeness, just as with geographical isolation. Darlington (1939) and Muller (1939), following out the suggestions of earlier workers, set forth numerous examples of how inversion and translocation may isolate small portions of the hereditary outfit from the rest, thus providing a basis for the selective divergence of the two types, the original and the inverted (or translocated). When, as is frequently the case, the sectional chromosome-mutation also shows reduced interfertility with

---

[1] It is worth pointing out here that, though cases such as I have been mentioning are now being brought to light, in which morphological differences between true species are negligible, yet where such morphological differences exist, their use by taxonomists, even when the characters involved are apparently trivial, seems almost always to be sound (Diver, 1939). Where experimental analysis has been undertaken it has, in the great majority of cases, confirmed the validity of the morphological criterion (especially when combined with the geographical one) as a firm basis for minor taxonomy.

the type, the door is opened to an important method of speciation, undreamt of by earlier generations of biologists. On the
other hand, Muller (1939) gives reason for thinking that such
chromosomal changes are less important than they were supposed to be in the first flush of their discovery, and in any case,
in animals at least, less important than gene-mutations for
bringing about discontinuity between species.

One particular type of genetic isolation is unusually striking,
since it produces new good species at a bound. I refer, of course,
to allotetraploidy following on a species-cross. The other forms
of genetic isolation, like geographical and physiological isolation, are gradual in their effects on divergence.

With regard to geographical isolation, this may be of every
degree of completeness. A river may effectively isolate the
populations on its two banks: the Chindwin river in Burma is
a good example (Thomas and Wroughton, 1916). But the effect
will clearly depend on the size of the river. Equally clearly it
will depend on the biological properties of the populations
concerned: large birds will be less likely to be isolated in this
way than say smallish mammals (though very small mammals
may again be more easily transported, in boats or on logs).

Geographical isolation may be effected in many ways. For
land forms, the isolating barrier may be sea, as for island forms
or the faunas of different continents; lakes, as in the African
pluvial period (Schwarz, 1929); rivers, as instanced above;
deserts; mountain ranges. For aquatic forms the barrier will in
general be land. Land-locked lakes are here the equivalent of
islands, and barriers like that formed by the isthmus of Panama
in the Miocene, the equivalent of an ocean between two continental land faunas.

Mere distance may promote geographical differentiation;
usually, however, as we shall see later (p. 29), it will by itself
produce no more than partial biological discontinuities. When
full speciation has occurred, it is probable that complete isolation has always been at work, and that when the two species are
now found together, this has been effected by later range-
changes.

Before dealing with geographical isolation and its results
more in detail, we may refer to the valuable light which has
been shed upon micro-evolution in nature by the intensive

analysis of cultivated plants. History here repeats itself. What Darwin's study of Animals of the Variation and Plants under Domestication accomplished in laying the foundation for evolutionary views in general and selection-theory in particular is now being accomplished for the detailed processes of evolution by the experimental, genetic, and cytological analysis of garden and crop varieties of plants. Crane (1939) points out that these have had four distinct (though often overlapping) modes of origin:

A. Within a single species:
    (1) By selection of gene-mutations.
    (2) By simple autopolyploidy.
B. As a result of species-crosses:
    (3) By allopolyploidy.
    (4) By selection from among the recombinations resulting from a species-cross without allopolyploidy or other chromosomal aberrations.

Two of these are selective processes, one relatively slow, the other relatively fast, while in the other two the new types are produced *per saltum*. (1), (2), and (3) have their direct counterparts in nature, while (4) also seems to occur as a result of selection among hybrid swarms. Isolation cannot easily be studied in cultivated plants (except by deliberate long-range experimentation) since it is provided artificially, ready-made, and complete, by human agency; but it is interesting to note how completely the other mechanisms of micro-evolution are paralleled.

Vavilov (1939) in his chapter approaches the matter from a somewhat different angle. He points out in the first place that the intensive studies of cultivated plants and their relatives undertaken in recent years, especially under his own auspices, have not only thrown new light on the groups concerned and brought to light many new wild species, but sometimes made it necessary to postulate new large Linnean species (as in wheat) to account for the cultivated varieties found.

Such studies have also led to the establishment of important new generalizations concerning primary and secondary centres of differentiation, confirmed selectionist views as to the close adaptations arising (in cultivated varieties) to local conditions of soil and climate, and extended our ideas as to the prevalence of parallel variation. Thus here the practical problems of plant-breeding have led to an enlargement of our views on evolution and systematics.

The Effects of Geographical Isolation

We may now revert to the study of isolation. Since geographical isolation has been more thoroughly studied than other kinds, we may here refer to one or two general points concerning its effects. In the first place, where isolation is relatively or quite complete and the isolated population small, the Sewall Wright effect (1931, 1939) will produce a certain degree of random, non-adaptive change. Additional random difference will often be introduced by initial sampling effects, the colonizers of new areas not being average representatives of the species. The total amount of diversification will thus be greater for a species broken up into numerous isolated population than if spread over a continuous area. Worthington (1939) draws attention to a case of this type, described by Miller in 1909, namely the marked differentiation of *Tragulus* into seven subspecies on the Rhio Linga archipelago, as against the absence of subspeciation on the 150 times larger but no less diversified area of Sumatra and Borneo. An equally striking case, in which initial sampling effects acting on a highly variable population seem to have played the major part, is the celebrated example of the snail genus *Partula* on the Society Islands (Crampton, 1916). Here the snails live in the bottoms of steep-sided mountain valleys, and can only cross the bare knife-edge ridges between the valleys rarely and with difficulty. Consequently almost every valley has its own distinctive type or range of types.

We may also note that even fully marine animals may show geographical subspeciation, while sedentary estuarine forms may be markedly differentiated according to their distance from the open sea (e.g. *Zoarces*; Schmidt, 1918). Here, as in many other cases, geographical grades into ecological differentiation.

The Tahiti snails also illustrate the effect of intrinsic biological factors on differentiation: the birds and most plants of Tahiti show no such diversification valley by valley. Rensch (1933) has used existing data to bring out this effect in a numerical way. Taking all the birds in Hartert's monumental avifauna of the palearctic region, and tabulating them according to size and habit, he reaches the following result:

	Per cent. of species which are monotypic	Number of subspecies per polytypic species
Large birds	54·5	1·6
Small birds, migratory . .	39·9	3·2
Small birds, non-migratory .	29·6	7·2

Somewhat similar results apply to bats as against non-flying mammals (data used by Rensch from Miller, 1912, 1924).

Our geographical and geological knowledge often allows us to state with some confidence the time at which isolation has been effected, and this in turn may provide evidence as to the rate of evolution. The first generalization thus reached is that the rate of evolution may differ markedly in different forms. The barrier between the Pacific and Atlantic fish faunas constituted by Central America came into being probably in the early Miocene, some 25 million years ago. Some of the fish on the two sides of the isthmus show only subspecific divergence, but the majority have differentiated into pairs of well-marked species (Regan, 1906–8).

The islands off the north of Scotland, including the Faeroes and Iceland, cannot have received their present fauna before the end of the Ice Age, some 15,000 years ago; yet numerous well-marked subspecies have evolved on them. Sometimes the rate of change may be extremely rapid. Jameson (1898) records an island population of house-mice which showed distinct mean adaptive colour-differences from those of the adjacent mainland (though with a much wider range of variability) within 100–120 years.

Kramer and Mertens (1938) have made an intensive study of the lizard fauna of a region of the Adriatic coast and its islands. Here the land has undergone submergence, so that the depth of water between an island and the mainland gives a measure of the length of time for which it has been isolated. The conclusions they reach are: first, that isolation *per se* promotes divergence; the mainland lizards show no subspeciation, while much subspeciation, often with no apparent correlation with environmental conditions, has occurred on the islands. Secondly, the degree of differentiation is correlated with the length of time during which isolation has been operative. But thirdly, it is also correlated, inversely, with the area of the island—in other words, the Sewall Wright effect of random change in small populations is operative. Neither of these correlations is complete, showing that, as is to be expected, chance plays a part, doubtless in regard to the occurrence of suitable mutations; but on the whole, the smallest islands which have been longest isolated show the greatest divergence of their lizard population from the mainland type.

Worthington (1939), after pointing out the rapidity of change in certain African freshwater fish since the middle or end of the pluvial period, draws attention to the fact that for all cold-blooded forms, evolution must proceed more rapidly in the warmer regions of the earth.

It only remains to point out that while subspecies may legitimately be called species in the making, this will only apply to a limited number. Many doubtless remain as subspecies. When not isolated, they may remain permanently as partially discontinuous groups (see below, p. 30). When isolated, they may fail to differentiate further, may show changes parallel to those of the mainland form, or may become extinct. But many undoubtedly diverge until they acquire the rank of full species.

Rensch has proposed the term *Rassenkreis* for a group of subspecies which replace each other geographically. In order to conform to accepted usage and to terms of international applicability, it is perhaps better to call such groups polytypic species, in contradistinction to the monotypic species (for which Rensch reserves the term *Art*), which show no subspeciation.

For groups consisting of forms which replace each other geographically and may be regarded as all descended from a common stock, but which are undeniably all of specific rank, Rensch has proposed the term *Artenkreis*. For this, we may substitute the term 'species-group', reserving the term 'supraspecies' for groups of an intermediate nature, in which it is dubious whether the constituent groups are best called subspecies or species, or in which some have remained obviously subspecies while others have differentiated to a stage at which they are, or appear to be, full species.

Practical convenience as well as the lack of clear alternatives dictates that we should stick to the classical terminology of genera and species and their subdivisions as general basis for minor systematics, even if there are certain groups such as the blackberries or the willows to which they will not apply, and even if in many cases we decide to coin special subsidiary terminologies for special purposes (see Turrill, 1938). However, we must remember that species and other taxonomic categories may be of very different type and significance in different groups; and also that there is no single criterion of species. Morphological difference; failure to interbreed; infertility of offspring; ecological, geographical, or genetical distinctness— all those must be taken into account, but none of them singly is decisive. Failure to interbreed or to produce fertile offspring is the nearest approach to a positive criterion. It is, however, meaningless in apogamous forms, and as a negative criterion it is not applicable, many obviously distinct species, especially of plants, yielding fertile offspring, often with free Mendelian recombination on crossing. A combination of criteria is needed, together with some sort of flair. With the aid of these, it is remarkable how the variety of organic life falls apart into biologically discontinuous groups. In the great majority of cases species can be readily delimited, and appear as natural entities, not merely convenient fictions of the human intellect. Whenever intensive analysis has been applied, it on the whole confirms the judgements of classical taxonomy.

It is clear that a great deal of the diversity produced by isolation is in a sense irrelevant to the main trends of evolution. The production of a crop of subspecies on a number of islands, or even of a new family on an archipelago; the specialization of a group of insects, so that each type becomes adapted to a particular food-plant, or the evolution of subspecies or species of snails in relation to different ecological habitals; the breaking up of a species of *Drosophila* into two intersterile groups, or the formation of a new plant type by autopolyploidy or by hybridization followed by allopolyploidy or apogamy—these have relatively little to do with long-range evolutionary changes, whether towards specialization, towards progress, or towards extinction. These main trends depend upon the basic biological facts of self-reproduction, mutation, and selection, perhaps with a little orthogenesis added—for although true orthogenesis, in the sense of directed mutation overriding selection, is incompatible with neo-Mendelism, as R. A. Fisher has pointed out, yet at least it is difficult, on the basis of our present knowledge, to account for certain apparently deleterious trends heralding extinction in Ammonites and other types without appealing to some degree of internally-directed evolution (Haldane, 1932). But the types of change we have been enumerating in the previous section depend essentially upon accidents which are unrelated to these major forces— accidents of geography or of ecology, or accidents to the hereditary machinery. Thus taxonomy in the ordinary sense, though it may show us evolution at work, for the most part is concerned with the less important aspects of evolution. In order that he may not lose sight of these, it is essential that the taxonomist should keep before him the facts and ideas of comparative anatomy, of embryology, and especially of palaeontology.

Different Modes of Speciation and their Consequences

Reverting to the mechanism of evolution, it is clear that isolation (apart from the accidental fixing of new combinations of genes already present) is powerless to effect differentiation without mutation, and, in most cases, without selection.

Selection will be everywhere at work, shaping the material provided for it by mutation and recombination (Timofeeff-Ressovsky, 1939). This material may differ both in quantity and quality from organism to organism, and the use that selection can make of it will vary with features of the reproductive mechanism. Even where gene-mutation is the sole or main source of heritable variation, its rate may differ in different types. We know comparatively little as yet on this subject, but it is quite possible that in certain species the rate may vary cyclically to quite a considerable extent, and also as between different species. The rate of mutation may then be a limiting factor of evolutionary change, condemning some forms to stability, stagnation, or eventually extinction. In general, however, mutation-rates in the comparatively few types investigated are all of the same general order of magnitude.

The rate will also vary with temperature, chiefly because of the effect of temperature in increasing the number of generations in all except warm-blooded organisms. This, as Worthington (1939) points out, will imply a more rapid rate of evolution in the tropics than in colder regions.

The size of the group, in number of individuals, will also be important. Sewall Wright (1939) points out that large inter-breeding groups separated by partial discontinuities into sub-groups (subspecies) provide the greatest reservoir of evolutionary potentiality, in regard to numbers of mutations and of course to recombinations as well. Isolated and numerically small groups, on the other hand, exhibit various anomalous features. Any mutations which are selectively more or less neutral can spread through them with great rapidity, and useless or even slightly unfavourable recombinations have an opportunity, denied to them in large groups, of becoming the predominant type owing to mere chance. This accidental non-selective change may with time reach any extent.

In general, as has long been clear, isolation is correlated with differentiation. A knowledge of the genetic machinery involved has shown, as Wright (1939) and Muller (1939) stress, that, granted a normal rate of mutation and degree of variance, it actually *promotes* differentiation, a fact which could not have been prophesied on any *a priori* grounds.

Sectional chromosomal mutation is another source of change. This, according to Muller (1939), is in most cases less important than gene-mutation; but where prevalent it encourages partial genetic isolation of blocks of genes, giving them the opportunity of evolving into harmoniously balanced partial genetic systems.

Genome-mutation involving the ploidy may be of great importance. It is rare in higher animals, however, owing to their X-Y sex-determining mechanism, and also to the rarity of self-fertilization among them. But, as Darlington (1939) points out, it has been of great evolutionary and taxonomic importance in many plants. Both allo- and auto-polyploidy have played their parts. Of recent years numerous examples have been established of a process which would have profoundly shocked most earlier taxonomists, namely the formation of good new species *per saltum*, by species-hybridization followed by chromosome-doubling.

Hogben (1939) draws attention to another interesting fact concerning the chromosomes, namely that while some groups, such as the urodeles, the gymnosperms, and most families of

Diptera, are extremely constant in their chromosome number and arrangement, others, such as the Drosophilidae among Diptera, are highly variable in this respect. In passing, it may be mentioned that a good example of the same phenomenon in plants is afforded by the genus *Carex*, with over 1,000 distinct species, and great diversity in chromosomal number and arrangement. He is tempted to draw the conclusion that such chromosome-variability is correlated with high genetic variability in general, and therefore with evolutionary plasticity and actual rate of change.

Hogben also, after drawing an important distinction between the extrinsic and intrinsic factors promoting, modifying, or limiting evolutionary change, gives some interesting examples of differences in intrinsic factors and their effects. The chances of chromosome inversions or translocations becoming established in a homozygous condition will be much greater where periods of agamic reproduction occur, as in gall-wasps, and their establishment in this condition will provide a measure of genetic isolation between different sections of the species, which will then promote more rapid speciation. Inbreeding in isolated populations, and widespread or compulsory self-fertilization will obviously have important and on the whole similar effects, though the latter will act much more rapidly.

Again, the type of the distinctive characters evolved in related species whose ranges overlap will vary with the reproductive mechanisms employed. A common and simple method of providing a barrier to intercrossing is to have non-overlapping breeding seasons. In entomophilous plants this result may be achieved by adaptation to distinct insect-pollinators, which will usually involve distinctive floral coloration or scent. In higher animals, sexual recognition-characters are likely to be involved. Where, as in birds, the territorial system and the desirability of avoiding combat with rivals is superadded, such distinctive characters will be at a still higher premium. Thus the much greater diversification of the males than of the females in so many groups of birds, whether in colour, pattern, or song, is a special evolutionary consequence of their particular type of reproduction. Mode of life will exert still further subdivision of this effect. Thus in birds which can be readily seen at a distance, visual distinctiveness will be encouraged (e.g. stonechat and whinchat), while in those which frequent dense cover of any sort, the distinctive characters will tend to be auditory (e.g. songs of chiff-chaff and willow warbler) (see Huxley, 1938).

This leads on to a further interesting conclusion. Where forms differentiate in complete isolation, no selective value will attach to characters tending to hinder intercrossing. If in point of fact such barriers do arise, they will be merely consequential upon the general genetic divergence. But where their geographical ranges overlap and they come into contact with each other, such barriers will, speaking in teleological shorthand, be encouraged by selection, so as to prevent the biological wastes consequent upon intercrossing. These biological wastes will be of two main types—those concerned with the poorer adaptation of the results of a cross, and those concerned with their lower fertility or constitutional viability. Thus in groups where barriers to interbreeding depend on characters such as pattern, readily available to the taxonomist, the degree of visible differentiation between closely-related forms will tend to be greater among overlapping than among non-overlapping species.

The biological environment may also have an effect upon the degree of differentiation achieved, as Worthington (1939) points out. Where predator-pressure is less intense, selection is not so rigorous, and a greater degree of radiation is found in a given group. Presumably this principle can be still further generalized so as to include selection exerted through competition as well as through predation. In extreme cases the radiation may apparently become in large measure non-adaptive, and the variation excessive, as seems to have been the case with the ground-finches (*Geospizidae*) of the Galapagos (Swarth, 1934), with results that are biologically very interesting, but deplorable to tidy-minded taxonomists.

Timofeeff-Ressovsky (1939) draws the important distinction between micro-evolution and macro-evolution, the latter consisting of the large-scale trends which by reason of their biological magnitude and their extent in time cannot be made amenable to experimental analysis, the former of the small-scale changes with which experiment, in many cases at least, is able to come to grips. Evolution is going on here and now under our noses. Sometimes it consists in changes of range, sometimes in hybridization consequent upon such range-changes, sometimes in selective alteration consequent upon change in environmental conditions, or in non-selective alteration due to mutation or re-combination in isolated groups. Related groups, whether species, subspecies, or merely regional sections of a specific or subspecific population, are found to differ. The existing differences clearly represent a cross-section through the process of evolutionary change.

Our knowledge of their habitats and of the environmental changes that have occurred in the 15,000 years or so since the last glacial period enable us to draw certain general conclusions as to the correlation of micro-evolutionary with environmental change. Cytological, ecological, and physiological investigation may enable us to push the analysis still farther, and genetical and physiological experiment may complete it so that we have a clear picture of how small-scale evolution actually operates.

Classical taxonomy has provided a firm foundation for micro-evolutionary studies wherever it has been pushed below the specific level and has taken cognizance of geographical subspecies, ecotypes, cytological variants, and so forth. Population studies, drawing on all relevant biological disciplines, are now needed to complete the edifice.

Taxonomic Theory and Practice

This brings us to the more strictly taxonomic aspects of our subject. These, as already noted, largely centre around the concept of species. After a period in which many general biologists reacted against what they considered the dogmatic or arbitrary employment of the term, often going so far as to deny any greater objective validity to the species-category than to categories of higher order such as genus, family, or class, there seems now to be a general recognition among those who have concerned themselves with the taxonomic facts, whether from the standpoint of the museum systematist, the ecologist and physiologist, or the geneticist, that species are in some valid sense natural groups. Dobzhansky (1937) has drawn attention to the fact that they are the most stable units in taxonomic practice, as compared either with infra-specific categories such as variety or subspecies, or supra-specific ones such as genus, subfamily, or family. When, however, he tries to define the species-level as that stage in taxonomic differentiation after which fertile interbreeding is impossible, he goes far beyond the facts. It is certainly right to attempt a dynamic, in place of a static, definition by thinking of subspecies and species as stages in a process of evolutionary diversification: but it is impossible to insist on infertility as the sole criterion of this stage. Many groups, especially among plants, universally recognized as species by taxonomists, are capable of fertile intercrossing, and in many others we find sterility between mere strains of obvious species. Thus either Dobzhansky's definition is untrue, or, if true, taxonomic practice must be so re-cast as to rob the term species of its previous meaning.

Muller (1939), like Dobzhansky, stresses the unique character of the species (in sexually reproducing organisms), regarded as a stage in group-differentiation.

Within well-knit species, at any rate, an interchange of new mutations will eventually take place, which will result in selection favouring harmonious combinations and eliminating such mutants as are mutually disharmonious and lower viability or fertility on crossing. But when two good species are involved, this adjustment of mutations cannot occur, and the two groups must automatically and progressively diverge both in visible appearance and physiological compatibility. 'There is no other stage of divergence', Muller writes, 'which, like speciation, involves the entrance of a qualitatively different factor, having a direct influence upon the process of divergence itself.' As he is careful to point out, this statement needs a little qualification, notably in regard to different types of subspecific isolation; but it is broadly and substantially true, and of great importance.

Rensch (1933, 1934) has recently discussed at length the concept of natural and artificial taxonomic units, and in the present volume Gilmour (1939) attacks the problem from a more philosophical point of view.

It would appear that species may be properly regarded as natural units, in that they are groups which (a) have a geographical distribution-area; (b) are self-perpetuating as groups; (c) are morphologically (or in rare cases only physiologically) distinguishable from other related groups; and (d) normally do not interbreed with related groups, in most cases showing partial or total infertility on crossing with them (though neither the lack of crossing or of fertility is universal). In regard to (a), (b), and (c), species resemble subspecies, except that the group-individuality of subspecies may be slightly less on account of gene-flow from neighbouring subspecies; but they differ from them as regards (d). They differ also from Rensch's *Artenkreise* (supra-species) as regards (b).

Species may differ markedly both in regard to their size and their degree of difference from related species. This is due to the facts (1) that size of population at any moment is a variable quite uncorrelated with degree (though not with rate) of evolutionary differentiation, and (2) that evolutionary differentiation can arise in several quite distinct ways. It must also be recognized that the species-concept, however loosely framed, will not apply to all groups. It is inapplicable, for instance, to purely apogamous forms, and to groups with markedly reticulate descent (Turrill, 1936, 1938). Here other terminologies must be devised.

Difficulties of another sort arise when we consider species in the time-dimension as palaeontologists perforce must do. These are thoroughly discussed in the present volume by Arkell and Moy-Thomas (1939). The chief taxonomic problem raised by paleontology, however, is that of the genus rather than of the species. When, as often happens, more or less parallel evolution occurs in undoubtedly distinct lineages, should generic names be given to the horizontal stages—in which case the genus is not monophyletic—or to the lineages—when extreme practical inconvenience will result? This appears to provide an opportunity for subsidiary taxonomic terminology. We should, in such cases, continue to use generic names for horizontal stages, frankly recognizing the absence of all phylogenetic basis to them, but for purposes of further biological analysis should give other names, not to be part of the formal nomenclature, to the lineages as well.

The time-dimension also enters into ontogeny. De Beer (1939), in his chapter in this book, gives numerous interesting examples of the need for taking ontogenetic time into account—in this case by thinking in the dynamic terms of processes and their rates, instead of in the static ones of characters and their measurable differences—if ontogeny is to take its due place as an aid to taxonomy.

Reverting to the question of phylogeny, we find that Calman

(1939) and Sprague (1939) in their chapters in this book, writing from the point of view of the professional systematist dealing with existing forms, proclaim the phylogenetic basis of natural classification. Sprague considers that a natural classification is necessarily phylogenetic, while Calman states that 'the great majority of systematic zoologists still believe, with Darwin, that "the Natural System is founded on descent with modification" '. Gilmour (1939), however, starting from a general philosophical standpoint, reaches the conclusion that a natural classification is merely one based on the maximum number of relevant attributes, and points out numerous cases in which it will not square with phylogeny, together with others where the phylogenetic interpretation is at best dubious. This was also the standpoint of T. H. Huxley, quoted by Calman (1939), who, however, agreed that the results of taxonomy 'readily adapt themselves' to a phylogenetic interpretation.

It would seem that these two views, apparently so dissimilar, can be reconciled. In the first place we may admit that taxonomic classification actually arrives at its results by evaluating resemblance and difference in the largest possible number of characters, and not by means of phylogeny, which can only be subsequently deduced, and is only measurable, if at all, in terms of the characters used in taxonomic evaluation. In the second place, however, it is certainly true that it can have what I may call a phylogenetic background, in that it can most often be interpreted phylogenetically ; and, further, that such a phylogenetic interpretation may sometimes suggest an improved taxonomy. But it must, finally, also be admitted that there are certain cases where taxonomy does *not* have a phylogenetic basis. We have just mentioned those paleontological cases where to introduce a phylogenetic classification would rob the taxonomic system of practical convenience. Then in lower taxonomic categories such as species and subspecies, parallel mutation may make a phylogenetic interpretation an almost impossible ideal, of little practical help or even theoretical significance. Even in larger groups, such as those of higher plants, phylogeny may be almost hopelessly obscured by parallel or convergent evolution, added to the lack of fossil material in early evolutionary stages. And further, taxonomy can only represent phylogeny adequately when differentiation is divergent. Wherever it is reticulate, whether by allotetraploidy in plants, by hybridization followed by apogamy, or by the meeting and crossing of subspecies originally differentiated in isolation from each other, as seems not infrequent in animals, our existing taxonomic methods inevitably fail to denote phylogeny.

A natural system is then one which enables us to make the maximum number of prophecies and deductions. It also in the majority of cases follows the lines of phylogenetic descent, though these are not always discernible; but there are a certain number of exceptions where a phylogenetic interpretation is meaningless, and others where taxonomy and phylogeny cannot be made to square with each other.

Meanwhile Smart (1939), in another chapter, draws attention to a purely practical problem, namely the overburdening of the entomological systematist by the mere number of kinds of insects, of which approximately 10,000 new species are still being described every year. In view of this fact, it is clear that the main task here is the provision of additional workers, and that any discussion of the refinements of taxonomy adumbrated by Turrill and others in this volume must wait for many years before being adequately discussed or put into practice in this, by far the largest group of organisms.

Returning to the species problem we find, of course, what is to be expected on any evolutionary theory, namely a number of exceptions and of border-line cases. There are border-line cases such as *Silene maritima* and *S. cucubalus* (references in Turrill, 1939), which behave as 'good species' over most of their range, but cross freely to produce a hybrid intermediate population in some smallish areas. From this it is but a step to other cases where extension of range has brought good species into contact, and where in the region of contact one species has ceased to exist as such, but exists only in the form of various gene-combinations in the hybrid progeny, while the other in some parts of the region remains reasonably pure, as in the two species of *Centaurea* in Britain. In some cases, indeed, the hybrid product may be regarded as a new polymorphic species (Turrill, 1939). From such cases, it is only a step to the hybrid swarms described by Allan (1939) among New Zealand plants, by Turrill (1929) in Balkan plants, and by Sweadner (1937) in one region of North America in moths.

In regard to hybrid swarms the species-concept breaks down. So it does in various plants which exhibit reticulate instead of divergent descent (Turrill, 1936), such as *Rubus* or *Salix*. So it does in man, who exhibits a peculiar form of reticulate descent consequent upon extreme migration. So it does in entirely apomictic forms. In this last case species may be simulated, in that we may find assemblages of types showing a certain limited degree of variability, more or less sharply marked off from each other: but this presumably depends on differential advantage enjoyed by certain main types. Divergence accompanied by differential multiplication has produced pseudo-species.

Other border-line cases exist where a chain of forms, each at least subspecifically nameable, but all connected by inter-grading zones of interbreeding, is continued so far that its extremes would immediately be styled distinct species if the intermediates did not exist, and would doubtless behave as such if tested genetically. Carabid beetles provide an excellent example of this. Sometimes nature has actually performed the crucial experiment and range-extensions have brought the end-forms together in nature, when they do behave as 'good species' in refusing to cross. Examples are known from birds (*Parus*: Rensch, 1933) and butterflies (*Junonia*: Forbes, 1928).

In still other cases range-changes have brought forms together which, though differentiated far enough to look like good species on first inspection, are still capable of free inter-crossing. Such cases grade down from those where hybrid swarms exist in large regions, as mentioned above, through those like the flickers (*Colaptes*) of North America (see Bateson, 1913), where interbreeding is confined to a long and moderately broad belt, to others like the crows (*Corvus*) of Europe and Asia, where the zone of interbreeding is very long and quite narrow (Meise, 1928). It is probable on general grounds that the breadth of the belt is in inverse proportion to the physio-logical-genetic divergence between the two forms, narrowness implying reduced fertility and/or viability of the mixed popula-tion. If so, we can define the various stages of speciation in such cases.

Every stage of speciation can also be found among forms which enjoy complete geographical isolation, as land forms on islands or aquatic forms in lakes. When differentiation has been but slight, we must obviously assign only subspecific rank to the isolated form: when it has been really marked, we have every right to assign specific rank. But there must remain an array of cases in which it will always remain a matter of taste and convenience whether to call them species or subspecies: and this again is to be expected on the postulate of evolution.

Fischer-Piette (1935) has recently described another type of border-line case in a section of the limpets (*Patella*). He finds that in certain areas the group is biologically a single inter-breeding one, whereas in other areas it is divided up into discontinuous non-interbreeding sub-groups. It is one species in one place, several species in another.

But the important fact remains that in the majority (and apparently the great majority) of cases there are no such intrinsic difficulties. Either a group exhibits no or negligible inter-breeding with related groups and is sharply marked off as an entity, or else it exhibits geographical replacement in regard to other very closely similar groups, and if its range abuts on that of any of these, the two interbreed freely. In other words, most groups are either definitely species or definitely subspecies. To the question of subspecies we shall return. Meanwhile Diver (1939) has emphasized how the ecologist, coming to his task in a critical spirit and animated by quite other aims than that of conveniently naming and pigeon-holing types, finds in the very great majority of cases that even surprisingly similar forms to which the taxonomist has assigned specific rank are in point of fact truly distinct as natural assemblages.

In other words, the nature of organisms and the conditions under which they exist are such that on the basic continuity of life is normally superposed a discontinuity of the distinct groups or populations for which the term species still remains the most suitable. True, that these discontinuities are not permanent: traced back into the past, they always converge; traced forward, any single group may again undergo fission and diverge. But the time during which the discontinuities remain complete is far greater than that during which they are partial; and accordingly the number of 'good species' is far greater than that of difficult border-line cases.

As Turrill (1938) has emphasized, the fact that groups may

or might show fertile intercrossing when artificially or in other ways secondarily brought together does not disprove their right to be styled species. It is the actual facts of nature, not its every potentiality, with which the systematist has to deal. The fact of their separate existence *qua* self-perpetuating interbreeding groups, together with *either* a reduction or absence of fertility in intercrossing, *or* a certain empirically evaluated degree of morphological or physiological characters, should be taken as the basis of decision.

The mechanisms by which specific discontinuity may be produced are very various. The main types of speciation, as already mentioned, are those due to geographical isolation, to physiological isolation, to ecological isolation, and to genetic isolation. Each main method of isolation will tend to produce different types of speciation. We have already noted that sex-recognitional specific characters are more likely to be fostered by ecological than by geographical isolation. Physiological isolation, as in phytophagous insects and parasites, is likely to promote a relatively large degree of physiological difference accompanied by relatively feeble difference in the morphological and visual characters usually relied on by the museum taxonomist (see Thorpe, 1939). Genetic isolation originating in the partial isolation produced by sectional chromosome-rearrangements, as investigated in *Drosophila* for instance, is likely to leave the two groups similar both in physiological and morphological characters for a much longer time, since they will still both be inhabiting a similar environment, and differentiation will be in the main merely an accidental consequence of their isolation. Speciation due to genetical isolation arising *per saltum*, as happens by the alteration of the ploidy, will often be accompanied by changes consequent on the changed genome-constitution, but again is unlikely to be accompanied by nearly so much character-differentiation as geographical or ecological speciation.

Certain practical difficulties remain. Are the 'physiological races' of insects, &c., to be given specific rank when they are partially or wholly intersterile but yet show very little morphological distinction? The museum systematist naturally shrinks from this course, as it puts the main onus of assigning specimens to their correct category, on ecological or experimental methods for which there is neither space nor time in the routine work of a museum.

What again is to be done with forms like the two 'races' of *Drosophila pseudo-obscura*, discussed by Muller (1939)? These are only slightly less differentiated morphologically than are *D. simulans* and *D. melanogaster*, yet while the latter have passed into current scientific literature as species, the former continue to be described as 'races' A and B, in terminology not subject to the international rules of nomenclature, although the biological distinctness of the two groups, owing to their intersterility, is of the same order of magnitude.

What again is to be done with the new type of group-unit recently discovered in mosquitoes (Hackett, 1937; Swellengrebel and de Buck, 1938), and usually still called by the non-committal term 'race', which shows extremely slight morphological distinction from other such units, does not exhibit geographical replacement, but is markedly distinct in ecological preference and in behaviour? (see Thorpe, 1939). They do not fit into the category of subspecies since they also show marked sterility barriers, even in artificial conditions. Yet they can sometimes not be distinguished morphologically except by egg-characters.

What, finally, is to be done with triploid and other polyploid types which are macroscopically almost or quite indistinguishable from the diploid, especially if they coexist with it over all or some of its range?

In triploid and other anisoploid plant types the problem is linked with that of apomixis, since they cannot maintain themselves by sexual reproduction. In general, polyploid varieties will perhaps be best dealt with by rule-of-thumb methods. When the morphological distinction is slight, and there is no marked difference in geographical range or ecological habitat, the sum of the forms will best be called the species, and the separate forms simply designated by the addition of the ploidy in brackets—$(3n)$, $(6n)$, or whatever it may be. But when there are recognizable macroscopic differentiae, and in addition the range and/or the habitat is distinct, as in the $2n$ or $4n$ forms of *Biscutella laevigata* (Manton, 1937), it would seem advisable to give specific names to the two forms. Borderline cases will, of course, exist, and in relatively large numbers: it would seem desirable to treat them conservatively and not to assign specific rank to them.

The same sort of method cannot so readily be applied to the other kinds of difficult case. Polyploidy can be indicated by a special convention, showing that we are dealing with a group-category which is *sui generis*. But the only nomenclatorial possibility with the others, if they are not assigned specific rank, is to introduce trinomials and call them subspecies: and this gives a false picture, since they are not on the same level of biological discontinuity as the classical subspecies of higher animals with their geographical replacement but capacity for fertile intercrossing. There is also a very real practical point. These forms are often of great practical importance, either as pests or counter-pests of crops or as vectors of human or animal disease, and the different groups differ precisely in regard to characters of economic or medical importance. It is therefore eminently desirable that they shall be kept apart in collections, and also that their difference shall be emphasized in that fundamental aid to distinctiveness, their name. The agricultural or medical entomologist or mycologist may with some justice feel that museums, like the Sabbath, were made for man and not vice versa. In any case, taxonomy aims not only at practical utility but at reflecting the facts of natural grouping, and these are natural groups demanding to be fitted into our taxonomic scheme: shall we insist on using that scheme as a Procrustean bed, or shall we modify it to suit the newly discovered facts of nature?

It is hard to see what precise form the answer should take. It may be tentatively suggested that when the groups do exhibit marked biological discontinuity they shall be accorded specific names, but that when their morphological distinctions are so slight that it is impossible to assign specimens to one group or another without such ecological or experimental data as are not normally forthcoming, a collective name for the whole group should also be retained as a binomial when needed. This collective group should be regarded as of supra-specific rank, on the analogy with Rensch's geographical supra-species, and perhaps distinguished by some abbreviation in brackets: (sp.l.), denoting *species lata*, might be better than (s.sp.) for *supra-species*, since this latter might be taken for an abbreviation for subspecies. The supraspecific name should, of course, never be the same as any of the specific names applied to the separate groups.

Some procedure of this type should also presumably be employed for cases such as those mentioned by Arkell and Moy-Thomas (1939), where fossil brachiopods indistinguishable externally have been placed in different species or even genera on the grounds of internal anatomy. However just the biological grounds for this may be, the determination can only be made with the aid of petrographic sections, and the geologist can still make profitable use of the collective group for stratigraphical purposes. In such cases presumably a collective generic as well as a collective specific name is needed.

The Problem of Subspecies

We now come to the subspecific category. There do exist systematists who refuse to see in taxonomy any function but the purely pragmatic one of pigeon-holing and ready identification, and who therefore wish to abolish trinomialism root and branch. If, they would say, a group which has been assigned subspecific rank is sufficiently distinct to merit a separate name, it should be called a species, and assigned its place with other binomials. Even from the practical point of view, however, this has grave disadvantages. It is almost always an advantage to have an easy way of showing relationship between the closely allied groups usually called subspecies; and this is automatically done by means of trinomials, while no such clue is given by a large number of separate binomials.

In passing, very similar considerations apply to genera and subgenera. The all-too-common practice of splitting genera until many are monotypic defeats one of the main aims of Linnaeus's great invention. The subgenus, or perhaps preferably some other infra-generic category such as *section*, is the proper category for such detailed classification. We thus should normally recognize as our ideal a quadrinomial system. Genus and species will be the categories normally used by the general zoologist, while section and subspecies are needed for full accuracy and are essential for certain purposes. Subgenera or sections indicate affinities of species within genera, while subspecies define geographical or physiological differentiations, and are all-important for certain studies, including genetical and ecological analysis as well as zoogeographical and faunistic problems. As already noted, for certain special cases a further supra-specific category would appear to be desirable.

Returning to the subspecies problem, there is an even more important argument against the view that trinomial subspecific naming should not be employed. That is that taxonomy has an intellectual as well as a practical aim, namely to give a picture of the facts of nature. And it is a fact of nature that groups do exist which are differentiated from each other, but between which the biological discontinuity is of a qualitatively different nature from that between obvious species.

Subspecies, like species, may be of various types. Geographical subspecies are the best analysed: to them we shall return. Then there are excellent examples, as Thorpe (1939) shows, of physiological subspecies, among parasitic and phytophagous forms, where the differentiation and the reproductive discontinuity are both incipient. There are also ecological subspecies adapted to different habitats. These are best known among higher plants. It is possible that many so-called ecological subspecies among animals will turn out to be better subsumed under the head of clines (see below, p. 31). We may presume that genetical subspecies will be revealed by further analysis. Forms like *Drosophila simulans* or the 'races' of *D. pseudo-obscura* must have passed through a subspecific phase of genetic discontinuity.

There are authors who, like Rensch (1933, 1934), are so much impressed with geographical subspecies that they would not only assign an overwhelming role in speciation to geographical as opposed to other forms of isolation, but would reserve the category of subspecies entirely for geographical groups. This is assuredly both illogical and impracticable. If physiological, ecological, and genetical isolation can promote the formation of full species, such species must *in statu nascendi* pass through a phase of less than specific distinction; and if we call them all species once they are formed, we must call them all subspecies during the transitional period in their formation. And even Rensch himself is driven to use trinomials for certain physiological races. He raises the theoretical objection that both geographical and some other type of differentiation might operate simultaneously within a species, so that, for instance, different physiological races might also show geographical subspeciation. If such cases turn up, taxonomists will presumably have to reconcile themselves to conferring two subspecific names, with '(phys.)' and '(geogr.)', or '(ecol.)' and '(geogr.)' added after them in brackets.

The numerous plant species enumerated by Salisbury (1939) in his chapter in this book, which can only have differentiated in relation to ecological differences, constitute strong presumptive evidence for the existence of ecological subspecies as stages in ecological speciation. He, like Turrill (1939), also draws attention to the great differences in plasticity seen in different plant species; while Diver (1939 b) mentions some similar examples in snails. This is another proof of the wide range of phenomena included under the species-concept. Some species achieve variability by means of high environmental plasticity; others by means of high genetic variability and the selection of different genetic types by different habitats; and still others are highly specialized, with restricted variability, both genetic and modificational.

The existence of high genetic variability coupled with restriction of certain types to certain habitats, examples of which are also given by Salisbury, constitutes another possible means by which real ecological subspeciation and speciation may later occur.

Subspeciation, however, can undoubtedly best be studied in its geographical aspect. And here certain important general conclusions emerge. In the first place, there exist two rather distinct kinds of geographical subspecies. There are those which are completely or almost completely isolated, like island populations among land forms, or lake populations among freshwater forms. Even when the isolation is not absolute—for instance in avian subspecies on islands close to the mainland—any intercrossing which occurs will only reduce the difference between the groups or at most render one margin of each a little more like the adjacent margin of the other, but can never give rise to a continuous zone of intergradation.

Such continuous zones of intergradation, however, are characteristic of many subspecies of continental areas. Wherever a large species exhibits biological continuity over a considerable continental area and is also divisible into subspecies, it is found that these do often present the phenomenon of intergradation at the margins of their areas. Thus, whereas in isolated sub-species we see incomplete differentiation, in non-isolated sub-species we are in addition confronted with what may be called partial biological discontinuity.

Numerous examples of subspeciation of this latter type are known from mammals and birds, e.g. *Peromyscus* (Osgood, 1909; Sumner, 1932), squirrels (Ingoldby, 1927), wrens (Chapman and Griscom, 1924), shrikes (Miller, 1931), warblers (Ticehurst, 1938), &c.

There seems to be a tendency for the 'joints' between the subspecies to recur in the same or neighbouring localities in many species (many cases in Grinnell, 1928; see also Reinig, 1938), but this is by no means universal. Its absence is doubtless often due to range-changes subsequent to differentiation (Sumner, 1932).

A question immediately poses itself: how is the stepped con-dition maintained, by which large areas of comparative uni-formity of characters are separated by narrow belts of rapid character-change, in spite of interbreeding continuity in the population as a whole?

In some cases their condition is doubtless due to the narrow zones being areas with low population-density, so that gene-flow is restricted across them: here the partial biological dis-continuity reflects a partial geographical discontinuity. In other cases again, the narrow zones of intermediacy mark zones of abrupt environmental change, for instance from plain to mountain, from forest to open country, &c. But numerous cases remain where no such simple environmental correlation appears to exist. In them, why does the flow of genes not gradually break down the abrupt step and flatten and broaden it out so as to convert it and the two adjacent subspecies into a simple gradation of characters running across the whole area?[1]

One possible answer exists, based on the principle of harmoni-ously stabilized gene-complexes (Fisher, 1930 *a* and *b*; Timo-

[1] Diver (1939) draws attention to the important fact that the spread of genes may be effected in two rather distinct ways—either by actual migration of indi-viduals, or by the handing on of genes by reproduction, with negligible movement of the individuals in any generation. These he distinguishes as zygotic and gametic migration respectively.

feeff-Ressovsky, 1939). If different regions of a continental area differ considerably in environmental properties, selection will operate to adapt the population to the different conditions. Where population is densest or selection most intense, such selection will tend to build up a gene-complex which not only includes what we may call the extrinsic adaptations or character-adaptations which adapt the organism to the prevailing conditions, but also the intrinsic adaptations or gene-adaptations which render the resultant gene-complex more harmonious and viable (see Timofeeff-Ressovsky, 1939). These latter will consist of modifiers to the genes which are concerned with the character-adaptations, and the action of these modifiers will be to enhance the phenotypic expression of the main genes and at the same time to confer the maximum viability on the gene-complex containing them.

If the area inhabited by the population is sufficient, and the 'biological tension' between different regions is great enough, two or more of such centres of adaptation will arise at different points of it. But by virtue of the viability conferred by the harmonious stabilizations of the resultant gene-complexes, these will be enabled to extend over greater areas than those to which they are in the first instance adapted. And where such stabilized gene-complexes come into contact, the resultant intermediates will *ex hypothesi* be less well adapted and, what is more important, less viable. In consequence, the zones of interbreeding and intergradation will remain narrow. Some confirmation of this is given by the fact that characters may exhibit greater variability in the zones of intergradation than in the subspecific areas, as has been established for colour-characters in *Peromyscus* (see Huxley, 1939, on Sumner's case). This is consonant with the view that the subspecific characters have been harmonized by adjuvant modifiers, though other interpretations are of course possible. Definite proof of the view here put forward is so far only forthcoming for one example, namely that of the geographical colour-patterns of certain lady-beetles (Timofeeff-Ressovsky, 1932). Genetic analysis has here shown that the various patterns depend on numerous genes, and that the gene-combinations responsible for the patterns characteristic of large areas are constitutionally more viable than most of the other combinations. This automatically restricts the area of the less viable combinations to narrow zones of intergradation, where they are constantly produced by intercrossing, but as constantly destroyed and prevented from spreading by their negative selective value. Reduction of fertility in the intermediates would, of course, have a similar effect.

In any case, this interpretation is adequate, while so far as I am aware no other suggestion has been advanced which will explain the facts. If this view is confirmed, we have the interesting and novel principle that in certain ecological conditions, selection acting upon the Mendelian mechanism of heredity will introduce partial biological discontinuities into a geographically continuous population. It is difficult to see how comparable partial discontinuities could arise except on a geographical basis, since the selective prevention of gene-flow between geographically separated areas seems to be the only way in which narrow zones of intergradation could be maintained.

In passing, this same general principle will presumably account for the narrow zones of interbreeding between subspecies which have met after differentiating in separate areas (p. 21). The width of the zone will presumably be inversely proportional to the biological difference between the two forms, since the greater the reduction of viability or fertility of the hybrids, the narrower the zone will remain.

Character-gradients (clines) and Taxonomy

Consideration of the regional adaptation of a continuous population brings us to a further point, namely the existence of character-gradients within groups. For these I have proposed the word 'cline' (Huxley, 1939) as a convenient technical term. So far clines have been comparatively little investigated, but a cursory inspection of taxonomic literature indicates that in one form or another they are widespread.

Clines may be of several distinct types. The first distinction is between group (inter-group) clines, where the characters measured concern only the mean value for a group (subspecies or species), and internal (intra-group) clines, where the mean value of the character changes gradually through a continuous population. So far, inter-group clines have been much more thoroughly studied. Many of the results are embodied in the various geographical rules, of Allen, Gloger, Bergmann, &c.,

which have recently been well summarized by Rensch (1936). In all these cases, the gradient in characters is correlated with some gradient in climatic conditions (temperature, humidity, &c.), and the most obvious prima facie explanation is a selective one. Sometimes, as in the increase of size with latitude in small warm-blooded animals, the character measured has a direct selective value, whereas in other cases, as in the alteration of pigmentation in relation to temperature and humidity, it must be a 'correlated character' in Darwin's sense, the selection operating on some physiological property with which the visible character is correlated. Evidence for such indirect selection is provided by the observation of Yocum and Huestis (1928) that heavily pigmented subspecies of *Peromyscus* from humid regions are characterized by a thyroid structure which is quite different from that of lightly pigmented subspecies from more arid regions. The existence of invisible physiological regional adaptations to climate has been proved by Timofeeff-Ressovsky (1935) in his interesting study of the temperature-adaptations of *Drosophila funebris* in different areas of Europe. Other colour-clines may be of direct selective value, namely those correlated with change in the colour of the background in cryptically coloured species (see, e.g. Dice and Blossom, 1937).

Reinig (1937) has advanced the view that the inter-group clines subsumed under the various geographical rules are due to the gene-elimination, both selective and random, which has occurred during the spread of groups from the areas they occupied during the glacial (pluvial) period. Rensch (1938) has shown that this is untenable as the sole or main cause of the phenomenon, but in view of Vavilov's work on the genetical peculiarities of the marginal zones of species, it may hold for certain cases.

Internal clines have as yet been little investigated, owing to the laborious nature of the work involved; but their study is likely to yield results of great importance. Sometimes, as in the British and Irish subspecies of Cole Tit (*Parus ater*), specimens characteristic of one subspecies are found within the range of a second, and when this is so, they occur solely or in greater abundance in the region geographically nearest to the range of the first (see Huxley, 1939). This may be due to either of two causes, singly or in combination: either there is a limited gene-flow by zygote migration (in this case across the Irish Channel), or else the conditions which impose the inter-group cline also operate within the separate groups.

Christy's analysis (1929) of the races of African buffaloes shows that colour and size are here directly correlated with environment, forms from dense equatorial forests being small and reddish, while those from arid plains are large and black throughout life. Forms from intermediate areas show intermediate characters. Some darken from red to brown; others from red to black, the black only appearing in a few aged individuals; others from red to black before maturity; while in the extreme forest types the red phase is passed through before birth.[1] Furthermore, in many areas there exists a gradual change of type as the character of the country changes, and a full analysis will doubtless show that extensive clines alternate with well-delimited regional forms meriting the name of subspecies.

Sumner's beautifully analysed case of two subspecies of *Peromyscus* (1929; see also Huxley, 1939) seems best explicable on the basis of the interaction of (1) a not very intense selection for cryptic coloration; (2) gene-flow between two adaptively different groups; (3) restriction of gene-flow with consequent formation of a narrow zone of intergradation and high variability due to the two groups possessing gene-complexes stabilized in different ways. The result is a stepped cline for increased pigmentation from the coast inland, eventually flattening out altogether.

On the basis of this case and of general considerations, we may expect that when inter-group clines exist between subspecies separated by narrow intergrading zones, there will be gentle internal clines within the separate subspecies for the same characters that show the inter-subspecific cline. The cline within the species as a whole will then take the form of a stepped ramp, long gentle inclinations alternating with short steep ones. The steep clines across the intergrading zones will have a purely genetic cause, while the general inter-group cline and the internal clines will be adaptive.

---

[1] In passing it may be noted that this case, as well as that of the cole tits and doubtless many others, appear to have as their genetic basis rate-genes controlling the speed of some developmental process, as analysed in detail for the eye-colour of *Gammarus* by Ford and Huxley (1929).

In other cases it is possible that the biological tension has not been sufficient to produce partial discontinuities, when we may expect a single uniform geographical cline, or at least one without abrupt changes of slope, throughout the population. Such a cline appears to exist as regards the tongue-length and other characters of hive-bees (Alpatov, 1929). It is likely that certain cases falling under the geographical rules will on closer investigation turn out to be of this nature. Mr. Moreau of Amani, Tanganyika, informs me that he believes numerous East African birds will prove to show clines of this sort.

Continuous clines of more or less uniform slope, but extending over much shorter distances than do those of a geographical nature correlated with broad climatic changes, are those of an ecological nature, correlated with changes in the habitat. These are best known from plants, although Rensch (1933) believes that much of the ecological variation of land molluscs may be capable of being subsumed under this head.

In the few cases which have been subjected to full analysis, like the sea-plantain, *Plantago maritima*, the cline appears to come into being by a selective action of the graded environment upon a large assemblage of genotypes, the proportions of the different forms gradually changing from place to place (Gregor, 1938). Ecoclines of this particular sort could thus arise only in species with a large internal variability; but others where a single main type is modified by selection in accordance with the habitat conditions are theoretically possible.

A special type of cline is that in the proportions of two (or a few) sharply contrasting types. A recently analysed case is that of the common guillemot (*Uria aalge*) in western Europe (Southern, 1939). Here the spectacled or bridled variety exists as a rare 'aberration' in the southern part of the range. The proportion of bridled forms then rises steadily, with occasional sharp rises after geographical discontinuities, until at the northern margin of the species the bridled type outnumbers the 'normal'. This case is complicated by the existence of two named subspecies.

Similar dimorph-ratio clines are known as regards the colour phases of the Arctic and the North American red fox (*Alopex lagopus* and *Vulpes fulva*), and also in the lady-beetle, *Adalia bipunctata* (Timofeeff-Ressovsky, 1939). In the last-named animal certainly, and probably in the others also, the proportions of the different types varies cyclically with the periodic fluctuation in numbers of the species. This would confirm Fisher's view (1930 *b*) of the selective balance involved in all cases of the coexistence of a few sharply distinct types within a species, and further analysis of such cases will throw much light on the mode by which selection acts.

Finally there are cases of dimorph-ratio clines for which the most natural explanation is the occurrence of a mutation and its subsequent spread owing to its conferring some selective advantage. Examples of these are the 'simplex' variation in the teeth of the field-vole *Microtus arvalis* (Zimmerman, 1935) and the black variety of the Tasmanian subspecies of the long-eared opossum, *Trichosurus vulpecula* (Pearson, 1938, and discussion in Huxley, 1939; see also Timofeeff-Ressovsky, 1939). In both these cases, the large numbers examined permit the plotting of contour lines showing the percentage distribution of the character, and examination of the way these 'phenocontours', as we may call them,[1] are distorted by geographical features provides strong evidence in favour of the theory of selective spread. Periodic re-examination of such cases should provide interesting data as to selection in nature.

One important fact remains to be noted, namely, that clines for different characters may be quite independent of each other. The clines for two characters may run parallel for some distance and then one may reverse its sign when the environment changes, the other not: this occurs in the honey-bee (Alpatov, 1929). Or different clines may run in different directions, as in shrikes (Miller, 1931), &c.

This fact alone makes it desirable to employ the cline concept as an auxiliary aid in taxonomic practice, additional to the classical method of specification by named areal groups. Further, it can be of use in summarizing regularities of variation in the subspecies of a polytypic species (or in the species of an *Artenkreis* or supra-species), which otherwise must be laboriously picked out from the subspecific descriptions. It further may assign a convenient place to groups whose differ-

---

[1] Diver (1939 *b*) has proposed the term *isomar* for such lines of equal phenotypic manifestation. In spite of the hybrid derivation of *phenocontour*, I prefer it as being more self-explanatory.

ences from other groups, though definite, are too slight for the bestowal of a separate subspecific name, as is the case with the wrens (Troglodytes) of Fair Isle (Witherby, 1938). Similarly, many subspecific names conferred on the basis of slight differences may appropriately drop into desuetude if the groups concerned fall into recognizable clines, as may well prove to be the case with the new 'subspecies' of blackbird and thrush (*Turdus merula* and *T. ericetorum*) and other birds recently described from the west of Scotland (Clancey, 1938).

Here some brief notes on terminology may not be out of place. In the first place, monotypic genera should be avoided where possible, as defeating the ends of binomial nomenclature. Where, as often occurs, genera require some subdivision, this should be effected by the erection of subgenera or preferably sections—a subsidiary form of nomenclature.

With regard to species, the principle of geographical replacement should, wherever possible, be adopted, thus reducing the number of species while increasing that of subspecies. Similar principles of ecological or genetic replacement should also be adopted as knowledge increases.

When distributional and morphological data make it certain that a group of distinct species (or forms on the border-line between subspecies and subspecies) have had a common origin, Rensch's term *Artenkreis* may be employed, or preferably *supraspecies*. Rensch's alternative term *genus geographicum* should be avoided, as in it *genus* is used in a different sense from the normal.

It is undesirable to separate monotypic from polytypic species (with one and more than one subspecies respectively), as Rensch originally proposed under the different terms of *Art* (species) and *Formenkreis*; we must frankly recognize that *species* is a wide term, embracing many distinct kinds of natural groups. Rensch himself has later withdrawn his suggestion.

The term subspecies should be reserved for natural groups of the same general nature as species, but exhibiting a lower degree of morphological differentiation and/or reproductive isolation. When subspecies are again divisible or when large numbers of single isolated populations show appreciable differentiation (as occurs in *Zoarces*, Schmidt, 1917; and in certain grasshoppers, Uvarov, *in verbis*), the term 'microsubspecies' (microgeographical races, Dobzhansky, 1937) may be used as a subsidiary term, but the names of such micro-races, even if they are named at all, should not be incorporated into the nomenclature.

In addition to the differentiation of natural groups, i.e. processes of the same type as those involved in speciation, organic diversity may be manifested by the occurrence of differentiation within groups, the differences usually depending on one or a few mutant genes with marked effects. Such diversity may either manifest itself in the form of sporadic individuals or small groups of individuals (as in albino plants or animals) or in that of two or more well-marked contrasted types or 'phases', all regularly present in appreciable numbers. The latter condition is that of polymorphism, as defined by Ford (1939) in his chapter in this book, and is maintained by balanced selection. The former is maintained by mutation-pressure, sometimes combined with the Sewall Wright effect of isolation. For such variation, the terms *form* or, in certain cases, *aberration* or *phase*, should be applied. The name should not be incorporated into the nomenclature subject to the international rules.

The term *variety* should be dropped, as having been employed in so many senses. If a general term is wanted for any form differing from the mean of the group, some neutral word such as *paramorph* may be employed. In general, as Rensch has stressed, it is highly desirable to retain a certain number of wholly neutral and general terms, with no theoretical or technical connotations, such as *group, population*, &c.

In some cases the cline concept may be actually incorporated in the nomenclature—e.g. when a complete gradation exists between two well-marked subspecies. This is the case in the European nuthatch *Sitta europaea*, between the white-breasted eastern *S. e. europaea* and the chestnut-breasted western *S. e. caesia*. Løppenthin (1932), in describing the gradation, assigns three subspecific names to arbitrary stages in it. This, however, appears illogical and confusing, since the essence of a subspecies should be that it is a form with definable geographical range and distinctive characters. It would be preferable, after describing the two subspecies, to add a description of the cline *S. e. cl. europaea-caesia* (*cl.* being an abbreviation for *cline*), with

notes as to its area, &c. Stages in the cline could then be delimited by some arbitrary descriptions, not incorporated into
the nomenclature, such as roman numerals or capital letters.

When a cline exists, but the end-terms are not subspecies in
the sense of being reasonably constant over a considerable area,
it might be specified solely by a hyphenated trinomial.

Thus Thomas & Wroughton (1916) describe no fewer than
seven subspecies of *Callosciurus sladeni* from collecting stations
along 250 miles of the east bank of the Chindwin river. Inspection of their paper indicates that the three southern 'subspecies'
represent a N.-S. cline from dark grey to rufous, while the
four northern ones are undoubtedly much better described as
a N.-S. cline in increasing pallor from brownish-grey to cream.
In this latter group, the two end-forms have been given the
subspecific names *shortridgei* and *harringtonii*. It would be preferable to describe the whole series as the cline *C. s. cl. shortridgei-
harringtonii*.

Finally, the description of internal clines, when such exist
within subspecies or monotypic species, will serve as a useful
corrective to the false sense of regional uniformity conferred by
a binomial or trinomial name, though here, as in the case of
external clines, between subspecific means, the term should
only be used in an auxiliary way, and not incorporated into the
nomenclature.

Conclusion

If practical suggestions are in order in a work of this kind,
the following, which arise directly out of the articles of other
contributors or have arisen in discussion, may be noted.

In the first place, an increase in the scientific staffs of the
world's great museums, especially in the entomological departments, is urgently needed if they are to escape from the burden
of routine description and naming and take full part in the
activities which may be described under the head of the New
Systematics. Secondly, better liaison must be established
between museum taxonomy and other branches of biology. In
part, the effective liaison may be secured by a more co-operative
spirit on the part of geneticists, ecologists, and others in university departments and research institutions. But in part it
should be secured by the provision of appropriate laboratories

and field stations, with adequate staff, attached to the museums themselves. An important beginning along these lines has been made in such institutions as the American Museum of Natural History or the Museum of Vertebrate Zoology of the University of California, with eminently satisfactory results. It is desirable that such facilities should be provided within the framework of museum organization in order that the ecological and genetical work should be carried out in a taxonomic atmosphere and with constant attention to the needs of taxonomy, and also in order that the classical taxonomists should be in immediate contact with other relevant aspects of biology.

Once adequate staff exists, much-needed refinements in taxonomic practice can be undertaken in all those groups which have already been comparatively well worked out. Richards (1938), in a valuable article, after drawing attention to the steady improvement that has taken place in the standard of taxonomic description, points out the extent to which taxonomy (and all the branches of biology dependent upon it) would benefit by adopting a few comparatively simple additions to its routine.

First and foremost comes the need for more measurement. Linear measurements of, say, half-a-dozen characters should be made on reasonably long series. The parts to be measured will, of course, differ from group to group. In presenting the data, the number of specimens measured, the mean value of the measurements, and their standard deviation, should always be stated. Allometric constants can often then be deduced, and these and simple ratios of proportion of parts will frequently prove useful.

In addition to linear measurements, those of qualitative characters will also be valuable, even if stated only on some arbitrary grading.

Richards points out that mean linear (and other) measurements appear to be just as diagnostic as the characters usually employed by taxonomists, while they enjoy the additional advantage of quantitative expression and direct comparability.

The use of correlation methods is also recommended, and will often permit important conclusions to be drawn.

The calculation of standard deviations gives a measure of the variability, which will not only be of great biological interest, but may suggest further lines of taxonomic analysis.

If such methods were adopted, he concludes that, in regard to the broad biological problems of micro-evolution, the taxonomic and biometric method of study will for many organisms prove at least as effective as the genetic. Genetical analysis, where practicable, is necessary as an intensive tool. But it is often not practicable, and accordingly extensive methods of study are just as important.

Adequate provision should also be made for research in what may be called Comparative Systematics, meaning thereby work which utilizes data already in existence, whether already published or in the form of specimens in the museum collections. Valuable results may be expected on various subjects of general biological interest, such as dimorphism and polymorphism and their zoological and geographical distribution, the different degrees of subspeciation and other obvious variation in different groups; inter-group clines; the applicability of Lameere's and Geoffrey Smith's rule concerning the influence of absolute size on the relative size of parts in related forms; and many other topics.

All large museums should have trained statisticians on their staff, partly in order to ensure the proper statistical treatment of taxonomic data (a feature often conspicuous by its absence in current practice), and partly in order to undertake special investigations on such problems as the greater variability of common species (abundant in individuals) than of rare ones (Fisher and Ford, 1928; Fisher, 1937), the comparative variability of different genera or families, &c.

Another urgent need is that for a priority list of problems for museum taxonomy. While in some groups, notably in insects, the main necessity for some considerable time to come will be the amassing and description of fresh general collections, in other groups, for instance birds, mammals, diurnal lepidoptera, or flowering plants, this may well involve waste of energy and time. In such groups it may be advisable to concentrate the limited resources available first upon special sub-groups, secondly upon special areas, and thirdly upon special problems. The special groups will be chosen for phylogenetic interest, for abnormal variability, for a profusion of 'difficult' species, or for other reasons. The special areas will be those where recent migration has intermingled differentiated faunas and floras with consequent overlap of related species, hybridization, or formation of relict groups, those where subspecific boundaries are especially frequent, where well-marked clines exist, and so on. The special problems will be best dealt with by *ad hoc* expeditions designed to study the ecology, physiology, or behaviour of taxonomically interesting groups *in situ*, to bring back material of such groups for further genetical and ecological analysis, and so on (see Vavilov, 1939).

Detailed genetic work will usually be best undertaken in universities or special institutes, though simple breeding tests may well be carried out in relation to museums.

Muller (1939) points out how, in the few cases where intensive genetic analysis is possible, this may be directed towards a better understanding of the process of taxonomic differentiation, especially in its early stages. For instance, the mutation-frequency in wild populations can be calculated from the number of naturally occurring sex-linked lethals; and once this is known, the degree of inbreeding can be determined by a further study of the frequency of autosomal lethals. By determining the geographical and local variation of these values, and also of naturally occurring chromosome-rearrangements and gene-mutations, a rational picture of the breeding structure, incipient divergence, and evolutionary potentialities of a population can be arrived at. Already such studies have indicated that, for instance, *Drosophila pseudo-obscura* is in all probability more prone to geographical differentiation than most other species of the genus.

Timofeeff-Ressovsky (1939) makes still wider suggestions for population study, and he and Muller agree in stressing the need for an internationally planned co-operative attack on these laborious problems.

Among other problems of a general nature which ought to be undertaken, preferably as part of the regular work of the great museums, we should especially mention the detailed mapping of the boundaries and range-changes of species and subspecies. Such work, if undertaken on the proper scale, would be the biological counterpart of the International Star Map in astronomy, and should have equally valuable consequences.

Of the special types of research which, though with taxonomic bearings, are perhaps best undertaken by workers in other institutions, population studies clearly take a foremost place. Such studies may aim merely at a more detailed description of populations, e.g. with regard to internal clines; or they may be concerned with the genetic detection of the amount of available variability, by discovering the number of mutant genes carried in the population; or they may undertake intensive ecological surveys of the whole fauna and flora of a limited area, like that of South Haven Peninsula (references in Diver, 1939); or they may apply genetic and ecological methods to the analysis of the peculiarities of a species or group of species, as in the work on *Peromyscus* by Sumner (1932) and Dice (1937) or that on the lady-beetles by Dobzhansky (1933) and Timofeeff-Ressovsky (1932, 1939), or they may seek to investigate the intensity of mortality or selection in nature (e.g. Dowdeswell, Fisher, and Ford, 1939 *b*), notably in relation to cycles of abundance (Ford and Ford, 1930).

It is safe to prophesy that such micro-evolutionary studies will become increasingly important in the near future. Besides this, the steady amassing of cytological, genetical, ecological, physiological, and behaviour data with an eye on their taxonomic bearings will clearly be needed.

As such work proceeds, the New Systematics will gradually come into being. It will in some ways doubtless help classical taxonomy in its practical pigeon-holing functions; it will give a much more detailed picture of the actual facts of the diversity of organic nature and its distribution in groups and in character-gradients over the globe; it will reveal many facts and principles of great importance to general biology; and through it taxonomy will become the field of major interest for all those concerned with the study of evolution at work.

REFERENCES

ALLAN, H. H. (1939). 'Natural Hybridization in relation to Taxonomy', in *The New Systematics*. Oxford.

ALPATOV, W. W. (1929). 'Biometrical Studies on Variation and Races in the Hive-bee, &c.', *Quart. Rev. Biol.* **4**, 1.

ARKELL, W. J., and MOY-THOMAS, J. A. (1939). 'Palaeontology and the Taxonomic Problem', in *The New Systematics*, Oxford.

BATESON, W. (1913). *Problems of Genetics*. Oxford.

DE BEER, G. R. (1939). 'Embryology and Taxonomy', in *The New Systematics*. Oxford.

CALMAN, W. T. (1939). 'A Museum Zoologist's view of Taxonomy', in *The New Systematics*. Oxford.

CHRISTY, G. (1929). 'The African Buffaloes.' *Proc. Zool. Soc.* (1929), 445.

CLANCEY, P. A. (1938). 'Some Remarks on western Scottish birds.' *Ibis* (14), **2**, 746.

CRAMPTON, H. E. (1916, 1932). *Studies on the Variation, Distribution, and Evolution of the Genus Partula, &c.*, Publ. Carnegie Inst. Wash. Nos. 228, 410.

CRANE, M. B. (1939). 'The Origin and Behaviour of Cultivated Plants', in *The New Systematics*. Oxford.

CHAPMAN, F. M., and GRISCOM, L. (1924). 'The House Wrens of the Genus Troglodytes.' *Bull. Amer. Mus. Nat. Hist.* **50**, 279.

DARLINGTON, C. D. (1939). 'Taxonomic Species and Genetic Systems', in *The New Systematics*. Oxford.

DEMENTIEV, G. P. (1938). 'Sur la distribution géographique de certains oiseaux, &c.' *Proc. 8th Int. Congr. Ornith.*, 243.

DICE, L. R. (1931). 'The Occurrence of two Subspecies of the Same Species in the Same Area.' *J. Mammal*, **12**, 210.

—— (1937). 'Variation in the Wood-mouse, &c.' *Occ. Papers Mus. Zool. Univ. Michigan*, No. 352, 1.

DICE, L. R., and BLOSSOM, P. M. (1937). *Studies of Mammalian Ecology, &c.*, Publ. Carnegie Inst. Wash. No. 485.

DIVER, C. (1939). 'The Problem of Closely-related Species living in the Same Area', in *The New Systematics*. Oxford.

—— (1939 *b*). 'Aspects of the Study of Variation in Snails.' *J. Conchyl.* **21**, 91.

DOBZHANSKY, T. (1933). 'Geographical Variation in Lady-beetles.' *Amer. Nat.* **67**, 97.

—— (1937). *Genetics and the Origin of Species*. New York.

DOWDESWELL, W. H., FISHER, R. A., & FORD, E. B. (1939 *b*). 'The Quantitative Study of Populations in the Lepidoptera (I)' *Proc. Roy. Soc.* (B), *127*, S. 57.

ELTON, C. S. (1930). *Ecology and Evolution*. Oxford.

FISCHER-PIETTE, E. (1935). 'Systématique et Biogéographie: les Patelles d'Europe et d'Afrique du Nord.' *J. Conchyl.* **69**, 5.

FISHER, R. A. (1930 *a*). *The Genetical Basis of Natural Selection*. Oxford.

—— (1930 *b*). 'The Evolution of Dominance in Certain Polymorphic Species. *Amer. Nat.* **64**, 385.

—— (1937). 'The Relation between Variability and Abundance, &c.' *Proc. Roy. Soc.* (B), **122**, 1.

—— and FORD, E. B. (1928). 'The Variability of Species in the Lepidoptera, &c.' *Trans. ent. Soc.* **86**, 367.

FORBES, W. T. M. (1928). 'Variation in Junonia lavinia, &c.' *Journ. N. Y. entom. Soc.* **36**, 306.

FORD, E. B. (1939). 'Polymorphism and Taxonomy', in *The New Systematics*.

—— and HUXLEY, J. S. (1929). 'Genetic Rate-factors in Gammarus.' *Arch. Entw. Mech.* **117**, 67.

FORD, H. D., and FORD, E. B. (1930). 'Fluctuation in Numbers and its Influence on Variation, &c.' *Trans. ent. Soc.* **78**, 345.

GILMOUR, J. (1939). 'Taxonomy and Philosophy', in *The New Systematics*.

GREGOR, J. W. (1938). 'Experimental Taxonomy, II.' *New Phytol.* **37**, 15.

GRINNELL, J. (1928). 'Distributional Summary of the Ornithology of Lower California.' *Univ. Calif. Publ. Zool.* **32**, 1.

HACKETT, L. W. (1937). *Malaria in Europe.* London.

HALDANE, J. B. S. (1932). *The Causes of Evolution.* London.

HOGBEN, L. T. (1939). 'Problems of the Origin of Species', in *The New Systematics.* Oxford.

HUXLEY, J. S. (1938). 'The Present Standing of the Theory of Sexual Selection', in *Evolution*, ed. G. R. de Beer. Oxford.

—— (1939). 'Clines: an Auxiliary Method in Taxonomy.' *Bijdr. Dierk*, **27**, 491.

INGOLDBY, C. M. (1927). 'Notes on the African Squirrels of the Genus Heliosciurus.' *Proc. zool. Soc.* (1927), 471.

JAMESON, H. L. (1898). 'On a Probable Case of Protective Colouration in the House Mouse', &c. *J. Linn. Soc.* (*Zool.*), **26**, 465.

KOROTNEFF, A. (1905–12). *Wissenschaftliche Ergebnisse einer zoologischen Expedition nach der Baikal—see*, &c. Kiev and Berlin.

KRAMER, G., and MERTENS, R. (1938). 'Rassenbildung bei westistrianischen Inseleidechsen', &c. *Arch. Naturgesch.* (N.F.), **7**, 189.

LØPPENTHIN, B. (1932). 'Die Farbenvariation der europäischen Baumkleiber', &c. *Vidensk. med. Dansk. naturh. For.* **94**, 147.

MANTON, I. (1937). 'The Problem of Biscutella laevigata, II.' *Ann. Bot.* (N.S.), **1**, 439.

MEISE, W. (1928). 'Die Verbreitung der Aaskrähe', &c. *J. F. Ornith.* **76**, 1.

MILLER, A. H. (1931). 'Systematic Revision and Natural History of the American Shrikes (Lanius).' *Univ. Cal. Publ. Zool.* **38**, 11.

MILLER, G. S. (1912). *Catalogue of the Mammals of Western Europe, &c.* London.

—— (1924). 'List of North American Mammals.' *Bull. U.S. Nat. Mus.* **128**, 1.

MULLER, H. J. (1939). 'The Bearing of the Drosophila Work on Systematics', in *The New Systematics.* Oxford.

OSGOOD, W. H. (1909). 'Revision of the Mice of the American Genus Peromyscus.' *U.S. Dept. Agric., N. Amer. Fauna*, **28**.

PEARSON, T. (1938). 'The Tasmanian Brush Opossum', &c. *Pap. Proc. Roy. Soc. Tasmania for 1937*, 21.

RAMSBOTTOM, J. (1939). 'Taxonomic Problems in Fungi', in *The New Systematics.* Oxford.

REGAN C. T. (1906–8). *Biologia Centrali-Americana: Pisces.*

REINIG, W. F. (1937). *Elimination und Selektion.* Jena.

—— (1938). *Die Holarktis.* Jena.

RENSCH, B. (1933). 'Zoologische Systematik und Artbildungsproblem.' *Verh. Deutsch. Zool. Ges.* (1933), 19.

—— (1934). *Kurze Anweisung für zoologisch-systematische Studien.* Leipzig.

—— (1936). 'Studien über klimatische Parallelität', &c. *Arch. Naturgesch.* N.F. **5**, 317.

—— (1938). 'Bestehen die Regeln klimatischer Parallelität bei der Merkmalsausprägung von homöothermen Tiere zu Recht?' *Arch. Naturgesch.* N.F. **7**, 364.

RICHARDS, O. W. (1938). 'The Formation of Species', &c., in *Evolution*, ed. G. R. de Beer, Oxford.

SALISBURY, E. S. (1939). 'Ecological Aspects of Plant Taxonomy', in *The New Systematics*. Oxford.

SCHMIDT, J. (1918). 'Racial Studies in Fishes, I.' *J. Genet.* **7**, 105.

SCHWARZ, E. (1929). 'On the Local Races and distribution of the Black and White Colobus Monkeys.' *Proc. Zool. Soc.* (1929), 585.

SMART, J. (1939). 'Entomological Systematics examined as a Practical Problem', in *The New Systematics*. Oxford.

SOUTHERN, H. N. (1939). 'The Status and Problem of the Bridled Guillemot.' *Proc. zool. Soc.* (A), **109**, 31.

SPRAGUE, T. A. (1939). 'Taxonomic Botany, with Special Reference to the Angiosperms', in *The New Systematics*. Oxford.

SUMNER, F. B. (1929). 'The Analysis of a Concrete Case of Intergradation between Two Subspecies, I and II.' *Proc. Nat. Ac. Sci.* **15**, 110, 481.

—— (1932). 'Genetical, Distributional and Evolutionary studies of the Subspecies of Deermice (Peromyscus).' *Bibliogr. Genet.* **9**, 1.

SWARTH, H. S. (1934). 'The Bird Fauna of the Galapagos Islands', &c. *Biol. Rev.* **9**, 213.

SWEADNER, W. R. (1937). 'Hybridization and the Phylogeny of the Genus Platysamia.' *Ann. Carneg. Mus.* **25**, 163.

SWELLENGREBEL, N. H., and DE BUCK, A. (1938). *Malaria in the Netherlands*. Amsterdam.

THOMAS, O., and WROUGHTON, R. C. (1916). 'Scientific Results of the Mammal Survey, XII.' *J. Bombay Nat. Hist. Soc.* **24**, 224.

THORPE, W. H. (1939). 'Ecology and the Future of Systematics', in *The New Systematics*. Oxford.

TICEHURST, C. B. (1938). *A Systematic Review of the Genus Phylloscopus*. Brit. Mus. (Nat. Hist.), London.

TIMOFEEFF-RESSOVSKY (1932). 'The Geno-geographical Work with Epilachna chrysomelina, &c.' *Proc. 6th Inter. Congr. Genet.* **2**, 230.

—— (1935). 'Ueber geographische Temperaturrassen bei Drosophila funebris.' *Arch. Naturgesche.* N.F. **4**, 245.

—— (1939). 'Mutation and Geographical Variation', in *The New Systematics*. Oxford.

TURRILL, W. B. (1929). *The Plant Life of the Balkan Peninsula*. Oxford.

—— (1936). 'Contacts between Plant Classification and Experimental Botany.' *Nature*, **137**, 563.

—— (1938). 'The Expansion of Taxonomy', &c. *Biol. Rev.* **13**, 342.

—— (1939). 'Experimental and Synthetic Plant Taxonomy', in *The New Systematics*. Oxford.

VAVILOV, N. I. (1939). 'The New Systematics of Cultivated Plants', in *The New Systematics*. Oxford.

WITHERBY, H. F. (ed.) (1938). *The Handbook of British Birds*. London.

WORTHINGTON, E. B. (1939). 'Geographical Differentiation in Freshwaters', &c., in *The New Systematics*. Oxford.

WRIGHT, SEWALL (1931). 'Evolution in Mendelian Populations', *Genetics*, **16**, 97.

WRIGHT, SEWALL (1939). 'The Statistical Consequences of Mendelian Heredity in Relation to Speciation', in *The New Systematics*. Oxford.

YOCUM, H. B., and HUESTIS, R. R. (1928). 'Histological Differences in the Thyroid Glands from Two Subspecies of Peromyscus.' *Anat. Rec.* **39**, 57.

ZIMMERMAN, K. (1935). 'Zur Rassenanalyse der mitteleuropäischen Feldmäuse.' *Arch. Naturgesch.* (N.F.), **4**, 258.

EXPERIMENTAL AND SYNTHETIC PLANT TAXONOMY

By W. B. TURRILL

BY far the greater part of taxonomy is based on morphology. While for reasons which in the broad sense can be termed historical it could scarcely be otherwise, it is also a matter of general convenience that determinations should be as easily and quickly made as possible. On the whole, taxonomists have every reason to be proud of the work they have accomplished since the time of Linnaeus by the use of descriptive and comparative morphological methods. There is no doubt that the hierarchical classification of plants into varieties, species, genera, families, and larger groups has produced a system without which many of the modern developments in ecology, cytology, genetics, histology, and even physiology would have been impossible. Classification is a *sine qua non* of any biological research, and there has been no system of classification proposed that could replace the system[1] conveniently known as alpha or orthodox taxonomy, though the desirability of subsidiary classifications for special purposes is not questioned. On the other hand, no taxonomist would say that the existing system, or any large part of it, is complete or perfect. Further, it is becoming more and more obvious that recent discoveries in cytology, ecology, and genetics have often a bearing on taxonomy. There is, indeed, a recipro-cal advantageous reaction between them. The taxonomist has to be prepared to use the constructive criticisms of his colleagues and to incorporate into his system relevant data supplied by them. He may thus be able gradually to develop the existing system and progress from the present relative beginning towards an ideal perfected system which is his goal. Daring the reproaches of his biological colleagues, the taxonomist maintains that his subject is the alpha and has the potentiality of becoming the omega of a very considerable part at least of biological knowledge.

[1] The variations of the morphological 'system' (Bentham and Hooker, Engler and Prantl, Hallier, Bessey, Hutchinson, &c.) are relatively insignificant from our immediate standpoint, and involve little more than a reshuffle of previously recognized units.

There are, of course, many difficulties to be met. Some of these have been considered at length elsewhere (Turrill, 1938). Here it must suffice to classify the new subject-matter to be incorporated in taxonomy very briefly and under two headings:

A. *Experimental*—including much genetics, some physiology, part of ecology, some cytology.

B. *Non-experimental*—including histology, much cytology, part of ecology, much biogeography.

Difficulties concerned with the latter group are not great and, indeed, have already been largely overcome. They are not considered in detail here because of the 'terms of reference' under which this chapter is written, not because their interest and importance is unrecognized by the writer. Here we are mainly concerned with the possibilities of using experiments and experimentally obtained data in taxonomy. It is important to remember that taxonomy has both 'practical' and 'theoretical' aspects. By 'practical' aspects is here meant simply determination, i.e. that it can be said definitely that a given specimen belongs to such and such a taxonomic group, and the methods in the broadest sense by which determination is made possible. Taxonomists claim, and can justify the claim, that they have problems additional to those of determination, and that these problems are partly peculiar to taxonomy proper and partly associated with other branches of biology. In other words, while taxonomy is the basis of all biological research, it is also something more and develops research along its own lines, by its own methods, and with independent aims. These points are, no doubt, developed elsewhere in this symposium, and both 'practical' and 'theoretical' aspects are intermingled in this chapter and the subheadings are based on the type of experiment.

1. *Simple Cultivation under approximately Uniform Conditions*

The taxonomist has to determine and classify phenotypes, but his taxonomic grading is based on the assumption that he can distinguish characters diagnostic of different genotypes from those representing the interaction of different environments with the same genotype. Without doubt the specialist in any group learns by experience to distinguish such kinds of phenotypes, often with a high degree of accuracy and by what comes to appear almost as intuition. Observation of abundant wild material living or growing *in situ* will often yield valuable experience. There are, however, many published instances showing difference of opinion, and final proof can only be obtained by fully recorded experiments.

Two or three simple examples will be first considered. *Cytisus scoparius* Link var. *prostratus* (Bailey) was first described (Bailey, 1866–7) from 'cliffs of serpentine rock about Vellan Head, situate about four miles north-west of the Lizard Lights'. The variety 'differs from the normal plant chiefly in its habit of growth, which, instead of being erect and bushy, is remarkably prostrate, the branches spreading out in fan-shaped patches, and growing flat upon the ground; the branches, particularly in the upper half, are densely clothed with short spreading hairs; the leaves have shorter stalks, with a greater tendency to suppress the two lateral leaflets, the majority of the leaves in fact being unifoliate; the pods are less numerous, have their dorsal and ventral sutures covered with long silky hairs, and are black rather than brown, shorter, and have fewer seeds'. Davey (1909) gives additional Cornish localities. The variety is also recorded from Guernsey and Alderney (Marquand, 1901) and probably is the same as the var. *maritimus* Rouy et Fouc. of the French flora (Rouy and Foucaud, 1897). Some authors have dismissed the var. *prostratus* with some contempt. Thus Lester-Garland (1903) says it is 'nothing but a form, entirely due to situation'. Seeds collected by A. K. Jackson on The Blaye, near Telegraph Tower, Alderney, and sown in the Herbarium Experimental Ground at Kew have reproduced the var. *prostratus* with the marked parental characters. Although no controlled breeding work has yet been done with this material, it is quite evident that the variety has a genetic basis and at the same time shows adaptation to the wind-swept habitats where it naturally occurs. It is, indeed, a very striking example of an ecotype as Turesson uses this term. This very simple illustration is also interesting because of an earlier published statement which, combined with our experiment, shows the danger of passing judgement from cultivation from seed when only negative results are obtained. Clement Reid (1899) says 'the prostrate maritime form of broom found in Cornwall (*Cytisus scoparius* var. *prostratus*) has similarly no claim to varietal rank, for Mr. Mitten tells me that seeds gathered by him grew in his garden into the common erect form of broom'. It appears that either the seeds sown were F_1 from the cross var. *prostratus* ♀ × var. *erectus* ♂, or that there is more than one prostrate variation of the broom.

Solanum dulcamara L. var. *marinum* Bab. is common on shingle around our British coasts. Material from Sussex grown at Kew retains the prostrate habit of the main branches, and other characters, year after year in ordinary garden soil. Other material, from Hampshire, grown at Potterne, similarly retains its characters, and from breeding work (unpublished) Marsden-Jones finds that the habit has a genic basis.

Cultivation from seed of *Silene subconica* Friv. var. *Grisebachii* David. (Turrill, 1933), with its elongated petal claws, shows that this character is maintained under conditions very different from those found in the native localities of the variety. The species has a wide distribution from south-east Italy, through the central parts of the Balkan Peninsula eastwards to Armenia. The variety is known only from the Aegean coastal districts of Thrace.

Similar examples could be multiplied from the writer's own experience and cumulatively justify Jordan's contention that cultivation is highly desirable for accurate taxonomic work concerned with species studies. This does not, however, mean that all Jordan's 'species' are advisably to be accepted with the taxonomic status assigned to them by their author. Thus it has been shown (Chaytor and Turrill, 1935) that in *Clypeola jonthlaspi* L. various characters occur in different combinations, often in one and the same wild population within a small area, that Jordan named some of these combinations as species, while the modern view is to regard them as variations having a genetic basis and due to various combinations of a small number of genes. Thus for size and indumentum of fruit alone it was shown that twelve character combinations could theoretically occur, and eleven of these were actually found. Further work at Kew (Turrill, 1937, and unpublished) showed that the characters were genically inherited.

Jordan's work has been extensively referred to by many writers (Bateson, Lotsy, &c.), and it seems desirable to offer a few further comments here. A clear account, by himself, of his methods is given in the Avant-Propos to his *Diagnoses* (Jordan, 1864). Jordan emphasizes that his researches are based on observable facts, not on hypotheses. To find that conspicuous

differences occur and are constant year after year, and 'qu'elles
se reproduisent héréditairement et invariablement pendant une
suite de générations', is a material fact. Differences of opinion
as to the interpretation of facts so obtained may be expected,
but the facts can be tested by repeated observation and experiment. He emphasizes the great importance of studying living
material and of testing the 'inheritance' of the diagnostic
characters. Thus: 'les espèces proposées par nous ne sont autre
chose que des formes végétales que nous avons appris à dis-
tinguer les unes des autres par la comparaison sur le vif de tous
leurs organes, en nous assurant, par les observations les plus
certaines, que leurs différences étaient héréditaires et ne pou-
vaient être attribuées à des causes accidentelles ou locales.' He
asserts that he has used these methods for 'l'immense majorité'
of his species, but confesses that others have been accepted on
the basis of the analogy of their characters with those of plants
submitted to experiment. He insists that it is logical to regard
his units as species and not as varieties of species already known,
because they can be recognized as 'vraies unités, parfaitement
limitées et distinctes, constantes et invariables dans leurs différences, complètement irréductibles les unes aux autres'. It is
not within my terms of reference to discuss in detail the various
connotations of the term 'species' stated or implied by biologists.
Jordan's definition is, however, worth quoting in his original
words, since it summarizes the theoretical background of his
practice: 'l'espèce . . . est l'unité renfermant un nombre indéter-
miné d'individus qui tous ont une même nature et sont consub-
stantiels les uns aux autres, de telle sorte qu'ils peuvent être
justement considérés comme issus originairement d'un seul et
même individu, premier exemplaire de toute l'espèce.' While
Jordan's conclusions are logically drawn from his accepted
premisses it is certain that they cannot now be maintained,
because some of his premisses have been experimentally proved
false and other important premisses were unknown to or ignored
by him. Thus, his view that species (even Jordanian ones) are
immutable and invariable is demonstrably incorrect, while the
results of natural hybridization are ignored. In *Clypeola* some,
at least, of Jordan's 'species' grow together in nature, and the
various character combinations suggest that intercrossing occurs.
Centaurea nemoralis Jord. crosses freely with *C. nigra* L. and with

C. jacea L. Some of Jordan's species are, of course, more distinct and more isolated. It also remains uncertain how far Jordan actually applied his own principles of testing, by simple cultural experiments, the 'constancy' of the diagnostic characters distinguishing his species. By himself or in collaboration he described over 1,300 new 'species' of vascular plants (nearly all Angiosperms), the vast majority from the French flora. Occasionally he gives details of their cultivation, but most often no mention is made of such tests. It is suggested that a much more exhaustive investigation from a definite standpoint of both Jordan's species and the 'Linneons' to which they are now most often relegated is required before the implications of the following statement by Bateson can be accepted: 'Between Jordan with his 200 odd species for *Erophila*, and Grenier and Godron with one, there is no hesitation possible. Jordan's view, as he again and again declares with vehemence, is at least a view of natural facts, whereas the collective species is a mere abstraction. . . .'

The deservedly well-known experimental researches of Turesson must, for the most part as at present published, be considered under the heading of simple cultivation. Turesson's most important papers have appeared in *Hereditas*. An adequate summary of the earlier ones (up to 1930) is given by Barton-Wright (1932). Briefly, Turesson transplanted to his experimental ground variations, of common species, which he found growing in and apparently correlated with distinct types of habitat. He found, with some exceptions, that these *ecotypes*, as he termed them, retained their diagnostic characters under conditions of cultivation. In this way ecotypes associated with dunes, sea-cliffs, woodlands, high altitudes, &c., were distinguished from the mass population of a considerable number of widely distributed 'Linnean' species. Most of Turesson's experiments were limited to Swedish material, though some were later extended to Alpine and other plants. There is no doubt as to the great value of Turesson's work. He has clearly shown not only that the species, as usually accepted by the taxonomist, is a complex assemblage of biotypes, but also that the species population varies in its biotype composition with habitat conditions. Further, he proves that in certain ecologically well-defined habitats the environmental factors limit the biotypes of a species to those possessing certain adaptational characters, that is to one or other ecotype. The term 'ecotype' was 'used as an ecological sub-unit to cover the product arising as a result of the genotypical response of an ecospecies to a particular habitat' (Turesson, 1922). The 'ecospecies' is 'the genotype compound narrowed down to the ecological combination-limit', while a 'coenospecies' is 'the total sum of possible combinations of a genotype compound'. By 'genotype compound' Turesson means the sum-total of gene-combinations, presumably within what he accepts as specific limits. These definitions were restated with slight changes in other publications, and new 'interpretations' (with certain improvements) are given by Gregor, Davey, and Lang (1936). The ecotype was originally proposed as an ecological unit, and it remains doubtful how far it can usefully be accepted in a taxonomic sense, either to replace such terms as 'subspecies' and 'variety', or as an additional taxonomic category. The ecotype is not synonymous with either the term 'genotype' or the term 'phenotype', for it is diagnosed only by characters 'arising as a result of the genotypical response of an ecospecies to a particular habitat'. Other characters, non-adaptational to the particular habitat, are ignored and may be present in sufficient numbers and genotypic diversity for a single ecotype to consist of numerous genotypes. Certain objections to the general taxonomic use of the ecotype theory have been published elsewhere (Turrill, 1938), but these do not deny either the validity of the results obtained by Turesson, Gregor, and others, or the desirability of testing on a large scale (and if necessary modifying) the original scheme. When the detailed distribution of more groups of organisms relative to the environmental conditions of their ranges has been studied it may be desirable to redefine assemblages and ecotypes, either in terms of naturally recurrent groups or in terms of ecological clines (Huxley, 1938). From our present standpoint the work of Turesson is accepted as a most valuable stimulus to experimental research, and it is to be hoped that many British botanists will adopt methods essentially similar.

Two aspects of simple cultivation, whether by transplant, from clones, or from seeds, may be emphasized. These are the value of studying living material and the value of studying abundant material at all stages of the life-history. Much taxonomic work has perforce to be done in herbaria and museums with preserved material. Many characters are obscured or disappear, or worse are changed, by even the best methods of preservation. This is particularly true of the most extensively used herbarium methods, and for certain groups of plants. It is also impossible adequately to represent many species on herbarium sheets because of peculiarities of habit or size. For the study of life-histories, from the seedling to the adult fruiting condition, cultivation is most often essential, partly because of the need constantly to watch and study the stages as they proceed, and partly to be quite certain that the same material is studied at the different stages. It is, then, obvious that cultivation is a most useful adjunct to herbarium and museum studies, just as herbarium methods are essential for careful work in other branches of biology (Marsden-Jones, Summerhayes, and Turrill, 1930).

2. *Cultivation under Varied but Controlled or Known Conditions*

Observations in the wild, as well as under garden conditions, show that genotypes are more or less plastic, but the degree of reaction of any genotype to different environmental conditions can only be known as a result of extensive and long-continued experiments.[1] The taxonomist has, most often, to classify organisms as they occur in nature. His interest in plasticity is therefore greatest when the variations occur under such conditions as are found in natural habitats. He is less directly concerned with the reaction of organisms to extreme laboratory conditions, though these can often throw light upon causes because of the high degree of control under which laboratory experiments can be conducted. The apical meristematic method of growth, with its formation of new lateral members and shedding of old, and the frequent formation of new branch systems from adventitious or dormant buds, is the rule in vascular plants. This gives scope for the display of plasticity of a kind different from that possible in most animal groups, including all higher animals. In the lower plants the widespread occurrence of vegetative multiplication by somatic cell-division, hyphal, protonemal, and gemmal spread and separation gives similar possibilities of varied reac-

[1] See L. T. Hogben, *Nature and Nurture* (London, 1933), for an extended discussion of this point in relation to animals.

tion by one clone. A number of well-known experiments have been made with the object of throwing light on the phenotypic variation of one genotype. Unfortunately, the published results of some of the most widely quoted of these are open to adverse criticism, to the extent that they certainly need repeating, under more careful control, before they can be accepted.

The French botanist, Bonnier, conducted transplant experiments on a large scale with native plants. His usual method was to choose plants of perennial herbaceous species, to divide a given individual into approximate halves, to plant one-half in a lowland garden (near Paris) and the other at a high altitude (in the French Alps or Pyrenees). Examination after shorter or longer periods showed very considerable differences between the ramets (the separated parts) of any one clone for many of the species. A concise summary of his results was published by Bonnier in 1920. A few of the plants taken from the plains to high mountain stations died, but a list is given of fifty-eight species that proved able to maintain themselves at high altitudes. These all underwent changes which often made them resemble indigenous high mountain species. The principal changes noted were: relatively large development of the subterranean as compared with the aerial parts, shortening of the leaves and of internodes of the stems, increased hairiness, and relatively larger development of bark and protective tissues. The leaves became thicker in proportion to their surface, had more highly developed palisade tissue, and were of a deeper green with a large number of chloroplastids per cell. The flowers were larger and more highly coloured. In at least seventeen species it was claimed that the changes in transplanted portions of individual plants were: so great that the plants had apparently been transformed into distinct alpine 'species'. Thus *Lotus corniculatus* L. began to show decided changes within ten years, and finally became identical with *L. alpinus* Schleich. *Helianthemum vulgare* Gaertn. in thirty years became *H. grandiflorum* DC., while *Leontodon proteiformis* Vill. in six years was completely transformed into *L. alpinum* Vill. The taxonomist may not be inclined to accept some of the recorded changes at their face value, while the experimenter may well suspect the dying out of the original ramet and its replacement by a seedling from a neighbouring plant of an allied but different species. In experiments extending over periods of years it is essential to watch for rogues almost weekly. The late Dr. H. M. Hall informed me that after a prolonged investigation in France he was unable to find preserved examples of plants showing the changes recorded or to obtain satisfactory evidence from Bonnier's contemporaries and assistants that proper precautions had been taken to ensure against errors in the experiments. This does not mean that Bonnier's published accounts have to be rejected *in toto*, but it does indicate the need for caution in accepting his conclusion that there was transmutation of species as a result of relatively quick and direct reaction to the complex of ecological factors involved in considerable differences of altitude.

Very extensive series of transplant experiments were commenced in 1900 by F. E. Clements. A summary account of the aims, methods used, and materials employed up to 1929 is given by Clements (1929). Some of the published results appear rather astounding to the taxonomist. Thus it is claimed that the production of 'an exact duplicate of an existing species from its assumed ancestor has been the conversion of *Phleum pratense* into *P. alpinum* by means of the water transect' (Clements, 1925), and 'the apparent change of *Epilobium angustifolium* to *E. latifolium* is, at least, remarkable' (Clements, 1925–6, 1924). The late Dr. H. M. Hall was also intimately connected with these experiments between 1922 and 1932, and has summarized some of his results and views (Hall, 1930, 1932). Since 1932 the work has been continued and considerably reorganized by J. Clausen and his associates. The more recent publications (Clausen, Keck, and Hiesey, 1934–7) give very brief summaries and suggest cautious and in part tentative interpretation of the results. Important particular and general conclusions may be expected from these extensive experiments.

The Transplant Experiments of the British Ecological Society were commenced at Potterne, Wiltshire, in 1928. While these experiments are more limited in aim and scope than those of Bonnier or of our American colleagues, they have been carefully standardized to give information on the reaction of a limited number of wild British species to different 'soil' conditions: sand, calcareous sand, clay, chalky clay, and Potterne Upper Greensand soil. Readers are referred to the biennial reports and the summary of results of ten years for details of the results so far obtained (Marsden-Jones and Turrill, 1930–8). It has been found that every species reacts differently from every other, though a classification of reactions is possible if any class is diagnosed by a certain range of behaviour. Thus, to take a few examples, *Centaurea nemoralis* survives well on all soils, but shows little morphological change on any; *Plantago major* L. very quickly reacts to the different soils by most conspicuous changes in size, number, orientation, &c., of vegetative and reproductive organs; *Phleum nodosum* and *P. pratense* show, on the five soils, strongly marked quantitative differences, but these are more slowly cumulative; several species show differential death-rates, with or without structural changes. The greatest and most rapid changes have been recorded for *Plantago major*, an extremely plastic species. Here phenotypes have been produced within two years, from seedlings and from ramets of a single clone, which have been classed as varieties and subspecies in a recent monograph of the genus. On the other hand, with the two pairs of congeners, *Silene cucubalus* Wibel (*S. vulgaris* Garcke) and *S. maritima* With. and *Phleum nodosum* L. and *P. pratense* L., there has been no approximation, on any soil, of one species to the diagnostic characters of the other. Since soil factors are known to be secondary to climatic factors in phytogeographical studies, though their great local importance is fully recognized, sensational results were not expected in these transplant experiments. It is suggested that experiments extended to different climates, the soil and other conditions being kept uniform, and conducted with the same degree of careful, constant, and regular control might yield striking and reliable results.

The modern taxonomist always welcomes information that may throw light upon the nature of the barriers which maintain his species as relatively distinct entities. It is therefore correct to include here a brief reference to such experiments as those of Tansley (1917) with *Galium saxatile* L. and *G. sylvestre* Poll. *G. saxatile* is a calcifuge, *G. sylvestre* a calcicole. Freed from competition either species can grow on calcareous or on non-calcareous soils, but when grown together *G. saxatile* becomes dominant on acid and heathy soils, *G. sylvestre* on calcareous soil with complete suppression of *G. saxatile*. Other examples, with bibliographical references, are given by Salisbury (1929) and by Clements, Weaver, and Hanson (1929). The work of the

Welsh Plant Breeding Station on competition between species in seeds mixtures is also relevant (Stapledon and Davies, and Davies, 1928).

Recent discoveries in the realm of growth-promoting substances (plant hormones, auxins, hetero-auxin) may be expected to throw light upon factors controlling some habits, leaf-shape, and other characters used in taxonomy. It may also be suggested that controlled experiments using degrees of mutilation at different phases of the life-history and also extensive experiments with seedlings under varied conditions are much to be desired.

3. Cytological Experiments

The relation of the new taxonomy to cytology is dealt with elsewhere in this symposium. Truly experimental cytology is, for plants, in its infancy. That X-rays, radium emanations, temperature extremes, and other external factors cause chromosomal and genic changes is established. Treatment with certain drugs (e.g. colchicine), fertilization with 'stale' pollen, mutilation, and the use of long-dormant seed are also known to give an increase in the mutation rate, the term 'mutation' being here used in the widest possible sense. To those interested in the taxonomy of wild plants the action of temperature and of dormancy are most suggestive. It has long been known that temperature and rainfall, and especially their relative seasonal distribution, are controlling factors in plant distribution, whether taxonomic units or plant communities be under consideration. Phytogeographical evidence suggests that relatively direct action on the chromosome and gene apparatus of extremes of temperature or of other ecological factors may well be a cause of the formation, for example, of some high mountain species altitudinally vicarious with lowland species. This is particularly well seen in the Greek flora (Turrill, 1929, pp. 117, 480). The possibility, even the proof, of such a cause of variation does not diminish the selective importance of environmental action or lead to the acceptance of a truly Lamarckian theory. That 'mutations' are of all 'sizes' and owe their origin to one or other of a variety of 'causes', some of which are constituents of the ever-varying natural environment, suggests strongly, to an experimental taxonomist who is not biased by acceptance of the views of any extreme school of evolutionists or phylogenists, that there may be a good deal to be accepted with advantage from more than one of the various theories that have been proposed to explain the mechanism of evolution.

Experimental cytology has, perforce, to be carried on under very carefully controlled laboratory conditions. The results are to that extent 'artificial', and the taxonomist has to use care in interpreting them from his standpoint. Nevertheless, extreme mutations, even if of a 'teratological' nature, may be significant in phylogenetic studies. Thus the family *Caryophyllaceae* is divided into the subfamilies *Alsinoideae* with free sepals and the *Silenoideae* with united sepals (Engler und Gilg, *Syllabus der Pflanzenfamilien*, &c.). A mutation of *Silene cucubalus* has been recently obtained with the sepals often separate to the base. Preliminary genetical studies with this mutant have so far been delayed because of sterility factors, but its direct and natural origin from the usual gamosepalous *S. cucubalus* is not in dispute. Numerous examples of equal value could be given if space permitted. If, then, gene or chromosome mutations underlie evolution, and, therefore, taxonomic and phylogenetic studies, it is of great importance to the taxonomist that the cytologist, by experiment or by cytological examination of the material of other experimental biologists, should provide information as to the cytological 'cause' in the causal chain. To carry this line of thought much farther would lead to a consideration of the nature and action of cytoplasm, chromosomes, and genes, but sufficient has, perhaps, been said to suggest that there is little in biology which has not a taxonomic use.

The taxonomist knows, only too well, that certain groups give him much more trouble than other groups. One cause is the occurrence of apomixis combined with variation. Thus, all the British *Taraxaca*, so far tested, are apomictic. The group is extremely polymorphic, and its history is slowly being elucidated by a combination of taxonomic, cultural, phytogeographical, and cytological methods (Turrill, 1938). Castration experiments can prove the occurrence of apomixis; cytological examination suggests hybridization previous to the adoption of apomixis and mutation since. Since individuals are also extremely plastic in reaction to different environmental conditions, and this plasticity sometimes overlaps phenotypic differences of different genotypes, intensive experiments arranged for or combined with cytological investigations might well throw light on gene-action and gene-change.

In other plants apomixis is less constant. Thus in *Ranunculus ficaria* L. it is frequent in some stocks; in *R. acris* L. it 'occurs in a low percentage of ovules, successfully in less than 1 per cent. under the most favourable experimental conditions tested' (Marsden-Jones and Turrill, 1935). Experiments with different stocks correlated with extensive cytological investigation might indicate or prove the causes of apomixis, its relation to hybridization, and the possible range of chromosomal and genic mutations in the absence of the phenomena normally connected with sexuality (e.g. meiosis and fertilization).

Surprisingly little experimental cytological research has been done with the lower plants. Wettstein's important results with Bryophyta and rather unco-ordinated research on certain genera of Algae, in addition to the known vegetative simplicity of many Thallophyta, suggest strongly that there is useful material available in the cryptogams for real experimental cytology with living plants. The relatively large size of cells and nuclei in many Algae and the fact that in unicellular and filamentous forms, at least, these can be viewed without section-cutting, both in somatic and reproductive parts, increase surprise that the pioneer work of the algal systematist has not been followed by much more detailed cytological research. The technical difficulties of controlled culture and *in vivo* examination should not be great. That cytological features are also direct taxonomic characters would increase the importance of such work to the taxonomist.

4. *Genetical Experiments*

Genetics, unlike morphology (including most of cytology) and much of ecology, is historically and basically experimental. It is therefore of the greatest importance to consider the actual and potential value of genetics in taxonomy. Genetics, in its modern form, may be said to date from Mendel's experiments with garden peas, and by far the greater part of modern genetical research in plants has been with cultivated material of unknown wild origin. There is, of course, no sharp line between wild and cultivated plants and no reason for believing that many, perhaps most, of the results obtained with garden plants cannot or do not obtain also in the wild. There are, however, certain differences in detail and in emphasis. Isolation and selection are different in kind and degree. Competition is generally greatly reduced. The phenomena of natural succession are absent. Soil, soluble food, water, and temperature are controlled and frequently kept near optimum conditions, or, at least, extremes are reduced. Possibilities of hybridization are changed—often they are increased or deliberately encouraged, or they may be lessened or prevented. Diseases and pests are more or less artificially controlled. Further, for long cultivated and domesticated races these artificial conditions have existed for many generations. All facts garnered under such conditions have biological value, which, in general terms, is equal to that for such facts as are obtained 'in the wild' or from the use of wild material, or under natural conditions. Their use to the taxonomist is, however, different, and they must often be used rather by analogy than directly, or at least with due regard to the differences to which the material has been subjected. Thus barriers between species which are valid in nature may be broken down under conditions of cultivation; mutations may appear and survive which cannot be found in the wild; extremes of plasticity may appear that are greater than those occurring in nature, and so on. Therefore, it is highly desirable that in addition to, not in place of, the genetical study of cultivated plants there should be corresponding studies on material of known wild origin, under a variety of conditions, some of which should be as natural as is possible with genetical methods. While it is true that considerable research is now being done on plants of immediate wild origin, the taxonomist is in the position to suggest to his genetical colleagues many more groups within which he would welcome such information as genetical experiments might be expected to give. Further, the taxonomist is often able to supply, directly or through his correspondents, much of the necessary material. Even within the British flora there are many species and groups of species within or between which simple controlled selfing and crossing, with adequate scoring, must yield valuable taxonomic data. Such research is not difficult and does not require expensive apparatus, though it needs concentrated effort, great care, and to be kept within the limits of what can be completed with precision in any one season. It is greatly to be hoped that

British botanists, including especially amateurs, will turn their attention to the intensive study by genetical methods of one wild species or small groups of wild species and correlate the results so obtained with data obtained from the observation and analysis of wild populations. The great interest and importance of such studies has been proved, but many more examples must be worked out before the widest reliable generalizations become possible. The data so obtained will not only aid the taxonomist but will go far towards settling such disputed questions as the origins of the British flora, or may be of direct economic use in the discovery or production of new and improved races of forage or other crops.

The limits to be assigned to species have frequently given rise to differences in practice and in theory. The taxonomist is right in giving prominence to 'species problems' since the species is the most used, because the most useful, taxonomic unit.

'With all its imperfections in practice, it is generally recognized that the species concept is essential. . . . No single absolute test for a species is yet known, and it is debatable if such is ever likely to be found, but as a working hypothesis the following criteria should be considered: a species is morphologically definable in that it has a sum-total of characters, and every individual within it has constant resemblances with every other individual within it, and constant differences from every individual of other species, even when the individuals are grown under diverse conditions; species are isolated one from another, sometimes geographically, sometimes by habitat preferences, sometimes by having different flowering periods, usually by not crossing naturally to produce completely fertile offspring; species may show chromosomal differences. A species is an isolated group of individuals whose sum of characters tends to keep constant by natural in-breeding' (Turrill, 1925).

The above quotation was written in 1923 (published in 1925). Only very slight alterations to give still greater precision would bring it into line with views now widely held. The limitations of out-breeding and the degree of freedom for in-breeding are frequently the concern of genetics as well as of taxonomy.

In a recent publication (Turrill, 1938) it is suggested that 'experimental methods should throw some light upon, at least, the following problems of importance to the taxonomist:

1. The degree of plasticity of genotypes.
2. The occurrence and constancy of correlation of characters.

3. The occurrence and nature of sterility barriers.
4. The evaluation of characters.
5. The recognition of hybrids.
6. The phylogeny of species.'

While the plasticity of genotypes is, from some aspects, a genetic as well as a taxonomic problem, it has already been considered in this chapter under other headings. The remaining subjects given in this list can be conveniently discussed in the following paragraphs.

The taxonomist, as already indicated, utilizes, partly for practical reasons, morphological characters, and requires that his species shall be defined inclusively and exclusively in morphological terms. Genetical research also involves the analytical study of characters which are often morphological and, in the genetically best-known organisms, very numerous. The occurrence of correlation between characters is important in the recognition of linkage, and the break-down of expected correlation has led to the theory of crossing-over and the development of much that is new in cytogenetic theory. In his preliminary studies the taxonomist determines his species by the constancy of association of certain characters, but has, by alpha methods alone, to describe this constancy from the examination of unequal and usually small samples. By combining genetical with taxonomic methods or by utilizing the results of geneticists the taxonomist is enabled to study correlation much more intensively and extensively and to reach conclusions much sounder statistically. The results are sometimes surprising to the taxonomist and indicate, as do other experimental methods, that at least many species (and many other taxonomic groups) must be accepted only as categories of scientific convenience with a very considerable amount of internal (intraspecific) variation and sometimes a large amount of character overlapping with other species.

Research on *Silene maritima* and *S. cucubalus* (*S. vulgaris*), the bladder campions, has been in progress at Kew and Potterne for more than twelve years, and over twenty papers have already appeared giving details of the experiments and observations (Marsden-Jones and Turrill, 1928–38). It is estimated that about half the work, as originally planned, has now been completed. Only a brief reference is possible here to one of the important results obtained. More than a dozen morphological differences, some of which are structural expressions of behaviour differences of selective value, can be enumerated as usually having specific value for diagnostic purposes, yet every one of these is found to 'break down' in some, mostly a few, individuals, and this apart from hybridization. Two simple examples may be given. *Silene maritima* has usually broad obloid capsules with reflexed teeth; *S. cucubalus* has ovoid capsules with erect teeth. The F_1 is intermediate and segregation is complex in F_2. In most inland populations of *S. cucubalus* a small number of plants (e.g. 2 to 3 per cent.) occur with capsules of the shape and with the teeth of fruits characteristic of *S. maritima*. Similarly, *S. cucubalus*-like capsules occur, though very rarely, in populations of *S. maritima*. 'Armadillo' seeds are usual in *S. maritima;* tubercled seeds in typical *S. cucubalus*. About 3 to 10 per cent. of *S. cucubalus* plants, however, have armadillo seeds in most wild populations, and in *S. maritima* wild populations have been analysed with up to 50 per cent. tubercled seeds, though usually the percentage is much lower unless recent hybridization has occurred with *S. cucubalus*. Armadillo is always recessive to tubercled, within each species and in both reciprocal crosses between the species, and the F_2 segregation is or usually approximates to $3:1$. The last pair of characters, of those so far studied, to 'break down' was zygomorphy versus actinomorphy. In spite of all such breakdowns in single characters, the two species keep essentially distinct, and the degree of correlation of the specific diagnostic characters is very high for plants not deliberately crossed. The species, as such, have no sterility barriers. Certain characters, conveniently referred to as 'habit', have a high selective value for certain different habitats in which the species naturally occur. Why other characters should show such high correlation with these remains, however, a stimulating mystery.

Anthyllis vulneraria L., the kidney-vetch, is another polymorphic species. Genetical research has shown that the varieties interbreed freely, both in nature and in the experimental ground, and that, in British material, there is no such constancy of correlation of characters as to justify the making of more than one species (Marsden-Jones and Turrill, 1933). A variation of *Solanum dulcamara*, the bittersweet, characterized by one-flowered inflorescences (*uniflora*) correlated with relatively retarded flowering and leafy inflorescences, was found to breed true for these characters, to be (somewhat incompletely and variably) recessive to the commoner '*multiflora*' variation, and F_2 from *uniflora* × *multiflora* to show segregation of a modified 3 : 1 type (Turrill, 1936).

Sterility is, in the widest use of the term, of many degrees and has many different causes. Complete sterility between genotypes must obviously result in their isolation and in the separation of those characters by which they are distinguishable. There are other kinds of isolation than that due to sterility barriers, and two or more kinds are often associated. Such association probably tends to increase with evolutionary divergence, as when two populations become geographically isolated and by retention and accumulation of different mutant genes develop different habitat preferences (which may become obligatory), i.e. they come to show ecological preferences, and, perhaps by other mutant genes, also inter-population sterility. By this time, given also morphological differences, even the taxonomist would accept the two populations as distinct species. It remains, however, that cytogenetical sterility is of the greatest importance to the taxonomist and cannot, with the present state of knowledge, be proved except by experiment. Species widely different morphologically may be fertile one with another and yield fertile offspring, as in many orchids, while species differing in few obvious characters may be inter-sterile, as in some buttercups. Distinct but morphologically closely related species of *Nemophila* have been shown to breed true to definite characters and to be intersterile, while their varieties are intraspecifically fertile (Chittenden and Turrill, 1926). *Centaurea scabiosa* L. will not cross with microspecies of the *C. nigra* group, though they frequently grow close together in the wild (Marsden-Jones and Turrill, 1937). Here the barrier to interbreeding is cytological (chromosomal) rather than genetical in the narrower sense. On the other hand, *Centaurea nigra*, *C. nemoralis*, and *C. jacea* hybridize freely, when they meet in the wild. Complex naturally occurring hybrid swarms have been analysed, and similar 'swarms' have been produced artificially by breeding. Most of the so-called species of the *Centaurea nigra—C. jacea* series have been both synthesized and analysed in the genetical work at Potterne (details unpublished) and have been found to be heterozygotes with *C. jacea* as one of the (original or immediate) parents. It is not improbable that genetical studies may reduce considerably the number of accepted 'species' in other genera of the British floras and lists.

Unpublished experiments also indicate strongly that certain *Saxifraga* populations in western Ireland and elsewhere are hybrid swarms, though certain plants have been collected from them and given special taxonomic treatment. Genetically, *Geum urbanum* L. and *G. rivale* L. may be considered as varieties of one species, in that they cross freely and produce hybrid swarms in which it is difficult or impossible to find plants showing a pure combination of the characters of either putative parent (Marsden-Jones, 1930). There is no sterility barrier between these species.

Anderson's studies, by the synthetic method, of American spiderworts (*Tradescantia*) has led to the elaboration of useful methods for dealing with hybrid swarms in which sterility barriers are absent or incomplete (Anderson, 1936).

Taxonomists undoubtedly evaluate (for the group with which they are working) the characters they observe. Not only are some characters considered of generic, some of specific, some of varietal rank, &c., but the practical selection of characters for diagnostic purposes or for artificial keys also sometimes gives unintentional theoretical emphasis to certain characters. Sometimes, too, there is what is little more than arbitrary choice of characters, especially for maintaining or making genera. On the whole, genetical research has not provided a more independent objective basis for evaluation of characters. Marsden-Jones and Turrill have so far found no essential difference in kind or in genetical behaviour between specific and intra-specific morphological characters in the species of *Silene* with which they are working. Certain characters have greater taxonomic importance because of their different selective values for the different wild habitats in which the species grow, but the genetical behaviour of these is similar to that of characters differentiating genotypes within the species. Other workers have reached similar tentative conclusions for the groups they have investigated. There is, however, the possibility that a critical review and experimental classification of numerous published genetical results might indicate certain general differences between 'varietal' and 'specific' characters or genes. Even if these differences were found to be 'tendencies' rather than absolutely diagnostic, new and significant lines of research might be suggested and facts of evolutionary importance might be brought to light. Thus specific characters might be due to more stable genes, varietal to more readily mutating genes; or there might be differences in the degree of gene interaction or in pleiotropy. Winge (1938), after a careful investigation of characters in crosses between two species of *Tragopogon*, discusses the 'basis of the taxonomically important characters—in particular whether they are due to (1) polymeric genes or (2) the alleles to lethal genes or (3) extraordinary stable genes'. He confesses that the general problems he raises are so far quite unsolved, and says: 'from the present investigation it is only possible to establish that the characters separating the two species of *Tragopogon*, are due to genes located in the chromosomes, and consequently the characters show Mendelian inheritance. The genetic analysis has not disclosed whether all genes are of taxonomic importance to the same degree or whether certain genes are especially active.' The reader is particularly referred to this important paper.

The taxonomist has to deal with material as it is sampled (often inadequately) from the wild. The monographer or worker in a large institution is largely dependent on collectors resident in or travelling over wide extents of the earth's surface. He frequently has to deal with specimens that do not exactly fit into his scheme of genera, species, and varieties. Sometimes he is fairly certain that the specimens are hybrids and he may be able to suggest the putative parentage. The occurrence of parallel mutations, which at or near the species level may be frequent, and the complexity of hybrid swarms due to back-crossing and crossing between segregates, make such suggestions more or less tentative, unless experiments can be made or the results of controlled experiments are available for reference. The geneticist can greatly assist the taxonomist by preserving material, adequately illustrating his results and fully documented, in an accessible, and preferably national, herbarium or museum. A permanently preserved collection of simple F_1 crosses and F_2 segregates, especially of interspecific origin, for the British flora and for economic (including horticultural) plants would be very valuable. Though a start has been made at Kew in the formation of such a collection, it can only be developed adequately through co-operation with a wide circle of geneticists.

The taxonomist, as a result of his more extensive experience, has often a wider appreciation of the wealth of form and structure than most of his biological colleagues. It is natural that he should speculate not only on the origin of the numerous and varied characters he uses but also upon that of the groups which he recognizes from their study. To discuss how far real or supposed phylogenetic data can or should be used in taxonomy would take us far beyond the realm of experimental taxonomy. It must suffice here to recall that cytogenetics has provided evidence, which must be accepted as conclusive, concerning the origin of some taxonomic units. While it is obvious that experimental methods are limited at present mainly to or below the species level, the definiteness of the evidence places it in a category quite apart from most of that used in phylogenetic theories. It is true that examples with published details are not yet numerous, but their number is increasing and is already sufficient to show that experiment combined with cytological and taxonomic study is likely to provide the phylogenist with many new facts in the future. Thus the origin of *Galeopsis tetrahit* L. (Müntzing, 1932, 1937), *Mentha nemorosa* Host (Stomps, verbally), and certain willows (Nilsson, 1937) by hybridization, and the cytogenetical relationships of some microspecies of *Oenothera* and apomicts of *Taraxacum*, show that hybridization is one important factor in evolution, and one which may, in part, explain the complex reticulation which the systematist finds when he attempts to classify a group of sexually or asexually reproducing plants. It is probable that taxonomically wider crosses can be made than any yet analysed genetically, and the behaviour of hybrids of diverse parentage, combined with cytological studies, may well throw light on the phylogeny of subfamilies and even of families. Research on the *Rosaceae* has suggested for the *Pomoideae* derivation from crossing between original polyploid forms with different numbers of chromosomes (Darlington, 1937).

Conclusions and Appendix

In this chapter certain possibilities of extending experimental methods as an aid to taxonomic studies have been considered.

It is obvious that such methods are as yet little developed and that they have limitations which will always prevent them replacing other methods. Nevertheless, sufficient is already known of their potentialities to make it certain that they can provide valuable data, unobtainable by any other method. Moreover, the data can be more precise and, since published results can be tested by repetition of the experiments, more 'objective' than interpretations of dead herbarium and museum specimens. The experimental methods suggested above, often with examples, are mostly simple and require neither elaborate and expensive apparatus nor highly technical training. The taxonomist must leave detailed genetical analysis to the geneticist, or must obtain his co-operation, and it is not his task further to complicate genetical theory.

While the importance of experiments has been intentionally emphasized here, it is important to remember that investigation of a species or group of species with the aim of reaching sound taxonomic, phylogenetic, or phytogeographical conclusions must be by a synthesis of methods. Thus Marsden-Jones and Turrill for the bladder-campions (*Silene*) have worked on the following principles: (1) a systematic investigation of material accumulated in herbaria and museums, correlating this with a critical reading of all published literature relevant to the subject; (2) a field investigation, by both phytogeographical and ecological methods, of the distribution of the species concerned in all their varieties and forms; (3) controlled selfing and crossing and growing in experimental grounds; (4) growing genetically investigated material under different environmental conditions in order to study the modifying effects of external factors; (5) cytological investigation of wild and cultivated material; (6) anatomical studies of vegetative and reproductive organs; (7) study of fossil material, so far as available.

It is only by a combination of all methods, herbarium or museum, library, laboratory, field, and breeding, that there is any hope of obtaining satisfactory evidence on the nature and genesis of taxonomic units. No method is sufficient by itself, yet each is essential. As an important part of the synthetic method experimental taxonomy will take its place in the scheme of 'The New Systematics'.

REFERENCES

ANDERSON, E. (1936). 'Hybridization in American Tradescantias.' *Ann. Missouri Bot. Gard.* **23**, 511, and references given here.

BAILEY, C. (1867). 'Notes on Varieties of Sarothamnus Scoparius, &c.' *Proc. Lit. & Phil. Soc. Manchester*, **6**, no. 6, Session 1866–7, 49.

BARTON-WRIGHT, E. C. (1932). *Recent Advances in Botany*, 77 seq. London.

BATESON, W. (1913). *Problems of Genetics*, 250. New Haven, &c.

BONNIER, G. (1920). 'Nouvelles observations sur les cultures expérimentales à diverses altitudes.' *Rev. Gen. Bot.* **32**, 305.

CHAYTOR, D. A., and TURRILL, W. B. (1935). 'The Genus Clypeola and its Intraspecific Variation.' *Kew Bull.* 1.

CHITTENDEN, R. J., and TURRILL, W. B. (1926). 'Taxonomic and Genetical Notes on Some Species of Nemophila.' *Kew Bull.* 1.

CLAUSEN, J., KECK, D. D., and HIESEY, W. M. (1935). 'Experimental Taxonomy.' *Carnegie Inst. of Washington, Annual Rep. Div. Plant Biology*, 201.

—— —— (1936). 'Experimental Taxonomy.' Ibid., 212.

—— —— (1937). 'Experimental Taxonomy.' *Carnegie Inst. of Washington, Year-Book*, no. 36, 212.

CLEMENTS, F. E. (1924). 'Ecology.' Ibid., no. 23, 257.

—— (1925). 'Ecology.' Ibid., no. 24, 311.

—— (1925–6). 'Ecology.' Ibid., no. 25, 337.

—— (1929). 'Experimental Methods in Adaptation and Morphogeny.' *J. Ecol.* **17**, 356.

CLEMENTS, F. E., WEAVER, J. E., and HANSON, H. C. (1929). *Plant Competition*. Carnegie Inst. of Washington.

DARLINGTON, C. D. (1937). *Recent Advances in Cytology*, 239–43. London.

DAVEY, F. H. (1909). *Flora of Cornwall*, 111. Penryn.

GREGOR, J. W., DAVEY, V. McM., and LANG, J. M. S. (1936). 'Experimental Taxonomy, I.' *New Phyt.* **35**, 323.

HALL, H. M. (1930). 'Méthodes expérimentales en taxonomie végétale.' *Bull. du Muséum*, 2ᵉ Sér. **2**, 564.

—— (1932). 'Heredity and Environment—as illustrated by Transplant Studies.' *Scientific Monthly*, Oct. 1932, 289.

HUXLEY, J. S. (1938). 'Clines: an Auxiliary Taxonomic Principle.' *Nature*, **142**, 219.

JORDAN, A. (1864). *Diagnoses d'espèces nouvelles ou méconnues*. Paris.

LESTER-GARLAND, L. (1903). *A Flora of the Island of Jersey*, 94. London.

MARQUAND, E. D. (1901). *Flora of Guernsey*, 74, 359. London.

MARSDEN-JONES, E. M. (1930). 'The Genetics of Geum intermedium Willd. haud Ehrh., and its back-crosses.' *J. Genet.* **23**, 377.

MARSDEN-JONES, E. M., and TURRILL, W. B. (1930–8). 'Reports on the Transplant Experiments of the British Ecological Society at Potterne, Wilts.' *J. Ecol.* **8**, 352 (1930); **21**, 268 (1933); **23**, 443 (1935); **25**, 189 (1937); **26**, 359, 380 (1938).

—— —— (1933). 'Studies in Variation of Anthyllis vulneraria.' *J. Genet.* **27**, 261.

—— —— (1935). 'Studies in Ranunculus III.' Ibid. **31**, 363.

MARSDEN-JONES, E. M., and TURRILL, W. B. (1937). 'Genetical Studies in *Centaurea scabiosa* L. and *Centaurea collina* L.' Ibid. **34**, 487.

—— —— (1928–38, and in continuation). 'Researches on *Silene maritima* and *S. vulgaris.*' *Kew Bull.* 1 (1928) to 254 (1938), and in press and preparation.

—— —— SUMMERHAYES, V. S., and TURRILL, W. B. (1930). 'Special Herbaria as Adjuncts to Modern Botanical Research.' *J. Ecol.* **18**, 379.

MÜNTZING, A. (1932). 'Cytogenetic Investigations on Synthetic Galeopsis tetrahit.' *Hereditas*, **16**, 105.

—— (1937). 'Multiple Allels and Polymeric Factors in Galeopsis.' Ibid. **23**, 371.

NILSSON, H. (1937). 'Ein oktonärer, fertiler Salix-Bastard und seine Deszendenz.' Ibid. **22**, 361, and references given here.

REID, C. (1899). *Origin of the British Flora*, 4. London.

ROUY ET FOUCAUD (1897). *Flor. Fr.* **4**, 204.

SALISBURY, E. J. (1929). 'The Biological Equipment of Species in relation to Competition.' *J. Ecol.* **17**, 197.

STAPLEDON, R. G., and DAVIES, W. (1928). 'Seeds Mixtures Experiments with special reference to the Influence of Environmental Factors'; and W. DAVIES (1928), 'The Factor of Competition between one Species and another in Seeds Mixtures', *Welsh Plant Breeding Station*, Series 8, no. 8.

TANSLEY, A. G. (1917). 'On Competition between *Galium saxatile* L. (*G. hercynicum* Weig.) and *Galium sylvestre* Poll. (*G. asperum* Schreb.) on Different Types of Soil.' *J. Ecol.* **5**, 173.

TURESSON, G. (1922). 'The Genotypical Response of the Plant Species to the Habitat.' *Hereditas*, **3**, 211.

TURRILL, W. B. (1925). 'Species.' *J. Bot.* **63**, 359.

—— (1929). *The Plant-life of the Balkan Peninsula.* Oxford.

—— (1933). 'Silene subconica *Friv.* var. Grisebachii *David.*' *Hooker's Icones Plantarum*, t. 3201.

—— (1936). 'Solanum dulcamara and its Inflorescence.' *B.E.C.* 1935 *Report*, 82.

—— (1937). 'A Contribution to the Botany of Athos Peninsula.' *Kew Bull.* 224.

—— (1938). 'Problems of British Taraxaca.' *Proc. Linn. Soc.*, Session **150**, 120.

—— (1938). 'Material for a Study of Taxonomic Problems in Taraxacum.' *B.E.C.* 1937 *Report*, 570.

—— (1938). 'Taxonomy and Genetics.' *J. Bot.* **76**, 33.

—— (1938). 'The Expansion of Taxonomy with special reference to Spermatophyta.' *Biol. Rev.* **13**, 342.

WINGE, Ö. (1938). 'Inheritance of Species Characters in *Tragopogon.*' *Compt. Rend. trav. Labor. Carlsberg, Sér. Physiol.* **22**, no. 9, 155.

MUTATIONS AND GEOGRAPHICAL VARIATION

N. W. TIMOFEEFF-RESSOVSKY

1. *Introduction*

THIS article will deal with one of the topics of the inter-relations of modern genetics with taxonomy and evolutionary studies. This special topic is the question of the role of mutations in geographical variability.

The present author regards this question as a fundamental one in the attempt at introducing modern genetic viewpoints into studies of the mechanism of evolution. Darwin formulated in a wonderfully clear and precise way the principle of natural selection and showed that this principle is the basic explanation of the mechanism of evolution. Since Darwin much very extensive and ingenious work has been done in the field of evolutionary studies, using palaeontological, morphological, embryological, and biogeographical data; these studies have allowed us to picture the main historical steps and events of the evolutionary process. The efficacy of these classical methods, which give a picture of what we may call 'macro-evolution', seems now to be more or less exhausted. Relatively much less work has been done in the field of what we may call 'micro-evolution', i.e. the evolutionary processes taking place within shorter limits of time, smaller groups of organisms, and lower systematic categories. But 'micro-evolution' is the evolutionary process in which we may expect to get exact scientific evidence regarding its mechanism; 'macro-evolution' is only accessible to descriptive historical methods, the conclusions regarding its mechanism being always deduced from other sources of evidence. And the main phenomenon of 'micro-evolution' is geographical variability and speciation.

It is curious that exactly at the moment when modern minor systematics, minor biogeography, and experimental ecology started their present development (at the end of the nineteenth and the beginning of the twentieth century) many evolutionists apparently became disappointed with Darwinism

L

and returned to various modifications of Lamarckian views on the mechanism of evolution. The cause of this reaction may perhaps lie in peculiarities of the development of our knowledge of organic variability. At the time of Darwin almost nothing was known about the distinction between heritable and non-heritable variation. During the whole period of classical evolutionism following Darwin very little attention was paid to an exact analysis of variability. Attention was concentrated on the major steps of evolution, neglecting the evolutionary material as such. Most evolutionists, taxonomists, and biogeographers also neglected the rapid development of experimental genetics since the beginning of this century, although the exact knowledge of the main traits and characteristics of heritable and non-heritable variability provided by this new branch of biology undoubtedly constitutes the most important advance in our knowledge with direct bearing on the mechanism of evolution, since Darwin. The neglect was reciprocal: most of the experimental geneticists, absorbed in their experimental analytical work, did not pay much attention to taxonomic and evolutionary problems. Only recently have both sides begun to feel that closer co-operation and reciprocal exchange of information will be of the greatest value for the further development of systematics, biogeography, and evolutionary theory.

Thus we regard as the main contribution of modern biology to the problem of evolution the knowledge of the mechanism of organic heredity and variability, which was provided by the development of experimental genetics. In Darwin's time and during the subsequent development of the theory of evolution, the mode of action of the known evolutionary factors, especially that of natural selection, could be considered and discussed only in a rather general and unspecified way. This was because almost nothing was known about the nature of the evolutionary material. To-day we are able to test in a precise and concrete way two questions which are important in this respect: (1) whether the variability of organisms, which provides the raw material for the evolutionary processes of adaptation and differentiation, is based merely on known genetic phenomena, or, in other terms, whether the genetically known and analysable units of variation constitute the only source of evolutionary raw material; and (2) whether these genetically known units of variation have all those qualities which must be assumed and required in order to explain their role as evolutionary material.

In the following sections these two questions will be briefly considered, followed by an examination of the actual participation of mutations in the formation of taxonomic units, and an evaluation of the various known evolutionary factors.

The author is much indebted to the editor, Dr. J. S. Huxley, for his help in correcting the English, and for his critical revision of the manuscript.

2. *Mutation as the Source of Evolutionary Material*

We know that the variability of organisms has two distinct components: the non-heritable modifications and the heritable variations. Only the latter ones are of primary importance in the process of evolution, the former being important merely in regard to the plasticity of the type and in being, in the last instance, based on its type of hereditary constitution. Almost all cases of well-analysed hereditary differences between individuals or groups of individuals have proved to depend upon combinations of Mendelian 'unit-characters'. And we know that all segregating unit-differences are due, in respect to their origin, to mutations in the broadest sense of the word. We thus can say that mutations and their combinations constitute the basis of almost all analysable hereditary differences. The only known exceptions are certain plastid and plasmon differences in plants. The non-Mendelian plastid-characters are due to the far-reaching autonomy of plant plastids in regard to reproduction, variation, and segregation. We have good reason to believe that such heritable, extra-nuclear plastid-differences originate as sudden, reproducible changes of single plastids. If we define the term 'mutation' as sudden changes of heritable units, transmitted in a more or less constant new form to subsequent cell-generations, we may speak of these as plastid-mutations. If so, the only cases of heritable differences which in their origin cannot yet be regarded as due to mutation are certain plasmatic differences, found in some species and varietal crosses in plants; these so-called plasmon-differences seem to be more or less independent of the genetical factors localized in the chromosomes, and nothing is yet known about their origin. But this phenomenon of autonomous plasmon-differences does not seem to be of very general importance, since it has been found in only a few cases.

Thus we can say that by far the most important source of the origin of heritable variation is mutation. We must accordingly examine the following three questions: (1) whether the general character of the known and genetically analysable process of mutation may explain the whole of the heritable variability of organisms; (2) whether mutations and their combinations produce such differences in the relative viability of individuals as to enable a sufficiently differentiated action of natural selection to take place; and (3) whether mutations are present in sufficient numbers in free-living populations of organisms. This examination will show us whether the mutation-process can really be regarded as the sole or main source of evolutionary raw material. If this question can be answered in the affirmative, the same examination will also show us the real characters and qualities of the evolutionary material, thus permitting a much more specialized and exact consideration of the mechanism of action and the relative value of the various factors of evolution.

(a) *Types of mutations, mutant characters, and mutation-rates.* As mutations we design sudden changes of heritable characters, leading from one more or less stable condition to another. Mutations have been found to occur spontaneously, i.e. without the application of any special mutation-inducing factors, in all species of protista, plants, and animals so far analysed in this respect. We thus have good reason to believe that spontaneous mutation is a general character of all living beings.

Cytogenetic work has revealed several different distinct types of mutational change in the hereditary material. According to the unit of change mutations can be classified into the following three groups: (1) gene-mutations, i.e. changes or losses of single genes; (2) chromosome-mutations, i.e. structural changes in single or several chromosomes (deletions, duplications, inversions, translocations); and (3) genome-mutations, i.e. changes in the number of single, several, or all chromosomes (haplo- or polysomy, heteroploidy, polyploidy). In plants, plastid-mutations may occur besides these three types.

All hypoploid chromosome-mutations (i.e. those lacking a piece of one or more chromosomes), and many of the hyperploid ones, are lethal in homozygous condition. Deficiencies for one or more genes often produce phenotypic character-changes even when heterozygous. Some of the chromosome-rearrangements show so-called 'position-effects' of the gene or genes near the point of breakage of the chromosomes; these 'position-effects' consist in character-changes, brought about by the abnormal functioning of the genes near the point of breakage and rearrangement, due to their proximity to other genes than in normal chromosomes.

Extensive observations of the mutation-process in different plants and animals show that all types of morphological and physiological character-changes can be produced by mutations. Mutant characters vary from ones so slight, that they can be detected only by means of special methods, up to changes so profound that they can be regarded as of more than normal specific value or produce death or serious pathological symptoms. All species of plants and animals extensively analysed in respect to their mutability show that mutations and their combinations are capable of producing the whole range of morphological and physiological character-variability of the species in question.

In genetically well-analysed species quantitative studies of their mutability have been made. They showed the following traits of spontaneous mutability. The total mutation rates[1] per generation are rather low, lying in the order of magnitude of 1–10 per cent. Variation in the factors of the normal environment of the organisms have little or no influence upon the mutability. Different single mutation-steps have different rates of change, lying in the order of magnitude of 0·001–0·00001 per cent.

(*b*) *The relative viability of mutations.* It was mentioned in the preceding paragraph that all possible kinds of character-changes may be produced by mutations. This already shows that different mutant characters and their combinations must show pronounced differences in their biological value. In all species extensively enough analysed in respect of their mutability, a

---

[1] By the 'rate of mutation' we understand the percentage of gametes or haploid genomes containing a mutation. In this case, by 'total mutation rate' is meant the percentage of gametes (of one generation) containing any kind of mutation. In other cases the rates of single definite mutation-steps, or of mutations of a certain gene or group of genes, or of mutations producing a certain type of character-changes may be analysed. For details and difficulties of determination of mutation-rates see Timoféeff-Ressovsky, 1937.

very large proportion of newly arising mutations show a more or less pronounced decrease of viability (many of them being even lethal when homozygous). This characteristic of mutation is not at all surprising: we must admit that by a permanent natural selection the 'best' mutations are taken up into the so-called normal type of the species or race in question, so that most mutations (i.e. alleles and chromosome-structures not belonging to the 'normal' type) must be rather 'worse' than the 'normal' type, which by natural selection is permanently kept in harmonious relation to its environment. The fact that most mutations are more or less deleterious has often led to the conclusion that mutability is of no importance as providing the raw material of evolution. But this conclusion is evidently wrong. The deleterious nature of many mutant homozygotes merely decreases the mutation-rate which is of evolutionary significance.

In order to get more information on the viability relations of mutations and their combinations special experiments can be performed. In such experiments some special aspect of the general phenomenon of 'viability' must be chosen and studied quantitatively. It is, for instance, possible to study the relative viability of different genotypes by comparing their hatching-, survival-, or fertility-rates under definite constant conditions. In *Drosophila funebris* and *melanogaster* experiments on the relative viability of mutations and their combinations were performed by studying the hatching-rates of a normal and various mutant genotypes, in culture-bottles started with equal numbers of the two types of eggs and kept under definite conditions of crowding, food, and temperature.

Some examples of the results are shown in Fig. 1. The upper row of this figure shows the viability of several single mutations as compared with that of the normal type: most of the mutations have a lower, but some a higher, viability than the normal type under given conditions. The viability of combinations shows sometimes a purely additive effect of the viabilities of the single mutations in question; but in other cases it may be lower or higher than is to be expected on the assumption of an additive effect of the single genes—three different typical cases are shown in the lower row of Fig. 1. The viability of a 'large' mutation may be specifically changed not only by the presence of another large mutation but also by many 'small' mutations or so-called modifiers, as is shown by the action of plus- and minus-selection upon the relative viability of a definite single mutation in heterogeneous cultures. Thus the general statement can be made that the relative viability of single mutations is partly

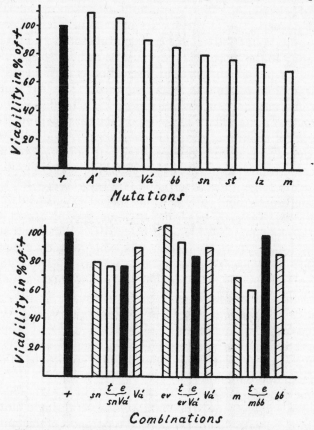

FIG. 1. The relative viabilities of eight mutations and three combinations in *Drosophila funebris* (hatching-rates in percentage of the normal type, in constantly crowded cultures held at 25° C.). For combinations two values are given: the empirical (*e*), and that calculated on the assumption of a purely additive effect of the two genes (*t*). (Timofeeff-Ressovsky, 1934.)

dependent upon the 'genotypical environment' provided by the gene-complex in which they find themselves.

The relative viability of different mutations and combinations may also differ under different environmental conditions. The upper row of Fig. 2 shows some typical examples: the viability of the three mutations behaves differently with change of temperature. Similar differences were also found in the reactions of the relative viabilities of different mutations to other environmental factors.

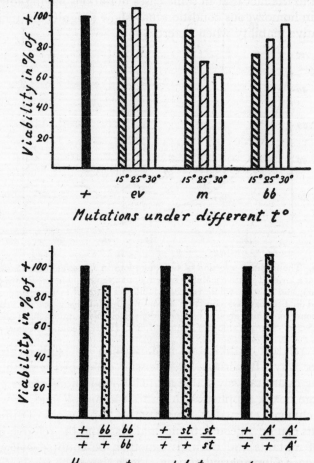

FIG. 2. The relative viabilities of three mutations at different temperatures, and the comparison of the relative viabilities of heterozygotes and homozygotes of three mutations at 25° C. in *Drosophila funebris* (all the experiments at constant degree of crowding of the cultures). (Timofeeff-Ressovsky, 1934.)

The lower row of Fig. 2 shows some different typical examples of the dominance-relations of the relative viability of different mutations. Just as in the case of morphological character, the viability effects of different mutations can show different degrees of dominance or recessiveness, which do not always correspond to those of the morphological character. Attention is drawn to the fact that in some cases mutations having low viability in homozygous condition may show a significant increase of relative viability when heterozygous.

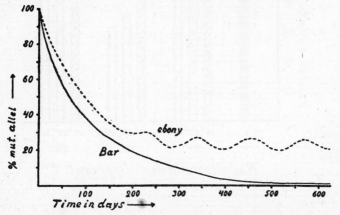

Fig. 3. The negative selection of two mutations in *Drosophila melanogaster*, one which has a lowered relative viability both in homozygous and heterozygous condition (Bar), and another whose relative viability is lowered in homozygous, and increased in heterozygous condition (ebony). Quantitatively stable 'artificial' populations (containing about 4,000 individuals each) of the mutations in question, were 'infected' by small amounts of normal flies. (L'Héritier and Teissier, 1937.)

The relative viability of mutants can be studied also in another way. L'Héritier and Teissier developed a method of keeping quantitatively stable artificial populations of *Drosophila* (in large boxes, supplied with dishes containing food, of which one is changed every day). Such stable populations of different mutants can be 'infected' by normal flies, and the relative numbers of mutants and normals can then be counted every few weeks over a long period of time. Fig. 3 shows the result of such experiments with the mutants Bar and ebony of *Drosophila melanogaster*. Both mutants decrease rapidly in number at first; then Bar continues to be gradually replaced by normal, finally disappearing from the population; ebony is after a while stabilized at a certain, rather low percentage. This latter effect is due to the counter-action of the negative selection of homozygotes by the positive selection of heterozygotes. It is interesting to note that in our own previous, quite independent, experi-

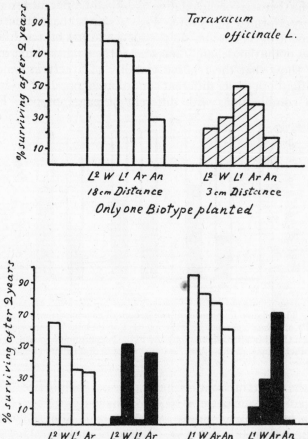

Fig. 4. Survival rates in artificial populations of five different biotypes of *Taraxacum officinale* L. (Compositae) from: Leningrad 1, Leningrad 2, Archangelsk, Wologda, and Askania-Nova. The populations were planted in two densities: 3 cm. and 18 cm. distance between the plants; above—each population contained only one of the biotypes; below—each population contained a mixture of four biotypes in equal numbers. (Sukatschev, 1928.)

ments on the relative viability of mutations it was found that ebony behaved in the same way as the mutation A on the right side of the lower row of Fig. 2: it showed a lowered relative viability in homozygous condition but increased relative viability of the heterozygote.

Still further tests of the relative viability of different genotypes can be performed in nature. Fig. 4 shows the results of an experiment of Sukatschev on the survival rates of five different biotypes of the dandelion, *Taraxacum officinale*; these experiments clearly show that the relative viability of a certain genotype may differ both under different conditions of population-density and in combinations with different other genotypes. Fig. 5

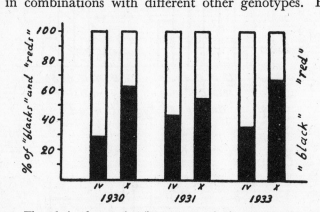

FIG. 5. The relative frequencies of two groups of colour-pattern-forms ('black' and 'red') of *Adalia bipunctata* L. (Coleoptera, Coccinellidae) in the early spring population (IV; just after hibernation) and in the late autumn population (X; just before hibernation) during three seasons near Berlin. (Timofeeff-Ressovsky, unpubl.)

shows the results of counting the relative numbers of two different monogenic colour-pattern types of the lady-beetle *Adalia bipunctata* in the early spring and the late autumn populations near Berlin during three years: this beetle has about three generations a year in this locality and shows a decrease of one of the genotypes after hibernation and of the other one just before it. This result shows that during different seasons of the year these two genotypes have different, opposite selective values; this is probably the cause of the permanent polymorphism of almost all populations of the species.

All the above-cited experiments were performed on 'large' mutations. Our experience of intraspecific variability shows us that the latter is in most cases due to 'small' mutations, slightly affecting some quantitative characters. It is thus important to know whether 'small' viability mutations, not causing pronounced character changes, also occur in organisms. Special experiments can be performed in *Drosophila* on the production of sex-linked mutations, differently affecting the relative viability of males. Fig. 6 shows the results of such experiments;

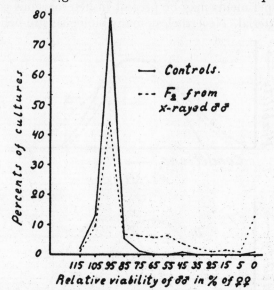

FIG. 6. Production of sex-linked mutations with lowered viability by X-rays in *Drosophila melanogaster*. Distribution of the sex-ratios in control cultures and in F₂-cultures from X-rayed ♂♂. (Timofeeff-Ressovsky, 1935.)

they clearly proved that 'small' viability mutations are the most frequent group of mutations in *Drosophila*. These results were confirmed by similar experiments of Kerkis (1938).

We thus see that mutations and their combinations may affect the relative viability of the organism in an extremely manifold and plastic way, permitting a most variable, specialized, and delicate action of natural selection. Fig. 7 shows schematically different types of mutational changes of viability in respect to an environmental factor; some of these changes do not replace the optimum, others do. The first type of viability changes may be classified as changes of 'resistance' to a certain environmental factor; the second as 'adaptational' changes. Anyhow, we see that as regards viability, mutations fulfil all requirements expected from the raw material of evolution.

(c) *Mutations in free-living populations.* We have now to prove whether mutations fulfil the last requirement: Are they present in sufficient frequency in free-living populations? Many incidental observations in different species of plants and animals have shown that mutations of the same type as those found in genetic experiments may be present in heterozygous condition in wild material. Nevertheless, many biologists still believe that

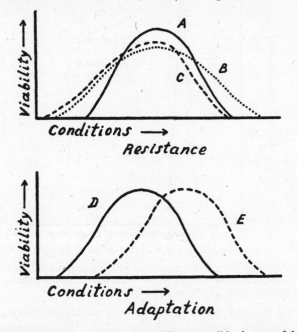

Fig. 7. Graphical representation of the different possible changes of the relative viability produced by mutations. Above: the optimum in respect to a certain environmental factor (e.g. temperature) is not changed in B and C; they differ from A merely in respect to their resistance to extreme conditions (change of 'resistance'). Below: E differs from D in its optimum in respect to the environmental factor ('adaptational' change). (Timofeeff-Ressovsky, 1934.)

mutations are of no evolutionary importance, since mutation-rates are so low and since most mutations are of no biological value. There are even some biologists who still think that mutations are a kind of 'artefacts' produced in the laboratory or under conditions of domestication in 'genetical' objects. Our whole knowledge of the mutation-process together with the numerous incidental observations of mutations in wild populations speak against these views, and show that mutation must occur in nature just as in our laboratory cultures.

In *Drosophila* and some other objects special experiments have been performed in order to test quantitatively the presence and concentration of different mutations in free-living populations. The method of these experiments is very simple and consists in arranging for the segregation of all recessives present in individuals taken from wild populations. The simplest way is the

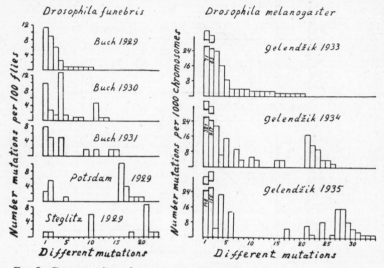

FIG. 8. Concentrations of mutations in different free-living populations of *Drosophila melanogaster* (Dubinin and associates, 1936), and *D. funebris*. (Timofeeff-Ressovsky, 1939a.)

inbreeding of wild-caught females, already fertilized in nature, for two generations, by making a large number of single pair-crossings from the F_1; any recessive present in heterozygous condition in either of the wild parents will then segregate in one of the F_2 crosses. Using this method, extensive tests of free-living populations of *Drosophila melanogaster* from Berlin (Timofeeff-Ressovsky, 1927) and from the Caucasus (Tschetverikov, 1928) showed that numerous mutations were present in different concentrations in these populations. Substantially similar results have later been found in other populations of the same species (Dubinin and co-workers, 1934, 1936, 1937; Gordon, 1935; Timofeeff-Ressovsky, unpubl.) in different populations of *Drosophila funebris* (Romashoff, Timofeeff-Ressovsky), of *D. obscura* (Gershenson, 1934), *D. subobscura* (Gordon, 1936), *D. pseudo-obscura* (Dobzhansky and Queal, 1938), *D. phalerata, D. transversa,* and *D. vibrissina* (Balkashina and Romashoff, 1935), and of the amphipod *Gammarus chevreuxi* (Sexton and

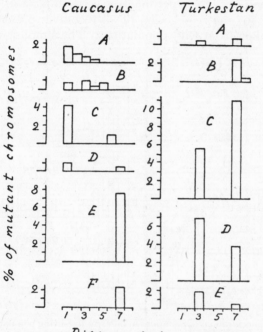

FIG. 9. Concentrations of inversions in different free-living populations of *Drosophila melanogaster*. Caucasus: A, Kutais; B, Gori; C, Batum; D, Baku; E, Gelendžik; F, Derbent. Turkestan: A, Osh; B, Samarkand; C, Bukhara; D, Stalinabad; E, Leninabad. (Dubinin and associates, 1937.)

Clark, 1936). Different populations may contain different, or sometimes the same mutations, the concentrations of different mutations within the same populations being sometimes very different. The content of mutations in the same population in successive years may vary very much; but the mutations present in high concentrations may persist in the populations for several years, i.e. for many generations of *Drosophila*. Fig. 8 shows the results of such experiments in *Drosophila funebris* and *D. melanogaster*. All these experiments thus show that numerous mutations of the same type as those studied in genetical experiments are present in wild populations, sometimes in surprisingly high concentrations. Special experiments in *D. pseudo-obscura* (Dobzhansky and Queal, 1938) showed that 'small' mutations

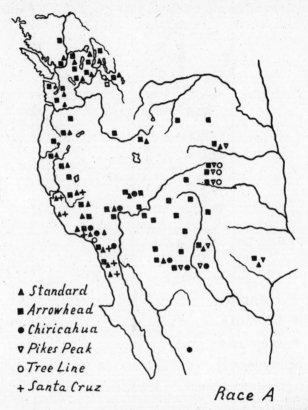

▲ *Standard*
■ *Arrowhead*
● *Chiricahua*
▽ *Pikes Peak*
○ *Tree Line*
+ *Santa Cruz*

Race A

FIG. 10. Geographical distribution of different types of gene-arrangements (inversions and combinations of inversions) in the III-chromosome of *Drosophila pseudo-obscura* race A, in North America. (From Dobzhansky, 1937*b*.)

are also abundantly present in wild populations. In *D. melanogaster* and in *D. pseudo-obscura* special experiments were designed in order to test the presence of chromosome-mutations in free-living populations. Fig. 9 shows the concentration of inversions in different *D. melanogaster* populations. Figs. 10 and 11 show the geographical distribution of different inversions and combinations of inversions in one of the chromosomes of *D. pseudo-*

obscura A and B in North America. Both of these extensive sets of experiments show that inversions especially are present in rather high concentration in all populations examined.

Thus both the *ad hoc* analysis in *Drosophila* and the whole evidence from other species shows that mutations are abundantly

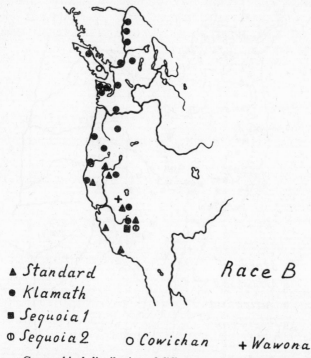

▲ *Standard*

● *Klamath*   *Race B*

■ *Sequoia 1*

◐ *Sequoia 2*   ○ *Cowichan*   + *Wawona*

FIG. 11. Geographical distribution of different types of gene-arrangements in the III-chromosome of *Drosophila pseudo-obscura* race B, in North America. (From Dobzhansky, 1937*b*.)

present in free-living populations, so that the second requirement also is fulfilled. The study of inversions and combinations of inversions of a certain chromosome is of interest also in another respect. A special analysis of inversions and different combinations of inversions in the giant chromosomes of the salivary glands of *Drosophila* may show the sequence of their origin (Sturtevant and Dobzhansky, 1936), so that following up their geographical distribution, the accurate phylogenetic relations of the different types may be found. Fig. 12 shows the result of such investigations in *D. pseudo-obscura* A and B and *D. miranda*.

(*d*) *Mutations as the raw material of evolution.* We thus have seen that gene-mutations, chromosome-mutations, genom-mutations, the position effects accompanying some of the chromosome-mutations, and the plastid-mutations in plants are the only known sources of heritable variation of organisms. Even if other still unknown sources of heritable variation exist, the

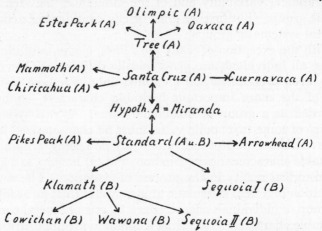

FIG. 12. Scheme of the phylogenetic relations of the different populations of *Drosophila pseudo-obscura* race A, race B, and *D. miranda*, constructed according to the assumed sequence of origin of repeated inversions in the III-chromosomes contained in these populations. (From Dobzhansky, 1937*b*.)

known ones and their combinations undoubtedly constitute by far the majority. The general features of the mutation-process, the special experiments on the relative viability of mutations and their combinations, and the analysis of the mutation-content of free-living populations, show that the assumption that mutation, as made known by modern genetics, is the only source of evolutionary material, fulfils all necessary requirements. It is thus legitimate to consider evolutionary questions and problems on the basis of this assumption.

3. *Mutations and the Formation of Taxonomic Groups*

If we consider mutations as the only source of evolutionary material, we must expect that the analysis of the genetic constitution of different subspecific and specific taxonomic groups will show that the differences between those groups are merely due to different combinations of mutations (i.e. show Mendelian segregation); furthermore, we should expect to find cases of the formation of taxonomic groups *in statu nascendi*, due to the spread of single mutations or of definite combinations of mutations.

In this chapter some examples will be given proving that mutations and combinations are in point of fact the basis of geographical variability and of the differences between taxonomic groups. But first we must briefly consider the definition of 'real systematic groups'.

With the exception of really pure lines, clones, and identical twins, all individuals are genotypically different. Thus a biotype, even if classified and identified only in respect to rather few of the more important heritable characters, cannot be regarded as a group of taxonomic value. A 'real systematic group' of some taxonomic value must be characterized in two ways: It is a group of individuals (1) possessing a number of heritable characteristics in common, and (2) having, as a group, an historical reality in the process of evolution. The simplest definition of a 'real systematic group' would then be as follows: A group of individuals characterized by one or several common heritable characters and having a common area of distribution. The definition of an area of distribution should not be limited merely to a closed geographical territory, but extended to cover cases of ecological areas: in the latter case, two or more areas may overlap within a larger geographical area.

According to the above definition, a clear detection of the lowest intraspecific systematic categories can be made. The relative taxonomic evaluation of higher groups remains very difficult in particular cases, and must depend upon the general knowledge and 'biological tact' of the systematist. These difficulties already arise in connexion with any general definition of the species. This question can be here considered only very briefly. I believe that we have no reason to doubt the reality of species as natural taxonomic units; but, on the other hand, I doubt whether it is possible to give a general and simple definition of the species, applicable in all the larger groups of organisms. The most general but at the same time cautious definition of a species may perhaps be given as follows: a species is a group of individuals that are morphologically and physiologically similar (although comprising a number of groups of the lowest taxonomic category), which has reached an almost complete biological isolation from similar neighbouring groups of individuals inhabiting the same or adjacent territories. Under biological isolation we understand the impossibility or non-occurrence of normal hybridization under natural conditions.[1] The practical difficulties of a general definition of the term species, and of using one or two simple criteria in distinguishing what is a species and what is not, may be seen from some examples of 'good' species which practically show no pronounced morphological differences (e.g. *Drosophila melanogaster* and *D. simulans*, *D. miranda*, and *D. pseudo-obscura*), and on the other side also 'good' species showing typical specific traits in their morphology, physiology, and distribution, but producing fertile hybrids with other species under laboratory conditions (e.g. some Lepidoptera, birds, and many plants).

Another question must still be briefly considered. Some biogeographers assume a fundamental difference between individual and geographical variation. This assumption is based on the obvious fact that not all the characters of the individual variation seen in a single local population are included in the geographical variability. But deductions about fundamental differences between geographical and individual variation based on these facts are wrong. The individuals differ in all those characters which are included in the geographical variation, but not vice versa, since the geographical variation is the result of the selection of only a few possible character-differences and character-combinations. The mutations and their combinations form the basis of the individual heritable variability; but only a few of them are used in the process of evolution to build up what were above described as 'systematically real groups'; and it is these latter which exhibit geographical variability. In many cases the same character may in different groups of organisms behave as an individual aberration, as a characteristic of a geographical race, or even as a species-character. Fig. 13 shows an example of this kind: a mutant wing-vein character in the genus *Andrena* (Hymenoptera).

[1] A more detailed classification and description of the various types of isolation is given in the next section (p. 107).

(*a*) *Taxonomic groups in statu nascendi.* We will now first examine the question whether cases can be found, in which certain mutations or combinations of mutations are just beginning to produce geographical races. If mutations really participate in the formation of taxonomic groups, such cases of races *in statu nascendi* should be found.

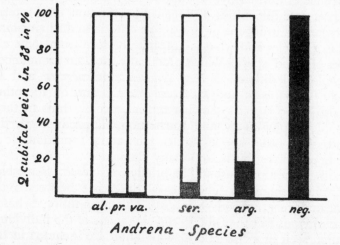

Fig. 13. A mutant character ('second cubital crossvein') in the populations of six different species of the genus *Andrena* (Hymenoptera): as a rare aberration (*A. albicans, A. praecox, A. vaga*), as a frequent aberration (*A. serica, A. argentata*), and as a species-character (*A. neglecta*). (Zimmerman, 1933.)

The participation of mutations in the formation of geographical races can be directly observed in the following cases. First of all when races, distinguishable in some other respects, show pronounced differences in the concentration of certain alternative heritable characters. Next, when species are polymorphic in respect of certain alternative heritable characters, and show pronounced differences in the concentrations of some of these characters in different populations (some of these populations reaching monomorphism by the total elimination of some of the character-alternatives). And finally in cases where a certain mutation, spreading around its centre of origin, occupies a definite distribution area, and thus can be designed as a good geographical race. There are undoubtedly many cases of all these types, but only a few of them have been described, because of our lack of knowledge of the minor systematics and bio-geography even of our commonest species.

Cases of the first two types are nevertheless well known, especially amongst birds and beetles. In birds such cases were described by Stresemann in his *Mutationsstudien* (1926). In beetles a thoroughly analysed case has been described by Dobzhansky in *Harmonia axyridis* (1924, 1937). Fig. 14 shows

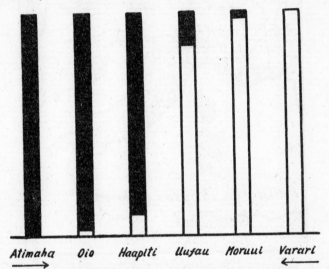

FIG. 14. Relative frequencies of an alternative heritable character, dextrality (black, →) and sinistrality (white, ←) of coiling in the mollusc *Partula suturalis*, in different populations on the island Moorea. (Crampton, 1916.)

a similar case in the mollusc *Partula suturalis*, analysed by Crampton, and showing different frequencies of an alternative heritable character in different populations on Moorea. Many other cases are known in the *Carabid beetles* from mountainous regions. Population-statistical studies on various of our most common species of plants and animals would reveal a large volume of interesting data on the distribution of single heritable characters, their dynamics, and their participation in the process of geographical variability.

The following figures will show some cases of the formation of geographical races by single mutations. Fig. 15 shows the present geographical distribution of the semi-dominant mutation *Elaterii* in a part of the north Mediterranean population of the lady-beetle *Epilachna chrysomelina*. This mutation causes a conspicuous, specific colour-pattern, and must be classified as a good geographical race. The *Elaterii*-population also shows some differences in minor heritable characters, genetically inde-

FIG. 15. Geographical distribution of the semidominant gene 'Elaterii' in the north Mediterranean populations of *Epilachna chrysomelina* F. (Coleoptera, Coccinel-lidae).

pendent of the *Elaterii*-mutation; this is to be expected according to our knowledge of the relative viability of mutations and combinations: every mutation selected or distributed for any reason must automatically 'select' a genotypical environment which is optimal for its relative viability. Fig. 16 shows the distribution of a recessive mutation affecting the structure of the molar teeth in the north German population of *Microtus arvalis* (Zimmerman, 1935). From Schleswig-Holstein the concentration of this mutation decreases southwards. Fig. 17 shows the distribution of three heritable colour-types, the normal and two different recessive mutations, in the German population of the squirrel *Sciurus vulgaris*; both mutations seem to be limited, so far as any considerable frequency is concerned, to northern or mountainous regions (they frequently recur in northern

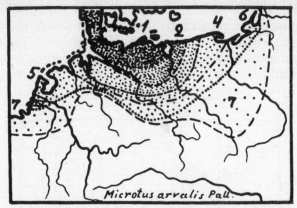

FIG. 16. Geographical distribution of the recessive mutant character 'simplex' (molar teeth) in the population of *Microtus arvalis* Pall. (Rodentia) from northern Germany. Concentrations of phenotypically detectable homozygotes: 1 = over 85 per cent.; 2 = 65–85 per cent.; 3 = 50–65 per cent.; 4 = 25–50 per cent.; 5 = 10–25 per cent.; 6 = 5–10 per cent.; 7 = less than 5 per cent. (Zimmerman, 1935.)

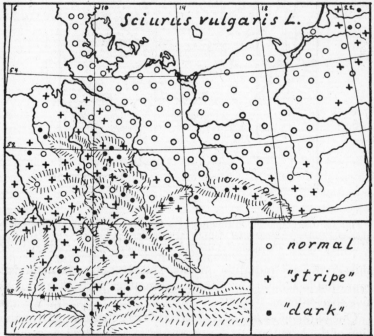

FIG. 17. Geographical distribution of three heritable colour-types ('normal', dark dorsal 'stripe', and 'dark' colour) in the squirrel, *Sciurus vulgaris* L. (Rodentia) in Germany. (Lühring, 1928.)

Russia and the Ural district), but as single aberrations may be found anywhere. Figs. 18 and 19 show definite, limited distribution areas of high concentrations of recessive colour-mutations within the populations of the polecat *Putorius putorius* and of the hare *Lepus timidus* in western Russia; as rare aberrations

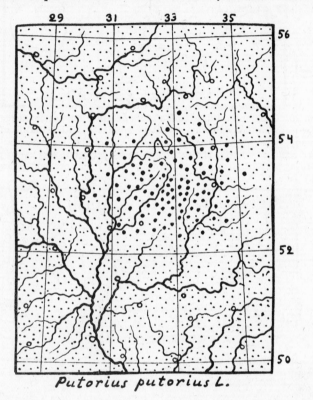

Putorius putorius L.

FIG. 18. Geographical distribution of a recessive erythristic mutant colour-character (subspec. *Stanchinskii* Mel.) in the polecat, *Putorius putorius* L. (Carnivora) in western Russia. (According to the data of Melander, 1926, and other sources.)

this erythristic mutation in the polecat and this melanistic mutation in the hare are also found in other parts of the respective species-areas.

One of the most interesting cases of the geographical distribution of single mutations is represented in Fig. 20. Here is shown the present distribution of a recessive melanistic colour-mutation in the hamster *Cricetus cricetus*. This mutation occurs sporadically as an aberration in various populations of the hamster. The well-known Russian geographer Lepekhin, at the end of the eighteenth century (in the years 1771–2), during his scientific journey to northern Bashkiria, observed that in a certain region between the rivers Kama and Belaia the hamster population contained a high percentage of melanistic animals. Since then

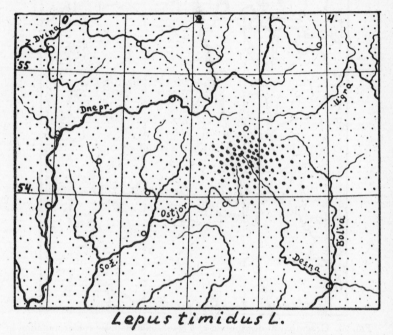

Lepus timidus L.

Fig. 19. Geographical distribution of a recessive melanistic mutant colour-character in the hare, *Lepus timidus* L. (Rodentia), in western Russia. (According to the data of Melander, 1930, and other sources.)

up till the present the distribution of this black mutant has been followed up (Kirikov, 1934, and additional data). An exact study of its distribution was possible because hamsters play an important role on the fur-markets in eastern Russia. In the course of the last 150 years this mutation has spread from its original centre of high concentration along the northern border of the species-area. To-day the populations of northern Bash-kiria and in the adjacent western parts of eastern Russia are almost homogeneous for this mutation; and populations with rather high concentrations of this gene are spread westwards as far as the river Dnieper. The hamster is a typical rodent of the xerophytic zone of the steppes; but this melanistic mutation seems to be better adapted than the normal form to the cooler and moister climate of the wood-steppe subzone along the northern border of the distribution area of this species.

FIG. 20. Geographical distribution of a recessive melanistic colour-mutation in the hamster, *Cricetus cricetus* L. (Rodentia), along the northern limit of its distribution-area in eastern and middle Russia. (According to the data of Kirikov, 1934, and other sources.)

What appears to be a very similar case is that of the spread of the melanic mutant of the opossum *Trichosurus vulpecula* in its Tasmanian subspecies (Pearson, 1938), except that the area in which the black form is abundant is geographically isolated from the main area of the species, in which melanics occur only as rare aberrations. As with the previously cited case of the tooth-mutant in *Microtus arvalis*, the geographical distribution of the frequencies of the mutant type provide evidence that it is still in process of spreading, the spread being totally prevented or partially held up by such features as mountains, large rivers, or narrow isthmuses. It is also to be noted that the region in which the black form has been favoured is cooler and moister than the rest of the range, in *Trichosurus* as well as in *Cricetus*.

These examples show clearly enough that although our knowledge of the population-statistics of wild plants and animals is rather meagre, nevertheless enough direct cases of the participation of mutations in the origination of geographical races may be observed. That this refers not only to gene-mutations but also to chromosome-rearrangements is shown by the *Drosophila pseudo-obscura* work, some results of which are shown in Figs. 10 and 11.

(b) *The genetic structure of races and species.* Another way of proving the participation of mutations in the origin of taxonomic groups is to test the genetic nature of the differences between these groups.

In many different cases, involving different groups of plants and animals, different geographical races or subspecies or even different species have been crossed. Although a thorough monographic analysis of the whole intraspecific variability has been carried out only in a few cases, the general impression of all such genetic experiments is that all heritable differences between races and even species are dependent upon segregating units of genetically familiar type, the origin of which is known to be due to gene- or chromosome-mutations. Only in a few cases, as was mentioned before, some plant crosses show plasmatic differences the origin of which is not yet known. In any case we may state that the great majority of the differences between taxonomic groups are due to mutations and their combinations.

The experiments show that most of the 'good' geographic races, even the closely related ones, differ in a large number of genes, most of which cause only very small quantitative character-deviations. Thus we get typical multifactorial segregations, like the one shown in Fig. 21. But this is just what is to be expected according both to our knowledge of the history of species and races and to our knowledge of the interrelations of the relative viabilities of mutations and combinations.

In many cases it is still impossible to discover the detailed relations between the biological values of single race characters or their combinations and the local environmental conditions. But in some cases the local biological value of the geographical

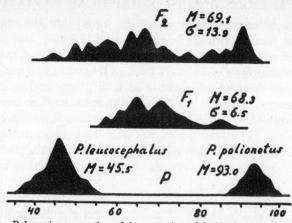

Fig. 21. Polygenic segregation of the extension of dark colour in a cross between two subspecies of deer-mouse, *Peromyscus polionotus polionotus* × *Peromyscus polionotus leucocephalus*. (Sumner, 1932.)

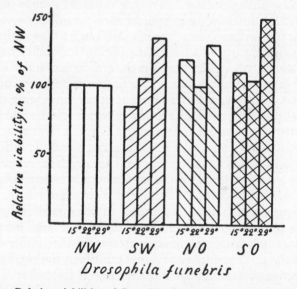

Fig. 22. Relative viabilities of *Drosophila funebris* from various regions of the western Palaearctic: the north-west (seven populations from: Germany, Sweden, Norway, Denmark, Scotland, England, and France), the south-west (six populations from: Portugal, Spain, Italy, Gallipoli, Tripolis, and Egypt), the north-east (six populations from: Leningrad, Kiev, Moscow, Saratov, Perm, and Tomsk), and the south-east (five populations from: Crimea, northern Caucasus, southern Caucasus, Turkestan, and Semiretchje), in different temperatures (15°, 22°, and 29°), expressed in percentage of the viability of the north-western form. (Timofeeff-Ressovsky, 1935a.)

races can be shown experimentally. The relative viability of
Drosophila funebris flies from twenty-four different populations
of the western Palaearctic was studied at three different temperatures (15°, 22°, and 29° C.). A summary of the results is shown
in Fig. 22; the north-western and south-western populations
differ clearly in respect to their viabilities at low and high

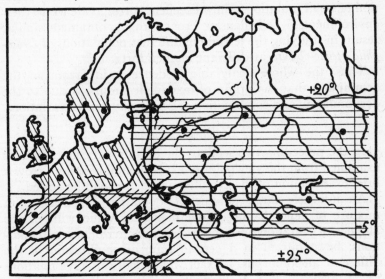

FIG. 23. Map of the approximate distribution of the three 'temperature-races'
in *Drosophila funebris*; the distribution fits the climatic peculiarities of this region,
characterized by the isotherms of July (+20° C.), and January (−5° C.), and by
the isoline of a difference of 25° C. between the mean temperatures of July and
January (±25°). (Timofeeff-Ressovsky, 1935*a*).

temperatures, the northern population being more resistant to
low, the southern more resistant to high temperatures. All the
eastern populations, the north-eastern as well as the south-
eastern ones, show higher resistance both at low and at high
temperatures. At first glance the results for the eastern populations do not show the same correspondence with the local
climate as the western ones. But if, as it is shown on Fig. 23, we
consider the climatic peculiarities in this part of the palaearctic
region, we find an excellent correspondence of all populations
with the climates of their habitats. As is seen on the map of
Fig. 23, the January isotherm of −5° C. runs from the northernmost part of Norway to the south-west point of Russia on the

Black Sea coast; on the other hand, the July isotherm of $+20°$ C. runs from Lisbon in the west up to about $63°$ latitude in the east. These isotherms characterize the continental climate of eastern Europe and northern Asia, with both extremely high and low temperatures. Thus these 'temperature races' of *Drosophila funebris*, which are due to the accumulation by selection of small mutations, show excellent correspondence to their environments. Dobzhansky (1935, 1937) obtained similar results in studying the fertility of different populations of *Drosophila pseudo-obscura* at different temperatures.

Thus, the whole analysable evidence is in favour of the assumption that the origin of taxonomic groups is due to the accumulation and combination of genetically known variations.

4. *Evolutionary Factors*

In the preceding two sections the evolutionary material was examined from the viewpoint of experimental genetics. Now a brief examination of the evolutionary factors will be added.

An infinitely large panmictic population consisting of a mixture of genes having equal biological value will, in the absence of mutation and under constant environmental conditions, be stabilized in a certain state of equilibrium of the different allelomorphs. Exact mathematical investigations (R. A. Fisher, J. B. S. Haldane, S. S. Tschetverikov, S. Wright, and others) show that three different factors may disturb this equilibrium and lead to a change of the relative gene-frequencies, i.e. to an evolution of the previously stable population. These factors are: (1) mutability, introducing, by mutation, changes into the genetic constitution, the amount of the change being expressed by the mutation-pressure depending upon the rate of mutation; (2) selection, depending upon differences in the biological value of the different genotypes, and quantitatively characterized by selection-pressure; and (3) the limitation of panmixy, leading to accidental fluctuations of the concentration of single genotypes, and, in cases of continued isolation, to a statistical divergence of the different parts of a mixed population. The interrelation of these three factors constitutes the mechanism of adaptation and differentiation, i.e. the mechanism of evolution.

Mathematical analysis shows the quantitative values and

limitations of the efficiency of each of these three factors and their interrelations under various arbitrary conditions and values of mutation-pressure, selection-pressure, and isolation. This type of mathematical work is of the greatest importance, showing us the relative efficacy of various evolutionary factors under the different conditions possible within the populations (Wright, 1932). It does not, however, tell us anything about the real conditions in nature, or the actual empirical values of the coefficients of mutation, selection, or isolation. It is the task of the immediate future to discover the order of magnitude of these coefficients in free-living populations of different plants and animals; this should form the aim and content of an empirical population-genetics (Buzzati-Traverso, Jucci, and Timofeeff-Ressovsky, 1938). Here we can consider the evolutionary factors only in a rather general way, with the aim of testing whether the known qualities of the evolutionary material and of the conditions in natural populations are of such a nature that the known evolutionary factors, applied to the known evolutionary material, are capable of explaining the mechanism of evolution.

Although we know only the three above-mentioned groups of mechanisms leading to changes in the genetic constitution of populations, we may distinguish four different evolutionary factors: mutation, selection, isolation, and population-waves. For biological reasons (which will be mentioned in due course) we differentiate the 'mathematical' factor of isolation into two biological factors, that of isolation proper and that of population-waves.

(a) *Mutation.* The biological content and significance of this first evolutionary factor are at present better known than those of the other factors, due to the extensive genetical experiments on the process of mutation in different plants and animals.

As we have seen in the previous sections, mutation is the sole, or in any case the most important, source of new evolutionary material. In this sense the significance of mutation as an evolutionary factor is quite clear. But it is often asserted that mutation may also act as a directing factor in evolution. Even some geneticists have thought that, for instance, some of the so-called orthogenetic series in palaeontological evolution may be explained by 'directed' mutations (Jollos). However, there are two general features of mutation which make it impossible to explain directed evolutionary series simply by correspondingly directed mutation—first, the random nature of mutation and, secondly, the relatively very low rate of mutation. These two properties show that the process of mutation as such could influence the direction of evolutionary change only in the extremely improbable event of mutation-pressure being high enough over long periods of time to override the effects of the other factors, selection and isolation. The evolutionary fate of two mutations A and B will thus normally depend not upon the very small difference in their very low mutation-rates but upon their relative selective value and the structure and history of the populations. This being so, even cases of strictly directed mutations (which are so far unknown from exact experimental data) would have no importance as an explanation of chronologically or territorially 'directed' series of phenotypes. A directive influence of mutation is possible only in so far as the mutability of any species is limited, and in so far as any step in differentiation at the same time constitutes a certain limitation of further possibilities of variation.[1]

Mutation as an evolutionary factor is thus of importance as the source of new heritable variation; it has no, or at best very little, importance as a directive factor in evolution.

(b) *Selection.* The significance of natural selection as an evolutionary factor is well known, so that we need here only examine whether and to what extent the genetically known evolutionary material may be subject to selective processes.

In a mixture of two or more different genotypes, that one which under given conditions has the highest total probability of producing mature offspring will gradually increase its relative frequency within the population: this is the general process of natural selection. Selection-pressure can be numerically expressed in the form of selection-coefficients which represent the relative probabilities of reproduction of the genotypes in ques-

---

[1] Perhaps some cases of the reduction of vestigial organs which no longer retain the selective value which they possessed when fully developed can be ascribed to an automatic accumulation of mutations, most of which would produce a reduction of the organ. But this would be only a special case of a very general phenomenon: without the sifting, and thus directive, action of natural selection, mutation alone would lead to a general regression of highly differentiated organisms (since most mutations are 'deleterious' or 'regressive').

tion. It has been shown by numerous mathematical studies (Fisher, Gause, Haldane, Tschetverikov, Volterra, Wright, and others) that even very small selective advantages may, although only within large populations and over long periods of time, significantly increase the concentration of genotypes previously present in low concentrations, and thus change the genotypic constitution of the population. Most evolutionists have been very cautious in their assumptions concerning the quantitative values of selection-coefficients, and seem in general to have rather underestimated the amount of selection-pressure to be found in nature. All that we know about the relative viability of different mutations and combinations under different environmental conditions shows that we can, in point of fact, reckon with quite high positive and negative selective values for different genotypes under different conditions and in combination with different other genotypes. Experiments on the relative viability of mutations and combinations have shown that the selective values of mutations may be very different in the heterozygous and the homozygous condition, in different combinations with other genes, and in different environments. From these findings a highly differentiated and plastic action of natural selection may be deduced.

Our present knowledge of the relative viability of mutations readily explains the possibility of the differentiation by natural selection of different 'harmonious' genotypic combinations in different regions within the geographical range of a species; they are due to the fact that every process of selection automatically involves (even in cases when one character is mainly being selected) many different genes connected with the primary character by their viability interrelations. This is the way in which many so-called physiological correlations arise, and the apparently 'neutral' characters that often are diagnostic of species and subspecies. It is evident that not only positive but also negative selection will be of importance in building up physiologically correlated gene-combinations. The heterogeneity of almost all natural populations provides the species with potential 'candidates' for evolution, ready to undergo positive or negative selection in different regions of the species area. The same mutation may clearly have different selective values in different populations, due to differences in the external or the genotypic environments. The genetic heterogeneity of a species constitutes a reservoir of potential adaptability to heterogeneous and fluctuating environments.

Thus, the properties of the genetically known material of evolution permit an extremely powerful, plastic, and differentiated action of natural selection, leading to the most specialized and minute adaptations. And different selective adaptations, when combined with isolation, may lead to differentiation. We know that rather high selection coefficients may occur; but we still know very little concerning the actual intensities of selection-pressures to be found in nature.

(c) *Isolation*. For biological reasons we must distinguish two evolutionary factors, which are rather similar in the mechanism of their action: first, isolation, and, secondly, population-waves. The essential properties of both these factors are the limitation of panmixy, leading to a limitation of interbreeding between neighbouring groups of organisms, and the restriction of population-size. The limitation of interbreeding and mixture hinders the dissipation of incipient local processes of differentiation and localizes them; the reduction of population-size significantly increases the relative importance of accidental fluctuations of gene-concentrations.

Isolation we define as the more constant, longer-lasting limitations of panmixy, their most essential result being a partial or total prevention of interbreeding between two or more groups of organisms. A definition of population-waves will be given later.

Various different forms of isolation exist. Isolation as a whole comprises two main kinds—biological and territorially-geographical (hereinafter simply called geographical). Biological isolation may be subdivided (without pretending to give a definitive classification) into the following main groups: (1) genetic isolation *sensu stricto*, consisting in the lowering of hybrid viability or fertility (in extreme cases producing complete hybrid sterility or inviability), and brought about by genetic differences between the parental groups of organisms; (2) physiological isolation, consisting in a limitation (by sexual or gametic incompatibility) on the production of hybrids, although the hybrids themselves, if produced, are more or less normal; (3) ecological isolation, limiting the possibility of interbreeding through ecological differences between the parental groups of organisms. It is evident that all types of biological isolation are in the last resort due to genetic differences. Geographical isolation, on the other hand, is brought about by unequal distribution of the individuals within the species area, by disjunction between different parts of the distribution area, or by unsurmountable geographical obstacles within the species area.

All the types of biological isolation above mentioned have been observed in different plants and animals, although sometimes it is rather difficult to say which type is primary. The problem of genetic and physiological isolation has been extensively analysed by Dobzhansky, Sturtevant, and their colleagues in *Drosophila pseudo-obscura* A and B, *D. miranda*, *D. athabasca*, and *D. azteca* (Dobzhansky, 1935, 1937; Dobzhansky and Koller, 1938; Sturtevant and Dobzhansky, 1936). Physiological and ecological isolations have been extensively studied in *Trichogramma* (Harland and Attek, 1933) and in Aphids (Cholodkowsky, 1910). Sexual selection leading to partial physiological isolation has been experimentally tested in some mutant stocks of *Drosophila melanogaster* and *funebris* (Nikoro and collaborators, 1935; Spett, 1931; Sturtevant, 1915; Timofeeff-Ressovsky unpublished), and in different strains of *Drosophila pseudo-obscura*, *D. miranda*, *D. azteca*, *D. athabasca* (Dobzhansky and Koller, 1938). Apart from *Drosophila*, the limitations of the fertility and viability of hybrids due to differences in the structure and number of chromosomes are especially well known in Lepidoptera and plants (Federley, 1915–16; Karpechenko, 1935).

In many, if not in most cases, the various types of biological isolation are secondary, the primary isolation being geographical. The latter type of isolation may occur in very different forms. Fig. 24 shows an extreme case of a geographical disjunction of a species area; such cases are known in different groups of plants and animals, and are due to post-diluvial disjunction during the reimmigration of the species into their previous area from the south-western and south-eastern refuges into which Palearctic organisms were driven during the glacial period. Fig. 25 shows an example of a territorially fractionated species area, due to the lack of suitable biotopes between the various occupied parts of the total distribution area; such cases of geographical isolation are also very frequent. An example of secondary fragmentation, due to partial extermination by man,

FIG. 24. Postdiluvial disjunction of the distribution-area of *Cyanopica cyanus* Pall. (Aves, Corvidae). (Meinertzhagen, 1928.)

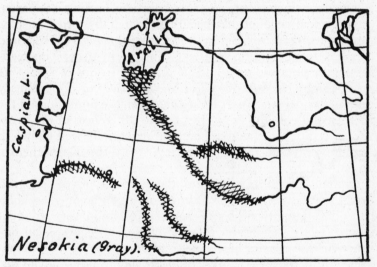

FIG. 25. Ecological disjunction of the distribution-area of *Nesokia* (Rodentia) in middle Asia. (Geptner, 1936.)

is shown in Fig. 26. Territorial fragmentation of the population of a species may occur also on a smaller geographical scale, as shown on Fig. 27.

An examination of the real distribution of individuals within the species-area shows that total or partial territorial isolation may occur on a still smaller scale, even within small local popula-

FIG. 26. Secondary fragmentation of the distribution-area of *Martes zibellina* L. (Carnivora), by extermination. (Ognev, 1931.)

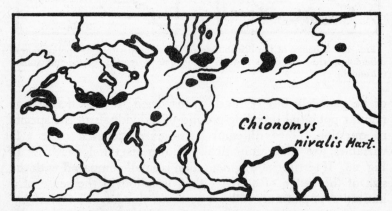

FIG. 27. Orographical disjunction of the populations of *Chionomys nivalis* Mart. (Rodentia) in the Alps. (Mohr, 1930, from Geptner, 1936.)

tions. The distribution of individuals is never quite uniform, and shows either small isolated population-areas or at least more or less pronounced differences in population-density in different parts of the inhabited territory; this is schematically shown in the upper row of Fig. 28. But such minor fragmentations of the population do not always lead to isolation. Isolation, in the sense of a limitation of panmixy, depends upon the relation between territorial fragmentation of the population and what we may call the 'range of activity' of the individuals of the species in question. By the term 'range of activity' we mean the area within which individuals of one generation may move

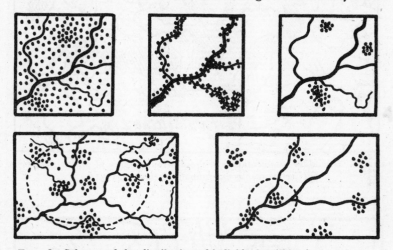

FIG. 28. Schemes of the distribution of individuals within the population of different species, and of its relation to the 'activity-regions' of the individuals. (Original.)

or be passively but regularly transported; it thus defines the regular potential breeding-ground of individuals of the species in question. Two different possible relations of these two variables are diagrammatically shown in the lower row of Fig. 28. If territorial fragmentation is small compared with the size of the range of activity, then isolation in the sense of a limitation of panmixy will not necessarily occur. The following example shows how misleading conclusions concerning the degree of geographical isolation may be, if based merely upon territorial fragmentation of the population. The common teal, *Nettion crecca*, occurs in widely separated biotopes within the distribution area of the species, so that a pronounced degree of geographical isolation of the various single populations might be assumed. But, as shown on Fig. 29, young birds taken from the nest and ringed in central England were already in their next year caught as nesting-birds in different parts of a huge region, extending from Iceland and the northern Urals in the north to central France and central Russia in the south. This implies a tremendous dissipation of the young birds in every generation, i.e. a very large range of activity, so that territorial

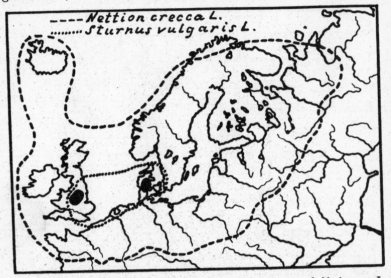

FIG. 29. The nest-regions ('activity-regions'): of the common teal, *Nettion crecca* L. (Aves, Lamellirostres), marked as young birds in England and caught as nesting birds during the next year; of *Sturnus vulgaris* L. (Aves, Passeres), marked as young birds in Denmark and caught during the subsequent eight years. (Original, according to the data of Schütz and of Promptov.)

fragmentation is of no importance as an isolating factor. The same figure shows the considerably smaller activity-range found in the starling *Sturnus vulgaris*.

Our knowledge of the real distribution of individuals within populations, and of their ranges of activity, is still very limited, so that we know little about the relative importance and frequency of small-scale territorial isolation. In suitable objects both questions can be easily studied. Fig. 30 shows the results of a study of the distribution of individuals in three different species of *Drosophila* on a small area near Berlin. Fig. 31 shows the result of an experiment on the determination of the activity-range in one of the species, using non-deleterious mutations as markers. These studies show that the regular activity-ranges in *Drosophila* are rather small, so that even small territorial fragmentations of the population may result in partial isolation. Further experiments of this type should be carried out, both in *Drosophila* and in other organisms.

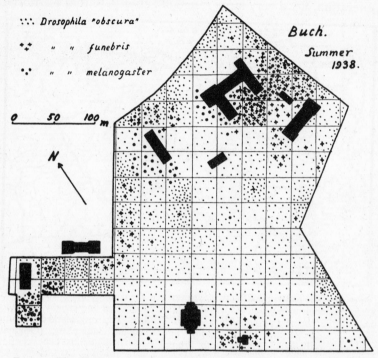

FIG. 30. The distribution of three species of *Drosophila* on a tenement in Buch. In the middle of each square a bottle with food was placed for 3–4 days; these bottles were inspected twice on each day, and the flies caught in them were counted and recorded; such experiments were repeated every 3–4 weeks during the whole season. (Original, according to the data of H. A. Timofeeff-Ressovsky.)

We thus see that various forms of isolation are widespread in all organisms, down to the territorially smallest populations. But, just as in the case of selection, we still possess very few exact data about the real amount and the relative significance of biological and small-scale geographical isolation.

(*d*) *Population-waves.* The fourth evolutionary factor, population-waves, consists in quantitative fluctuations of the number of individuals and of the territorial distribution of single populations. As with isolation, the mechanism of action of population waves consists essentially in the limitation of panmixy and population-size; but population-waves differ from isolation in not being definitely-directed and long-period processes, but accidental short-period fluctuations in both directions. Their

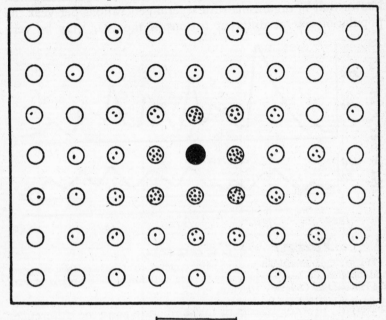

ca 25 m

FIG. 31. The 'activity-region' of *Drosophila funebris*. 1,200 marked flies were put with a supply of food at the place marked with a black circle; 99 bottles with food were placed at regular distances around this place, and the marked flies caught in these bottles were counted and recorded once a day during a period of two weeks. The circles represent the bottles, and the black dots the marked flies caught in these bottles. (Original.)

most important effect consists in the production of accidental fluctuations of gene concentrations. The evolutionary importance of these processes was first recognized by Tschetverikov (1905, 1915), who called them 'life-waves'; Elton (1930), Dubinin (1931), and Dubinin and Romaschoff (1932) pointed out their evolutionary significance under the name of 'genetically-automatic processes', and Wright (1932) gave an exact mathematical analysis of the mechanism of their action.

In all organisms, the population-size is not constant but is subject to more or less pronounced quantitative fluctuations, usually periodic (Elton, 1930). It is, for instance, well known that only a small fraction of the young produced in each generation reaches maturity; this indeed implies only a difference in the numbers of individuals of different ages. But it is also well known that in organisms with several generations per year the population-size at different seasons of the year may be very

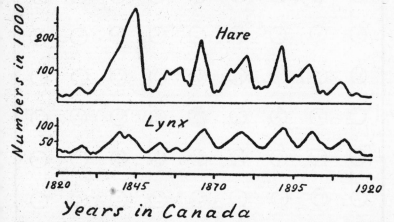

FIG. 32. Quantitative fluctuations of the populations of the hare *Lepus americanus* and the lynx *Lynx canadensis* in eastern Canada, as shown by the fur-market data of the Hudson Bay Company. (Hewitt, 1921.)

different; in some insects of the temperate zone the differences in number of individuals before and after hibernation may be of the order of magnitude of 1 : 1,000 or even more. Finally, in many organisms non-seasonal fluctuations recurring at more or less regular periodic intervals of several years are also known; Fig. 32 shows such correlated fluctuations of the populations of hare and lynx in Canada during the last century.

In most cases fluctuations in number of individuals are accompanied by corresponding fluctuations of the 'micro-territories' of the sub-populations. In addition, there may occur larger and more permanent increases or decreases, both periodic and aperiodic, of the territory occupied by larger populations (species or subspecies); the causes of these fluctuations are in most cases not yet exactly known. Fig. 33 shows the rapid expansion of the European cornborer *Pyrausta nubilalis* in North America; and Fig. 34 the expansion of the American musquash

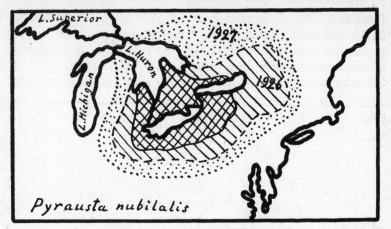

FIG. 33. Expansion of *Pyrausta nubilalis* Hb. (Lepidoptera) in North America in the years 1926–7. ▒▒▒—territory occupied before 1926. (Felt (1928), from Geptner (1936).)

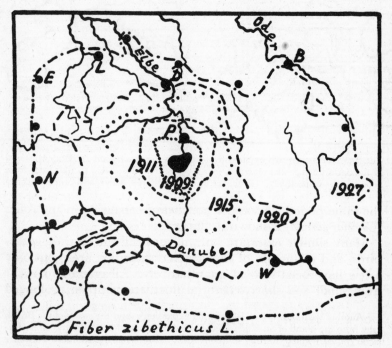

FIG. 34. Expansion of the musquash (muskrat), *Fiber* (*Ondathra*) *zibethicus* L. (Rodentia) in central Europe since its introduction in 1905. (Ulbrich, 1930.)

(muskrat) *Fiber zibethicus* in central Europe since its introduction in the first years of the present century. Fig. 35 shows the expansion of the common hare, *Lepus europaeus*, in a north-eastern direction during the last century; and Fig. 36 that of the Siberian bunting, *Emberiza aureola*, in a western direction during

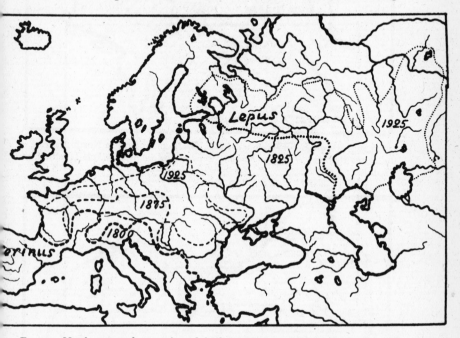

FIG. 35. North-eastward expansion of the hare *Lepus europaeus* L. (Rodentia) and of the Serin finch *Serinus canaria serinus* L. (Passeres) from 1825 to 1925, and from 1800 to 1925 respectively. (From the data of Folitarek, Mayr, and other sources.)

the same period. A case of northward expansion in the roller (*Coracias garrula*) is shown in Fig. 37.[1]

Many similar cases are known, especially in insects, game-birds, and mammals, of changes in distribution area; but only a few have been studied quantitatively. All gradations occur from small and short territorial fluctuations up to prolonged

[1] Another well-known case is the rapid expansion round the coasts of the British Isles from the island of St. Kilda, of the breeding-range of the Fulmar Petrel (*Fulmarus glacialis*) which, starting in about 1887, has now reached southern Yorkshire on the east, and Pembrokeshire and southern Ireland in the west. See S. Gordon (1936).

and pronounced range-changes, gradually leading over to processes of historical expansions or migrations of species. Most important from our present point of view are the small quantitative fluctuations of single populations, especially at the limits of the distribution areas of subspecies and species. Every field-naturalist is aware that at the margins of distribution areas the

FIG. 36. Westward expansion of the bunting *Emberiza aureola* Pall. (Passeres, - - - - 1825) and of the warbler *Acanthopneuste viridana* Blyth. (Passeres, · · · · 1880), from 1825 to 1925, and from 1880 to 1930 respectively. (From the data of Promptov, and other sources).

waves of population may result in what we may call 'breakers'. Fig. 38 shows diagrammatically such 'population-breakers' at the margin of a distribution area. As an evolutionary factor, both numerical and territorial population-waves are of great importance.

The periodic numerical fluctuations of small populations will produce a pronounced accidental fluctuation of the concentration of single genotypes. They may lead to the total disappearance of many genotypes present in low concentrations (irrespective of their selective value), while other rare genotypes may also irrespective of their selective value reach rather high concentrations. This process is of the greatest importance. The action of selection (even with high selection-coefficients) can be shown to be very slow in the case of low concentrations of a genotype; it becomes very much more rapid when the concentration is higher. Thus only the genotypes which reach higher

FIG. 37. The northward expansion of the roller, *Coracias garrula* L. (Aves, Coracii-formes) during a period of fifty years.

concentrations as a result of accidental fluctuations become exposed to a really effective selection. Further, the selection of homozygotes can only begin when the concentration of hetero-zygotes has reached a rather high level. Population-waves are thus important as an historical factor in the fixation or dis-appearance of mutations. The high concentration of many mutations in free-living populations is undoubtedly due to population-waves. On the other hand, the further fate of those genotypes which have already reached a higher concentration depends mainly on selection and not on accidental fluctuations.

Population-waves may also exert an influence upon the mechanism of selective action. The territorial fluctuations of a population increase environmental variability, thus making it

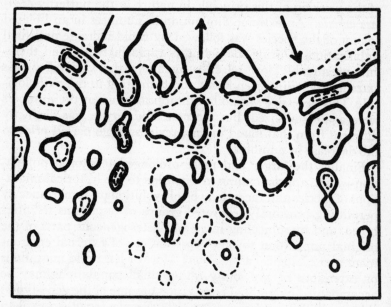

FIG. 38. Territorial progression (↓) and regression (↑), building of 'drop'- or 'island'-populations, their growth and disappearance, at a border (southern) of the distribution-area of a species. ------ former conditions; ——— present conditions. Roughly diagrammatic, but based on actual data.

possible for some of the 'evolutionary candidates', in the shape of mutations and recombinations, to find a specially suitable environment. Of especial importance in this respect are the 'breakers' at the margin of distribution areas; and an extensive geno-geographical analysis of cultivated plants has shown that many recessive mutants are actually found at the periphery of the distribution areas of species (Vavilov, 1927). In cases of pronounced numerical fluctuations extending over several generations, the intensity of selection is also affected, rising while the population is decreasing and vice versa; its type also will change at different points in the cycle (Elton, 1930, p. 27). Thus one method of studying the real intensity of natural selection will be by careful and exact population-statistical analysis of the total number of individuals and the relative frequency of various characters through the course of several periodic population-waves; a rough approximation to this type of analysis is shown in Fig. 5. Ford and Ford (1930) have given an example of the working of this principle in nature in the butterfly *Melitaea aurinia*. An extreme diminution in numbers in an isolated colony of the species was followed by rapid increase and final stabilization. During the period of rapid increase (and therefore presumably low selection-intensity) the variability was extreme, including even forms approximating to the pathological. This excessive variability disappeared when the numbers were again stabilized, but the new modal type was distinctly different from that found in the previous stable period prior to the decrease in numbers.

Finally, the larger and more prolonged territorial population-waves, approximating in extension to the historical migrations of species and races, may be of evolutionary importance by permitting previously separated groups of organisms to interbreed, and by subjecting large and heterogeneous parts of the original population to new constellations of external environment and biological association. More or less rapid migrations or extensions of previously rather small populations may be accompanied by gradual elimination of some of the geno-types: this possibility was recently used by Reinig (1938) to explain cases of geographical character-gradients ('clines' according to the new terminology of Huxley, 1939).

(*e*) *Relative evaluation of evolutionary factors.* It is obvious that all four evolutionary factors are necessary in the process of evolution. Thus their relative importance can only be evaluated in respect of their particular significance for different parts of the complex evolutionary mechanism.

As already mentioned, three basic mechanisms can be distinguished which may alter the genetic composition of a population: mutation-pressure, selection-pressure, and limitations of panmixy and population-size. We must now discuss how far the single evolutionary factors, with the aid of these three mechanisms, are able to exert a directive influence upon the evolutionary process.

Mutation cannot be regarded as a directive factor in adapta-

R

tion and differentiation, because, as we have seen, mutations arise at random and individual mutation-rates are extremely low; a directive influence of the mutation-process is possible only in those few cases where mutation-pressure is for some reasons greater than the pressures of selection and of accidental fluctuations in the concentrations of single genotypes. Mutation must thus be regarded mainly as a factor supplying new evolutionary material. We must assign essentially the same significance to population-waves. By rapid changes in the concentrations of single genotypes they produce pronounced changes in the genotypic content of populations, and expose some of the mutations more intensively to selective action by rapid accidental increase of their concentrations; and by territorial fluctuations of populations (range-changes) they create permanently new environmental constellations for the process of adaptation by natural selection.

The directive factors are selection and isolation. Selection permanently maintains an optimal relation between organisms and their surroundings, and also produces an adaptive morphophysiological differentiation in time. The first result we normally call adaptation, the second specialization or evolutionary progress. Isolation is the main factor of differentiation in space. The latter may be also produced by selection, acting on different parts of the population under different conditions; but here too differentiation is markedly accelerated by isolation. Different forms of biological isolation, especially genetical isolation *sensu strictu*, constitute the most important step in the process of speciation.

The four evolutionary factors may thus be divided into two groups: mutation and population-waves are providers of evolutionary material; and selection and isolation are the directive factors of evolution, the first being the only factor in adaptation and progressive differentiation, and the latter the most important factor in regard to differentiation in space. Other suggested evolutionary factors, such as, for instance, a direct Lamarckian influence of the environment upon organisms, or immanent heritable orthogenetic variation, have never been proved; conversely, the whole evidence of experimental genetics disproves their existence and shows that there is really no need to assume it to explain the mechanism of evolution.

5. *Conclusions*

The facts set forth in the preceding sections lead to the conclusion that in the known and genetically analysable material of evolution (mutations and combinations), and in the known evolutionary factors (mutability, selection, isolation, and population-waves) we possess all the theoretical premisses at present needed to explain the mechanism of micro-evolution and of geographical variation. No attempt is here made to give a complete theory of the mechanism of micro-evolution; only certain features regarding geographical variation will be briefly discussed.

The examination of groups exhibiting geographical variation shows that they may be characterized by three types of characters and character-combinations: neutral characters, clearly adaptive ones, and harmonious character-combinations (i.e. characters which in a specific combination have a specifically adaptive relation to a local environment and to each other). On the basis of the known properties of mutations and combinations, and of the mechanism of action of different evolutionary factors, it is easy to understand the origin of all three types of geographically varying characters. The first group undoubtedly includes, on the one hand, really 'neutral' characters, whose origin has nothing to do with selective adaptation, but is due to historically accidental plus-fluctuations of the relevant gene-concentrations. On the other hand, many characters appear to us to be 'neutral' merely because we cannot find any plausible relation between them and the local environment; in many cases a selective value must be ascribed not to a character as such, but to the influence of the gene responsible for it upon the relative viability of a specific gene-combination in a specific local environment. The obvious cases of adaptive characters or character-combinations owe their origin to the selective advantage of the morphological or physiological properties of the character as such under given environmental conditions, mimicry and protective coloration being extreme examples of this type. We should not forget that the selective advantage or the survival-rate represents the numerical sum of a large complex of different biological properties (such as, for instance, degree of sexual affinity, fertility-rate, spontaneous embryonic mortality, resistance of different developmental stages to diseases or enemies, specific qualities in the struggle for existence, and competition with other groups of organisms, &c.), influencing the relative viability of a genotype under given conditions. It is thus evident that the selective value of a mutation may in some cases be connected with the obvious main morphological or physiological character phenotypically manifested by the gene, while in others it will not be. This leads us to the question of harmonious character-combinations. Their origin is based on automatic simultaneous selection of several ancillary genes by any one selected for some specific reason; this simultaneous selection is due to the specific viability-interrelations of the various genes (see section 2 (b)). Even the fixation of a mutant character by chance (accidental plus-fluctuation of the gene-concentration) must inevitably induce the selection of an optimal genotypic environment for itself. A mutation producing a character, which as such, morphologically, is of importance for the organism under local conditions, may be positively selected, although its spontaneous 'physiological' viability may be lower than that of the original type; but after a while it will improve its physiological viability by selection of other genes, leading to an optimal, harmonious combination. These selective interrelations of genes assuredly explain some at least of the cases of relatively narrow zones of interbreeding, and relatively few natural hybrids between two 'good' and numerically large subspecies: both optimal gene-combinations lose their selective value if destroyed by crossing and subsequent segregation of their components. On the other hand, some zones of mixture may sometimes give origin to many new combinations of positive selective value.

The methods of geographical differentiation may be very various. In section 3 (a) were described some cases of the geographical expansion of single mutations. This is undoubtedly one of the methods by which geographical races (subspecies) originate; while *in statu nascendi*, such races differ primarily in one character, but soon, by the above-mentioned process of simultaneous selection, 'good' races differing in several characters must result. Another method by which geographically localized polygenic character-combinations originate is the meeting and overlapping of originally independent distribu-

tion- and expansion-areas of different single mutations or combinations; in some cases this will simply lead to an irregular
polymorphism of the population, but in others it may result in
the formation of a harmonious combination having a local
selective advantage. Such cases are probably not infrequent,
but their detection demands a detailed 'phenogeographic' and
if possible 'genogeographic' analysis of the species—i.e. an
analysis of the distribution and concentration of single, more or
less elementary, characters and of the genes responsible for
them. Studies of this type in lady-beetles (*Epilachna*, *Coccinella*)
and mice, which are still in progress, have revealed such
cases.

Both these methods of subspeciation occur within species-
areas which are more or less geographically continuous; pronounced and long-continued intraspecific isolation will certainly
lead to a corresponding differentiation; such cases of 'historical'
subspecies-formation are well known in biogeography. Another
'historical' mechanism leading to the origin of new races is the
migration and crossing of previously separated and already
well-differentiated groups. Probably many of the local races of
the northern Palearctic are in their origin partly due to such
mixture after reimmigration of subspecies which were differentiated in separate isolated refuges during the glacial period.

In many cases the intraspecific (and sometimes also the interspecific) variability shows the phenomenon of geographical
character-gradients, for which Huxley (1939) has recently proposed the term 'cline'. A special case of geographical clines is
represented by those characters which follow the so-called
'geographical rules' (the rules of Bergmann, Gloger, Allen, &c.).
Clines, and especially the cases embodied in the 'geographical
rules', are a favourite field of research and discussion in modern
biogeography. Such cases are of interest in two respects: (1)
They present certain purely technical difficulties to the taxonomist, sometimes making it difficult to distinguish and describe
the different geographical forms. But this will present really
serious difficulty only in a few cases and in a few groups of
organisms, since it is rather seldom that we encounter a really
continuous geographical variation, without any sharp steps of
difference, within the whole area of a species. Geographical
clines without more or less well-marked 'steps' are found only

for single quantitative characters; and to the different populations within a continuous cline concerned with a single character, no names of taxonomic value should be given, if they do not also show other characters allowing them to be described as races. (2) There is much discussion about the validity and the mechanism of origin of the geographical rules. Some biogeographers undoubtedly exaggerate the frequency of the cases which obey these rules; others try to deny the reality of almost all of them. The explanation of this controversy may lie in the rather curious phenomenon that some of the most radical upholders of the zoogeographical rules have used them as arguments in support of their Lamarckian views (e.g. Rensch, in his earlier work, 1929).[1] Many cases of parallel geographical clines and of geographical convergence undoubtedly exist within larger systematic categories. Their explanation on selectionist lines encounters no fundamental theoretical difficulties, although we know very little about the special ecological and physiological relations of the characters in question to their environments; a selectionist explanation of geographical convergence is much facilitated by the well-known fact that related species and genera show a far-reaching parallelism in their heritable variation (phenomenologically summarized by Vavilov (1922) in his 'law of homologous series in variation'). But equally undoubtedly the exceptions to the geographical rules are much more numerous than is admitted by their most radical upholders; we should always keep in mind that only relatively few groups of organisms have been analysed extensively enough on a large enough scale, and including the whole area of distribution, in respect of their geographical variation. Many clines appear to have no relation at all to the geographical rules, but to represent phenotypic gradients of polygenic quantitative characters around the centre of their highest development, or along the paths of distribution, migration, or expansion of the mutations or groups of organisms in question; in some cases such clines may be due to what Reinig (1938) called 'elimination', i.e. a reduction of the genetic heterogeneity of populations from the centre of origin or of diversity, to the periphery of the species-area. But this explanation too should not be overstressed,

---

[1] In later publications (e.g. 1939, *Arch. Naturgesch.* N.F. **8**, 89) Rensch has adopted a selectionist interpretation of the 'geographical rules.'

since geographical convergences and geographical clines probably originate in quite a different way.

The last question to be mentioned concerns the relation of intraspecific variability to speciation. Here, too, opinions differ markedly. Although, as pointed out in an earlier section, it is very difficult to give a definition of the species which would be of general value and of practical use in all groups of organisms, we nevertheless know that a high degree of biological isolation is the most important criterion. Since, as we have seen, there are many types of biological isolation, all due to genetic differences of the parental groups, we may expect also different mechanisms of speciation. The one extreme would be the origin of biological isolation, and thus of full speciation, by long-continued geographical isolation. The groups which in this way reached a certain degree of biological isolation may then, by migration or expansion, penetrate into each other's territories without crossing; or they will occupy adjacent regions without forming a hybrid population in the zone of transgression or common border of their distribution areas (geographically vicariant species). The other possible extreme would be the local origin and expansion of a genotype biologically isolated in some way from the surrounding genotypes; the degree of biological isolation would increase by accumulation of further genetic differences. And we can imagine all intermediates between these two extremes. We still know very little about species *in statu nascendi* in nature.

As an example of the first type of speciation may serve the subspecies *major* and *minor* of *Parus major*; these two geographically extreme races (*major* being the north-eastern, and *minor* being the south-eastern in the ring of subspecies around the great Asian deserts) meet in Manchuria and the Ussuri district without showing any tendency to hybridization. The second type is perhaps realized in the origin of different species in the 'obscura'-group in *Drosophila*. In genetic experiments 'good' species have been produced experimentally in *Drosophila* (Dubinin, 1936; Kozhevnikov, 1936) and in *Datura* (Blakeslee, 1932), in using chromosome-mutations.

The general impression obtained by a review of the relations of modern genetics to geographical variability and microevolution is first, that by now we are sufficiently supplied with general, fundamental principles and mechanisms for the explanation of micro-evolution. But there is still very little empirical material from field biology and micro-systematics to supply coefficients and numerical values in our general formulae. The immediate future should be devoted to intensive work in the field of empirical population-genetics. Modern taxonomy, ecology, and biogeography should devote special attention to the study of phenogeography, population-statistics, and population-waves in suitable common species of plants and animals. In these studies the results and viewpoints of modern genetics must be taken into account, in order to avoid *a priori* fruitless work and methodologically incorrect conclusions. Only when the mechanisms and explanatory principles of present-day experimental genetics have been exhausted (and they are still not fully understood or appreciated by the majority of taxonomists, biogeographers, and ecologists) must we search for new ones; and they then must be analysed with the aid of exact experimental methods. Anti-selectionist and anti-genetical evolutionary speculations have to-day no scientific value, even in connexion with the problems of macro-evolution.

REFERENCES

ANDERSON, E. (1936). 'The Species Problem in Iris.' *Ann. Missouri Bot. Garden*, **23**, 457.

BALDI, E., e POROCCHI, L. (1938). 'Prospettive genetiche in Limnologia.' *Atti d. Reun. d. Soc. Ital. di Genet. ed Eugen.* (Roma.)

BALKASHINA, E., und ROMASHOFF, D. (1935). 'Genetische Struktur der Drosophila-Populationen. I. Swenigoroder Populationen von Dros. phalerata, transversa und vibrissina.' *Biol. Žurn.* (*Moscow*), **4**, 81.

BAUER, H. (1936). 'Structure and Arrangement of Salivary Gland Chromosomes in Drosophila Species.' *Proc. Nat. Acad. Sci.* (*U.S.A.*), **22**, 216.

—— (1937). 'Cytogenetik.' *Fortschr. d. Zool.* **1**, 521 and **2**, 547.

BAUR, E. (1925). 'Die Bedeutung der Mutationen für das Evolutionsproblem.' *Z. indukt. Abstamm.- u. Vererb.-Lehre*, **37**, 107.

—— (1932). 'Artumgrenzung und Artbildung in der Gattung Antirrhinum.' *Z. indukt. Abstamm.- u. Vererb.-Lehre*, **63**, 256.

BLAKESLEE, A. (1932). 'The Species Problem in Datura.' *Proc. 6th Int. Congr. Genet.* **1**, 104.

BUZZATI-TRAVERSO, A., JUCCI, C., e TIMOFEEFF-RESSOVSKY, N. W. (1938). 'Genetica di popolazioni.' *Cons. Nat. d. Ric.*, Roma.

CARPENTER, G. D. H. (1936). 'The Facts of Mimicry still require Natural Selection for their Explanation.' *Proc. Roy. Soc. Lond.*, B, **121**, 65.

CHARUSIN, O. A. (1929). 'Versuche zur Bestimmung der natürlichen Gattungsgrenzen.' *Zool. Zurn. (Moscow)*, **9**, 85.

CHERUVIMOV, O. S. (1928). 'Analyse einer Population in Bezug auf ein geschlechtsgebundenes Merkmal.' *Zurn. Eksper. Biol. (Moscow)* **4**, 181.

CHOLODKOWSKY, N. (1910). 'Ueber biologische Arten.' *Bull. Acad. Imper. St. Petersburg* (Ser. 6), **4**, 751.

CRAMPTON, H. E. (1916–32). 'Studies on the Variation, Distribution, and Evolution of the genus Partula. I and II.' *Carn. Inst. Wash. Publ.* Nos. **228** and **410**.

DICE, L. R. (1934–5). 'Studies of Ecology and Genetics of North-American Mammals.' *Carn. Inst. Wash. Yearbook*, **33**, 268 and **34**, 278.

DIVER, C. (1936). 'The Problem of Closely Related Species and the Distribution of their Populations.' *Proc. Roy. Soc. Lond.*, B, **121**, 62.

DOBZHANSKY, Th. (1924). 'Die geographische und individuelle Variabilität von Harmonia axyridis.' *Biol. Zentralbl.* **44**, 401.

—— (1927). 'Die geographische Variabilität von Coccinella 7-punctata.' *Biol. Zentralbl.* **47**, 556.

—— (1933a). 'Geographical Variation in Lady-beetles.' *Amer. Nat.* **67**, 97.

—— (1933b). 'On the Sterility of the Interracial Hybrids in Drosophila pseudo-obscura.' *Proc. Nat. Acad. Sci. (U.S.A.)*, **19**, 397.

—— (1935a). 'Fecundity in Drosophila pseudo-obscura at Different Temperatures.' *J. exp. Zool.* **71**, 449.

—— (1935b). 'A Critique of the Species Concept in Biology.' *Philosophy of Science*, **2**, 344.

—— (1937a). 'Genetic Nature of Species Differences.' *Amer. Nat.* **71**, 404.

—— (1937b). *Genetics and the Origin of Species.* Columbia Univ. Press, New York.

—— (1938). 'The Raw Materials of Evolution.' *Sci. Monthly*, **46**, 445.

—— and KOLLER, P. C. (1938). 'An Experimental Study of Sexual Isolation in Drosophila.' *Biol. Zentralbl.* **58**, 589.

—— and QUEAL, M.L. (1938). 'Genetics of Natural Populations. I. Chromosome Variation in Populations of Drosophila pseudo-obscura inhabiting Isolated Mountain Ranges.' *Genetics*, **23**, 239.

—— —— (1938). 'Genetics of Natural Populations. II. Genic Variation in Populations of Drosophila pseudo-obscura inhabiting Isolated Mountain Ranges.' *Genetics*, **23**, 463.

—— and STURTEVANT, A. H. (1938). 'Inversion in the Chromosomes of Drosophila pseudo-obscura.' *Genetics*, **23**, 28.

DUBININ, N. P. (1931). 'Genetico-automatical Processes and their Bearing on the Mechanism of Organic Evolution.' *Zurn. Eksper. Biol. (Moscow)*, **7**, 463.

—— (1936). 'Experimental Alteration of the Number of Chromosome Pairs in Drosophila.' *Biol. Zurn. (Moscow)* **5**, 833.

—— and collaborators (1934). 'Experimental Study of the Ecogenotypes of Drosophila melanogaster, I and II.' *Biol. Zurn. (Moscow)*, **3**, 166.

—— —— (1936). 'Genetic Constitution and Gene-dynamics of Wild Populations of Drosophila melanogaster.' *Biol. Zurn. (Moscow)*, **5**, 939.

—— —— (1937). 'The Aberrative Polymorphism in Drosophila melanogaster (fasciata).' *Biol. Zurn (Moscow)*, **6**, 311.

DUBININ, N. P., and ROMASCHOFF, D. D. (1932). 'Die genetische Struktur der Art und ihre Evolution.' *Biol. Žurn. (Moscow)*, **1**, 51.

—— and SCHASKOLSKY, D. W. (1935). 'Die Rolle des Genbestandes der Geschlechtschromosomen in der Struktur der Populationen.' *Trudy Gos. Univ. Charkov.*

—— SOKOLOV, N. N., and TINIAKOV, G. G. (1937). 'Intraspecific Chromosome Variability.' *Biol. Žurn. (Moscow)*, **6**, 1007.

DUNN, L. C. (1921). 'Unit Character Variation in Rodents.' *J. Mammal.* **2**, 125.

EAST, E. M. (1936). 'Genetic Aspects of Certain Problems of Evolution.' *Amer. Nat.* **70**, 143.

ELTON, C. S. (1924). 'Periodic Fluctuations in the Numbers of Animals, their causes and effects.' *Brit. J. exp. Biol.* **2**, 119.

—— (1930). *Animal Ecology and Evolution.* Oxford.

FEDERLEY, H. (1915–16). 'Chromosomenstudien an Mischlingen. I–III.' *Öfr. Finska Veten. Soc. Förhandl.* **57**, Nr. 26, Nr. 30; **58**, Nr. 12.

FISHER, R. A. (1930). *The Genetical Theory of Natural Selection.* Clarendon Press, Oxford.

—— (1932). 'The Evolutionary Modification of Genetic Phenomena.' *Proc. 6th Int. Congr. Genet.* **1**, 165.

—— (1936). 'The Measurement of Selective Intensity.' *Proc. Roy. Soc. Lond.*, B, **121**, 58.

—— (1937). 'The Wave of Advance of Advantageous Genes.' *Annals Eugen.* **7**, 355.

FORD, H. D., and FORD, E. B. (1930). 'Fluctuations in Numbers and its Influence on Variation, in Melitaea aurinia.' *Trans. Ent. Soc. Lond.* **78**, 345.

FROLOVA, S. L. (1936). 'Several Spontaneous Chromosome Aberrations in Drosophila.' *Nature*, **138**, 204.

—— (1932). 'Polyploidie und ihre Rolle in der Evolution.' *Zool. Žurn. (Moscow)* **11**, 190.

—— and ASTAUROV, B. L. (1929). 'Die Chromosomengarnitur als systematisches Merkmal.' *Z. Zellforsch. mikr. Anat.* **10**, 201.

GAUSE, G. (1934). *The Struggle for Existence.* Baltimore.

GERSHENSON, S. M. (1934). 'Mutant Genes in a Wild Population of Drosophila obscura.' *Amer. Nat.* **68**, 569.

GEPTNER, W. (1936). *Allgemeine Zoogeographie.* Moscow.

GIMMEL, W. G. (1928). 'Geographische Verteilung der Größe der Hühnereier in Rußland.' *Arb. Zentral-Station Genetik, Moscow*, **3**.

GOLDSCHMIDT, R. (1929–33). 'Untersuchungen zur Genetik der geographischen Variation. II–VII.' *Roux' Arch. EntwMech.* **116**, 136; **126**, 277, 591, 674; **130**, 266, 562.

GORDON, C. (1935). 'An Analysis of two Wild Drosophila Populations.' *Amer. Nat.* **69**, 381.

—— (1936). 'The Frequency of Heterozygosis in Free-living Populations.' *J. Genet.* **33**, 25.

GORDON, S. (1936). 'The Fulmar Petrel.' *Nature*, **137**, 173.

GREGOR, J. W., and SANSOME, F. W. (1927–30). 'Genetics of Wild Populations. I–II.' *J. Genet.* **17**, 349, and **22**, 373.

HALDANE, J. B. S. (1924–34). 'A Mathematical Theory of Natural and Artificial Selection. I–X.' *Proc. Cambr. Philos. Soc.* **23, 26, 27, 28**; *Genetics*, **19**.

—— (1932). *The Causes of Evolution.* Longmans, Green & Co., London.

—— (1932). 'Can Evolution be Explained in Terms of Known Genetical Facts?' *Proc. 6th Int. Congr. Genet.* **1**, 185.

—— (1932). 'The Time of Action of Genes and its bearing on some Evolutionary Problems.' *Amer. Nat.* **66**, 5.

—— (1936). 'Primary and Secondary Effects of Natural Selection.' *Proc. Roy. Soc. Lond.*, B, **121**, 67.

—— (1937). 'The Effect of Variation on Fitness.' *Amer. Nat.* **71**, 337.

HARDY, G. H. (1908). 'Mendelian Proportions in a Mixed Population.' *Science*, **28**, 49.

HARLAND, S. C. (1936). 'The Genetical Conceptions of the Species.' *Biol. Rev.* **11**, 81.

—— and ATTECK, O. M. (1933). 'Breeding Experiments with Biological Races of Trichogramma minutum in the West Indies.' *Z. indukt. Abstamm.-u. Vererb.-Lehre*, **64**, 54.

HEINCKE, F. (1898). 'Die Naturgeschichte des Herings.' *Abh. D. Seefischer. Ver.* **2**, 1.

L'HÉRITIER, Ph. (1932). 'Comparaison de cinq lignées de Drosophila, type sauvage, au point de vue de leur survivance en présence d'une nourriture toxique.' *C.R. Soc. Biol.* **111**, 982.

—— and TEISSIER, G. (1933). 'Étude d'une population de Drosophiles en équilibre.' *C.R. Ac. Sci. Paris*, **197**, 1765.

—— —— (1934). 'Une expérience de Sélection naturelle. Courbe d'élimination du gène 'Bar' dans une population de Drosophiles en équilibre.' *C.R. Soc. de Biol.* **117**, 1049.

—— —— (1935). 'Recherches sur la concurrence vitale. Étude de populations mixtes de Drosophila melanogaster et de Drosophila funebris.' *C.R. Soc. de Biol.* **118**, 1396.

—— —— (1936). 'Contribution à l'étude de la concurrence larvaire chez les Drosophiles.' *C.R. Soc. de Biol.* **122**, 264.

—— —— (1937). 'Élimination des formes mutantes dans les populations de Drosophile.' *C.R. Soc. de Biol.* **124**, 881.

HEWITT, C. G. (1921). *The Conservation of the Wild Life of Canada.* New York.

HUXLEY, J. S. (1936). 'Natural Selection and Evolutionary Progress.' *Rep. Brit. Ass. Adv. Sci.* (1936), 81.

—— (1939). 'Clines: an Auxiliary Method in Taxonomy.' *Bijdr. t. d. Dierk*, **27**, 491.

JENKIN, T. J. (1936). 'Natural Selection in Relation to the Grasses.' *Proc. Roy. Soc. Lond.*, B, **121**, 52.

JOHANNSEN, W. (1903). *Über Erblichkeit in Populationen und in reinen Linien.* Fischer, Jena.

KAMSCHILOW, M. M. (1935). 'Über phänotypische Variabilität in Biotypen und in Populationen.' *Biol. Zurn.* (*Moscow*), **4**, 385.

—— (1935). 'Selektion unter verschiedenen Bedingungen der Merkmalsmanifestierung.' *Biol. Zurn.* (*Moscow*), **4**, 1005.

KARPECHENKO, G. D. (1935). *Theory of Remote Hybridization*. Selchosgis, Moscow.

KERKIS, J. (1938). 'Study of the Frequency of Lethal and Detrimental Mutations in Drosophila.' *Bull. Acad. Sci. USSR, Cl. math. natur.* **1**, 75.

KINSEY, A. C. (1937). 'Supra-specific Variation in Nature and in Classification from the Viewpoint of Zoology.' *Amer. Nat.* **71**, 206.

KIRIKOV, S. V. (1934). 'Sur la distribution du hamster noir et ses relations avec la forme normale de Cricetus cricetus.' *Zool. Zurn. (Moscow)*, **13**, 361.

KIRPITCHNIKOV, V. S. (1935). 'The Role of Non-hereditary Variability in the Process of Natural Selection (a hypothesis of indirect selection).' *Biol. Zurn. (Moscow)*, **4**, 775.

KNAPP, E. (1938). 'Über genetisch bedeutsame Zellbestandteile außerhalb der Chromosomen.' *Biol. Zentralbl.* **58**, 411.

KOLTZOFF, N. K. (1933). 'Das Problem der progressiven Evolution.' *Biol. Zurn. (Moscow)*, **2**, 475.

KOZHEVNIKOV, B. (1936). 'Experimentally produced Karyotypical Isolation.' *Biol. Zurn. (Moscow)*, **5**, 727.

LANCEFIELD, D. E. (1929). 'A Genetic Study of Two Races or Physiological Species in Drosophila obscura.' *Z. indukt. Abstamm.- u. Vererb.-Lehre*, **52**, 287.

LEVITSKY, G. A. (1926). 'Karyo- and Genotypical Variations in the Process of Evolution.' *Bull. appl. Bot.* **15**, No. 5, 3.

—— (1931). 'The Karyotype in Systematics.' *Bull. appl. Bot.* **27**, No. 1, 187.

LÜHRING, R. (1928). 'Das Haarkleid von Sciurus vulgaris L und die Verteilung seiner Farbvarianten in Deutschland.' *Z. Morph. Oekol.* **11**, 667.

LUSH, J. L. (1937). *Animal Breeding Plans*. Ames (Iowa).

MEINERTZHAGEN, R. (1928). 'Some Biological Problems Connected with the Himalayas.' *Ibis* (12th ser.), **4**, 480.

MELANDER, W. A. (1926). 'Rufinismus beim Iltis im Gouv. Smolensk.' *Izv. Smolensk. Univ.*, Smolensk.

— (1930). 'Some Cases of Mutations in Wild Mammals.' *Trudy 4. Sjezda Zool. Anat. Gist.*, Kiev.

MOHR, E. (1930). 'Zur Kenntnis der Schneemaus, Chionomys nivalis.' *Z. Säugetierk.* **4**, 193.

MORGAN, T. H. (1932). *The Scientific Basis of Evolution*. New York.

MULLER, H. J. (1925). 'Why Polyploidy is rarer in Animals than in Plants.' *Amer. Nat.* **59**, 346.

—— (1929). 'The Method of Evolution.' *Sci. Monthly*, **29**, 481.

—— (1936). 'On the Variability of Mixed Races.' *Amer. Nat.* **70**, 409.

MÜNTZING, A. (1936). 'The Evolutionary Significance of Autopolyploidy.' *Hereditas*, **21**, 263.

NIKORO, Z. S., GUSSEV, S., PAVLOV, E., and GRIASNOV, I. (1935). 'The Regularities of Sex Isolation in some stocks of Drosophila melanogaster.' *Biol. Zurn. (Moscow)*, **4**, 569.

NILSSON-EHLE, H. (1909–11). 'Kreuzungsuntersuchungen am Hafer und Weizen. I and II.' *Lunds Univ. Arsskr.*

OGNEV, S. I. (1931). *The Mammals of Russia*. Moscow.

ÖKLAND, F. (1937). 'Die geographischen Rassen der extramarinen Wirbeltiere Europas.' *Zoogeographica*, **3**, 389.

PÄTAU, K. (1935). 'Chromosomenmorphologie bei Drosophila melanogaster und Drosophila simulans und ihre genetische Bedeutung.' *Naturwissensch.* 23, 537.

PARK, T. (1937). 'Experimental Studies of Insect Populations.' *Amer. Nat.* 71, 21.

PEARSON, K. (1904). 'On a Generalized Theory of Alternative Inheritance.' *Phil. Trans. Roy. Soc. A*, 203, 53.

PEARSON, T. (1938). 'The Tasmanian Brush Opossum: its Distribution and Colour Varieties.' *Pap. Proc. Roy. Soc. Tasmania* (1938), 21.

PERELESHIN, S. (1928). 'Essay on a Biometrical Analysis of the Term Subspecies.' *Zool. Zurn. (Moscow)*, 8, 37.

PETROV, S. G. (1928). 'The Genetic Analysis of the Poultry Population in the Vetlouga-district.' *Arb. ZentrStat. Genetik, (Moscow)*, 3.

—— (1936). 'The Population of Fowl near Shabalino.' *Biol. Zurn. (Moscow)*, 5, 57.

PHILIPTSCHENKO, J. A. (1924). 'Über Spaltungsprozesse innerhalb einer Population bei Panmixie.' *Z. indukt. Abstamm.- u. Vererb.-Lehre*, 35, 257.

PICTET, A. (1936). 'La Zoogéographie expérimentale dans ses rapports avec la Génétique.' *Mém. Mus. Hist. Nat. Belgique*, ser. 2, 3, 233.

PROMPTOV, A. N. (1934). 'The Evolutionary Significance of the Migrations of the Birds.' *Zool. Zurn. (Moscow)*, 13, 409.

RASMUSSON, J. (1933). 'A Contribution to the Theory of Quantitative Character Inheritance.' *Hereditas*, 18, 245.

REINIG, W. F. (1935). 'Über die Bedeutung der individuellen Variabilität für die Entstehung geographischer Rassen.' *Sitzber. Ges. naturf. Freunde*, Berlin (1935), 50.

—— (1937). *Melanismus, Albinismus, Rufinismus.* Thieme, Leipzig.

—— (1938). *Elimination und Selektion.* Fischer, Jena.

RENNER, O. (1934). 'Die Plastiden als selbständige Elemente.' *Ber. Math. Phys. Kl. Sächs. Akad. Wiss.* 86, 241.

RENSCH, B. (1929). *Das Prinzip geographischer Rassenkreise.* Borntraeger, Berlin.

ROMASHOFF, D. D. (1931). 'On the Conditions of Equilibrium in Populations.' *Zurn. Eksp. Biol. (Moscow)*, 7, 442.

ROSANOVA, M. A. (1928). 'Experimentell-genetische Methode in der Systematik.' *Zurn. Russk. Botan. Obšč.* 13.

—— (1930). 'Modern Methods of Plant Systematics.' *Bull. appl. Bot. (Leningrad) Suppl.*, 41.

SALTYKOVSKY, A., and FEDOROV, V. (1936). 'Chlorophyll Abnormalities in Wild Synapis alba.' *Bull. appl. Bot.*, ser. II, 9, 287.

SCHITKOV, B. M. (1932). 'Über zoogeographische Forschungsarbeit an der Fauna der eine gewerbliche Bedeutung besitzenden Tiere.' *Zool. Zurn. (Moscow)*, 11, 3.

SEMENOV-TIANSCHANSKY, A. P. (1910). *Die taxonomischen Grenzen der Art und ihre Unterabteilungen.* Friedländer, Berlin.

SEREBROVSKY, A. S. (1927). 'Genetic Analysis of the Population of Domestic Fowl in Daghestan.' *Zurn. Eksper. Biol. (Moscow)*, 3, 62.

—— (1928). 'Genogeography and the Gene-staff of the Domestic Animals in Russia.' *Naučn. Slovo (Moscow)*, 9, 3.

SEREBROVSKY, A. S. (1929). 'Problems and Methods of Genogeography.' *Trudy Sjezda Genetiki, Leningrad*, 2, 71.

SEXTON, E. W., and CLARK, A. R. (1936). 'Heterozygotes in a Wild Population of Gammarus chevreuxi Sexton.' *J. mar. biol. Assoc.* 21, 319.

SEWERTZOFF, S. A. (1933). 'Zur Dynamik der Herde bei Wirbeltieren.' *Bull. Acad. Sci. USSR.* Ser. VII (1933), 1005.

—— (1934). 'Vom Massenwechsel bei den Wirbeltieren.' *Biol. Zentralbl.* 54, 337.

SINSKAJA, E. N. (1931). 'The Study of Species in their Dynamics and Interrelations with Different Types of Vegetation.' *Bull. appl. Bot.* 25, No. 2, 1.

SPETT, G. (1931). 'Gibt es eine partielle sexuelle Isolation unter den Mutationen und der Grundform von Drosophila melanogaster?' *Z. indukt. Abstamm.- u. Vererb.-Lehre*, 60, 63.

SPOONER, G. M. (1932). 'An Experiment on Breeding Wild Pairs of Gammarus chevreuxi.' *J. mar. biol. Assoc.* 18, 337.

STORER, T. J., and GREGORY, P. W. (1934). 'Color Aberrations in the Pocket Gopher and their Genetic Explanation.' *J. Mammal.* 15, 300.

STRESEMANN, E. (1926). 'Übersicht über die Mutationsstudien I–XXIV und ihre wichtigsten Ergebnisse.' *J. f. Ornith.* 47, 377.

STUBBE, H. (1934). 'Einige Kleinmutationen von Antirrhinum majus.' *Der Züchter*, 6, 301.

—— (1937). *Spontane und strahleninduzierte Mutabilität.* Thieme, Leipzig.

STURTEVANT, A. H. (1915). 'Experiments on Sex-recognition and the Problem of Sexual Selection in Drosophila.' *J. anim. Behaviour*, 5, 351.

—— (1918). 'An Analysis of the Effects of Selection.' *Carn. Inst. Wash. Publ.* No. 264.

—— (1929). 'The Genetics of Drosophila simulans.' *Carn. Inst. Wash. Publ.* No. 399.

—— and DOBZHANSKY, Th. (1936). 'Geographical Distribution and Cytology of Sex-ratio in Drosophila pseudo-obscura.' *Genetics*, 21, 473.

—— —— (1936). 'Inversions in the Third Chromosome of Wild Races of Drosophila pseudo-obscura, and their use in the Study of the History of the Species.' *Proc. Nat. Acad. Sci. (U.S.A.)*, 22, 448.

—— and TAN, C. C. (1937). 'The Comparative Genetics of Drosophila pseudo-obscura and Drosophila melanogaster.' *J. Genet.* 34, 415.

SUKATSCHEW, W. (1928). 'Einige experimentelle Untersuchungen über den Kampf ums Dasein zwischen Biotypen derselben Art.' *Z. indukt. Abstamm.- u. Vererb.-Lehre*, 47, 54.

SUMNER, F. B. (1932). 'Genetic, Distributional, and Evolutionary Studies of the Subspecies of Deer Mice (Peromyscus).' *Bibliog. Genet.* 9, 1.

SVESCHNIKOVA, I. (1936). 'Translocations in Hybrids as an Indicator of Caryotype-Evolution.' *Biol. Zurn. (Moscow)*, 5, 303.

TAN, C. C., and LI, J. C. (1934). 'Inheritance of the Elytral Color Patterns of the Lady-bird Beetle Harmonia axyridis.' *Amer. Nat.* 68, 252.

TIMOFEEFF-RESSOVSKY, H. A., and N. W. (1927). 'Genetische Analyse einer freilebenden Drosophila melanogaster-Population.' *Roux' Arch. EntwMech.* 109, 70.

TIMOFEEFF-RESSOVSKY, N. W. (1932a). 'Verschiedenheit der normalen Allele der white-Serie aus zwei geographisch getrennten Populationen von Drosophila melanogaster.' *Biol. Zentralbl.* **52**, 468.

—— (1932b). 'The Genogeographical Work with Epilachna chrysomelina.' *Proc. 6th Int. Congr. Genet.* **2**, 230.

—— (1933). 'Über die relative Vitalität von Drosophila melanogaster und Drosophila funebris unter verschiedenen Zuchtbedingungen, in Zusammenhang mit den Verbreitungsarealen dieser Arten.' *Arch. Naturgesch.*, N. F. **2**, 285.

—— (1934a). 'Über die Vitalität einiger Genmutationen und ihrer Kombinationen bei Drosophila funebris und ihre Abhängigkeit vom genotypischen und vom äußeren Milieu.' *Z. indukt. Abstamm.- u. Vererb.-Lehre*, **66**, 319.

—— (1934b). 'Über den Einfluß des genotypischen Milieus und der Außenbedingungen auf die Realisation des Genotyps.' *Nachr. Ges. Wiss. Göttingen, Biologie*, N. F. **1**, No. 6.

—— (1935a). 'Über geographische Temperaturrassen bei Drosophila funebris.' *Arch. Naturgesch.*, N. F. **4**, 245.

—— (1935b). 'Experimentelle Untersuchungen der erblichen Belastung von Populationen.' *Der Erbarzt*, **2**, 117.

—— (1935c). 'Auslösung von Vitalitätsmutationen durch Röntgenbestrahlung bei Drosophila melanogaster.' *Nachr. Ges. Wiss. Göttingen, Biologie*, N. F. **1**, No. 11.

—— (1936a). 'Qualitativer Vergleich der Mutabilität von Drosophila funebris und Drosophila melanogaster.' *Z. indukt. Abstamm.- u. Vererb.-Lehre*, **71**, 276.

—— (1936b). 'Some Genetic Experiments on Relative Viability.' *Proc. Roy. Soc. Lond.*, B, **121**, 45.

—— (1937). *Experimentelle Mutationsforschung in der Vererbungslehre.* Steinkopff, Dresden.

—— (1933a). 'Mutabilità sperimentale', in *Genetica*. Milano.

—— (1939b). *Le Mécanisme des mutations et la structure du gène.* Edit. Hermann, Paris (in press).

—— and ZARAPKIN, S. R. (1932). 'Zur Analyse der Formvariationen.' *Biol. Zentralbl.* **52**, 138.

TSCHETVERIKOV, S. S. (1915). 'Waves of Life.' *Dnevn. Zool. Otd. Moscow*, **3**.

—— (1925). 'Theoretical Premises of the Genotypical Analysis of a Species in the genus Drosophila.' *Trudy 2. Sjezda Zool. Anat. Gist.*, Moscow.

—— (1926). 'On Certain Features of the Evolutionary Process from the Viewpoint of Modern Genetics.' *Zurn. Eksper. Biol. (Moscow)*, **2**, 3.

—— (1927). 'On a Problem of Evolution and on its Experimental Solution.' *Trudy 3. Sjezda Zool. Anat. Gist.*, Leningrad.

—— (1928). 'Über die genetische Beschaffenheit wilder Populationen.' *Verh. 5. Int. Kongr. Vererb.* **2**, 1499.

TURESSON, G. (1922). 'The Species and Varieties as Ecological Units.' *Hereditas*, **3**, 100.

—— (1925). 'The Plant Species in Relation to Habitat and Climate.' *Hereditas*, **6**, 147.

TURESSON, G. (1929). 'Zur Natur und Begrenzung der Arteinheiten.' *Hereditas*, 12, 323.

—— (1930). 'The Selective Effect of Climate upon Plant Species.' *Hereditas*, 14, 99.

—— (1931). 'The Geographical Distribution of the Alpine Ecotypes of some Eurasiatic Plants.' *Hereditas*, 15, 329.

—— (1932). 'Die Pflanzenart als Klimaindikator.' *Kgl. fysiogr. Sällsk. Förh. Lund*, 2, No. 4.

ULLRICH, J. (1930). *Die Bisamratte: Lebensweise, Gang ihrer Ausbreitung in Europa, wirtschaftliche Bedeutung und Bekämpfung.* Dresden.

VAVILOV, N. I. (1922). 'The Law of Homologous Series in Variation.' *J. Genet.* 12, 47.

—— (1926). 'Studies on the Origin of Cultivated Plants.' *Bull. appl. Bot.* 16, No. 2, 1.

—— (1927a). 'Geographical Regularities in the Distribution of the Genes of Cultivated Plants.' *Bull. appl. Bot.* 17, No. 3, 411.

—— (1927b). 'Essais géographiques sur l'étude de la variabilité des plantes cultivées en Russie.' *Rapport à l'Institut Intern. d'Agricult. de Rome*.

—— (1928). 'Geographische Genzentren unserer Kulturpflanzen.' *Verh. 5. Int. Kongr. Vererb.* 1, 342.

—— (1931). 'The Linnean Species as a System.' *Bull. appl. Bot.* 26, No. 3, 109.

—— (1935). *The Geographical Basis of Plant Breeding.* Selchosgiz, Moscow.

VOLTERRA, V. (1931). *Leçons sur la théorie mathématique de la lutte pour la vie.* Paris.

WETTSTEIN, F. v. (1934). 'Über plasmatische Vererbung.' *Wiss. Woche zu Frankfurt a. M.* 1.

WRIGHT, S. (1931). 'Evolution in Mendelian Populations.' *Genetics*, 16, 97.

—— (1932). 'The Roles of Mutation, Inbreeding, Crossbreeding, and Selection in Evolution.' *Proc. 6th Int. Congr. Genet.* 1, 356.

—— (1935). 'Evolution in Populations in Approximate Equilibrium.' *J. Genet.* 30, 257.

ZARAPKIN, S. R. (1934). 'Zur Phänoanalyse von geographischen Rassen und Arten.' *Arch. Naturgesch.*, N. F. 3, 161.

—— (1937). 'Phänoanalyse von einigen Populationen der Epilachna chrysomelina.' *Z. indukt. Abstamm.- u. Vererb.-Lehre*, 73, 282.

—— and TIMOFEEFF-RESSOVSKY, H. A. (1932). 'Zur Analyse der Formvariationen. II.' *Die Naturwissensch.* 20, 382.

ZIMMERMANN, K. (1933). 'Über Mutationen in wilden Populationen.' *Mitt. Zool. Mus. Berlin*, 19, 439.

—— (1935). 'Zur Rassenanalyse der mitteleuropäischen Feldmäuse.' *Arch. Naturgesch.*, N. F. 4, 258.

—— (1936). 'Die geographischen Rassen von Epilachna chrysomelina und ihre Beziehungen zu E. capensis.' *Z. indukt. Abstamm.- u. Vererb.-Lehre*, 71, 527.

TAXONOMIC SPECIES AND GENETIC SYSTEMS

By C. D. DARLINGTON

1. *Methods of Inference*

SYSTEMATICS is concerned in the first place with separating and defining species so that the same name shall always have, as nearly as possible, the same meaning when applied to an organism or a group of organisms. We must have exact names for the plants and animals we use. In order to do the sorting out necessary for this purpose no more certain criterion is known, as John Ray put it, than 'distincta propagatio ex semine'. For clearly, if an organism does not in nature produce offspring fit to be called by the same name as itself (as has sometimes happened, when the test has been made (Erlanson, 1934)), it will be a waste of time to give it a name and a place in a general catalogue. The first assumption of systematics is therefore that species are groups of individuals that breed true within their own limits.

But in practice the systematist cannot apply this assumption to the definition of every species. He has to use practical rules, rules of summary diagnosis. The first question is, therefore, how he is to test these rules in particular instances. The rules that he has applied in the past are based on the forms of individuals and the geographical distributions of related groups of such individuals. He assumes that certain degrees of dissimilarity in form and of isolation in space imply a capacity for 'distincta propagatio' while lower degrees do not. This method works well enough in certain groups, while in others it breaks down, for two broad reasons. Sometimes the clear discontinuity which is taken to imply 'distincta propagatio' fails to appear within a widely varying group, as in some sections of *Rosa* and *Rubus*; and sometimes discontinuity occurs so freely that the forms, though true enough to be taken as species, are, on account of their inconveniently large number and small dissimilarity, degraded to a lower rank, as in some sections of *Hieracium*.

The twin disciplines of experimental breeding and chromosome study have largely grown up in the endeavour to make out what the 'distincta propagatio' of the systematist depends on. The cytologist is able to determine the changes in the structures, proportions, and positions of the genes in the chromosomes on which the external differences observed in experimental breeding depend. The experimental breeder is able to show the relationship between these changes and the differences found in natural forms. These laborious methods cannot be applied to the detailed consideration of the whole body of systematics. But the rules to be deduced from them can be so applied. Now the rules which have guided taxonomy (implicitly since De Candolle, and explicitly since Darwin) are rules derived by individual systematists in various ways and with varying results from the doctrine of relationship by descent. Genetic experiments support these rules in some ways, contradict them in others. Let us see how this comes about.

2. *The Origin of Discontinuity*

We must first consider the nature of species as they are found characteristically in most groups of higher plants and animals. The individuals that are subjected to systematic study are diploid zygotes. They reproduce by sexual reproduction. They produce haploid gametes, and the system of mating is so controlled that gametes, usually from different parent zygotes, mate to give new diploid progeny zygotes. The hereditary elements carried by different parent zygotes within a spatially limited mating group are therefore reassorted in each generation. When we examine the hereditary elements, the chromosomes, in the course of meiosis (by which the diploid cells give rise to the haploid), we find that in all such organisms the maternal and paternal chromosomes are reassorted in all possible combinations in the haploid cells produced. Not only this, but the corresponding maternal and paternal chromosomes cross over at different places in each cell undergoing meiosis, so that all possible combinations of *parts* of chromosomes are also produced. The unit of crossing-over of the chromosome determines the size of these parts and is known as the gene. It follows, therefore, that where corresponding genes differ in different individuals within the mating groups, sexual reproduction leads to a different recombination of genes as far as possible within every individual of the mating group. Such a mating group distributed over a sufficient range of space and time is a species in the sense of Ray.

Usually in sexually reproducing groups of plants or animals every act of reproduction requires cross-fertilization. This system arises either by a differentiation of individuals into opposite sexes or by a barrier of a physiological or structural kind establishing self-sterility. In this way the maximum diversity is attained within a freely mixing group. One might suppose that genetic changes occurring within such a group would increase the range of diversity within it and gradually break it up. This we can in fact see happening within certain groups which the systematist has conveniently classified as species. We can see that discontinuities are arising which break them up into distinct self-perpetuating and inter-sterile groups. This comes about in various ways and with various results which must be specially considered.

The minimum discontinuity that we can discover in variation is that we ascribe to single and sudden changes in genes. We must first ask ourselves whether such changes can establish a new species. In sexual systems they cannot do so, for the following reason: the changed form will cross with the unchanged, and the gene-hybrid will not breed true.

It is true that the basis of distinction between species in *Malva* (Kristofferson, 1925), *Galium* (Fagerlind, 1937), *Nicotiana* (Goodspeed, 1934), and *Tulipa*, and even of the division of the genus in *Primula* (to mention only a few examples) has proved to be a single-gene difference. But when the facts of inheritance are known, such distinctions can no longer be upheld on ground of either principle or convenience. Ray will not allow it.

It might be supposed that in a rare case a single change would itself prevent interbreeding. But in practice this is just what does not happen. There are many single-gene changes known which sterilize the changed form. And there are others (as in *Zea mays* L.; Darlington, 1933) which prevent crossing in one way between the normal and mutant types. But there are none which prevent crossing in both ways without sterilizing the changed form. The reason for this is plain. A single change may alter a sexual stimulus, the style-length, or the mating season, but it is not likely to make at the same time changes in sexual response, in pollen growth, or in fruit ripening which are necessary for the success of the first change.

On the other hand, if the barrier between species is purely external there might seem to be no reason why complex genetic differences should be necessary. They are necessary, however, for no adaptive discontinuity can be determined by single genes. Gene-changes are based on chemical stability of the genes, not on the adaptive value of their results. Every single gene-change will therefore demand others. To put the matter in another way, any single change so far as it is significant at all thrusts the organism into a new environment. Related groups of plants and to a lesser extent animals are extremely variable in their breeding seasons. Any gene-change affecting the breeding season, however, calls for complementary gene-changes affecting the rate of development or general habits, for the progeny will be brought forth at a different season. The effective environment of the progeny and therefore of the species will be changed. Thus every mutation demands a chain of co-ordinated successors. How is this co-ordination to be made compatible with the crossing-over and recombination provided by sexual reproduction? We admit that differences between species which are to be worth naming must depend on the action of several genes. And these genes must be permanently inherited together. A group of genes must by their behaviour contradict their description as genes. We know that from the progeny of crosses between two species, like *Tragopogon pratensis* L. and *T. porrifolius* L. (Winge, 1938), individuals exactly resembling the wild ancestors can be selected in later generations. Yet this mixing and unmixing does not as a rule take place in nature. How does this contradiction come about? The answer is, in a broad sense, isolation.

Isolation is of many kinds and its modes and meanings are only just becoming understood. Between some pairs of species it is immediately external. They are separated geographically or ecologically in nature, and when brought together by man they cross freely. The improvement of cultivated plants is largely due to this de-isolation. Between other pairs of species the isolation is immediately internal. They live side by side, but do not cross owing to one of the reproductive disharmonies already referred to. This is not to say that even in such cases it is possible to disentangle the internal and external elements in isolation. Geographical isolation may itself have been determined by a genetic discontinuity that is not apparent, and genetic isolation may be fitted to an ecological discontinuity that is also not apparent. Genotype and environment are so closely bound up that the order of events must usually be obscure on a first examination.

It is in these circumstances that we turn to the evidence of chromosome mechanisms. Perhaps the most obvious of these is polyploidy. In many genera of plants species include within their described limits not only diploids but also tetraploids, hexaploids, and types with even higher multiple numbers of chromosomes. These may arise by accidental failure of cell division, giving nuclei with the double number. In other groups, as in *Dactylis* (Müntzing, 1937) and *Vallisneria* (Jorgensen, 1927), on the other hand, tetraploid forms and the diploids from which they have been derived have been assigned, as they should be assigned, to different species.

These changes in chromosome number arise through failure of cell-division. A nucleus divides either by mitosis or meiosis, and its two products later fuse again. Where the new polyploid has arisen from a non-hybrid diploid it is less fertile and may even depend on asexual reproduction, as in the branchiopod *Artemia* and in many grasses. In this way in *Allium nutans* L., side by side with the diploid ($2x$) forms, others with $3x$, $4x$, $5x$, $6x$, $8x$, and even $12x$ have arisen, differing little from one another in external form (Levan, 1935).

Sometimes a doubling of the chromosomes takes place in a more or less sterile hybrid. The new polyploid is then always fairly fertile and, in proportion to its fertility, true-breeding. These properties are due to the dissimilar chromosomes of opposite parents no longer pairing with one another but with the new identical mates produced by their own doubling. In this way new polyploid forms such as *Aesculus carnea* Wats., *Galeopsis tetrahit* L., *Spartina townsendii* H. & J. Groves, *Triticum sativum* Lam., and *Prunus domestica* L. have arisen and multiplied, some with and some without the assistance of man (Darlington, 1937a).

New polyploids have two new modes of variation open to them. First they are buffered by their doubled genetic outfit against the ill effects of loss or gain of chromosomes or parts of chromosomes. The effects of unbalance are toned down and unbalanced forms often therefore survive in nature (e.g. in *Cochlearia anglica* L.; Maude, 1939). A new type of instability is thereby introduced. In those polyploids which arise from hybrid diploids a second and special method of change appears. Crossing-over occasionally takes place between chromosomes from opposite parental species, and new combinations are formed. Accordingly, in the young polyploid species of cereals, tobacco, and many other forms, 'mutations' characteristically arise which are due to the loss of parts of chromosomes, or to variations in their number, or to mere recombination. By selection of such variants it seems the new polyploid usually loses its initial gigantism, for old polyploids are on the average no larger than their diploid relatives.

We have seen that the separation of two endogamous and genetically different groups within one old one requires not only the presence of several genetical differences but also a restriction of combinations between them. Where this restriction is absent the range of variation within a species may be so great that hybrids may occur within it of the same degree of hybridity as those that would arise from crossing two species. Hence a widely cross-fertilized diploid species may contain sufficient variation and hence sufficient hybridity within itself to produce a fertile hybrid tetraploid. It thus happens that within the same species *Allium schoenoprasum* L. (Levan, 1935) we may have both types of tetraploid, one non-hybrid and fairly fertile and the other hybrid and highly fertile; probably combinations of the two occur here and in such complex groups as *Galium mollugo* L.

New polyploids, whether they arise with or without hybridity, whether they are fertile or sterile, and whether they are sexual or parthenogenetic, usually fail to cross with their diploid parents or, if they cross, they give progeny that is highly sterile. Further, it should be noticed that the polyploid forms within a species, although often not morphologically easy to distinguish from the diploids, necessarily have a geographical range of their own, smaller than that of the diploids at the beginning (as in *Biscutella laevigata* L.; Manton, 1937) and often greater later on (as in *Aconitum*, Schafer and La Cour, 1934, or *Tradescantia*,

Anderson and Sax, 1936). Ecologically also the diploid and polyploid forms usually differ (as in *Myosotis*; Geitler, 1936). New polyploids are therefore inevitably new species. But they go farther than this, for in several ways they escape from the isolation of their diploid parents. Thus spreading, they will come to overlap new species in distribution: they escape from

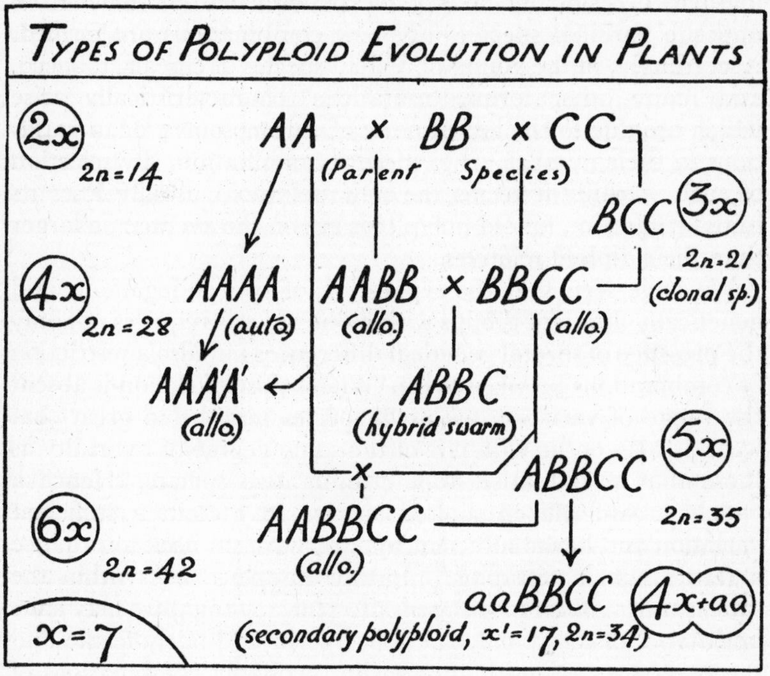

FIG. I.

the spatial isolation of their parents. They may also cross, as has been found in artificial *Raphanus-Brassica* tetraploids and in species of *Saxifraga* (Skovsted, 1934) and *Veronica* (Scheerer, 1937), with related tetraploid species with which their diploid parents would not cross; they escape from the genetic isolation of their parents. Convergence will therefore follow divergence and will create a complicated system such as the systematist actually finds in genera like *Galium* and *Saxifraga* (Fig. I). In such cases chromosome numbers are not merely an indispensable guide; they actually provide a rigorous basis of classification which is not to be found amongst the welter of morphological types. In the cereals and fruits, and indeed in all cultivated groups of plants, this rule is always followed by the practical breeder. The chromosome number tells him at once which of two or three endogamous groups of *Triticum* or *Fragaria* a plant falls into, and what kind of results can be expected from each of the possible crosses that he may undertake.

For the systematist it is equally true that, in a group where the number of chromosomes varies, no plant or animal can be accurately defined without a knowledge of its chromosome number. So much can be said on the basis of our present knowledge. In a few years all species of flowering plants whose range and variation are known will have been examined, and it will then be possible in this special field to draw conclusions far more numerous in detail and far broader in scope than are now within the reach of inference.

3. *The Role of Structural Change*

The importance of polyploidy is obvious. Admirable studies of chromosome number and behaviour have helped in clearing up the systematic confusion which it had created in many plant genera. But as an agent of variation polyploidy is sporadic and secondary to the universal and fundamental changes that take place within the chromosomes. In all diploid species such changes are continually going on and have the effect of imposing other kinds of major discontinuity on populations with many freely recombining differential genes; these are structural changes.

Structural changes in the chromosomes come about in the following way. Two chromosomes or parts of the same chromosome become interlocked, and owing to the strain this imposes on them while they are changing their shapes in the course of nuclear division, they break. The broken ends reunite and a new arrangement of genes is produced in the chromosome threads. The new arrangement usually has the same physiological properties as the old one. Its importance consists in its changed mechanical properties. The simplest of these changes is the inversion of a part of the chromosome, so that the genes, instead of running *abcdefgh*, run *abfedcgh*. The result is that the ten or a hundred genes in the inverted piece *fedc* cannot regularly cross over with those in the normal piece *cdef* in the hybrid (or heterozygote) which has the changed and the unchanged chromosomes. If they happen to be a good working combination of genes as compared with homologous combinations in the species, or even if mutations occur within the inversion to produce such a combination, progeny with this inversion will be favoured. The combination will be held together because in heterozygotes crossing-over is suppressed by the inversion, while in homozygotes crossing-over has no effect (Darlington, 1938). This is of the first importance, because, as we saw, the unit of selection and adaptation must always be a combination of genes. Recombination between old and new genes within a working group will be disastrous. An inversion which will hold them together will save the situation. The inversion will then spread in the species. So it often happens. In the first place, we find (so far as our evidence goes) that all individuals of large species with fairly free mating (whether a grasshopper or a paeony) are heterozygous for one inversion or another. There is a certain hybridity equilibrium in the species, an equilibrium depending on the rates of change, crossing, selective elimination, and on hybrid vigour. Not only this, but particular inversions are more frequent in one part of the species range than in another. Take the species *Drosophila pseudo-obscura*. Specimens from some parts of North America have inversions in certain parts of the chromosomes which are not found elsewhere. And if flies of this species are examined from different parts of its range, they are all found to differ in one or more of these inversions. Furthermore, one type is found covering a large part of the whole range, which represents the highest common denominator of the species in this respect. Other special types differ less from this standard type than from one another. The species can therefore be shown to have diverged from this original type. Its racial phylogeny can be traced with Euclidean rigour (Dobzhansky and Sturtevant, 1938).

The importance of recognizing these structural changes, however, depends on the principle to be inferred from their behaviour that, although they do not usually establish genetic differences themselves, they isolate any groups of gene-differences that are already present. In simple cases this happens, as we saw, merely through failure of regular crossing-over. More complicated

U

results follow when two individuals differing in regard to several inversions, whether members of the same species or not, are crossed. They produce a hybrid whose chromosomes, on account of these differences, are unable to pair at meiosis. Such a hybrid is therefore sterile, and the sterility of many interspecific hybrids, both of plants and of animals, is largely due to this cause. An inverted segment therefore acts as an isolating agent either on itself alone or on the whole race that carries it. It is the former and less obvious action which explains why we find that, in two related species or subspecies in *Malva*, *Triticum*, or *Avena*, for example, the significant differences are often inherited as though they were a single gene-difference, that is, as a single block (Darlington, 1937*a*). They have not arisen by a single mutation, but successive mutations have accumulated together in the inversion, sheltered by its immunity from crossing-over within the chromosome, just as they might be sheltered by the immunity from crossing of whole organisms given by a mountain range. It is not therefore surprising that where related species with chromosomes of the same sizes and numbers are crossed together we nearly always find the hybrid is heterozygous for inversions or other dislocations of pieces of chromosomes. The mechanism is universal, although again it varies enormously in importance in different groups. While in *Crepis*, *Campanula* (Darlington and Gairdner, 1937) or *Drosophila* it is clearly an essential agent, in *Lolium* or *Festuca* it is a superfluous incident. The differences in its importance depend on the stage in isolation at which other agents become decisive.

The recognition of structural hybridity from chromosome behaviour in germ-cell formation enables us to say that some species are permanently hybrid: all individuals are regularly derived from the fusion of gametes which are as different both in hereditary properties and in chromosome structure as those of two different species, yet nevertheless they breed true. Evidently the advantages of permanent hybridity in preventing the segregation of new and unsatisfactory combinations have made it possible for them to sacrifice some of their fertility, and these species have stabilized their hybrid condition. This they have done in *Oenothera*, *Paeonia*, *Rosa*, and elsewhere by special adaptations of structural change and chromosome movement (Darlington, 1937*a*). What is significant about these mechanisms for our present purpose is that structural change has made it possible to develop and maintain a major discontinuity between chromosomes within the species just like that occurring between chromosomes of different species.

The same kind of device, as we may call it, has arisen to distinguish and isolate from one another the homologous sex chromosomes in one sex, the heterozygous sex, of species with differentiated sexes. Both of these types of isolation arise most clearly from internal causes. But the differentiation of the sex chromosomes is remarkable for its secondary effect. It is responsible for the high sterility of the heterozygous sex in crosses between species, and thus contributes to the genetic isolation of species and, in *Drosophila pseudo-obscura*, of races within the species.

The occurrence of structural change as a basis for major discontinuity has bearings on the work of the systematist that are perhaps unexpected. In the first place, it means that discontinuity can arise not merely between individual plants and animals but between small parts of their chromosomes. An inversion or other structural change can *float* in a species, picking up, as it were, by chance combination with differential genes the elements from which a cleavage of a higher order will ultimately develop in the species; a cleavage, that is, depending on the isolation of zygotes and not of parts of their chromosomes. This process of accumulation will be subject to ecological selection, and races of *Drosophila* (Dobzhansky and Tan, 1936) arising in this way show, as we might expect, different optimum temperatures for survival and reproduction, just as polyploid races of plants do. Thus just as geographical or ecological isolation may lead to genetic isolation, so also genetic isolation may lead to geographical or ecological differentiation and isolation. Further, this ecological differentiation may then come to establish a genetic isolation at a higher level than that which established it—the level of organisms instead of the level of chromosomes.

The opposite side of the picture is shown where, as sometimes happens, the discontinuity of structure or number of chromosomes occurs within a group which is in other ways so stable that no discontinuity of a higher order develops from it. Genetic changes undoubtedly occur in such systems, but of a morphologically compensating kind so that new genetic species may arise without any external signs of cleavage.

We have already seen how such hidden changes may arise from polyploidy followed by compensating anti-giant selection. 'Hidden' species were first discovered in *Drosophila*. The existence of *D. simulans* was detected by breeding experiments in 1919 and that of *D. pseudo-obscura* by chromosome studies in 1929. In 1935 yet another new species, *D. miranda* (Dobzhansky, 1935) was distinguished from the last by the same means. The two proved to be inter-sterile. All these species escaped the morphologist successfully, and no doubt they represent an abundant type of *cryptic* species. Cryptic species, like permanent hybrids, show that discontinuity may arise from internal factors alone, even when the external factors are working against it.

When we turn back to consider all these conditions of species-formation together we see that the development of discontinuity is inherent in the genetic system because the chromosomes, while potentially permanent, are also inherently subject to change in the properties, positions, and proportions of their component genes. And further, in groups where gene-discontinuities having a morphological effect are eliminated by selection, those chromosome discontinuities having a merely isolating effect may even be favoured. The organism may change without appearing to do so, and genetic species may in this way arise without morphological change.

4. *The Decay of Sexual Reproduction*

We have seen that sexual reproduction implies the recombination of genes within mating groups. We have also seen that the development of discontinuity establishes isolation of various kinds and stops the indefinite extension of these groups. Such isolation limits the freedom of recombination and hence the scope of sexual reproduction. When sexual reproduction is not so limited, another and more violent kind of break-down stops it altogether, for wide crossing leads to excessive recombination and sexual sterility. It is in these circumstances that plants and animals turn to a new method of reproduction which gives an entirely different face to the system of variation and the nature of species.

We can see the origins of this method in many species which

are reproductively versatile. Some individuals of *Poa pratensis* L., for example, reproduce sexually, others can also develop their seed from vegetative buds within the ovule. The two methods of reproduction or, more strictly, the progeny of the two methods, compete within the ovule as well as within the species and survive according to their individual merits. Such facultative or cyclically asexual methods of reproduction have no significance for the species concerned beyond permitting greater variability within it and economizing its reproductive resources. Facultative parthenogenesis in *Rubus* and *Rosa* and probably elsewhere also has the use that it is stimulated when pollination with another species has taken place: it thus becomes an agent of genetic isolation. The importance of these methods lies in their helping us to understand how obligatory asexual reproduction may arise.

Take the simplest case of a triploid. Owing to a failure of chromosome pairing (often in a hybrid) a diploid organism produces unreduced diploid gametes which, fusing with reduced gametes, yield triploid offspring. Triploids are nearly always sexually sterile, since they cannot undergo regular reduction. But for this very reason they often themselves produce unreduced gametes. When these are capable of developing without fertilization (and a capacity for parthenogenesis is very widespread in plants and animals) the triploid will reproduce itself. A new self-perpetuating strain will have been established. Such is the method of origin of obligatorily parthenogenetic forms alike in Crustacea and in Flowering Plants (e.g. *Trichoniscus* and *Hieracium*). The last sexual act in their history was an act of hybridization—haploid mating with diploid gametes—and this act of necessity brought sexual reproduction to an end and established the hybrid as a new species.

Amongst plants parthenogenesis is not the only means of survival of a sterile triploid. Many triploid species of Liliaceae are known. When they are examined they are found to have some special vegetative device for reproduction: the vivipary of many *Allium* species, the runners of *Tulipa saxatilis* Sieber ex Spreng., the bulbils of *Lilium tigrinum* Ker-Gawl. So striking is the association of triploidy with vegetative mechanisms that it has often been thought to have the inherent property of encouraging them. We can now see that the story is the other way round. Triploids can survive only with the help of vegetative propagation. Their existence as plant species, like the absence of males in animal species, proclaims the decay of sexual reproduction.

Obligatorily parthenogenetic species are, however, often diploid. Can we attribute the same origin by sterility to them? Undoubtedly in some cases we can, since hybridization in experiment has been known to determine parthenogenesis. It is equally certain, on the other hand, that a genetic property, arising by mutation or segregation, can break down meiosis and, causing sterility as effectively as triploidy, will likewise inaugurate parthenogenesis, either obligatory or cyclical.

The effect of obligatory parthenogenesis is immediately and permanently to isolate the new strain from any sexual or parthenogenetic kindred it may have. It constitutes at once a new species by itself. The character of this species will depend on such properties of variation as it may still possess. These properties have so far been most inadequately studied, but we know their essential character: it depends on mutation occurring without recombination. Every mutation will breed true and will be selected individually. These mutations are probably very frequent in the early life of a species, owing to the survival of crossing-over as a means of segregation of differences after reduction has itself been suppressed. They resemble the mutations of *Oenothera*, which are also due to crossing-over in hybrid species. The variant forms are entirely and permanently isolated from one another. They are, each of them, genetically the best of good species. How far they can be arranged in groups of common descent having a systematic value only the combination of experimental breeding, chromosome studies, and distribution records will enable us to say.

5. *Genetic Isolation*

It has long been held, and as we see genetics shows no reason to doubt it, that isolation of their members is the agent which permits the cleavage of species. In fact, we may define species as the minimum permanently isolated groups. But, as we have seen, this isolation is of many kinds. It may be said to spring from two sources, external and internal. These sources are distinguishable at once in theory, and are sometimes at once distinguishable in practice. It is clear that a geological or climatic catastrophe can, as a purely external agent, separate one species into two parts which will be permanently isolated in space and inevitably diverge in form. It is also clear that polyploidy can, as a purely internal agent, split a species into two parts which will be isolated as reproductive units by intersterility and likewise in consequence diverge in form. These two types we may use as examples of geographical and genetic isolation. But the instances are simple and extreme. Between them there are many where internal and external agents must co-operate. How they co-operate we are only beginning to understand and the necessary experiments have not yet been made, but what we already know shows us the kind of problem we are dealing with and how to tackle it.

Let us suppose that an external discontinuity takes the lead in establishing isolation. The species occupies two different types of habitat. If it is genetically heterogeneous, genotypes differing in groups of genes will be favoured and consequently selected in the different habitats. Any genetic barrier between groups will reduce the reproductive wastage from recombination between the adaptive gene-groups. Such a barrier, as we have seen, can arise from a change in the structure of a chromosome preventing crossing-over. It can also arise through the action of gene or structural changes causing differences in pollen-tube growth, or mating season, or reducing the fertility of an F_1 from crossing between the two groups. Genetic variations of all these kinds occur in countless species. Once genetic isolation has been completely established in these ways it will inevitably lead to further genetic divergence. It is perhaps self-evident that this divergence will develop in a certain evolutionary sequence, the *isolation sequence* which may be stated in principle to follow the reverse course to that of individual development. Thus if isolation is established by failure of crossing-over, at a later stage of divergence fertility of the F_1 will be affected or the mating of the gametes, and finally of the parents themselves, will become impossible (Fig. 2).

While the whole of this series may spring originally from an external cause it seems that in general internal, genetic, changes are of predominant and even primary importance. External conditions can directly determine only the last stage of the isolation sequence—the mating of parental zygotes. The changes which are continually taking place in the genes and chromosomes of a species are, most of them, of altogether negligible importance in fitting an organism to its environment. In fact most of them are definitely unfitting in effect. But they are of inevitable importance in causing discontinuity within the species irrespective of any discontinuity in its environment. Thus genes which determine the preferences of mating of *Drosophila simulans*

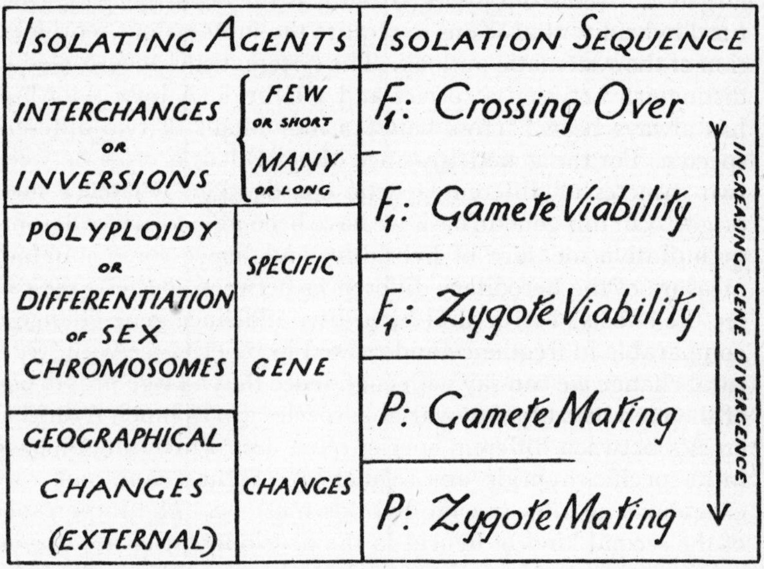

ISOLATING AGENTS		ISOLATION SEQUENCE	
INTERCHANGES OR INVERSIONS	FEW OR SHORT	F_1: Crossing Over	INCREASING GENE DIVERGENCE
	MANY OR LONG	F_1: Gamete Viability	
POLYPLOIDY OR DIFFERENTIATION OF SEX CHROMOSOMES	SPECIFIC GENE	F_1: Zygote Viability	
		P: Gamete Mating	
GEOGRAPHICAL CHANGES (EXTERNAL)	CHANGES	P: Zygote Mating	

FIG. 2.

and *D. melanogaster* have nothing to do with the environments of these species, but they have a great deal to do with the mating of individuals and the genetic isolation to which the separate existence of the species is due. They have arisen, we can hardly doubt, as *endo-adaptations*, concerned with the breeding relations of parts of one species, as opposed to the *exo-adaptations* with which we are familiar in the relationship of the species to its general environment.

The genetic analysis of this differentiation of two species by comparison for example of the relative mating behaviour (in animals) or relative pollen-tube growth of F_1s and F_2s with their parental species has not yet been attempted. Our problem is, therefore, knowing the genetic agents from which the isolation of pairs of species is built up, to find out in what order and in what relationship these different agents have worked to produce this isolation. Again, the joint study of form, function, habitat, and heredity will be needed for any significant advance.

6. *Hybridity*

Our inferences of structural change in chromosomes are largely derived from hybrids, and it is the occurrence of structural hybridity that seems to require the most serious reorientation of the systematic outlook. The systematist is accustomed to distinguish between a species and a hybrid. A hybrid for him has always been a cross between individuals of two different species. For the geneticist (since Mendel) it is a cross between two gametes of different genetic constitution, whatever their origin. On this genetic basis we have been able to arrive at some quantitative measure of hybridity, and hence some standard measure of the hereditary differences between species. We can see the effects of structural hybridity, and since gene-change is comparable in frequency and related in inheritance with structural change we can say with confidence that a large proportion of the members of many variable species are as much hybrid as crosses between different species often are. Furthermore, such intra-specific hybrids are regular occurrences and not rare exceptions as inter-specific hybrids must be. The importance of the second kind of hybrid in the development of new forms, particularly polyploids, has long been known. The importance of the first kind is little known and is far greater. For purposes of genetics the distinction has no particular value, but for purposes of systematics it is altogether vital. It depends on the similarity in the form of the parents and not on the abundance or variability of the progeny.

Broadly speaking, three types of intra-specific hybrid are systematically important. The first is the kind which gives rise to a fertile tetraploid, like that derived from a species-cross. This kind has been referred to earlier. The second kind is the triploid which has arisen, perhaps by self-fertilization, from a diploid parent through the formation of an unreduced diploid gamete. Such a plant is a numerical hybrid and in consequence is usually sterile. It is important, as we saw, wherever non-sexual reproduction is possible. Such a triploid form of *Lolium perenne* L. has been described as a species of *Festuca* (*F. loliacea* Curt.) and appears in the London Catalogue as a cross between *F. pratensis* Huds. and *L. perenne*. Its alleged inter-specific origin, as in other triploids, has no doubt been deduced from its sterility which in fact results from the purely numerical hybridity of any triploid. The third kind of hybrid is that already referred to in *Oenothera* and *Rosa*, where a special system of structural and numerical changes in the chromosomes has enabled the species to continue reproducing sexually while gradually generating hybridity within itself. This internal generation of hybridity is also important in non-sexual species and in garden plants which are propagated vegetatively, for as a result of these inherent and internal changes they come to develop a hybridity (and sterility) which is no necessary indication of their having arisen from the crossing of dissimilar gametes. As we saw earlier, a species may similarly diverge into two intersterile forms without any corresponding morphological change. Such cryptic variation is analogous to the compensating genetic changes inferred in stable species and to the dwarfing reversion inferred in new polyploids. All these are genetic changes which either produce no morphological change, or actually cover up such a change when it has been produced by other means.

From all these considerations it follows that the term 'hybrid' can have no meaning to the systematist unless he knows how the particular genetic system works. An enormous number of plant species that are validly described as species both on taxonomic and genetic grounds are hybrids. In fact, as we saw, many asexual species are species by virtue of an act of hybridization which established their sexual sterility. Other species are the fertile and true-breeding polyploid derivatives of hybrids. There are even more kinds of hybrids than of species, and the systematic importance of the different kinds depends on their genetic classification.

7. *Phylogeny*

Chromosome studies unrelated to the evidence of experimental breeding have another bearing on systematics, namely, in the elucidation of relationships between species and larger groups that will not cross. We all know that the reproductive system is the most conservative part of the organism in evolution. Its conservatism is due to its being most sensitive to the ill effects of unco-ordinated change, and co-ordination of groups of genes is, as we saw earlier, the crux of adaptation. In general the chromosomes are not the most conservative part of this system, nor are they uniformly conservative in different groups, but we sometimes find in them the means of recognizing the common descent of groups of species and even of genera and families. We have already seen how the changes in structure of the chromosomes enable us to trace the phylogeny of races and individuals within a species with great accuracy. A similar, although necessarily less accurate, method may be used in tracing from the mere numbers and shapes of chromosomes at mitosis the relationships between species which will not cross. Some sections of the Orthoptera may be readily recognized by the constant forms and numbers of the chromosomes found within them, and the whole of the Pomoideae, embracing perhaps 1,000 species, have a constant set of 17 chromosomes, which distinguishes them from the rest of the Rosaceae.

This kind of comparison of course establishes no general standard of classification. The degree of conservatism of chromosome organization depends, as we saw earlier, on the whole system of reproduction and variation, and this system is characteristic of each group. In some groups differences of number as well as form of chromosomes occur within the species in consequence of special kinds of structural change resulting in fragmentation and fusion. Only exceptionally do we find a genus like *Crepis* (Babcock and Cameron, 1934) or *Primula* (Smith, 1933), where probably all species (over a hundred having been examined) can be recognized by their chromosome numbers and forms, and their relationship and descent consequently inferred in some detail from this alone.

Such diversity implies considerable instability in chromosome number. Instability might be due to more frequent breakages and fusions of chromosomes than usual. More probably it is due to the survival of the results of such changes, and this survival in turn must depend on the genetic properties of the parts of the chromosomes near their dynamic centres, the centromeres. These organs cannot be created *de novo*. Gain or loss of chromosomes must therefore depend on the gain or loss of centromeres, together with such adjoining parts of the chromosomes as happen to be broken off with them. If these parts are inert their reduplication or loss will make no difference. The chromosome complement can then change its number freely. If they are genetically active, on the other hand, they will compel the chromosome complement to be relatively stable. In *Drosophila* (Kozhevnikov, 1936), where these parts are inert, changes of chromosome number have been produced artificially and occur in nature. Again we see that the possibilities of variation inherent in a species depend on the established arrangement of the hereditary materials in its chromosomes.

There is another way in which the conservatism of the genetic system is useful in discovering ancestral origins, namely, in the comparison of chromosome behaviour in different groups. The majority of organisms, plants, animals, and protista alike, show no significant variation from the two common types of nuclear division found in body-cell and gamete formation. Several groups of animals, however, are peculiar in the chromosome movements found at meiosis in one sex, the heterozygous sex, as well as in the special genetic organization of this sex. Thus it is possible to distinguish the Hymenoptera and some other groups by their having haploid males, and the section of Diptera with short antennae by their having abnormal meiosis without crossing-over in the males (Darlington, 1937a). It is consequently possible in certain cases of difficult subdivision to resolve a systematic dilemma by reference to chromosome behaviour. For example, it seems likely that a division of the Neuroptera (Klingstedt, 1937), according to the pairing and non-pairing of the sex-chromosomes, has a finality that could not be attained by purely morphological methods.

Comparison of chromosome behaviour, more particularly in gamete formation, has another implication than that of relationship between living forms; it shows how certain rare and critical changes in evolution have taken place. The most significant of these is found in certain polyploids where one or two of the chromosomes, instead of being represented, say, four times, like the others, are represented six times. In this way a species such as *Dahlia merckii* Lehm. comes to have 36 or $4x$ for 6 chromosomes and $6x$ for 2, instead of 32 or $4x$ for all 8. Such unbalanced multiplication of some chromosomes at the expense of others always carries with it a change in the system of growth of the organism.

We can have no doubt, therefore, that this species must largely owe its specific properties to the change in balance which took place earlier in its history. Plants having this constitution are known as secondary polyploids. They can be recognized more or less distinctly by a number of special properties. In some groups the change is no doubt so remote that its traces have vanished. In others, as in the Pomoideae, we can still see the evidence of the whole of this large group of species, all of which as we saw have a set of 17 chromosomes, having arisen by a change of balance from an earlier rose-like ancestor with 7 chromosomes (Fig. 1, and Darlington, 1937a).

We may notice parenthetically that changes in balance or proportion amongst genes, of which secondary polyploidy is a violent example, are going on unobtrusively all the time in most species of animals and plants. The mechanism depends on small structural changes in the chromosomes. Segments are broken off and moved from one part of a chromosome to another, and new chromosomes are formed having such segments lost or reduplicated. It is often said that gene-changes alone will not account for differences between species. The changes in position and proportion of which we have evidence in the structural and numerical hybrids found in nature when superimposed on the changes in the internal properties of the genes themselves will account for the differences between species, and every one of these differences is paralleled by the single differences found within species and also produced in experiments. The distinction between these single differences and the multiple differences revealed by the behaviour of crosses between species lies in integration. The three types of change in the individual properties and the relative positions and proportions of genes are integrated in the course of isolation from an old species and adaptation to a new environment. Species-formation accompanied by morphological divergence is therefore a symptom of the efficient use of the available genetic materials for evolutionary change.

8. *The Species Concept*

The many kinds of isolation which establish species mean that the species established are themselves of many different kinds. How these kinds are to be recognized is a question demanding a collaboration of geneticist and systematist that is only now being attempted. But there is another way, already open to us, by which species may be classified.

We have now seen that it is possible to consider separately and as a unit the organization of an inter-mating group of plants or animals as it affects the genetic properties of that group. This organization depends equally on the adaptation of the fine chromosome mechanism of heredity and variation and on the gross mechanisms of reproduction. It exists as an organization on account of the continual adaptive interaction of these different mechanisms, and it is for this reason that I describe the whole organization, taken together, as the *genetic system* (Darlington, 1939). In terms of this system we can now attempt to classify kinds of species.

We can trace evolution proceeding from the asexual to the sexual stage of reproduction and back to the apomictic or subsexual, from the sexually undifferentiated to the differentiated, from the haploid to the diploid, and from the diploid to the polyploid. Most of these steps are irreversible. All of them show a characteristic type of species-formation simply because the conditions of origin of discontinuity are characteristic at each level of development. In the virus the definition of a species is clearly a matter of molecular structure. In the asexual protozoa the classification is beyond any genetic experiment and has no necessary genetic significance. In the higher plants a morphologically uniform species may conceal intersterile diploid and polyploid forms. In the higher animals, similarly, cryptic species may arise by the differentiation of mating instincts establishing a genetic isolation without any change of form. In plants and animals equally, sterility may enforce a return to asexual reproduction with an unlimited efflorescence of individuals, every one of which constitutes a valid species. Before we attempt to divide a complex group into species we must therefore know from combined genetic and cytological inquiry what kind of species we are likely to find in it.

The evidence of breeding and chromosome behaviour therefore shows that systematics cannot always obey the rules that are expected of it. There are many kinds of species and many kinds of discontinuities between species; there are also many kinds of hybridity and isolation. These differences depend on the different kinds of genetic systems at work in plants and animals; but they cannot be arranged in a simple table because they occur at different levels of integration. The uniformity of systematic nomenclature so convenient for description suggests to us that the species is a proper subject for inductive consideration. We feel that we ought to have a 'species concept'. In fact, there can be no species concept based on the species of descriptive convenience that will not ensnare its own author so soon as he steps outside the group from which he made the concept. The only valid principles are those that we can derive, not from fixed classes but from changing processes. To do this we must go beyond the species to find out what it is made of. We must proceed (by collaboration) to examine its chromosome structure and system of reproduction in relation to its range of variation and ecological character. From them we can determine what is the genetic species of Ray, the unit of reproduction, a unit which cannot be used for summary diagnosis, but which can be used for discovering and relating the processes of variation and the principles of evolution.

REFERENCES

ANDERSON, E., and SAX, K. (1936). 'A Cytological Monograph of the American Species of *Tradescantia*.' *Bot. Gaz.* **97**, 433–76.

BABCOCK, E. B., and CAMERON, D. R. (1934). 'Chromosomes and Phylogeny in *Crepis*, II.' *Univ. Cal. Pub. Agr. Sci.* **6**, 287–324.

DARLINGTON, C. D. (1933). 'Chromosome Study and the Genetic Analysis of Species.' *Ann. Bot.* **47**, 811–14.

—— (1937a). *Recent Advances in Cytology.* 2nd ed. London.

—— (1937b). 'The Early Hybridizers and the Origins of Genetics.' *Herbertia*, **4**, 63–9.

—— (1939). *The Evolution of Genetic Systems.* Cambridge.

—— and GAIRDNER, A. E. (1937). 'The Variation System in *Campanula persicifolia*.' *J. Genet.* **35**, 97–128.

DOBZHANSKY, TH. (1935). '*Drosophila miranda*, a New Species.' *Genetics*, **20**, 377–91.

—— (1937). *Genetics and the Origin of Species.* New York.

—— and STURTEVANT, A. H. (1938). 'Inversions in the Chromosomes of *Drosophila pseudo-obscura*.' *Genetics*, **23**, 28–64.

—— and TAN, C. C. (1936). 'Studies on Hybrid Sterility, III.' *Z. indukt. Abstamm.- u. Vererb.-Lehre*, **72**, 88–114.

ERLANSON, E. W. (1934). 'Experimental Data for the Revision of the North American Wild Roses.' *Bot. Gaz.* **96**, 197–259.

FAGERLIND, F. (1937). 'Embryologische, zytologische und bestäubungs-experimentelle Studien in der Familie Rubiaceae nebst Bemerkungen über einige Polyploiditätsprobleme.' *Acta Hort. Berg.* **11**, 195–470.

GEITLER, L. (1936). 'Vergleichend-zytologische Untersuchungen an *Myosotis*.' *Jahrb. wiss. Bot.* **83**, 707–24.

GOODSPEED, T. H. (1934). 'Nicotiana Phylesis in the Light of Chromosome Number, Morphology, and Behaviour.' *Univ. Cal. Pub. Bot.* **17**, 369–98.

GUSTAFSSON, A. (1935). 'The Importance of the Apomicts for Plant Geography.' *Bot. Notiser*, **1935**, 325–30.

JØRGENSEN, C. A. (1927). 'Sex and Chromosomes in *Vallisneria*.' *J. Genet.* **18**, 63–75.

KLINGSTEDT, H. (1937). 'Chromosome Behaviour and Phylogeny in the Neuroptera.' *Nature*, **139**, 468.

KOZHEVNIKOV, B. TH. (1936). 'Experimentally produced Karyotypical Isolation.' *Biol. Zhurn. (Moscow)* **5**, 727–52.

KRISTOFFERSON, K. B. (1925). 'Species Crossings in *Malva*.' *Hereditas*, **7**, 233–356.

LEVAN, A. (1935). 'Zytologische Studien in *Allium Schoenoprasum*.' *Hereditas*, **22**, 1–128.

MANTON, I. (1937). 'The Problem of *Biscutella laevigata*, II.' *Ann. Bot.* N.S. **1**, 439–62.

MAUDE, P. (1939). 'The Merton Catalogue. A List of Chromosome Numbers of British Species of Flowering Plants.' *New Phytol.* **38**, 1–31.

MÜNTZING, A. (1937). 'The Effects of Chromosomal Variation in *Dactylis*.' *Hereditas*, **23**, 113–235.

RICHARDSON, M. M. (1936). 'Structural Hybridity in *Lilium Martagon album* × *L. Hansonii*.' *J. Genet.* **32**, 411–50.

SCHAFER, B., and LA COUR, L. (1934). 'A Chromosome Survey of *Aconitum*, I.' *Ann. Bot.* **48**, 693–713.

SCHEERER, H. (1937). 'Experimentelle und zytologische Untersuchungen innerhalb der Veronica-Gruppe Pentasepala.' *Flora*, **51**, 287–323.

SKOVSTED, A. (1934). 'Cytological Studies in the Tribe Saxifrageae.' *Dansk bot. Ark.* **8**, 1–52.

SMITH, W. WRIGHT (1933). 'Some Aspects of the bearing of Cytology on Taxonomy.' *Proc. Linn. Soc.* **145**, 151–81.

STEBBINS, G. L. (1938). 'Cytogenetic Studies in Paeonia, II.' *Genetics*, **23**, 83–110.

UPCOTT, M. B. (1937). 'The Genetic Structure of *Tulipa*, II.' *J. Genet.* **34**, 339–98.

WADDINGTON, C. H. (1939). *An Introduction to Modern Genetics.* London.

WINGE, Ø. (1938). 'Inheritance of Specific Characters in *Tragopogon*.' *C. R. Carlsb. (Physiol.)*, **22** (9).

THE STATISTICAL CONSEQUENCES OF MENDELIAN HEREDITY IN RELATION TO SPECIATION

By SEWALL WRIGHT

THE most obvious starting-point, in attempting to relate laboratory genetics to speciation in nature, is the phenomenon of mutation. The term 'species' primarily means 'kind', and mutations are the elementary observable changes in kind along lines of descent. The abruptness of origin of mutations and their stability after origin appear to give a simple explanation of the traditional distinctiveness and internal homogeneity of species in their essential characters. While it has been obvious that most mutations do not produce changes in kind directly comparable to species-differences, yet from the viewpoint that the term 'species' denotes a certain critical step in the hierarchy of degrees of difference in kind, it has appeared legitimate to identify the origin of species and even of higher categories with mutation, with the qualification that only occasional mutations are of specific rank and still rarer ones of generic, familial, or higher rank. This is a viewpoint taken by certain geneticists, most notably in recent years by Goldschmidt.

Few systematists, however, seem ever to have been at all satisfied with this identification of speciation and mutation (cf. Osborn, 1927). In part this has been because of the apparent dissimilarity in the type of difference referred to above, but more, perhaps, because of a change from the traditional conception of the species, imposed by the findings in those groups which have been studied most exhaustively. It has become necessary to shift the emphasis in the definition of species from the essentially physiological concept, kind, to the ecological one, the interbreeding population. It has come to be recognized that most species must be divided into subspecies, differing rather consistently in kind at their centres of distribution but connected by statistically intergrading populations, and that even within the taxonomically recognizable subspecies, sufficiently careful studies show that no two local populations have exactly the same statistical properties (cf. Schmidt, 1917; Sumner,

Y

1932; Turesson, 1925; anthropologists in general). In the other direction, numerous recognized species living in different regions and supposedly distinct because of marked differences in kind have had to be assembled in species-complexes (or *Rassenkreise*) because of the discovery of intergrading populations between them (cf. Rensch, 1929).

The ideal has been to apply the specific name to groups within which all subdivisions interbreed sufficiently freely to form intergrading populations wherever they come in contact, but between which there is so little interbreeding that such populations are not found. But it is becoming apparent that this ideal is often unrealizable. A chain of intergrading populations may return on itself around a circle, leading to populations which occupy the same territory without interbreeding (e.g. *Peromyscus maniculatus bairdii* (Hoy & Kennicott) and *P. m. gracilis* (Le Conte) in Michigan; Osgood, 1909; Dice, 1931). The most remarkable case of this sort so far reported seems to be that found by Kinsey in the American gall-wasps of the genus *Cynips*. Long branching chains of intergrading 'species' loop back repeatedly to the same region and host, leading ultimately to types so different in kind that they have been considered subgenera. From the standpoint of continuity one of these chains (with 76 to 86 races in one case) must be considered as a single giant *Rassenkreis* (cp. Goldschmidt, 1937), but from the standpoint of sufficient differentiation to permit occupancy of the same territory without interbreeding some 8 or 9 good species must apparently be recognized in the above case, and finally from the standpoint of character-differences there are 86 taxonomically distinguishable 'species' to be grouped arbitrarily in 9 'complexes' and the 2 subgenera, *Acraspis* and *Philonix*.

From the population viewpoint, a single mutation can give rise to a new species only if its descendants form a group not interbreeding in nature with the parent species. But this at once implies coincidence of another sort of evolutionary factor, isolation, unless the mutation itself has isolating effects. Thus such mutations as the trisomics of *Oenothera lamarckiana* Ser. and of *Datura stramonium* L., which can only exist as types segregating from the parent populations, cannot form species in this sense, though the difference in kind may seem fully comparable to that of true species. On the other hand, a tetraploid mutation, fertile by itself, but producing a largely sterile triploid hybrid with the parent species, may give rise to a population which may properly be considered a new species from the population viewpoint even though the character-differences, at least at the time of mutation, may be very slight. Most of the character-differences in species which have had this mode of origin probably trace to other evolutionary processes, the tetraploidy being significant largely as an isolating factor which gives an opportunity for the action of these other processes. Tetraploidy in a species-hybrid, however, produces a type which satisfies the usual criterion for degree of difference in kind from pre-existent species as well as the more essential criterion of isolation. There can be no doubt that both auto- and allotetraploidy have played a role in the multiplication of genuine species, especially in higher plants (cf. Müntzing, 1932, 1936), but also in some groups of animals. Nevertheless, it appears that this role is a subordinate one in the evolutionary process in general. No other type of mutation is known which can bring about the origin of a new species by itself, at least under prevailing biparental reproduction. We will not here consider the meaning of the term 'species' as applied to forms with exclusive or nearly exclusive vegetative reproduction.

Genetic analyses of species-crosses show that in most cases the differences are not such as could have arisen at one step. An array of differences of all grades of coarseness is usually found in each case: gross chromosome-changes such as inversions, translocations, and duplications, gene-differences with major effects, comparable to those of the familiar laboratory mutations, and finally apparent blending differences, due presumably to a multiplicity of individually minute or subliminal gene-effects (cf. Dobzhansky, 1937). Moreover, a certain degree of variability may be an essential characteristic of a species. Kinsey (1929) compares the extraordinary variability of *Cynips erinacei* (Walsh) within all parts of a range of some 500,000 square miles with the approximate uniformity of *C. pezomachoides* (O-S.) in a large adjoining territory. He also (1937) compares the usual high variability of 'continental' species with the relative uniformity of 'insular' ones.

These findings indicate that the occurrence of single mutations can be of little importance in speciation in general. For the significant factors we must look to statistical processes which can carry certain genes to fixation or hold them at certain constant frequencies in the population. We must consider such factors as the pressure of *recurrent* mutation, the pressure of selection, both between individuals and between populations, and finally the effects of isolation, partial or complete.

These constitute a very heterogeneous group of factors. In order to discuss their roles intelligently it is necessary to compare their effects on a common scale. Such a scale is to be found in *gene-frequency*, applicable, it may be noted, to most types of chromosome aberration as well as to single gene-mutations. Because of the symmetry of the Mendelian mechanism, the relative frequencies of two allelic conditions tend to remain unchanged in a large randomly breeding population in the absence of recurrent mutation, selection, or immigration. From this viewpoint, an adequate genetic description of a species would consist of a list of gene-frequencies such as

$$(p_1 a_1 + q_1 A_1)(p_2 a_2 + q_2 A_2)...(p_n a_n + q_n A_n)$$

rather than of a single typical genotype such as

$$A_1 A_1 A_2 A_2 ... A_n A_n.$$

The elementary evolutionary process becomes change of gene-frequency rather than mutation.

It is easy to see how recurrent mutation tends to change gene-frequency. If q is the frequency of a given gene, $(1-q)$ that of its alleles, and the latter, considered collectively, mutate to the given gene at the rate v per generation, the mutation pressure is obviously $\Delta q = v(1-q)$. Since mutation is known to be a reversible process in many cases (Muller, 1928; Timofeeff-Ressovsky, 1932), reverse mutation should also be represented in the formula. If the rate per generation is u, the net mutation-pressure may be written

$$\Delta q = v(1-q) - uq.$$

A graphic representation is given in Fig. 1.

There is a certain point on the scale at which the opposed pressures balance each other $\left(\Delta q = 0 \text{ at } \hat{q} = \dfrac{v}{u+v}\right)$. At this point there is stable equilibrium. This situation differs from the persistence of gene-frequencies found in the absence of any evolutionary pressure in the tendency for the population to return always to the same equilibrium point after a change in either direction. A species in which a few important gene-differences or many minor ones are held in equilibrium at frequencies not too close to 0 or 1 is characterized by a constant high degree of variability as well as by constant average values of each character.

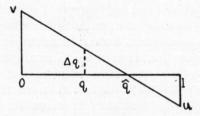

FIG. 1. Mutation-pressure (Δq) on an exaggerated scale in relation to gene-frequency (q). $\Delta q = v(1-q)-uq$. At equilibrium $\Delta q = 0$, $\hat{q} = \dfrac{v}{u+v}$.

The effect of selection can also be measured on the scale of gene-frequencies. As there can be no selection relative to a gene, if it is either completely fixed or absent ($q = 1$ or $q = 0$), selection-pressure may be expected to contain the term $q(1-q)$. The simplest case is that in which there is a constant difference in adaptive value (W) between the two homozygous conditions, with the heterozygote exactly halfway between

$$(W_{AA} = 1, W_{AA'} = 1-s, W_{A'A'} = 1-2s).$$

Selection-pressure here takes the simple form $q = sq(1-q)$ (Fisher, 1930). The consequences of many other special cases have been worked out by Haldane, who, however, has expressed his results in terms of the frequency ratio of alleles, equivalent to $q/1-q$ in the symbolism used here.

The assignment of selection coefficients to individual genes does not give as realistic a representation of natural selection as is desirable. It is the organism as a whole that is more or less adaptive in relation to prevailing conditions, not single genes. A gene that produces a more favourable effect than its allele in one combination is likely to be less favourable in others. Thus if a certain proportionality in the development of two parts of an organism is more adaptive than deviations in either direction, genes that increase the relative size of one part will be adaptive in combinations in which this part is unduly small because of other factors, but will be antiadaptive in combinations which make this part too large. It can be shown that if an average adaptive value (W), relative to prevailing conditions, can be assigned each genotype as a whole, the net selection-pressure on a single gene (in a population of diploid organisms) can be expressed by the formula

$$\Delta q = \frac{q(1-q)}{2\overline{W}}\frac{\partial \overline{W}}{\partial q},$$

where $\overline{W}$ is the average of the adaptive values of all possible genotypes, giving due weight to their frequencies.

These frequencies are functions of the frequencies of the component genes. Thus for the array of gene-frequencies given above, the frequencies of all possible genotypes, under random mating, are given by the appropriate terms in the expansion of the expression

$$(p_1 a_1 + q_1 A_1)^2 \; (p_2 a_2 + q_2 A_2)^2 \; \ldots \; (p_n a_n + q_n A_n)^2.$$

This means that in general the selection-pressure on any gene is a function not only of its own frequency but of that of all other genes.

There may be a stable equilibrium due to selection alone under conditions in which a heterozygote is selected over both homozygotes. The extreme case is that of balanced lethals, exhibited in nature in the permanent heterozygosis of many species of *Oenothera*. It is probable that polymorphism in many species rests on a slight advantage of the heterozygote (Fisher, 1930*b*).

In most cases in which one allele has an appreciable selective advantage under the prevailing conditions, equilibrium is probably established between opposed pressures of selection and mutation. The net rate of change of gene-frequency, due to selection and mutation together, may be written as follows by combining preceding formulae:

$$\Delta q = v(1-q) - uq + \frac{q(1-q)}{2\overline{W}}\cdot\frac{\partial \overline{W}}{\partial q}.$$

A special case is shown graphically in Fig. 2.

Another possibility of change of gene-frequency is exhibited by the well-known tendency towards fixation of one or another chance combination of genes in closely inbred strains. The effect depends on accidental, rather than selective, factors which determine the individuals which become the parents of the next generation. It requires $2N$ gametes to reconstitute a population of N mature individuals. Random samples of this size, from a population in which a given gene has the frequency q, vary in gene-frequency with a standard deviation,

$$\sigma_{\Delta q} = \sqrt{\frac{q(1-q)}{2N}}.$$

It may seem that this is an insignificant amount of variability if N is reasonably large, especially as the accidental variations

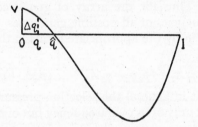

Fig. 2. Opposed pressures of mutation (v) and selection ($t = 25v$) in the case of a deleterious recessive. $\Delta q = v(1-q) - tq^2(1-q)$, $\hat{q} = \sqrt{(v/t)}$.

in the following generations are as likely to be in the reverse direction as in the same direction. However, variance of sampling is cumulative, being nearly doubled in two generations, multiplied threefold in three generations, and so on until damped by approach of q to 0 or 1. In the course of geologic time these chance variations may be expected to bring one allele or the other to fixation, even in rather large populations, in the absence of other factors. The rate of fixation here is $1/2N$ per generation. This process, occurring independently in all loci, may bring about any degree of differentiation of isolated populations in respect to indifferent characters.

We must again, however, consider the simultaneous effects of the various evolutionary factors. As described above, the directed evolutionary pressures, such as selection and mutation, in opposing each other, determine a certain point of equilibrium in gene-frequency. The inbreeding effect is opposed to such factors in a different sense from that in which they oppose each other. It tends to bring about random deviations in either direction from the equilibrium point. The resultant is a probability distribution relative to the scale of gene-frequencies (Fig. 3). The ordinates show how often, in the long run, the gene exhibits each frequency. The curve can also be interpreted as the frequency distribution at a given moment for all genes subject to the same conditions. A third interpretation is the distribution of frequencies for a given gene at a given moment in an array of completely isolated populations.

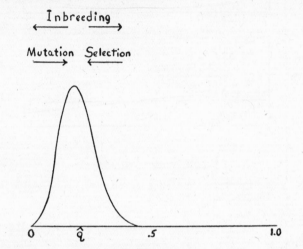

FIG. 3. Distribution ($\phi(q)$) of gene-frequencies for a recessive deleterious gene in a population of limited size (N). Mutation and selection-pressures as in Fig. 2 ($t = 25v$). $N = 1/v$. $\phi(q) = Ce^{-50q^2}q^3(1-q)^{-1}$.

As to the formula for this probability curve, it can be shown that it can be expressed in terms of the rate of directed change in gene-frequency (Δq) and the undirected sampling variance per generation ($\sigma^2_{\Delta q}$).

$$\phi(q) = (C/\sigma_{\Delta q})e^{2\int (\Delta q/\sigma^2_{\Delta q})\,dq}.$$

For the value of Δq given above and for a population of diploid individuals, this resolves into the following:

$$\phi(q) = C\overline{W}^{2N}q^{4Nv-1}(1-q)^{4Nu-1}.$$

Similar formulae can be developed for other cases such as sex-linked genes and polyploids.

The above expression brings together the effects of mutation, selection, and size of population. The ways in which its form varies in relation to severity of selection and size of population are illustrated in Figs. 4–6 for a recessive gene.

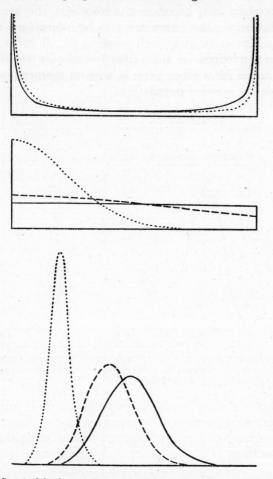

FIG. 4–6. Some of the forms taken by the distribution of frequencies of a recessive deleterious gene, $\phi(q) = Ce^{-2Ntq^2}q^{4Nv-1}(1-q)^{4Nu-1}$. Mutation rates to and from the gene are assumed equal ($u = v$). Effective size of populations is $N = \dfrac{1}{40v}$, $\dfrac{10}{40v}$, and $\dfrac{100}{40v}$ in Figs. 4, 5, and 6 respectively from top to bottom. In each case the solid line represents the least selection ($t = v/5$), the broken line selection 10 times as severe (not represented in Fig. 4, since practically indistinguishable from the preceding), and the dotted line represents selection 100 times as severe.

As already noted, $\overline{W}$ is a function of all gene-frequencies. In the practically infinite field of gene-combinations, possible from differences in only a few thousands, or even hundreds of loci, there are likely to be an enormous number of different harmonious combinations of characters. These would appear as peak values of $\overline{W}$, separated by valleys or saddles in a multi-dimensional surface. The distribution surface for all gene-frequencies, considered simultaneously, will show corresponding peaks.

$$\phi(q_1, q_2,..., q_n) = C\overline{W}^{2N} \prod_{i=1}^{n} [q_i^{4Nv_i-1}(1-q_i)^{4Nu_i-1}].$$

Fig. 7 illustrates a two-factor case with two peaks. It is assumed in this case that the grade of character is determined by two equivalent additive factors, but that the most adaptive combinations are intermediate, as is to be expected in any species long exposed to the same conditions.

Grade of character	Adaptive value (W)	Genotypes
5	$1-4s$	$A_1A_1A_2A_2$
4	$1-s$	$A_1A_1A_2a_2,\ A_1a_1A_2A_2$
3	1	$A_1A_1a_2a_2,\ A_1a_1A_2a_2,\ a_1a_1A_2A_2$
2	$1-s$	$A_1a_1a_2a_2,\ a_1a_1A_2a_2$
1	$1-4s$	$a_1a_1a_2a_2$

There are two peak combinations that may become fixed in populations ($A_1A_1a_2a_2,\ a_1a_1A_2A_2$) separated from each other in the two-dimensional system of values of q_1 and q_2 by a saddle which is shallow if s is a small fraction. The joint distribution of gene-frequencies shows two peaks determined by selection-pressures directed towards the peak combinations but opposed by mutation-pressures.

The peaks and valleys of the surface of adaptive values ($\overline{W}$) are so much exaggerated in the distribution of gene-frequencies (term $\overline{W}^{2N}$) that we are again confronted with the apparent unlikelihood of any appreciable non-adaptive drift away from the peak occupied by the species at a given time, if the size of population is at all large. The effective size of population may, however, be much smaller than the apparent size for various reasons. It refers, of course, only to sexually mature individuals. If mature individuals of one sex are much less numerous than those of the other, the effective size is largely determined by the former. It cannot be as much as four times as great. If there are wide variations in the numbers of offspring reaching maturity, left by different parents, the effective number may be reduced. If the species goes through a more or less regular cycle of numbers, the effective size is determined largely by the phase of small numbers. The situation is approximately as if the

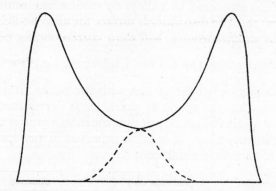

FIG. 7. The frequencies along the two diagonals of the joint distribution for two series of alleles with equal and additive effects on a character on which adverse selection acts according to the square of the deviation from the mean. The solid line shows the frequencies in populations along the line connecting the two favourable types $A_1 A_1 a_2 a_2$ and $a_1 a_1 A_2 A_2$. The broken line refers to the line connecting the extreme types $a_1 a_1 a_2 a_2$ and $A_1 A_1 A_2 A_2$. In the case shown, all mutation rates (u_1, v_1, u_2, v_2) are assumed equal, $N = 1/(2v)$, and $s = 5v$. Along the favourable diagonal $(q_1 = (1-q_2))$ the distribution is approximately $Ce^{-20q_1(1-q_1)}q_1^2(1-q_1)^2$. Along the unfavourable diagonal $(q_1 = q_2)$ it is approximately

$$Ce^{-20(1-3q_1(1-q_1))}q_1^2(1-q_1)^2.$$

population were characterized by the minimum number, but with the interval between generations as long as the length of the cycle. The significance of periodic reductions in size of population in making possible random variations in the character of populations has been stressed by Elton (1924).

In a large species the condition of random mating among all individuals is never realized. There are two limiting cases which can be represented conveniently by simple mathematical models. There may be continuity throughout the range, but restriction of the probable mates of any given individual to a small surrounding territory. The parents, grandparents, great-grandparents, and more remote ancestors trace to ever-widening territories. The standard deviation of gene-frequencies among populations separated by n generations of ancestors (or about $\sqrt{n}$

diameters of the elementary area) is $\sqrt{\{q_t(1-q_t)f\}}$, where q_t is the mean gene-frequency, and where f, the local coefficient of inbreeding, lies between

$$\frac{\sum}{2N+\sum} \text{ and } \frac{\sum}{2N-\sum} \text{ (or } 1), \sum \text{ being } \sum_{x=1}^{n} (1/x).$$

Under these conditions, the results are almost those of random mating, even for populations separated by thousands of diameters of the elementary territory, if the effective population number of the latter is in the thousands or more. There may be considerable fluctuating local differentiation (such as Anderson, 1936, has described in species of *Iris*) if the effective population number is less than a few hundreds. For an approach to fixation of different alleles in different regions, the elementary population number must be measured in 10's rather than in 100's.

In a species with a range that is essentially one-dimensional (shore-line, river, long chain of mountain ranges) the possibility of non-adaptive differentiation increases much more rapidly with distance than where continuity is over an area (as noted by Thompson, 1931, in a study of differences in number of fin-rays of small fishes in relation to water distance in Illinois). The quantity $\sum$ of the formula has the value $\sum_{x=1}^{n} \sqrt{(1/x)}$ in this case.

A model that fits rather better into the mathematical system developed here is appropriate where the range is subdivided into partially isolated territories. For a territory with effective population number N, replaced each generation to a small extent, m, by migrants derived at random from the species, there is a cross-breeding or migration-pressure $\Delta q = -m(q-q_t)$. This can be thrown into the same form as mutation-pressure, making it possible to introduce it into all of the formulae where mutation-coefficients appear, merely by substituting mq_t for v and $m(1-q_t)$ for u.

$$\phi(q) = C\overline{W}^{2N}q^{4Nmq_t-1}(1-q)^{4Nm(1-q_t)-1}.$$

Taking into account the fact that the effective population number (N) may be much less than the apparent number, and that the effective migration-coefficient (m) may be much less than indicated by the actual amount of immigration (largely from neighbouring, closely related populations), a large amount of non-adaptive differentiation of local populations is easily

possible. The standard deviation of q for indifferent loci $(\overline{W}=1)$
is

$$\sigma_q = \sqrt{\left(\frac{q_t(1-q_t)}{4Nm+1}\right)}.$$

The most extreme case is that in which there are many territories in which the populations are so isolated and so liable to
extinction that the lines of continuity of populations often pass
from territory to territory through single stray individuals.
Translocations are violently selected against, so long as rare,
because of the production of lethal duplications and deficiencies.
There can be little chance of their establishment in a subgroup
of a species in which reproduction is exclusively biparental,
except by some such process as outlined above. But translocations are among the differentials between closely allied species,
e.g. in the case of *Drosophila pseudo-obscura* (Frolown) and *D.
miranda* (Dobzh.), studied by Dobzhansky and Tan (1936). The
difficulties of fixation of such mutations are obviously much less
in species which can multiply vegetatively or under predominant self-fertilization (cf. Blakeslee, 1932).

The cross-breeding coefficient, m, is also important in connexion with the possibility of local differentiation under the
influence of differential selection. Taking s as the net selection-
coefficient for a local population, the net evolutionary pressure
being $\Delta q = sq(1-q)-m(q-q_t)$, it can be shown that there can
be no important amount of such differentiation if the variations
of s are small compared with m, while extensive adaptive
differentiation occurs if the reverse is true.

These statistical deductions from the Mendelian mechanism
do not in themselves give a general evaluation of the roles of the
various factors in evolution. They bring these factors under a
common viewpoint, however, and make it possible to form a
judgement as to the conditions under which one or another, or
a combination, may dominate the process.

The conditions under which mutation-pressures, at rates like
those usually observed in the laboratory, are likely to dominate
in the course of evolution appear to be decidedly restricted.
Even a very slight selective advantage (e.g. of the order 10^{-4} or
even 10^{-5}) would usually be more important. However, under
extreme reduction of size of populations ($4Ns$ much less than 1)
selection-pressure becomes ineffective, while mutation-pressure

is not affected. The one *systematic* effect of mutation seems to be a tendency towards degeneration (as may be seen from a casual survey of the effects of most of the *Drosophila* mutations). Thus a trend towards degeneration of structures of little or no use in small completely isolated populations (e.g. in caves or small oceanic islands) may be due to mutation-pressure. Even here there are possibilities of indirect control by selection which should not be ignored.

Great increases in mutation-rate at certain periods of the earth's history have been postulated by various authors to explain periods of rapid evolutionary advance. The real effect would depend on the prevailing balance with other factors. Such a change in mutation-rate would probably mean merely a degenerative trend unless the effects of all other influences were correspondingly speeded up.

In a large population with sufficient random interbreeding and no secular changes in conditions over a long period of time, all gene-frequencies may be expected to approach equilibrium values largely dominated by selection. Once the population has reached a certain peak in the surface of adaptive values there will be no further significant evolutionary change in spite of continual mutation, persistent variability, and rigorous selection. More rigorous selection will merely concentrate the species as a whole about the peak, raising the mean adaptive value, but reducing the variability on which further evolution must largely depend. The chance of occurrence of a wholly novel mutation, possibly adaptive from the first, is reduced, since the reduction in frequency of non-type alleles reduces the chance of occurrence of untried mutations at two or more removes from the type gene.

A secular change in the conditions to which the species must adapt itself changes the entire set of adaptive values. Peak combinations may be depressed while other genotypes may turn out to be more adaptive under the new conditions. A relatively rapid evolutionary process, controlled by the net selection-pressures on all genes, may be expected to start and to go on until the species reaches equilibrium about a new peak value of $\overline{W}$. Repeated changes in conditions, especially if involving changes in direction, mean a continuing evolutionary process. It can hardly be doubted that this has been one of the most important causes of evolution.

Extreme reduction in numbers, bringing a tendency towards random fixation of one or another combination which is almost certainly less adaptive than the previous type, should result in a degenerative evolution even before there is time for any appreciable effect of mutation-pressure. Extreme inbreeding is a factor that may be expected to lead to extinction of the species rather than to evolutionary advance.

In a large population subdivided into numerous partially isolated groups, both adaptive and non-adaptive differentiation is to be expected. A small value of the cross-breeding coefficient, m, favours both of these processes. On the other hand, the local population-size has opposite effects on these processes. Large numbers do not interfere with differential selection-pressures but, of course, prevent any appreciable random drifting apart, while the small numbers that make the latter possible reduce the effectiveness of selection. The greatest amount of differentiation should occur with a certain intermediate population number ($4Nm$ and $4Ns$ both in the neighbourhood of 1). Under this condition neither does random differentiation proceed to fixation nor adaptive differentiation to equilibrium, but each local population is kept in a state of continual change. A local population that happens to arrive at a genotype that is peculiarly favourable in relation to the general conditions of life of the species, i.e. a higher peak combination than that about which the species had hitherto been centred, will tend to increase in numbers and supply more than its share of migrants to other regions, thus grading them up to the same type by a process that may be described as intergroup selection. There is here a trial-and-error mechanism under which the field of factor combinations surrounding the prevailing peak combination is explored by the various subgroups with occasional crossing of a saddle from a lower to a higher peak. The species as a whole may evolve continuously even without secular change in conditions (although this process, occurring in all species, itself tends to bring about such secular changes and thus periods of rapid change controlled by natural selection). The combination of partial isolation of subgroups with intergroup selection seems to provide the most favourable conditions for evolutionary advance.

Partial isolation of subgroups is here considered as a factor in the evolution of the species as a whole. Splitting of the species depends on more complete isolation. It appears probable that the more or less complete cross-sterility that permanently separates most good species from their nearest allies is usually a by-product of the gradual accumulation of genetic differences in populations isolated at first merely by geography, habitat, &c. A direct origin (except in such cases as speciation by tetraploidy) is very difficult to understand. Selection, however, may play a role in perfecting cross-sterility where two groups which have drifted apart under complete isolation, later come in contact again, or where there is strong differential selection in other respects.

We have considered the possibilities for evolutionary change which may be deduced from the Mendelian mechanism. It is most important that such deductions be compared with conditions in nature.

There is a considerable body of data on the genetics of species and subspecies differences (cp. Dobzhansky, 1937), but more exhaustive investigations, made with the statistical consequences of Mendelian heredity in mind, must be made to establish the connexions on a secure basis.

There is an especially large amount of information on the chromosome differences of related species (cf. Darlington, 1937). Little is known, however, of the significance of these in determining character-differences (other than of the nucleus itself). Many major Mendelian differences have been isolated from crosses, but how these compare in importance with the cumulative effects of multiple minor factors is not clearly brought out in many cases. As it stands, widely different conclusions have been reached in different cases. Thus, Goldschmidt attributes most importance to certain major mutations (and to cytoplasmic differences) in distinguishing the races of *Lymantria dispar* Linn., although recognizing that the sharpness of segregation of the major factors is usually blurred by modifiers. Sumner, on the other hand, found no suggestion of unitary differences capable of analysis, in crosses between subspecies of *Peromyscus maniculatus* (Wagner). There was blending heredity with only a slight average increase of variability in F_2 over that of F_1. The closest approach which he observed to determination by major factors was in the case of a colour difference between subspecies of *P. polionotus* (Wagner) in which F_2 was so variable as to suggest that the difference might be due to as few as three or four factors. The most usual result in the many species and subspecies crosses in plants seems to be a hierarchy of differences ranging from a considerable number of major ones to an indefinitely large number of minor ones.

The genetic basis for cross-sterility is in some cases clearly chromosomal (as where a sterile hybrid produces a fertile allotetraploid), but in other cases is clearly genic (as in species-crosses in *Drosophila*; Dobzhansky, 1933). The relative importance of these mechanisms in different groups and, in the case of genic cross-sterility, the relative importance of single and multiple factors, need determination in more cases.

Data on the amount of hereditary variability within local wild populations are still rather scanty. One aspect is the determination of gene-frequencies where species are frankly polymorphic in respect to major genes. Another is the frequency of lethals and of other major factors that are strongly selected against. Several studies in *Drosophila* have shown that such factors are not uncommon in nature (Dubinin, 1934; Dobzhansky, &c.). Of perhaps greater evolutionary significance are biometric studies of the correlation between parent and offspring in quantitatively varying characters within local populations to determine how generally such populations are heterallelic in minor factors. Many such studies have been made in man, domesticated animals, and cultivated plants, but relatively few have been made for wild species. Sumner's data from *Peromyscus* subspecies are an example.

Estimates of typical mutation-rates are at present based on a very small number of organisms. Stadler found that 7 out of 8 genes of *Zea mays* Linn., chosen merely because of convenient endosperm effects, mutated repeatedly in samples of from 250,000 to 2,500,000 gametes. While the data suggested that rates between 10^{-5} to 10^{-6} per generation were most typical, one gene mutated at as high a rate as 5×10^{-4} and one failed to mutate in $1 \cdot 5 \times 10^{-6}$ gametes. Estimates of mutation-rates per generation are about the same in *Drosophila*. Haldane has estimated the rate of occurrence of the sex-linked mutation causing haemophilia in man as about 2×10^{-5} per generation. The rate per year is of course enormously less in man than in *Drosophila*. Whether these rates can be taken as typical or whether most loci mutate more rarely we do not know. It may be that all loci mutate much more frequently than is usually suspected, but that most of the mutations are so slight in effect as to make detection difficult (East, 1936). The discovery of genes which systematically affect the mutation-rates of other genes (Demerec, 1937) presents interesting questions on possible evolutionary regulation of mutation-rate itself (cf. Sturtevant, 1937). The extent to which possible mutations at a locus form indefinitely extended branching systems of multiple alleles, each allele capable of giving rise to others which cannot arise from the type gene directly, is a question with very important evolutionary implications, on which only a beginning has been made (cf. Timofeeff-Ressovsky, 1932).

Selection-coefficients have been determined ranging from 100 per cent. (complete lethality) down to perhaps 1 per cent. It is probable that most of the mutations which are important in evolution have much smaller selection-coefficients than it is practicable to demonstrate in the laboratory.

The phase of the theory that is most open to investigation in nature is that of breeding structure. It should be possible in many cases to estimate the effective size of the randomly-breeding units, and the effective amount of cross-breeding, with sufficient accuracy to form some judgement of the role which can be played by partial isolation. The distribution of frequencies for a single approximately neutral gene in a species gives an index of the amount of random differentiation.

That these coefficients may be relatively small even in species with enormous numbers of individuals has been shown in certain cases. Sturtevant and Dobzhansky (1936) have shown that chromosome-inversions in *Drosophila pseudo-obscura* behave as approximately neutral Mendelian units. Dobzhansky and Queal found three different inversions of one chromosome to be present in large numbers in the populations of the isolated mountain forests of the Death Valley region of California. The frequencies among 11 such populations ranged from 51 to 88 per cent. in one case, 2 to 20 per cent. in another, and 8 to 39 per cent. in the third. The standard deviations were such as to indicate an effective value of Nm (i.e. the effective number of migrants per generation) of about 5 (assuming approximate equilibrium). Some seventeen different inversions of the same chromosome have been found within the whole range of the species with frequencies ranging in one case from 0 to 100 per cent. (Dobzhansky and Sturtevant, 1938). For the species as a whole, the effective value of Nm is apparently only about one-tenth as great as its value in the restricted Death Valley region. Taking this as an indicator, there is the possibility of a great deal of non-adaptive differentiation in *Drosophila pseudo-obscura*. In the human species, the blood-group alleles are neutral as far as known. The frequencies vary widely from region to region and in such a way as to indicate that the historical factor (i.e. partial isolation) is the determining factor. The frequency distribution indicates a considerable amount of random differentiation even among the largest populations. The greater range of variability among small uncivilized groups (e.g. over 90 per cent. gene O in most tribes of American Indians, but about 80 per cent. A in Blackfeet and in Blood Indians and about 90 per cent. B in Patagonians; Gates, 1935) suggests that, during the major portion of the period in which man was evolving from lower primate ancestry, random local differentiation may have played a much greater role than at present.

Attempts to make general evaluations of the roles of adaptive and random differentiation have led to the most diverse conclusions because of the lack of objective criteria. The publication of Darwin's *Origin of Species* was followed by intensive and ingenious attempts to interpret all sorts of species-differences as adaptive under the belief that natural selection was the sole controlling principle of evolution (Wallace). In recent years Fisher has maintained on theoretical grounds that evolution of organisms is as completely subject to the net selection-pressures on the separate genes as the history of physical systems is subject to the increase of entropy. From the viewpoint of the present paper, however, this does not appear to be a necessary theoretical conclusion. Even from the first, certain authors (e.g. Gulick and Romanes) maintained that it was futile to look for a selective mechanism back of many of the differences between isolated populations living under substantially identical conditions. The majority of systematists have probably been sceptical of the adaptive significance of all taxonomic differences (cf. Robson and Richards, 1936).

The issue is complicated by the fact that the antithesis

'adaptive *v.* non-adaptive' does not necessarily correspond to the antithesis 'selection-pressure *v.* isolation-effect'. On the one hand, seemingly neutral character-differences may be interpreted as superficial by-products of adaptive but not easily observed physiological differences. On the other hand, an obviously adaptive difference does not necessarily imply intragroup selection-pressure as its cause. There may have been random differentiation of subgroups, followed by establishment of different types in different regions as a result of intergroup selection. There may even have been random differentiation accompanied by adoption of appropriately different environments or different ways of life in regions not necessarily different in their general conditions. Davenport has stressed the role of selection of suitable environments by organisms that differ merely by chance.

Goldschmidt, as noted earlier, makes a sharp cleavage between the origin of races and that of higher categories, based primarily on study of the gipsy moth (*Lymantria dispar*). He holds that the racial differences, in this case at least, are due to selection-pressure acting at the time of expansion of the species into regions to which it has been poorly adapted. These differences he finds to be largely quantitative and either directly adaptive (length of diapause, rate of larval development, &c.) or theoretically interpretable as indicators of unknown physiological adaptations (colour, pattern of larvae, &c.). He contrasts these with the qualitative differences between species (adaptive or otherwise) which he believes could not result from any amount of accumulation of the quantitative racial differences. He feels constrained to attribute their origin to mutations of a sort with which we have no experience in the laboratory ('hopeful monsters'). Cuénot is another recent author who has been impressed by the difficulty of accounting for many adaptations of species by a cumulative process and has urged that they must have arisen as pre-adaptations.

One may sympathize with these difficulties, but question whether it is necessary to bring in an unknown factor. Kinsey finds little indication of adaptiveness in the trivial taxonomic differences between adjacent populations of *Cynips*. But these apparently random differences accumulate along the species-chains and lead ultimately to differences apparently as qualitative (in character of galls, for example) as those which distinguish species of *Lymantria*.

There is no theoretical necessity for supposing that evolution has proceeded in the same way in all groups. In some it may proceed largely under direct selection-pressure following change in conditions, in other cases it may be determined by random differentiation of small local populations, with or without inter-group selection. It may even be dominated by mutation-pressure in special cases. It may be a gradual, fine-grained process or at times a coarse-grained process, new species arising directly from hybridization and polyploidy.

It has been pointed out, however, that the most favourable conditions for a continuing evolutionary process are those in which there is, to a first-order, balanced action of all of the statistical evolutionary factors. It is consequently to be expected that in most actual cases indications can be found of simultaneous action of all of them.

REFERENCES

ANDERSON, EDGAR (1936). 'The Species Problem in Iris.' *Annals Missouri Bot. Garden*, **23**, 457–509.

BLAKESLEE, A. F. (1932). 'The Species Problem in Datura.' *Proc. 6th Internat. Congress of Genetics*, I: 104–20.

CUÉNOT, L. (1925). *L'Adaptation*. Paris: G. Doin.

DARLINGTON, C. D. (1937). *Recent Advances in Cytology*. London: J. & A. Churchill.

DAVENPORT, C. B. (1903). 'The Animal Ecology of Cold Spring Sand Spit.' *The Decennial Publications, The University of Chicago*, **10**, 157–76.

DEMEREC, M. (1933). 'What is a Gene?' *J. Hered.* **24**, 369–78.

—— (1937). 'Frequency of Spontaneous Mutations in Certain Stocks of Drosophila melanogaster.' *Genetics*, **22**, 469–78.

DICE, L. C. (1931). 'The Occurrence of Two Subspecies in the Same Area.' *J. Mamm.* **12**, 210–13.

DOBZHANSKY, TH. (1933). 'On the Sterility of the Interracial Hybrids in Drosophila pseudo-obscura.' *Proc. Nat. Acad. Sci.* **19**, 397–403.

—— (1937). *Genetics and the Origin of Species*. New York: Columbia Univ. Press.

—— and QUEAL, M. L. (1938). 'Genetics of Natural Populations. I. Chromosomal Variation in Populations of Drosophila pseudo-obscura inhabiting Isolated Mountain Ranges.' *Genetics*, **23**, 239–51.

—— and STURTEVANT, A. H. (1938). 'Inversions in the Chromosomes of Drosophila pseudo-obscura.' *Genetics*, **23**, 28–64.

—— and TAN, C. C. (1936). 'Studies on Hybrid Sterility. III. A Comparison of the Gene Arrangement in Two Species, Drosophila pseudo-obscura and Drosophila miranda.' *Z. indukt. Abstamm.—u. Vererb Lehre* **72**, 88–114.

DUBININ, N. P., and fourteen collaborators (1934). 'Experimental Study of the Ecogenotypes of Drosophila melanogaster.' *B. Zh.* **3**, 166–206.

EAST, E. M. (1936). 'Genetic Aspects of Certain Problems of Evolution.' *Amer. Nat.* **70**, 143–58.

ELTON, C. S. (1924). 'Periodic Fluctuations in the Number of Animals: Their Causes and Effects.' *Brit. J. Exp. Biol.* **3**, 119–63.

FISHER, R. A. (1930). *The Genetical Theory of Natural Selection.* Oxford: Clarendon Press.

—— (1930). 'The Evolution of Dominance in Certain Polymorphic Species.' *Amer. Nat.* **64**, 385–406.

GATES, R. R. (1935). 'Recent Progress in Blood Group Investigations.' *Genetica*, **18**, 47–65.

GOLDSCHMIDT, R. (1933). 'Certain Aspects of Evolution.' *Science*, **78**, 539–47.

—— (1934). 'Lymantria.' *Bibliographica Genetica*, **11**, 1–186.

—— (1937). 'Cynips and Lymantria.' *Amer. Nat.* **71**, 508–14.

HALDANE, J. B. S. (1932). *The Causes of Evolution.* London: Harper & Bros.

—— (1935). 'The Rate of Spontaneous Mutation of a Human Gene.' *J. Genet.* **31**, 317–26.

KINSEY, A. C. (1929). *The Gall Wasp Genus Cynips.* Studies No. 84, 85, 86. Indiana Univ. Studies, **16**.

—— (1936). *The Origin of the Higher Categories in Cynips.* Indiana Univ. Publications, Science Series, No. 4.

—— (1937). 'An Evolutionary Analysis of Insular and Continental Species.' *Proc. Nat. Acad. Sci.* **23**, 5–11.

MULLER, H. J. (1928). 'The Production of Mutations by X-rays.' *Proc. Nat. Acad. Sci.* **14**, 714–26.

MÜNTZING, A. (1932). 'Cyto-genetic Investigations on Synthetic Galeopsis tetrahit.' *Hereditas*, **16**, 105–54.

—— (1936). 'The Evolutionary Significance of Autopolyploidy.' *Hereditas*, **21**, 263–378.

OSBORN, H. F. (1927). 'The Origin of Species. V. Speciation and Mutation.' *Amer. Nat.* **61**, 5–42.

OSGOOD, W. H. (1909). 'Revision of the Mice of the Genus Peromyscus.' *North American Fauna*, **28**, 1–285.

RENSCH, B. (1929). *Das Prinzip geographischer Rassenkreise und das Problem der Artbildung.* Berlin: Gebrüder Borntraeger.

ROBSON, G. C., and RICHARDS, O. W. (1936). *The Variation of Animals in Nature.* London: Longmans, Green.

SCHMIDT, J. (1917). 'Statistical Investigations with Zoarces viviparus L.' *J. Genet.* **7**, 105–18.

STADLER, L. J. (1930). 'The Frequency of Mutation of Specific Genes in Maize.' Abstract. *Anat. Rec.* **47**, 381. (See also Demerec, 1933.)

STURTEVANT, A. H. (1937). 'Essays on Evolution. I. On the Effects of Selection on Mutation Rate.' *Quart. Rev. Biol.* **12**, 464–7.

—— and DOBZHANSKY, TH. (1936). 'Inversions in the Third Chromosome of Wild Races of Drosophila pseudo-obscura, and Their Use in the Study of the History of the Species.' *Proc. Nat. Acad. Sci.* **22**, 448–50.

SUMNER, F. B. (1932). 'Genetic, Distributional, and Evolutionary Studies of the Subspecies of Deer Mice (Peromyscus).' *Bibl. Genetica*, **9**, 1–106.

THOMPSON, D. H. (1931). 'Variation in Fishes as a Function of Distance.' *Trans. Ill. State Acad. Sci.* **23**, 276–81.

TIMOFEEFF-RESSOVSKY, N. W. (1932). 'Mutations of the Gene in different directions.' *Proc. 6th Internat. Congress Genetics*, **1**, 308–30.

TURESSON, G. (1925). 'The Plant Species in Relation to Habitat and Climate.' *Hereditas*, **6**, 147–236.

WRIGHT, SEWALL (1931). 'Evolution in Mendelian Populations.' *Genetics*, **16**, 97–159.

—— (1932). 'The Roles of Mutation, Inbreeding, Crossbreeding, and Selection in Evolution.' *Proc. 6th Internat. Congress Genetics*, **1**, 356–66.

—— (1935). 'Evolution in Populations in Approximate Equilibrium.' *J. Genet.* **30**, 257–66.

—— (1937). 'The Distribution of Gene Frequencies in Populations.' *Proc. Nat. Acad. Sci.* **23**, 307–20.

—— (1938). 'Size of Population and Breeding Structure in Relation to Evolution.' *Science*, **87**, 430–1.

BEARINGS OF THE 'DROSOPHILA' WORK ON SYSTEMATICS[1]

By H. J. MULLER

THE bearings of the *Drosophila* work on systematics have so far lain chiefly in the light this work has thrown on the nature of the processes whereby the differentiation between groups of organisms takes place. A knowledge of these mechanisms is of help in deciding what kinds of differences are more indicative of major and what kinds of minor evolutionary changes, and so in deciding how our given groups of organisms should be arranged—which ones nearer, and which farther apart—in a system of classification that aims at reflecting natural relationships.

Evidence from *Drosophila* later to be referred to, corroborated by that from other forms, indicates that the origination of species, and still more so of higher categories, is very rarely at a single bound, especially in animals. This being the case, some of the heritable differences between individuals within a species must eventually become accumulated, and integrated, to make up the distinctions between species and finally too between higher categories. We should therefore be able to learn much about the genesis of these differences between taxonomic groups by investigating the nature of the heritable differences existing between the individuals of an interbreeding population.

1. *The Origination of Individual Differences, as found in Laboratory Material*

As is now so well known, it has been found that practically all of the heritable differences occurring in the laboratory between individuals of *Drosophila* have their basis in mendelizing differences residing in the chromosomes (see Morgan, Sturtevant, Muller, and Bridges, 1915). Amongst these, the most restricted and, from the evolutionary standpoint, least important class consists of simple losses or additions of whole chromosomes, or groups of chromosomes. All the other mendelizing differences are caused by changes belonging to one or the other of two

[1] Received for publication 28 Aug., 1938.

B b

major categories (the distinction between which may after all be only one of degree). These are known as 'gene-mutations' and 'gene-rearrangements' (or 'sectional rearrangements'), respectively.

The first of these is by far the more frequent of the two major categories in spontaneous origination, and is considerably more varied in its range of effects. This is the class of changes within those minute, probably ultramicroscopic portions of the chromosomes denoted as 'genes', of which thousands exist in each chromosome, arranged in linear order. These gene-mutations are so minute and of so discontinuous a nature as to resemble chemical changes in individual molecules, although recent evidence of the author and co-workers (Belgovsky, Raffel, Prokofyeva) suggests (as foreshadowed by Serebrovsky in 1929, and as very recently urged by Goldschmidt) that they *may* represent only the extreme limit, in smallness, of changes of the second category.

The second, and in its spontaneous occurrence far less frequent kind of change consists of alterations in the linear arrangement of whole blocks of these genes with regard to each other. Here, then, sections of the chromosome ranging in size from those too small to be seen even in salivary gland nuclei to those large enough to be seen in gonadic mitoses are removed, inverted, exchanged, or shifted in position, although always in such a way as to leave the final arrangement of genes still linear. We may postpone a more detailed consideration of the principles governing these sectional rearrangements, most of which have been made clear only in rather recent years, and note here only that these rearrangements are often accompanied by phenotypic effects like those of the gene-mutations proper, dependent on changes in the functioning of genes located near the points where the chromosome sections had become broken off and rejoined.

Exhaustive study has shown that neither the individual gene-differences nor those in the arrangement of sections originate continuously or gradually, but only by individually rare and sudden jumps, 'mutations', that are ordinarily preceded as well as succeeded by a period of high stability. The alterations, of both kinds, occur sporadically, in an essentially random fashion. Their direction (i.e. the quality of the effects they produce on the organism) is determined largely by ultramicroscopic, physicochemical accidents of the kinetics of the particles in and about the chromosomes, and the direction of the mutations consequently bears no relation—at least, none of any general directive importance in evolution—to the kind of environment under which they occurred. It is therefore not unexpected that only rare mutations have a chance of being beneficial, or even neutral. This situation calls for natural selection as the agent for deriving an adaptive result by the sifting of the valuable needles from out of the haystack which the other mutations constitute. And even these relatively few mutations are often of value only when in rather special gene-combinations or under special or rather limited environmental conditions—a fact which further accentuates the role of natural selection in the guidance of the process whereby adaptations—in the comprehensive sense of viable organizations in general—become built up.

At first the principles of chromosomal inheritance and mutation in *Drosophila* were known to apply only to certain more conspicuous and easily classified and studied differences, as these were naturally the first to be well investigated. There were other differences of a vaguer, more obscure kind, apparently fluid and continuous in their manner of variation and inheritance, which did not clearly fit the scheme. For the purpose of analysing such cases, with a view to determining to what extent they did conform, at bottom, to the regular principles above referred to, a special kind of method was elaborated by the author, the central feature of which was the use of conspicuous mutant genes of regular, known heredity to serve as 'identifying factors' or 'markers' of given chromosomes. The application of this method by the author and Altenburg (see Morgan, Sturtevant, Muller, and Bridges, 1915; Muller, 1918; Altenburg and Muller, 1920) showed that even the most refractory of these cases were in fact dependent entirely upon Mendelian, chromosomal genes that segregated regularly and were subject to change only by rare, sudden mutations.

It cannot be too strongly emphasized that no trace was found that could be attributed to some residuum of any other type of inheritable variation. The obscurement had been a result of the facts (1) that there were various gene-differences present, all of which affected the same character, in greater or lesser degree; (2) that these genes were sometimes linked up in a peculiar system known as 'balanced lethals' or 'balanced infertility genes', which did not allow the establishment of homozygous stocks, and (3) that environmental influences, interplaying with the gene-differences, further affected the character, in a manner which, although superficially similar to that of the genes, was without influence in heredity. Many further analyses, on other charac-ters—such as those by Zeleny (1915–29), Bridges and Mohr (1919), Sturtevant (1918 a), Timofeeff-Ressovsky (1927), &c.—have, in principle, borne out these earlier ones. Only one case, the recently published one of L'Héritier and Teissier (1938) on the transmission of susceptibility to carbon dioxide in a special stock of *Drosophila*, has seemed, after due genetic analysis, really to belong in a different category, one in which there is trans-mission outside of the chromosomes, and they have provision-ally postulated this difference to depend upon a virus.

2. *Individual Differences in Nature*

It was not reasonable to suppose that principles so generally applying to the differences found in the laboratory material would be confined to this domain. And there were in fact strong reasons for suspecting that some of the differences dealt with had been derived from wild populations. In addition, Sturtevant had early noticed several character-differences existing within species of *Drosophila* in a state of nature that closely resembled laboratory types, although on the whole wild *Drosophila* popula-tions gave the impression of considerable uniformity.

It remained for the genetic analysis of individuals of various species and races of *Drosophila* caught in nature, initiated by Tshetverikoff, and carried farther chiefly by Timofeeff-Ressovsky, Dubinin *et al.*, and Gordon, to show that in reality these popula-tions are full of gene-differences, although the abnormalities, when of a conspicuous kind, are, as expected, mostly latent: that is, recessives in heterozygous condition. The differences found clearly belong to the same category as those studied in laboratory strains. There can be no reasonable doubt that they too have been derived by mutation in the same manner, inas-much as experiments of the author have shown that far more drastic environmental differences, in temperature, nutrition, &c., than those to which the organisms are commonly subjected in nature have no directive influence upon the process of origination of inheritable variations. In addition to the mutant genes differentiating individuals from one another within wild populations of *Drosophila*, investigations of Sturtevant, Dobzhansky, Tan, of Koller, and of Dubinin and his collaborators (see section 10) have shown the widespread existence of differences in chromosome arrangement (chiefly inversions) between individuals of all species investigated in detail. Again, no basis has been found for postulating any residuum of other variation than these two general types.

The above work has also shown that, as was to be expected, the mutant genes and also the sectional changes of different kinds exist in widely different proportions in different local populations. As most of the gene-abnormalities studied, being conspicuous, are detrimental under all circumstances, these differences in frequency must be due in large part to accidental differences in the amount of multiplication of some genes or chromosomes. This chance process, first noted by Muller (1918, p. 481) in discussing balanced lethals, is favoured by the partial or temporary isolation of the local groups in question, and by the small numbers to which some of them must necessarily fall during certain seasons, and during the processes of migration whereby they are enabled to arrive at regions of greater multiplication. But Timofeeff-Ressovsky, through studies on temperature tolerance, has shown that there are also adaptive hereditary differences distinguishing *Drosophila* groups of the same species derived from widely different areas. Although these have not been analysed genetically, there is no reason to question their having arisen in the same way as the other hereditary differences; in their case, however, selection must have been a factor in their multiplication.

Much of the work on differences within and between *Drosophila* populations of the same species has, by reason of the methods used, been limited to the study of fairly conspicuous differences. On the other hand, the genetic analyses of obscure and variable characters above referred to showed that gene-differences producing slight effects detectable only under special genetic or environmental conditions were commoner than the conspicuous ones. Moreover, it is these 'small mutations' which (as pointed out by the author in 1918) would be less detrimental, or, to put it conversely, would oftener be neutral or favourable. They would then have a better chance of spreading and becoming established in considerable numbers within a population; in other words, they would supply most of the material for selection and evolution. And among these 'small mutations' would be many (possibly the great majority) whose existence could be detected only by physiological, or even chemical, tests.

Recent experiments carried out independently by Kerkis in collaboration with the author (see Muller, 1934, Kerkis, 1938) and by Timofeeff-Ressovsky (1935) have shown that, even among X-ray mutations—which, as they include many small deletions, favour the occurrence of lethals—detrimental mutations having a detectable effect on viability but a lesser one than out-and-out lethals (i.e. those resulting, roughly, in 10 to 90 per cent. reduction of the survival value under the culture conditions used) arise two to three times as frequently as the lethals themselves (those of 90 to 100 per cent. inviability); and the author has found the latter in turn to be five to ten times as frequent as the so-called 'visible mutations' ordinarily dealt with by the geneticist.

Not only because of their higher survival value, then, but also because of their higher frequency of occurrence, the 'small' and the 'physiological' mutations will tend to play a greater role than the conspicuous visible ones in the differentiation both of individuals and of localized populations or races from one another. And when large mutations do enter in, it is to be expected that their potentially detrimental effects would have been 'buffered'—as Huxley (1936) has aptly put it—by the selection of numerous small mutations having the function of more nicely adjusting the drastic effects of the large mutations with the other reactions of the organism.[1] Among the physiological mutations, those affecting fertility are, as we shall see later, very important in the process of species-splitting. Since even mutations causing outright sterility have been shown (in the

[1] In some cases the appearance of a large mutation having become established in evolution will be given by crosses between two groups in which one pair of alleles may have finally diverged widely through the successive establishment, with progressive 'buffering', of many small mutations of the same gene in the same direction. Again, a given gene-difference, the effect of which was small at first, may have become greatly increased in effect by the accumulation, over a long period, of modifiers that work only in the presence of a given one of the two alleles in question (the latter of which would then constitute a ' chief factor ' or 'primary gene' like that for hoodedness in Castle's rats).

work of Berg, of Neuhaus, of Schultz, and of Prabhu and the present author) to arise (in the X-chromosome) with a frequency nearly as high as that of mutations with a lethal action, it is to be inferred that those having a lesser effect on fertility are, like those with a lesser effect on viability, extremely common.

The prevalence of small and of physiological mutations in racial differentiation in *Drosophila* has been indicated not only by the experiments of Timofeeff-Ressovsky on temperature tolerance, and somewhat similar observations of Dobzhansky on races A and B of *D. pseudo-obscura*, but also by earlier work of Timofeeff-Ressovsky's showing differences in the so-called 'modifying genes' possessed by strains of flies derived from different localities, when tested by noting their influence in affecting some variable, sensitive character (of wing-venation, for instance). In the latter cases, the expression of the given character was made possible only by the introduction, into the genotype, of the suitable 'primary' mutant genes that, acting like a sensitizer, made the variability of the reaction possible. Dubinin's quantitative studies of bristle-number and of some other characters which appear, even normally, to be especially responsive to slight genetic differences, lead to a similar result—a more pronounced differentiation of local groups in these respects than in regard to genes having more conspicuous and clear-cut effects. And whenever refined methods of analysis are applied to such cases, it is found that these differences, though less clear-cut in expression, belong to essentially the same Mendelian, chromosomal category, and have just as clear-cut a method of inheritance and of mutation, as the others.

3. *Gene-differences existing between Species*

There is now evidence from various directions for the conclusion to which both Sturtevant and the author had come in the earlier days of the *Drosophila* work, and to which Baur had independently come on the basis of the *Antirrhinum* work, that the differences between species consist in the still greater accumulation, both by the processes of accidental spread and of natural selection, of Mendelian and chromosomal changes, arisen by mutation—and especially of those Mendelian changes which would usually be designated as 'small' or 'physiological'.

First there is the 'evidence by elimination', which has already been referred to. This involves the consideration that the species-differences must arise somehow. And unless they come at one bound—a phenomenon never observed for species-differences of this kind, i.e. not involving polyploidy, aneuploidy, or inter-specific hybridization—they must come by accumulation of the originally intraspecific hereditary differences. But virtually all of the latter are, as we have seen, of the chromosomal type, resulting from gene-mutation and rearrangement.

Secondly, as Sturtevant pointed out in his monograph on the North American species of *Drosophila* in 1921, practically every one of the differences that are observed between any two *Drosophila* species, and even between groups of higher rank, can be matched by similar intraspecies-differences that originated by mutation. This fact is not surprising, since mutations are to be found affecting any character studied (as must be the case if they provided all the building blocks of evolution). However, all taken together, the differences between most of the species are such as would be produced only by the accumulation of numerous mutations, mostly of the 'small mutation' type, and are not usually confusable with the differences produced by single conspicuous mutations.

Until very recently, actual genetic analysis of the visible phenotypic differences between species of *Drosophila* was impossible, as hybrids capable of any reproduction at all had been obtainable only in cases where the visible differences between the two groups crossed were vanishingly small, as in the *Drosophila pseudo-obscura* races A and B. But Spencer has now succeeded in obtaining hybrids, having a very small degree of fertility in both sexes, between two groups which differ noticeably in many morphological as well as physiological characters. These groups are the well-known *D. virilis* and his newly found *D. virilis americana* or *D. americana*—depending upon whether it is finally decided to distinguish them as separate subspecies or species. Despite the doubt concerning formal terminology, both morphological and physiological differences between these groups are (as Spencer informs me) greater than those between the groups *pseudo-obscura* and *miranda*, or *azteca* and *athabasca*, whose specific rank has not been questioned. And the differences between the chromosomes as seen in mitotic plates (as determined by Hughes) are considerably greater than between any other two

Drosophila species showing close kinship in other respects. Now when these two groups were crossed, it was found by Spencer, through a study of the offspring of backcrosses of the hybrids to both pure species, that all character-differences investigated were inherited in such a way as to show their dependence upon multiple mendelian genes, having individually small effects. That is, the results corresponded exactly with that conception of species-differences which we have been presenting above, and which was first founded only upon the less direct evidence to be found in the mode of origination and inheritance of inter-individual differences, and in the phenotypic appearance of interspecific differences.

That the same situation exists even with regard to the differences that are responsible for the infertility or sterility of the hybrids between physiologically isolated groups has been shown by the results of crosses between the so-called races A and B of *D. pseudo-obscura*. The first-generation male hybrids of these crosses are, as had first been shown by Lancefield, invariably quite sterile, but the females have a certain, very low fertility. Lancefield (1929) found that genes in both the X and other chromosomes took part in these effects, and Koller (1932) showed that the races differed in more than one pair of genes in the X, having complementary effects on fertility. By backcrossing to either original race hybrid females which had been provided with known genes to mark their chromosomes, according to the method of 'markers' previously referred to,[1] Dobzhansky has shown that the fertility of males of later generations depends wholly upon what combination of chromosomal genes they happen to receive. There prove to be numerous of these genes that we may, according to our point of view, call either fertility or sterility genes, distributed through all the chromosomes, and only combinations the same as those existing in the original subspecies are quite harmonious, i.e. fully fertile; but the degree of disharmony, or infertility, depends upon the extent and also upon the way in which either of these combinations is departed from, when some part of it is replaced

---

[1] The use of this method for heterozygous females meets with the difficulty caused by crossing-over in the latter, except where (as in the present crosses) sectional rearrangements are present that prevent or greatly reduce the frequency of crossing-over.

by a part of the other, in itself also harmonious, combination. For reasons to be mentioned later, the X-chromosome has an especial importance in these effects.[1]

Here, too, we should note that there is no residuum of fertility effect, dependent on non-chromosomal inheritable factors, since fertility is perfectly restored by the restoration of the original chromosome-combination. It should also be noted that different strains of the same subspecies show considerable genetic differences from one another in regard to their degree of 'crossability' with the other subspecies; the same phenomenon has been noted by Spencer in his *virilis* crosses.

4. *Gene-mutations carrying the Potentiality of Interspecific Incompatibility*

The readiness with which individual differences originate, of a kind which, by becoming established in separate lines, would lead to their partial genetic isolation, is indicated by the accidental discovery of a number of such cases among mutants of *D. melanogaster* which were being bred for other purposes. In all such cases it is of course necessary that some particular combination of genes, sometimes called 'complementary genes', give rise to the infertility (or inviability), where the same genes in their more usual genetic milieu fail to do so. It is natural that such cases, even though they may be relatively frequent in actual origination, are much more apt to escape discovery than simpler ones. But the very high frequency with which individual mutations arise that give infertility, sterility, and inviability should itself be taken as evidence that combinational effects of these kinds must be frequent also. For genes in general, producing their effects as they must, through chemical interactions, cannot be expected always to operate in a simple additive manner. And so in fact it is found, when morphological characters are studied, that besides the cases of additive action (which are of course the most abundant) there are also relatively frequent instances in which given types of effects depend upon given gene-combinations, involving so-called 'complementary factors', 'chief factors and intensifiers', 'specific suppressors', or

---

[1] As the recent work of Neuhaus (1938) shows, the Y-chromosome contains at least nine individually distinctive genes, all of which are necessary together for the motility of the spermatozoa, and hence for the fertility of the male.

even 'negative interaction'. It is cases of these kinds, among genes affecting fertility and viability, that must give rise to the infertility and inviability of hybrids. But whether some or all of the F_1's, or of the F_2's or backcross generation, are affected depends upon the details of the mode of action of the genes: upon their dominance relations, upon whether or not they have any 'delayed' or 'maternal' effect (as do one or more of the genes leading to non-development of eggs of certain genetic types from crosses of *pseudo-obscura* races), upon whether they lie in the X- or other chromosomes, and upon their homo- or heterozygous condition to begin with.

Among non-additive effects on fertility in *D. melanogaster* giving rise to phenomena essentially similiar to that of hybrid infertility, the fact may be mentioned that both the dominant mutant races 'curly wing' and 'moiré eye' breed satisfactorily as stock cultures (in 'balanced lethal' form), but that (according to unpublished observations of the author and Raffel) when they are crossed together, that class of F_1 males which have both curly wings and moiré eyes (25 per cent. of all the F_1 males) are exceedingly infertile and weak. Hence it has not been possible to maintain a stock of the two genes together.

In the case of both the mutants called 'scute-L8' and 'scute-4', the males are fertile, but Raffel and the author (in press) find that recombinational forms of males, having the section of the left region of the chromosome in which scute-4 had been contained, and a section from a particular part of the right region of the scute-L8 chromosome, are sterile. In the scute-L8 chromosome, then, an 'invisible' mutation had occurred which was a potential cause of sterility, but which worked harmoniously, not causing sterility, in its original genetic milieu; its combination with a 'complementary gene' in the scute-4 chromosome was necessary before the sterility ensued. The dominance relations in this case, however, do not happen to be such as to give sterile F_1 hybrids, but only sterile recombinants of a given class in F_2, though the principle is of course the same for dominant sterility genes as for recessive ones.

An essentially similar case is that of Bridges's sex-linked mutant called 'deltex-sterile'. Males carrying this gene but having an otherwise normal genotype have thickened wing veins and are quite sterile. In the stocks in which the gene was

found, however, the males were nearly normal, both morphologically and in respect to fertility, despite the presence of this
gene. Bridges found that the comparative normality of these
flies was due to the presence in them of another mutant gene,
which he called a 'suppressor of deltex', the only detectible
effect of which was its counteraction of the effects of the
'deltex-sterile' gene itself. Bridges in fact found three different
'suppressors' of this same abnormality (two autosomal and one
sex-linked), any one of which sufficed for fertility of flies having
the gene for 'deltex'. It was only the fact that the original line
of flies in which the 'deltex-sterile' mutant had arisen must also
have happened to contain one of these 'suppressors', that
enabled a fertile stock containing the gene 'deltex-sterile' to be
established in the first place. Now when flies of this fertile stock
were crossed with normals, a chance was provided for the
'deltex-sterile' gene to escape from the action of the suppressor,
in some of the flies of subsequent generations; hence some sterile
flies were produced by the interbreeding of the two fertile
stocks. Again it happens that the infertility is not expressed,
except in a minor degree, in the F_1, because of the dominance-
relations that happen to exist here—the suppressors being
partially dominant and deltex recessive.

In the case of viability, the same kind of process is at work.
It is so common an experience as not to occasion any remark to
find that two or more mutant genes, whose viability is not
noticeably low when in separate stocks, give a stock whose
viability is very much reduced—more than additively—when
in combination (though it is only dominant mutants which can
show such effects in F_1, and they are seldom obtainable in
homozygous stock). Cases are also known in which one
mutant, in combination with another, acts as a partial 'suppressor' of the inviability effect of the latter, so that the stock,
in itself of fair viability, gives some less viable forms on crossing
with the original type ('normal'). One supposed case in point
is the oft-quoted early one of Gonzalez, showing the higher
viability of purple eye and arc wing when together. In this,
however, we cannot be sure that the 'suppressor' was the mutant
gene which it was supposed to be, or even that it was a mutant
gene at all, since the stocks crossed had not been made 'isogenic',
i.e. alike in respect to all genes except the ones in question.

Other cases are reported by Timofeeff-Ressovsky in *D. funebris*, and here 'isogenic' stocks had been constructed. The best of these is the case of 'miniature bobbed', which has a considerably higher viability than either the 'miniature' or 'bobbed' alone. On account of the nature of the sex-linkage, crosses of females from a stock of miniature bobbed, having bobbed also in the Y-chromosome, to normal males, should result in miniature non-bobbed F_1 males, with lesser viability than males of either parental stock.

These examples should be sufficient to illustrate how genetic isolation, resulting in the inviability or sterility of some or all of the products of crossing of two groups, will arise in *Drosophila* if different mutations are allowed to accumulate in the two groups. For, given enough mutational differences, some at least of the genes, in recombination, will give non-additive effects on viability or fertility, and, as is always the case with effects not yet subjected to the sieve of selection, these effects will far oftener be adverse than beneficial to the organism concerned. Moreover, once such genetic isolation has begun, its existence will tend still further to separate the groups in their breeding, allowing still more mutations of the sort to accumulate. Thus the process, once begun, will tend to go farther and farther, causing the isolation to become more and more extreme.

If groups giving hybrids of poor fertility or viability are exposed to the possibility of crossing with one another, it then becomes an advantage for them to develop mechanisms that will stop the process of mixture at as early a stage as possible, so as to prevent wastage of zygotes and gametes. Thus, any mutations stopping the process earlier—e.g. those causing sterility of F_1 rather than of F_2, those causing inviability of F_1 instead of sterility of F_1, or best of all those preventing crossing between the P_1 in the first place—will after a time actually be favoured by the direct influence of natural selection.[1] Vice versa,

---

[1] It was pointed out by the author (1918) that in populations in which—on account of enforced heterozygosis caused by 'balanced' detrimental mutations—individuals of low fertility or viability are regularly produced, natural selection will tend to establish a system of mutations that will eliminate such individuals at earlier stages or that will, if possible, even prevent their being formed. The same argument was applied by Fisher (1930) in connexion with separate populations which on crossing with one another regularly give rise to sterile or inferior recombinants. That is, mutations would be preserved that reduced the wastage.

the prior existence of anything, such as geographical isolation, that prevents crossing will automatically (although not by direct operation of natural selection) lead to the form of isolation represented by sterile and inviable hybrids—although of course that effect can only become detectable when a way is found of circumventing the blocks to crossing. In other words, the non-mixing of two groups inevitably results in their immiscibility (Muller, 1937*b*).

5. *The Genesis of Interspecific Incompatibility through Gene-mutations*

In the light of the above examples, it will be clear that whenever two populations, originally of one type, are long prevented from interbreeding, by whatever means, the divergent processes of spread of rare accidentally arising mutations must tend to result in such disharmonious systems being formed as those cited above. Within any one population, of course, only such mutations can become established as leave the system harmonious. This is true no matter whether they become established by accidental spreading or by direct aid of natural selection, but in either case the harmoniousness of the result may be regarded as an aspect of natural selection, taken in a larger sense. But since there are so many genes, not only in the whole germ-plasm, but so many affecting any one given complex character, like fertility, or, to say the same thing in a different way, since so many mutations are possible that produce similar end-results though by different chemical mechanisms of development and physiology, some of the mutations which become established in the two isolated groups will be different from one another even when selection is tending in the same direction, or even when it is tending to maintain the *status quo* with regard to the character-effects in relation to which it is operating. For these character-effects are in a sense end-results, and it is these end-results, rather than the mechanism whereby they are produced, that determine whether or not a given mutation that accidentally arises and spreads to the point where it may be tested shall be allowed to persist. The nature of the mechanism only becomes important later, if two different mechanisms are mixed!

As those newly established mutations which differ in the two groups have not been selected for their compatability with one another, some must eventually arise which are more or less incompatible. Thus, if these two systems of mutations are later brought together by crossing, abnormalities will be engendered in the development or functioning of the character under consideration. In our present case, the character considered is fertility, but the same applies to viability, 'crossability', and, in general, to physiological as well as morphological characters. As a morphological effect of this kind we may cite the irregular development of the bristles noted by Sturtevant in F_1 hybrids of *D. melanogaster* and *simulans*, each of which in the original species has a regular set of bristles, of the same pattern in the two. Which kind of character becomes affected earliest, and to what degree, in the course of the evolutionary divergence, will depend in part upon its general complexity (which is correlated with the number of genes affecting it), in part on the nicety or instability of the equilibria of processes necessary for its proper functioning, and in part on the accidental circumstances that determined just which incompatible mutations happened to become established first. The large role of accident here is proved by the frequency and extent to which, in *Drosophila*, interspecific hybrid males (or, in general, hybrids of the heterozygous sex) from reciprocal crosses differ in the disturbance of their viability and of their germ-cell development.

In addition to this mutual incompatibility of the two genetically metamorphosing groups (groups which perhaps are changing little or not at all in their morphology and in the general features of their embryology and physiology), there will eventually arise incompatibilities between each of them and the original system from which both sprang, and the same general mechanism will also make them incompatible with other branches of the original species. For, once some mutations become established in an evolving group under consideration, even though these in themselves may still be harmonious in their action in connexion with the original system, they now provide a different genetic background for further mutations. That is, some of the latter can and will become established now which, though functioning innocuously or favourably in connexion with these genes which mutated earlier, act in a deleterious way when these are not present, or when (as in F_1 hybrids) they are less completely expressed. These earlier mutations thereby have their role changed from that of super-fluous or merely advantageous deviations to necessary parts of the system.[1] Now, even where no single mutations produced marked effects of the kinds in question (like those called the 'earlier' or the 'later' ones), nevertheless mutations having slight effects of this sort, on accumulating, will eventually bring about the same result, and so cause a complete sterility of the first-generation hybrids—although in some cases inviability of the F_1, or an inability to cross, or to cross-fertilize, on the part of the P_1, may arise first, by an essentially similar process (or in the case of non-crossability more directly, as explained in the third paragraph below).

Although no such cases have been observed in *Drosophila*, it is conceivable that, rarely, a single mutant gene might arise having the peculiarity of giving individuals that were viable and fertile *inter se*, but that were productive of infertile or inviable hybrids with those of the original stock (differing only in their non-possession of this gene). But unless this gene made its appearance in a selfable hermaphrodite, or in several indi-viduals at once, and unless it at the same time (!) fulfilled the very unusual condition of giving a strong tendency to individuals possessing it to undergo selfing, or assortative mating with the others like themselves, it would soon be wiped out through its unsuccessful crossings with the normal type. Moreover, as such a gene could hardly arise in homozygous condition to begin with, it would seldom be able to survive its preliminary period of heterozygosity (before it had 'made its appearance'), since

---

[1] 'Most present-day animals are the result of a long process of evolution, in which at least thousands of mutations must have taken place. Each new mutant in turn must have derived its survival value from the effect which it produced upon the 'reaction system' that had been brought into being by the many pre-viously formed factors in co-operation; thus a complicated machine was gradually built up whose effective working was dependent upon the interlocking action of very numerous different elementary parts or factors, and many of *the characters and factors which, when new, were originally merely an asset finally became necessary* because other necessary characters and factors had subsequently become changed so as to be dependent on the former. It must result, in consequence, that a dropping out of, or even a slight change in any one of these parts is very likely to disturb fatally the whole machinery; for this reason we should expect very many, if not most, mutations to result in lethal factors, and of the rest, the majority should be 'semi-lethal' or at least disadvantageous in the struggle for life, and likely to set wrong any delicately balanced system, such as the reproductive system.' (Cited from paper by the author, 1918, in *Genetics*, **3**, 463–4; italics in original.)

is no doubt that organisms of different kinds must differ greatly in this respect.

In the production of hybrid sterility and inviability the operation of Haldane's rule, stating that the heterozygous sex tends to be more affected than the homozygous one, is evident in *Drosophila*, as in other forms. Haldane in 1922 (but not in 1932) rightly gave as the explanation of it that the hybrid of the heterozygous sex, although having the distinctive genes of both systems represented in its autosomes, had those of only one system in its major sex-chromosome ('X' or 'Z'), and hence entirely failed to provide some sex-linked genes that might be necessary complements for those in the autosomes of one of the systems.

It may here be added that many of the distinctive genes in the one sex-chromosome that is present are especially strongly developed, as compared with those in the autosomes, because of the fact that some mutations (probably many) are more or less recessive. In the hybrid of heterozygous sex, then, those distinctive recessives and incomplete dominants that were (since the divergence of the two groups from their common ancestor) established in the sex-chromosome (X or Z) of one of the species, will, unlike the autosomal recessives and incomplete dominants, be as strongly expressed as in that parent species itself. Hence in the hybrids these sex-linked genes will find the expression of their autosomal complements especially inadequate, in relation to the strength of their own expression. Or, to put the matter conversely, they will be especially apt to meet with disharmonies of functioning, in reaction with the autosomal genes of the other system. But in the hybrid of homozygous sex, where the distinctive sex-linked genes of neither system have a tendency to be more strongly expressed than the autosomal ones, this additional cause of disharmony does not operate. The above causes of disharmony in the hybrid of heterozygous sex are further intensified by the fact, discovered by Berg in *D. melanogaster*, that the X-chromosome has, length for length, a far higher frequency of mutations affecting fertility, and probably also a greater number of loci affecting fertility, than do the autosomes. This is, as she points out, no doubt a consequence of the special role of the X in sex-determination. Hence a disagreement between the complement of genes in the

X and that in the autosomes would tend to be especially detrimental to fertility, much more so than would a disagreement between the complement of genes in any one of the autosomes and in the remainder of the chromosomes.

Although Dobzhansky in his important recent work *Genetics and the Origin of Species* (1937) does not offer any of these interpretations of Haldane's rule,[1] his own experiments with *D. pseudoobscura* A and B, above cited, clearly show the preponderant effect of the X-chromosome in relation to the others in producing the sterility of the F_1 and backcross individuals.

In cases where it is possible for the F_1 hybrids to breed, a special mechanism similar to that underlying Haldane's rule must operate in later generations with respect to the autosomes as well, so as to cause, in many of the individuals of succeeding generations, infertility, inviability, and various physiological and morphological disturbances, different in some of their genetic bases and developmental mechanisms from the infertility, &c. of the F_1. For, by recombination of chromosomes and of genes of the two species or subspecies, occurring in one or both parents of a given F_2 individual, the latter may come to receive certain of the genes of one system in homozygous condition, together with other genes of the other system. This will cause a malfunctioning of those recessive (or partly recessive) genes, now homozygous, that require complements (here missing, or relatively unexpressed) of the same system, or, to put the same thing conversely, certain dominants of the other system, necessary as complements for other genes of that system that are present, will be lacking. Where such genes are numerous, the offspring from crosses of F_1 by F_1, or from other similar crosses, would necessarily include many individuals containing some such disharmony, and the resulting abnormalities in reproduction and other processes might in consequence be considerably greater, on the average, than in the F_1 hybrid itself.

Such situations are well known in plants (where fertile F_1 hybrids in which regular segregation occurs may give progeny

---

[1] An explanation of it based on translocations (his pp. 252–3) can be shown to be inapplicable to some of the known instances of the rule in *Drosophila*. On the other hand, an explanation of hybrid sterility based on gene mutations (his p. 256) which does not take into account the special properties of the sex-chromosomes is also inadequate to account for Haldane's rule.

consisting of a majority of inviable and sterile types), but—
even until after the foregoing sentences were written!—they
had not been described in crosses of natural populations of
Drosophila, since the special crosses and tests necessary for their
detection had not been made. The above experiments on *D.
pseudo-obscura* A and B, for example, were not well adapted for
the detection of such effects, since the use of backcrosses alone
provides no opportunity for the combination of any homozygous genes from one race with others from the other race. But
I am informed by W. P. Spencer that tests of the requisite kind
have now been made in the cross of *D. virilis* and *D.* (*virilis*?)
americana, by means of the breeding of the F_1 hybrid females
and males with one another. Here it is found in F_2 that some
sterile recombinational individuals are formed, the eggs of
which are obviously more abnormal than those of the F_1.
It is suggestive in this connexion that Hughes has obtained some
provisional cytological evidence which seems to indicate that
more of the viable F_2 larvae of this cross have a salivary chromosome composition like that of F_1, or of the pure species, than
would be expected on the basis of equal viability of the different
expected classes; larger numbers are being obtained to determine whether this result is more than accidental. It seems
probable, because of the prevalence of recessive mutations, that
if a search were made, much sterility as well as inviability and
other abnormality due to the above cause might be found
among the heterogeneous descendants of crosses that had given
little or no noticeable infertility in F_1. In fact, we might expect
such effects usually to precede those of disturbances in the F_1,
of homozygous sex, at least, in the incipient stages of species
splitting.

6. *The Effects of Gene-mutations on Chromosome Conjugation*

Owing to the length and complexity of the process of germ-
cell development, and its sensitivity to disturbing influences,
there are probably many different developmental and genetic
paths whereby orderly meiosis and the production of functional
gametes may be interfered with in a hybrid. The hypothesis
has at times been held, however, that the major and primary
cause of the hybrid's lack of fertility lies in imperfect chromosome conjugation. This is, in many cases of animal hybrids

at least, putting the cart before the mule. Thus, Kerkis has
found that in hybrids of *D. melanogaster* and *simulans* maturation
of the germ-cells is interfered with in pre-oöcytic and pre-
spermatocytic stages, so that a true meiotic synapsis never has
a chance to occur. And Dobzhansky has found that in such
hybrids, even when two identical sets of chromosomes of one
species are provided, a condition obtaining in triploid hybrids,
or when two sets of both species occur, in tetraploid portions
of the gonads of diploid hybrids, nevertheless maturation fails
to occur, or is abnormal. Here, then, the cause of the sterility
must lie, as we have previously inferred, in gene-incompati-
bilities that result in some disturbance of physiological conditions necessary for the course of the normal germ-cell cycle.

There is also evidence to show that, even if there were some
inherent inability to conjugate on the part of the chromosomes,
this would not, in itself, act as a cause of such disturbances of
germ-cell development as the above. For, as Crew and Lamy
have recently found (1938) in *D. pseudo-obscura*, even haploid
gonadic tissue is capable of undergoing maturation, to the
extent of forming normally functioning gametes, although of
course many of the latter must have incomplete sets of chromosomes and hence form inviable zygotes.

On the one hand, then, it should be recognized that genic
disharmonies commonly produce sterility otherwise than *through*
an effect on chromosome conjugation, even though chromosome
conjugation is often disturbed secondarily, through the resulting
abnormal conditions in the germ-cells. But, on the other hand,
it should also be recognized that, quite apart from these effects,
the accumulation of gene-differences, arising by 'gene-mutations', must gradually result in a decrease of the synaptic
affinities of the chromosomes of the two groups. This effect,
which was deduced by the author (1918) on considerations of
the specificity of gene-attractions, has been illustrated in work
of Kerkis (1936), in which it was shown that in the salivary
glands of *D. melanogaster-simulans* hybrids the homologous
chromosomes conjugate with one another very imperfectly
even in regions where the microscopic arrangement of parts is
sensibly the same. Hughes has recently observed the same
phenomenon in the *virilis-americana* hybrids. That the imper-
fection of conjugation is, in the case of the *melanogaster-simulans*

hybrids, not due to the unsuitability of the developmental or physiological condition of the cells in question, was proved by the perfect conjugation, in such cells, of two homologous *simulans* X-chromosomes, when these had been especially provided by means of the crossing of *simulans* females having attached X's with *melanogaster* males; in the same cells as these X's, which were as perfectly conjugated as in either original species, were the autosomes, which were as imperfectly conjugated as both they and the X's were in ordinary *melanogaster-simulans* hybrids. A certain part of the effect is, to be sure, due to minute rearrangements, but if there were enough of these to account for the whole of it there should be far more cytologically visible minute rearrangements differentiating *D. melanogaster* and *simulans* than there actually are, unless we assume that there is an unusually high frequency of rearrangements of so extreme a grade of minuteness as to approach cytological invisibility.[1] But, since the latter would be undifferentiable, by present means, from gene-mutations, and since we would, in fact, not even have, at present, the right to make a fundamental distinction between them and gene-mutations, we should thereby return to the conclusion that the hindrance to conjugation was a direct one, caused by differences in the 'quality' (internal pattern) of the gene-material occurring at (formerly) homologous loci. And certainly even the 'individual genes', however these may eventually be defined and even if they should constitute a rather arbitrary delimitation of the 'genonema', must, through their mutations, change their synaptic affinities while still retaining the auto-specificity of the latter, otherwise these multitudinous diverse specific attractions of the now-existing genes could never have evolved.

If the incompatibility of gene-functioning referred to in the first paragraph of this section did not usually come into operation first, in *Drosophila* species, to cause interspecific hybrid sterility or inviability, the progressive weakening of synaptic attraction would itself eventually result in its own kinds of genetic isolation. We do not refer here so much to the partial and peculiar kind of isolation involved in the resultant reduction of crossing-over, as to the fact that the gametes formed by a hybrid in which conjugation did not occur effectively would,

[1] But see footnote on p. 228, concerning the recent observations of Horton.

although functional, seldom have complete 'orthoploid' sets of chromosomes, and so would seldom give rise to normally viable zygotes.

In the higher plants this cause of non-interbreeding of species seems to develop sooner, in relation to the other causes, than in animals, and in them often causes inviability of the haploid generation. It is also to be noted that the imperfect conjugation and disorderly disjunction of chromosomes caused by some kinds of sectional rearrangements necessarily tend, in a similar fashion, to give genetic isolation through their resulting in aneuploid gametes and zygotes, but it is probable that in flies this effect, too, seldom becomes pronounced before the engendering of more nearly complete genetic isolation by other means.

7. *Principles governing the Formation of Sectional Rearrangements*

In our account of the genetic mechanism of divergence we have so far focused our attention mainly upon gene-mutations, both because these furnish in themselves sufficient genetic material for the operation of the mechanism of divergence and because their frequency of origination as well as of establishment is so much greater than that of sectional rearrangements. The latter do take part in divergence, however, and in evolution in general, and their individual steps are not only more spectacular, usually, than those of individual gene-mutations, but they may at times furnish very precise and definite information regarding the relationships of groups.

To facilitate an understanding of the way in which sectional rearrangements enter into the process of divergence, it will be desirable first to consider the principles that have been found to govern their formation. The broadest of these principles— one which was put forward by the author in 1932 and which has recently been strongly supported by evidence obtained in collaborative work of Prokofyeva, Belgovsky, Kossikov, Raffel, and the author—is that changes of gene-arrangement which survive do not involve mere breakage or mere fusion of chromosome threads, but always an *exchange* of connexions of the threads, i.e. breakage, with reattachment at each surviving point of breakage. This brings all kinds of rearrangements under one general scheme. It involves the secondary principles (1) that, for a rearrangement to occur, breakage must take place at at least two points[1] (either in the same or different chromosomes); (2) that union of the resulting pieces can occur only between broken ends (surfaces of former attachment), not between two free ends or between a broken and a free end or between any end and the side of a chromosome, and (3) that, at any given point of reattachment, one broken end can unite with only one other. It is very possible that the parts previously connected may reunite again in the same order as before breakage, but in that case no detectable change will have occurred; a permanent rearrangement necessarily results only when the pieces unite in a different sequence from that which they originally had. This reassemblage of parts is such as to leave the arrangement of genes still linear, however.

It is not necessary to suppose that all broken ends invariably undergo reunion with other broken ends, but, if they do not, the chromosomes left with these permanently broken ends must be incapable of surviving long, since there is no good evidence of their ever having been recovered in subsequent generations. In any surviving chromosome, then, all broken ends have joined up again, with the resultant formation either of an 'endless' ring chromosome—which in some later generation, as a result of crossing-over, gives rise to a double chromosome with two centromeres, and so dies out—or of a chromosome the two ends of which are constituted of parts that even before breakage had functioned as free ends. The end genes thus constitute permanent chromosome structures, distinguished from all other genes by their constantly monopolar character; they have been denoted as 'telogenes' (or, for the visible bodies, 'telomeres') both by Darlington and myself and by Haldane. Similarly persistent structures are the 'centromeres' (as Darlington calls them), which mark the position of genes at which the spindle-fibres

[1] The very few apparent exceptions, involving seemingly one-break ('terminal') deletion, inversion, or translocation, are only what are to be expected as a result of one of the breaks occasionally happening to be so near to the end of a chromosome as not to be demonstrable. In view of the known fact that breaks occur oftener in chromocentral ('inert') regions, and that Prokofyeva has found small regions of this kind to exist at the free ends of the *Drosophila* chromosomes, cases of the above sort have scarcely been found as often as might have been anticipated.

However, although the rule of exchange appears valid for *Drosophila*, results obtained in maize by Stadler and by McClintock indicate that terminal deficiencies of chromosomes, involving a single break, may be produced in this plant by ultra-violet radiation. Here an interstitial gene evidently mutates to a terminal one.

become attached. Only such reconstituted chromosomes can
be properly transported to the daughter nuclei at mitosis, and
can thus survive to subsequent generations, as are 'monocentric', i.e. such as happen to have included within them one
and only one centromere, for those with none ('acentric')
cannot be transported at all, and those with two ('dicentric')
will often be pulled towards opposite poles at the same time
and will thus be broken or lost from both daughter nuclei.

All conceivable types of two-break, and most types of three-
break rearrangements consistent with the above principles have
been found, both as a result of irradiation and of 'spontaneous'
formation. The diagram (1) (pp. 212–13) will show all the types
of configurations capable of surviving indefinitely (hence, not
including ring chromosomes) that can result from two or three
breakages.   From rearrangements involving two breaks there
results, if the breaks are in the same chromosome, inversion or
deletion, according to which ends have united together.   If the
two breaks are in homologous (including sister) chromosomes,
the result is in effect a deletion in one reconstituted chromosome
and an adjoining 'repeat' (duplication) in the other.   If the
two breaks are in non-homologous chromosomes, there results
translocation of the ordinary 'mutual' type (also denoted as
'reciprocal' or 'exchange' translocation, or 'segmental interchange').   From three-break rearrangements there can result
various rather obvious combinations of the above changes,
adjoining one another, and also a type of rearrangement consisting of the deletion of an interstitial section from one part of
a chromosome and its insertion elsewhere, either into some
other part of the same chromosome, a phenomenon sometimes
called 'shift', or into a homologous chromosome, giving a repeat,
or into a non-homologous chromosome.   The latter change is
the non-mutual or 'insertional' type of translocation.   By
crossing-over or recombination of chromosomes, taking place
between a normal chromosome set and one having one or other
of the above rearrangements, or by crossing-over or chromosome recombination between two different rearrangements,
still other, more complicated types of rearrangements, involving
deficiencies or duplications of sections, or both, are produced.

Breakages can occur at any point along the chromosome
threads, but occur with far higher frequency, length for length,

in 'chromocentral' ('inert') regions than elsewhere. The most typical regions of this kind lie, normally, adjacent to the centromeres and telomeres. For this reason rearrangements not infrequently involve virtually the whole of the chromosome (in the case of chromosomes with nearly terminal centromeres) or of the chromosome arm (of a chromosome with more nearly median centromere). Two simultaneous breaks can be either close together or far apart, however, and it is possible that when they are closer together in space there is more chance than when they are far apart for the 'foreign' broken ends to find and become attached to one another, giving a new order, rather than for the old ends that were previously together to become reattached in the original order. This factor would favour the origination of smaller rearrangements. A factor certainly working in this direction is the following. As the relations between the frequency of various types of rearrangements and that of the induced ionizations in X-ray experiments show, the same inciting disturbance frequently produces more than one break, and these simultaneous breaks must be very close to one another; more usually they must be but a short 'map distance' apart in the same chromosome, though it is conceivable that they occasionally occur in different chromosomes or chromosome parts when these happen to be lying close together in the nucleus. In this way the production is favoured of minute inversions and deletions, and of shifts and insertional trans-locations of minute sections. The lower limit of size of these is not known, but it is questionable whether, when very minute, they may be included within the limits of a single 'gene' (as defined by tests of allelism), and thus constitute the individual 'gene mutations'. Whether the larger rearrangements always involve breaks between genes, as so defined, or may occur within them, is another disputable question at present.

8. *Factors favouring the Spread of Sectional Rearrangements*

It was noticed very early in the study of induced as well as spontaneous rearrangements (Muller, 1928, 1930) that they tended to be associated with lethal, sterilizing, and other abnormal somatic effects, and that the genetic bases of these effects were located at or near the points in the chromosome where the breakage and reattachment had occurred. Often

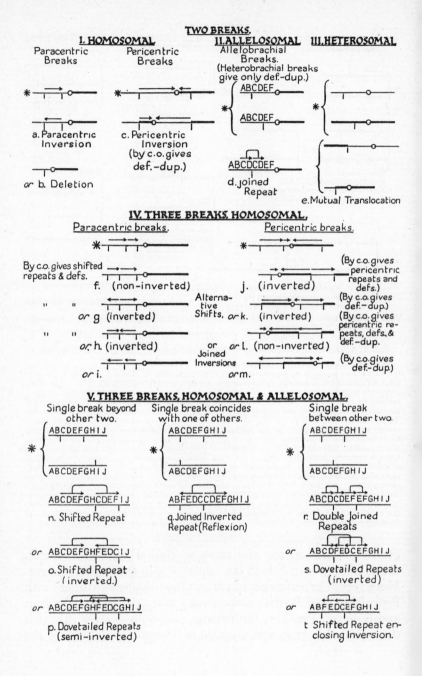

TWO BREAKS.

I. HOMOSOMAL   **II. ALLELOSOMAL**   **III. HETEROSOMAL**

Paracentric Breaks   Pericentric Breaks   Allelobrachial Breaks. (Heterobrachial breaks give only def.-dup.)

a. Paracentric Inversion

c. Pericentric Inversion (by c.o. gives def.-dup.)

d. Joined Repeat

or b. Deletion

e. Mutual Translocation

IV. THREE BREAKS, HOMOSOMAL.

Paracentric breaks.   Pericentric breaks.

By c.o. gives shifted repeats & defs.

f. (non-inverted)

or g. (inverted)

or h. (inverted)

or i.

j. (inverted)

Alternative Shifts, or k. (inverted)

or or l. (non-inverted)

Joined Inversions

or m.

(By c.o. gives pericentric repeats and defs.)

(By c.o. gives def.-dup.)

(By c.o. gives pericentric repeats, defs, & def.-dup.

(By c.o. gives def.-dup.)

V. THREE BREAKS, HOMOSOMAL & ALLELOSOMAL.

Single break beyond other two.

ABCDEFGHIJ

ABCDEFGHIJ

ABCDEFGHCDEFIJ

n. Shifted Repeat

or ABCDEFGHFEDCIJ

o. Shifted Repeat. (inverted.)

or ABCDEFGHFEDCGHIJ

p. Dovetailed Repeats (semi-inverted)

Single break coincides with one of others.

ABCDEFGHIJ

ABCDEFGHIJ

ABFEDCCDEFGHIJ

q. Joined Inverted Repeat (Reflexion)

Single break between other two.

ABCDEFGHIJ

ABCDEFGHIJ

ABCDCDEFEFGHIJ

r. Double Joined Repeats

or ABCDFEDCEFGHIJ

s. Dovetailed Repeats (inverted)

or ABFEDCEFGHIJ

t. Shifted Repeat enclosing Inversion.

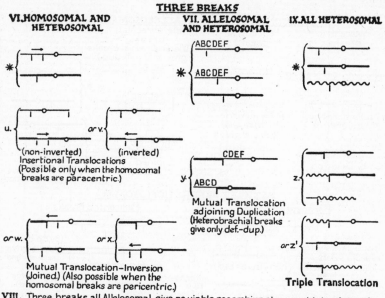

VI. HOMOSOMAL AND HETEROSOMAL

THREE BREAKS
VII. ALLELOSOMAL AND HETEROSOMAL

IX. ALL HETEROSOMAL

u.   or v.

(non-inverted)   (inverted)
Insertional Translocations
(Possible only when the homosomal breaks are paracentric.)

ABCDEF
ABCDEF

CDEF
ABCD

Mutual Translocation adjoining Duplication (Heterobrachial breaks give only def.-dup.)

or w.   or x.

Mutual Translocation–Inversion (Joined.) (Also possible when the homosomal breaks are pericentric.)

or z'

Triple Translocation

VIII. Three breaks, all Allelosomal, give no viable recombinants except joined repeats like those from two breaks.

FIG. 1. Chromosome Rearrangements resulting from Two or Three Breaks.

Except for deleted chromosome shown in I b, only such chromosomes or chromosome combinations are shown as might be capable of indefinite perpetuation: i.e. those in which each chromosome is monocentric and ditelic, and in which no net deficiency is involved. In three-break cases, only such recombinants, or combinations of them, are shown, as differ from any that could be formed by two breaks. Some of the results obtainable in later generations, by crossing-over between the recombinant and normal chromosomes, are stated in parenthesis, with the words 'by c.o. gives . . .', next to the respective recombinants; in these cases, 'def.-dup.' denotes a usually inviable combination having both deficiency and duplication of parts. Strokes vertical to chromosome mark positions where breakage will or has occurred. Circle (o) in course of line, where present, indicates position of centromere. Arrows indicate gene-sequence, those pointing towards centromere showing original, and those pointing away inverted, sequence with respect to position of centromere. 'Homosomal' denotes pertaining to same chromosome; 'allelosomal', pertaining to homologous or sister chromosomes; 'heterosomal', pertaining to non-homologous chromosomes; the words 'homobrachial', 'allelobrachial', and 'heterobrachial', referring to the same, homologous or sister, and non-homologous chromosome arms, are used analogously; 'pericentric' denotes on both sides of centromere, 'paracentric' on same side. In each figure the original chromosomes are represented above, with an asterisk, and with the positions of breakage marked, whereby the recombinants, represented and named below, become formed.

gene-mutations giving the same or similar effects, allelic to these, were known, which lay apparently in the same positions. More recent experiments of various investigators (Muller, with Prokofyeva and Raffel; Dobzhansky and Sturtevant; Dubinin and Sidorov; Panshin; Grüneberg; &c.) join to show that it is the actual change in arrangement of the genetic material of the region in question, that somehow causes the alteration of functioning observed in one or more genes of that region. This is the phenomenon known as the 'position effect'. It is conceivable that it is caused to some extent by breakages occurring within the limits of what are ordinarily considered individual genes, thus changing the nature of the latter. But the influence is not confined to the gene immediately at the breakage-point; it is known to extend out from the breakage-point for a distance of more than one gene (as a gene would ordinarily be defined). But however the effect may be brought about, it will follow as a consequence of the effect itself that re-arrangements of chromosome-sections, like ordinary gene-mutations, will provide direct objects of negative or positive selection.

Whether these effects will on the average have greater or lesser survival value than those of gene-mutations cannot at present be decided. The fact that genes in the neighbourhood on both sides of each of the two or more distinct breaks may be affected in each rearrangement would tend to result in a more multiple effect, hence one much more likely to be unfavourable, than that of an individual gene-mutation. But if the breaks of sectional rearrangements occur only between genes, it may be that each individual effect of a rearrangement would tend to be smaller and hence less unfavourable than that of a gene-mutation. On the other hand, the kinds of effects possible would in that case be far more limited for rearrangements than for gene-mutations. Comparing the amount of effect of large sectional rearrangements with that of small ones which are yet large enough to be recognizable as such, no consistent difference is to be noticed: a fact to be expected in view of the very small distance over which the position effect usually extends. On the whole, observations on rearrangements, whether large or small, in *Drosophila* indicate effects comparable in magnitude and diversity with those of the gene-mutations that have been studied, but we do not know to what extent the latter represent a class selected for conspicuousness by the observer.

In addition to producing phenotypic effects in themselves, the rearrangements may become permanently associated, through the suppression of crossovers that occurs in many heterozygous rearrangements, with ordinary gene-mutations that happened to arise in the same chromosome region. Thus the rearrangements may for a time—at least until a like mutation has arisen in some homologous chromosome without the rearrangement—become selected secondarily, in a negative or positive manner. In fact, if a given rearranged chromosome, not crossing-over effectively with the normal one, persists long, and attains considerable abundance, there must tend to develop within it a whole system of mutant genes, viable homozygously and also in heterozygous combination with the 'normal', a system harmonious if kept together but detrimental if somehow broken up. Thus something must eventually result that resembles speciation but is confined to a section of the germ-plasm, and that passes freely about, as a block, within the larger genotype of the species proper. It is conceivable that this might some time, in conjunction with some sort of isolation, even serve as the centre for the organization of a new departure in real speciation.[1]

On the other hand, as would follow from previous considerations, such a process is by no means a necessary condition for genetic isolation or speciation, and the state of affairs in which it forms the occasion for speciation is probably unusual. And certainly those cytologists and geneticists who thought of sectional rearrangements as leading immediately to an effective genetic isolation and so to speciation (or vice versa) had a vastly oversimplified view of the situation, as shown by the fact that those rearrangements which most commonly differentiate related species also exist commonly as variations within freely interbreeding populations. They do not, in themselves, prevent interbreeding, or cause infertility. In fact, it is a foregone conclusion that they must be able to persist fairly well as heterozygotes; otherwise they could not pass through that prolonged phase of heterozygosis which must usually precede their becoming established as the type of their own population.

An aid, of more or less temporary and limited character, in the process of spread or maintenance of numbers of a given rearranged chromosome is to be found in the fact that it may happen to carry the normal alleles of various detrimental genes

---

[1] Darlington (1934) has independently put forward substantially the same conception, but it did not come to the present writer's attention until after the above had been sent to press.

which are, collectively, more or less widespread in the non-rearranged (or otherwise arranged) chromosomes of the population. Being unable to exchange mutants with the latter, it will, in the process of accidental multiplication and decline of mutant genes (Muller, 1918), termed 'drift' by Wright, accumulate a divergent set of recessive detrimental mutant genes from that in the otherwise arranged homologous chromosomes of the population, thus being conducive to heterosis so long as it does not spread too much.[1]

But in addition, quite apart from any selective advantages or disadvantages attendant upon the phenotypic effects associated with them, rearrangements (that is, those which do not lead to inviable zygotes through recombination, as explained below) must be subject to the same processes of 'drift' as are gene-mutations themselves. In these ways, it is possible even for rearrangements of indifferent survival value to gain foothold in large populations. It is not conceivable, however, in the case of a population like that of the whole of *D. melanogaster*, which always remains large in numbers when the combined extent of all its local portions is considered, and in which these local portions remain so incompletely isolated from one another, that a given rearrangement which had gained some foothold through 'drift' should finally become established throughout the population simply by the same process. For the rearrangement could scarcely be, and remain, so extremely devoid of selective advantages, or disadvantages, primary and secondary,

---

[1] See also Sturtevant and Mather (1938), who have independently made similar suggestions concerning the relation between inversions and heterosis, as well as concerning the limitation of the abundance of inversions caused by the relatively detrimental effect of their restriction of recombination (as explained in the next section). Our own suggestions were made in ignorance of those by the latter authors, whose paper appeared two months after the above text had been submitted. In evaluating the heterosis effect quantitatively, the latter authors give the formula $\frac{p}{q} = \frac{b}{a}$, where p and q are the relative frequencies, at equilibrium, of two alternative non-recombining gene-rearrangements, A and B, in a population, and a and b are the respective depressions of the survival value of homozygous A and B as compared with the heterozygous individuals (in which the heterosis occurs). More important and more difficult is the question as to how a and b themselves may vary in the course of time, in response to needs for gene-recombination, and in correlation with mutation pressure, degree of inbreeding, population size, amount of migration, &c. Since some of these factors themselves vary with p and q it can be seen that the determination of the equilibrium, or, alternatively, of the manner of flux, of the latter, presents a complicated problem.

that these would not eventually overcome the effect of drift before the latter had a chance to go so far. On the other hand, in populations which over a protracted length of time remain small in total numbers, or pass repeatedly through periods of small numbers, no matter whether they be geographically diffuse or much localized, a rearrangement of comparatively indifferent survival value or, in exceptional cases, an actually detrimental one may, by drift, finally become established as the predominant, 'normal' form. The smaller the numbers, of course, the more readily will this occur, just as in the case of indifferent gene-mutations, including such as lead to genetic isolation.

9. *Factors hindering the Spread of Sectional Rearrangements*

Despite the factors above mentioned, which facilitate the spread and even establishment of sectional rearrangements, there are other factors, that tend to make their occurrence or establishment much rarer than that of gene-mutations.

One of these is the important circumstance, already referred to, that sectional rearrangements are far less frequent in spontaneous origination than gene-mutations.

Secondly, while allelic gene-mutations of virtually the same type (able to replace one another) recur with frequencies that appear to be approximately of the order of, or even higher than, one in a million gametes, each rearrangement constitutes a practically unique case. This is because of the fact that two rearrangements, to be mutually interchangeable, must have *both* of their points of breakage in sensibly identical positions— a circumstance which, instead of merely doubling the rarity of a given type of two-break rearrangement, as compared with that of a change affecting one locus, raises it as the square. (We leave out of account here the abundant but qualitatively limited class of rearrangements in which one or more of the breaks has occurred in a chromocentral region; other factors militate against the establishment of these.) If just one of the two points of breakage is sensibly different in two rearrangements, then not only will their phenotypic effects, if any, tend to be very different, but, on undergoing crossing-over or other recombination with one another, they will give rise to abnormal, usually inviable zygotes. This means that in any population all apparently identical gene-rearrangements (that is, those which are capable of giving normal recombinants with one another) which do not involve breakage of chromocentral or other duplicated regions are descended from a single original chromosome in which that rearrangement took place, no matter how widely scattered their representatives may now be. Given types of gene-mutations, on the other hand, can be polyphyletic, and this factor of recurrence has been shown by calculation to be of great help in their final establishment.

A third factor which acts to hinder the establishment, in a large population, of a chromosome with a rearrangement that interferes much with the production of crossovers is the disadvantage attendant upon its having so many genes not interchangeable with those of the general population. This handicaps the rearranged chromosome both in the minor, more temporary, processes of genetic adjustment and readjustment and in those longer-trend or large-scale processes that are more commonly thought of when the term 'evolution' is used. The rearranged chromosome has a much smaller stock of mutants to draw upon, corresponding with its lesser abundance, and this stock is in fact far less than correspondingly available for the furnishing of recombinants (by crossing-over). For the re-combinational forms of it can only arise from individuals homozygous for the rearrangement, and the relative frequency of such individuals is only the square of that of the rearranged chromosome itself. On the other hand, the more abundant the chromosome becomes in any given locality, the less will this factor operate against it there, and if it manages to exceed 50 per cent., the tide will even turn in its favour.[1] Considering a large population as a whole, this difficulty would seem to be one very rarely to be overcome, unless by the heterosis effect of the rearrangement, so long as the population remains large and thus subject to a steadier and more discriminating action of selection. For any advantageous trait attributable to a

[1] Sturtevant and Mather (1938, op cit.) point out that when one inversion has already attained, in some way, a high frequency (approaching 50%) in a population, as compared with the alternative, older arrangement, further inversions in the same type of chromosome suffer progressively less from that hindrance to their establishment occasioned by the detriment involved in their reduction of gene-recombination, since the *relative* reduction of recombination which they cause is less under these circumstances. In this way these authors seek to explain the fact that inversions are so much more abundant in the third than in the other chromosomes of wild populations of *Drosophila pseudo-obscura*.

rearrangement should also arise occasionally by gene-mutation, before the rearrangement can become established, and since the mutant gene would not suffer from the recombinational disadvantage of the rearrangement it should eventually prevail over the latter, except in the very rare cases where the rearrangement happens to be associated with a very advantageous combination of traits, not easily paralleled.

As Koller in 1932 pointed out, and Sturtevant and Beadle in 1936 developed further, there is a fourth, far more serious hindrance to establishment which applies to all the commoner types of sectional rearrangements, except inversions that are confined to one arm of a chromosome. This consists in the fact that individuals heterozygous for them give rise, as a result of crossing-over or of reassortment of whole chromosomes, to a certain proportion of 'aneuploid' germ-cells (not having just one complete set of genes), and the latter in turn result in offspring that are lethal or abnormal. In *Drosophila* the types of rearrangements having the largest reduction of productivity of this sort are the translocations, both those of the insertional and the mutual type (among these, mutual translocations that involve the exchange of practically whole arms give the best productivity). Inversions that include the centromere (i.e. *pericentric* inversions) have their productivity reduced approximately in proportion to their length, and in the case of shifts, whether within the same or to a different arm, a similar relation holds.

However, in the case of inversions that lie to one side of the centromere (intra-arm or *paracentric* inversions), it has long been known both that aneuploid (crossover) imagos are not produced, and also that there is no high death-rate of the zygotes in earlier stages. It was thought that this was because the inversion had prevented crossing-over and so prevented aneuploidy, but it has recently been found by Sturtevant and Beadle that the explanation lies mainly in another mechanism. In forms like *Drosophila*, where the three polar bodies are formed in a straight line directed radially outwards from the egg-nucleus, one of the non-crossover chromatids is shunted into the egg-nucleus at the maturation divisions whenever (as in such a case) the crossover chromatids are acentric or dicentric. For the latter chromatids, left lying in the middle of the spindle, repel the two movable chromatids—that is, the monocentric non-crossover ones—towards the two poles, i.e. into the egg and outer polar body nuclei, respectively. Thus the paracentric (intra-arm) inversions remain as the one type of more commonly occurring rearrangement not handicapped from the start by a definitely reduced productivity.[1]

It should be noted that a small pericentric inversion, as well as a shift of a short section for a fairly short distance, can give rise to very few crossovers of the aneuploid type. For this reason the selection militating against its survival will be less intense, and correspondingly more such cases should become established. Moreover, in the case of any shift or translocation transferring only a short section, the resulting aneuploidy may be too slight to reduce the viability much (at least, when heterozygous), and here, too, there will be less selection acting against the survival of the rearrangement.

[1] Sturtevant has pointed out—in a paper, 1938 / that appeared after the above text was submitted—that chromosomes differing by two overlapping (paracentric) inversions will give heterozygotes that are partially 'sterile', unlike individuals heterozygous for one inversion. For the heterozygotes for two inversions in the same chromosome pair are structurally like individuals heterozygous for shifts, and, unlike single-inversion heterozygotes, produce some inviable aneuploids by crossing-over. The same result is brought about no matter whether the two inversions have originated successively in the same chromosome, or separately in the different, homologous ones. Thus we must class paracentric inversions as being among those mutational changes which, like the complementary gene-mutations or 'suppressor' combinations considered in section 6, do not lower fertility, either heterozygously or homozygously, so long as they occur as individual steps, and so are able gradually to become established and accumulate, but do lower it in those heterozygotes the homologous chromosomes of which differ by more than one step, and hence finally contribute to hybrid infertility.

Sturtevant emphasizes further the point, discussed by us in section 6, that the existence of such partial hybrid infertility, where the two groups having the double or multiple differences come into contact, occasions a natural selection for changes that further increase the genetic isolation. It should be noted, however, that, as in the case of the complementary gene-differences for sterility, the very fact that the forms differing in respect to both changes at once (whether gene-mutations or inversions) would give partially sterile hybrids, would tend to have prevented the later of these two changes from gaining a foothold or becoming established, so long as the types having the double difference were liable to come into contact and cross with one another. If, on the other hand, they remained isolated from each other, not only could they become established but a succession of other, similarly acting changes could become established likewise, and so non-crossability would finally result even in the absence of any selective influence that directly favoured it. The selective mechanism proposed would therefore have the effect only of hastening the acquisition of immiscibility in the case of groups which had first been isolated and later brought into contact.

Aneuploids that entail duplications only, and not deficiencies, often have a fairly high viability even in homozygous condition, when the duplicated section is a small one. They will therefore become established at times, and as a result the germ-plasm will come to contain 'repeats', such as were demonstrated by Bridges (1935) to form a part of the normal constitution of the salivary chromosomes. Except for the method of polyploidy, which is far less important even when it is of common occurrence, as in many higher plants, the establishment of these 'repeats' constitutes the only effective means of gene increase in evolution. Thus the whole of the chromosome complement must really represent an accumulation of such repeats, most of which, however, are of such ancient origin that they have become changed beyond recognition. Small viable repeats may arise in various ways. Among these are: crossing-over between similar but non-identical inversions or translocations (Muller, 1930 *et seq.*); recombination following the occurrence of a small translocation, usually one of the insertional type (as in the case of scute-19; Muller, 1935); crossing-over involving a small shift; and—especially—unequal exchange or insertion between homologous chromosomes (as in *Bar*; Muller, Prokofyeva, and Kossikov, 1936, Bridges, 1936).

In the establishment of these repeats, however, as well as in the establishment of rearrangements of the type mentioned in the last paragraph but one, there will usually be a certain amount of selection, even though a small amount, acting against the new type. In the case of the repeats this is caused by the 'gene unbalance', while in the case of the rearrangements previously discussed it is caused by the production of a certain small proportion of inviable aneuploid crossovers. The greater the amount of this unfavourable selection, the more incapable of establishment would the change in question be, without the aid of that process of accidental reproduction which must attend the diminution of an isolated population to a number bordering on extinction. Each translocation, then, each shift, and each large 'repeat' which has become established in a species denotes the occurrence of such a 'bottle-neck' in its past history, when drift would outweigh selection. The same limitation in the mechanism of establishment applies with correspondingly more force to translocations and pericentric inversions of larger size; their establishment implies some former reduction to a few individuals, on the part of the population from which the group arose in which they were found to be established.

We may next consider a more complicated, though simple enough appearing, type of rearrangement, which is very little subject to the disadvantage occasioned by the production of aneuploids. This is the apparent division of a V-shaped chromosome to form two 'rods' or the reverse process—the apparent union of two 'rods' to form a V. It is easy to see that individuals heterozygous for such a change should be little subject to aneuploid formation. But for a change to occur from V to 'rods' according to the principles already set forth requires a very special concatenation, or succession, of breaks and reattachments, not a mere breakage of the V as formerly imagined. Hence this type of change could be expected to arise only on very rare occasions.

The difficulty of formation of two 'rods' from one V arises from the fact that, whereas the one V has but one centromere and two telomeres, the two 'rods', considered together, have two centromeres and four telomeres—no 'rods' being quite terminal in attachment.[1] These extra parts must be acquired by the duplication of sections including them, sections of the chromocentral regions too small for such duplication to be seriously detrimental. On any of the various possible configurations leading to such duplications, a considerable number of rather precisely placed breaks (in most cases, followed by a special type of chromosome assortment) must have occurred. The most readily occurring V-to-rod change is a mutual or insertional translocation between the V and some other chromosome such as the Y-, the fourth or the X-chromosome of *D. melanogaster*. This would have to be followed at some later time (if not accompanied) by deletions of the extra part or parts derived from this other chromosome. (See Fig. 2.) In the case of the X and fourth, there would be a tendency to the formation of some aneuploids until the deletion had occurred. If the V had undergone such a translocation with another large V, many aneuploids would be produced until the two necessary deletions had occurred. Another possibility, involving, however, four

[1] See Panshin and Khvostova (1938), Prokofyeva-Belgovskaya (1937a), and discussion by Muller (1938).

breaks at once, two sub-centric and two sub-terminal, is simultaneous deletion of the active region of different arms of homologous or sister V's, followed by non-disjunction of the deleted rod-like chromosomes. Other permutations of reattachment, following four simultaneous breakages in similar positions, would lead to the same result. It will be seen from the above that the Y-

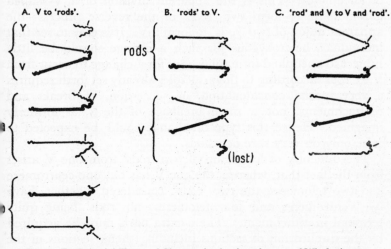

A. V to 'rods'. B. 'rods' to V. C. 'rod' and V to V and 'rod'.

Fig. 2. Preferential Types of Changes in the Attachment of Whole Arms.

Wavy line denotes 'inert' region, near centromere, position of which is here indicated by bend. Stroke vertical to chromosome indicates point where first break will or has occurred; where a later set of breaks occurs these are represented by an exclamation point. The original configuration is in each case shown above. Transformation A, of V-to-'rods', takes place by (a) mutual translocation between the V and Y, followed (b) by two deletions of the arms derived from the Y. Transformation B, of 'rods'-to-V, takes place by mutual translocation occurring within the subcentric 'inert' regions; the small chromosome thus formed may be superfluous and so may be lost. In each case the small 'inert' arm of the 'rod' is taken as being too small to be visible in the mitotic chromosome.

chromosome is the one best fitted to subserve the type of change in question, both because of its high breakage frequency (even higher than previously realized, according to results of Neuhaus, 1938) and because of the fact that, consisting so largely of 'inert' chromatin, its aneuploids (formed before the deletions mentioned had occurred) would be relatively normal. Hence it should be the Y which usually furnishes the 'anchorage' (centromere and adjacent chromocentral material) for newly formed 'rods' derived from V's, as suggested by Muller and Painter (1932). And so, after a succession of V-to-rod and rod-to-V changes had occurred in the evolutionary history, the chromocentral regions of all the chromosomes would tend to be of common origin, i.e. derived from the Y, and thus to be more or less homologous, as they in fact do seem to be.

The rods-to-V change should occur more readily than the reverse one, in cases where the 'rudimentary arms' of the rods consist only of dispensable chromocentral regions. For here only a mutual translocation, involving a subcentric break in the long arm of one 'rod' and in the rudimentary arm of the other, is required. But where there were genes necessary for life in either of the rudimentary arms such a simple exchange would not work. We have a simultaneous rod-to-V and V-to-rod change in the case of an exchange of one rod with an arm of a V. This would in fact occur with greater ease than either the pure rods-to-V or V-to-rods change, although the proportion of aneuploids from the resultant heterozygote is doubtful. It may also be noted that the transference (by mutual or insertional translocation) of a rod or arm of a V on to, or into, either arm of a small chromosome like the fourth of *D. melanogaster*, with resultant disappearance of the latter as a free chromosome, can occur with comparatively little disturbance of productivity through aneuploidy; so, too, can the insertion of the bulk of the latter into the former.

The establishment of rearrangements in which only one of the breakage points at which an exchange of connexions occurs lies in the chromocentral region, with the consequent removal of a part of this region from its position near the centromere or telomere to some interstitial position within a chromosome arm, is hindered by the special position-effect whereby a chromocentral region tends to cause a mosaic expression of genes in an originally 'active' region that has, by gene rearrangement, become transferred into the neighbourhood of a chromocentral region. This factor and others seem to have been fairly effective in keeping the more typical chromocentral ('inert') regions in positions near the centromeres and free ends.

10. *The Incidence of Rearrangements as found in Studies of Salivary Chromosomes*

Summing up the conclusions based upon our present knowledge of the genetics of rearrangements, we see that it can be stated definitely that by far the most frequent type of rearrange-

ment to become established in *Drosophila* must be that of paracentric inversions. Even these, however, should (as above explained) arise and become established far less frequently than
individual gene-mutations. Besides these rearrangements, there
may be occasional small shifts and repeats, small translocations,
and small pericentric inversions. None of the latter, however,
would be conspicuous, in ordinary cytological views of chromosomes in mitotic stages, in comparison with those rare but viable rearrangements which involve whole chromosome arms.
Throughout all of the changes mentioned, the total composition
(though not the internal arrangement) of genes within each
chromosome arm should be very stable. It would be altered
only very gradually, chiefly by the occasional occurrence of the
small pericentric inversions which, preceded and followed by the
more abundant paracentric inversions, would only in the course
of a very protracted evolutionary period give a chance for all
parts of one arm to become exchanged with the other arm of the
same chromosome. And, along with this process, the rare transfers of whole arms would only at long last accomplish the mixing
of the whole genotype.[1]

It is of interest to examine, in the light of the above considerations, the data that have been obtained with regard to sectional
rearrangements distinguishing individuals, local populations,
and species of various degrees of remoteness among the Drosophilinae. As early as 1913 inherited reductions of crossing-over
—so-called 'C-factors'—had been found and studied in *melanogaster* by Sturtevant, Muller, and Bridges. When heterozygous,
but not when homozygous, they prevented or reduced crossing-
over in that chromosome-region in which they lay. This led
King (1923) to interpret them as structural changes, but he
thought that they primarily involved alterations in the position
of the centromere. It was not possible to discover the real
structural basis of these phenomena until the linkage relations
existing in individuals homozygous for the 'C-factors' could
be studied in sufficient detail to show the gene sequences under
such circumstances. In 1926 Sturtevant (whose comparisons
of the *simulans* and *melanogaster* linkage maps had already in

---

[1] We do not take into account here the special adjustments that must arise,
through gene-mutation, when exchanged parts of the autosomes enter the sex-
chromosome system or vice versa (see p. 242).

1921 led him to postulate an inversion differentiating them and who, with Plunkett, proved its existence in 1926) succeeded in determining such sequences for 'homozygous C's', and thereby proved that the 'C-factors' in question really involved inversions of the corresponding part of the linkage map, a fact which completely explained their genetic behaviour. Since the finding of such 'C-factors', nearly all later proved to be inversions, had been not uncommon in laboratory stocks, even in those very recently derived from the wild, it became evident that inversions must be fairly frequent in natural populations of *melanogaster* (see Sturtevant, 1919, 1931). Lancefield (1925, 1929), followed by Koller (1932, 1936) and Tan (1935) obtained evidence that races A and B of *pseudo-obscura* were distinguished by inversions, and Koller (1936) and especially Sturtevant and Dobzhansky (1936) found inversions to be common within a given race (see p. 229). On the other hand, other kinds of gene rearrangements—deficiencies (Bridges, 1917, Mohr, 1919, 1923, Muller, 1935), translocations (Bridges, 1919, 1923), and 'repeats' (Muller, 1935, Bridges, 1935, Muller, Prokofyeva-Belgovskaya and Kossikov, 1936, Bridges, 1936)—were found with far greater rarity, as spontaneous variations.

It is true that Helwig, in 1929, following the earlier work of McClung, Carothers, and King, found cases of 'heteromorphic chromosomes' to be very abundant in certain Orthoptera, and rightly interpreted these as representing *pericentric* inversions. On them he made the first studies carried out in animals of the geographical frequency-distribution of intra-specific sectional rearrangements. But these are in all probability the exceptions that prove our rule of the infrequency of other sectional rearrangements than paracentric inversions in forms like *Drosophila*, that have non-localized crossing-over. For the above investigators' cytological studies of spermatogenesis showed that in their material, segregation of the unlike parts always occurred in the first meiotic division. This, as we now know, proves that, in the male at least, the chiasmata in these species are all localized in regions distal to these inversions. Thus (at least if the female is like the male in this) heterozygosis in respect to these pericentric inversions could not result in the production of aneuploids, as it would in species having non-localized chiasmata, and the abundance of such changes in the Orthoptera stands as a vindication of the general theory.[1]

In *Drosophila*, the largest scale study of the incidence of sectional differences between individuals as well as between local populations is the recent census by Dubinin, Sokolov and Tiniakov (1936, 1937) of 34,515 chromosomes derived from individuals of *D. melanogaster* captured in nature, in twenty widely different localities, as well as of thousands of chromosomes from numerous local populations of seven other species of the family (including *D. funebris* and *D. obscura*). Among all the chromosomes examined in *D. melanogaster*, only seven different rearrangements were found. Most of these, however, were widespread in their occurrence, so that, in all, 525 of the chromosomes examined (about $1\frac{1}{2}$ per cent.) showed one or another of these seven rearrangements. It is noteworthy that every one of these seven rearrangements was a paracentric (intra-arm) inversion. The frequencies of all of them showed considerable (but not parallel) geographical variation, and there were also local frequency changes from year to year. Similar results were obtained in the seven other species examined in similar fashion. In all (including *D. melanogaster*), thirty-five different rearrangements were found, and all of these were paracentric inversions excepting one shift (in an *obscura*-like species) and one small rearrangement that was probably an insertional translocation (in *D. obscura*).

The above results are decisive not only in the pronounced preference they show for one type of rearrangement as opposed to all others, but also in the evidence they give of the far lower frequency in the population of visible sectional differences than of gene-differences. For when it is remembered what a high proportion of wild individuals of all *Drosophila* species examined have been found to have detectable gene-mutations, and how diverse the latter are, especially when different localities are considered together, the contrast with the above situation regarding rearrangements is seen to be striking.

Similar facts emerge from comparisons that have been made between certain closely related species. Thus, *D. melanogaster*

---

[1] See in this connexion the considerations presented on p. 244 (written before we realized the significance of the Orthopteran results), where it is pointed out that such findings would be expected.

and *D. simulans* show only one large sectional difference; this is a paracentric inversion in the right arm of the third chromosome, found by Sturtevant and Plunkett by genetic methods in 1921–6. In addition, there is a very small inversion near the left end of the X-chromosome (Pätau, 1935; Kossikov and Kerkis, 1936), and there are some other still minuter differences that may depend only upon changes in the chromatinization of the genes resulting from their internal mutations.[1] Now, although superficially much alike, intensive study shows these two species really to differ phenotypically in very many ways, both in morphology (especially in structures of genitalia, eggs, and eyes), physiology, and behaviour. Most of these differences cannot be ascribed to the relatively few observable sectional alterations, since, as previously pointed out, the phenotypic effects of sectional changes are comparable in magnitude with those of individual gene-mutations. Hence it must be concluded that this high multiplicity of inconspicuous phenotypic differences has been caused by the accumulation of a multitude of 'gene-mutations' (leaving aside the question of whether these may themselves include sectional rearrangements too small to be visible). Similarly, in *D. virilis* and *D. (virilis) americana*—which, as previously mentioned, also show a multitude of phenotypic differences, each one of which that has been studied has been found to be, in its turn, multiple in its own genetic basis—Spencer and Hughes have found that (aside from two whole-arm changes, to be noted later) the chromosomes differ little except in respect to one large inversion in each of two chromosome arms and probably a shift, together with one inversion, in each of two others, while the minuter details of the salivary chromosome topography are on the whole very similar in the two forms.

Though such results as the above lead back to the conclusion that gene-mutations furnish the chief 'building blocks of evolution', it should be noted that in certain groups sectional rearrangements are to be found with greater frequency than in

[1] Horton (1938), in an abstract published since the above text went to press, reports five minute inversions visible in 'euchromatic' regions, four structural differences located within terminal chromocentral regions, and fourteen short areas which show a definite avoidance of synapsis in the inter-specific hybrids, and which may therefore represent minute rearrangements that involve no easily detectable structural alterations of the visible features of the banding.

those above considered. Sturtevant and Dobzhansky's (1936; Dobhansky, 1937) comprehensive studies of salivary chromosome configuration in populations of *D. pseudo-obscura* gathered from more than 70 different localities showed the existence of some 25 different rearrangements, virtually all intra-arm inversions, as contrasted with the 7 found in the above cited work on *D. melanogaster*. Of all these, 3 were in the X-chromosome, 4 in the second, 17 in the third, and 1 in the fourth chromosome. Some of these types were very widespread, but in any given region not all types of arrangement were observed. Thus, even in the case of the third, by far the most diversified chromosome, the usual number of types found in one locality was 1 or 2, and the greatest number was 4 (see Fig. 5). Local populations, then, differ from one another in respect to their sectional arrangement more in this species than in the others studied, but within a given local population the diversity in this respect is not much greater than in the other species, and it must be vastly less than the diversity in respect to the individual genes. That a considerable number of invisible differences between individual genes also exists between the local populations is strongly indicated by the prevalence of considerable differences between them in respect to their crossability with flies of the other race, and with *D. miranda* (Dobzhansky, 1937; Dobzhansky and Koller, 1938).

It is probably no mere coincidence that the species *pseudo-obscura*, giving the above high sectional diversity, has been found at the same time to be divided into two distinct 'races' or sub-species, A and B, giving sterile male hybrids and having a rather different geographical distribution. These subspecies are, as was pointed out on p. 193, differentiated in regard to many cross-incompatible 'fertility genes'. In regard to sectional arrangement, however, they do not, on the average, differ much more than some local populations of the same subspecies, for they show but two consistent differences in the X and one in the second chromosome (see Tan, 1935, Koller, 1936, and Sturtevant and Dobzhansky, 1936b). But in a comparison between *D. pseudo-obscura* and the rather closely related species, *D. miranda*, which give sterile F_1 hybrids with one another,[1]

---

[1] Dobzhansky has recently found that a race of *miranda* from Mt. Whitney gives hybrids with *pseudo-obscura A.* that have some (although a low degree of) fertility.

Dobzhansky and Tan (1936) estimate that at least 49 chromosome breaks must certainly have occurred in their derivation
from their common ancestor, and probably at least twice as
many. As Fig. 3 shows, the great majority of these are, as in
other cases, paracentric inversions, but there are also a number
of fairly small insertional translocations, as well as shifts and
one translocation (not shown because involving the Y) of
a whole arm. *D. athabasca* and *azteca*, which, according to
Dobzhansky, are 'not too widely remote systematically' from
D. pseudo-obscura and *miranda*, and which appear very similar
to one another and give sterile hybrids when crossed together,
show considerably more diversity from one another in their
salivary chromosome banding than *D. pseudo-obscura* and *miranda*
do, and show absolutely no recognizable homology in banding
with the two latter species (Bauer and Dobzhansky, cited by
Dobzhansky, 1937).

It must be left an open question why *D. pseudo-obscura* and
species not very distantly related to it (including here also
athabasca and *azteca*) show more divergence in their sectional
arrangement, for a given apparent amount of divergence in
other respects, than do other *Drosophila* species that have been
investigated. It must not be concluded without further evidence that their chromosomes undergo rearrangement more
readily, although the considerably greater diversity in chromosome III than in the other chromosomes of the *D. pseudo-obscura*
group would indicate[1] that certain conditions specific to the
given chromosome do play some part. It may be, for example,
that some difference in mobility or 'habit' of *D. pseudo-obscura*
and its relatives leads to a greater degree of isolation of its local
populations and so favours the accidental spreading ('drift') of
changes in given localities to the point where they may gain
a relatively stable foothold. If this is true, it should apply to
gene-mutations as well as to rearrangements, and this would
help to explain the observed tendency to divergence in respect
to the cross-fertility and crossability of local groups, even in the
face of a selection that tended to maintain a widespread resemblance in regard to more easily observable morphological
characteristics. However, even for a given degree of cross-
fertility and crossability the *pseudo-obscura* group diverges more

---

[1] But see footnote concerning this matter on p. 218.

widely in its sectional arrangement than do the other groups studied: *melanogaster-simulans* and *virilis-(virilis) americana*. The explanation of this fact, if not accidental, is harder to find. It might mean (1) that sectional rearrangements are less likely to be connected with characteristics of selective value than are gene-

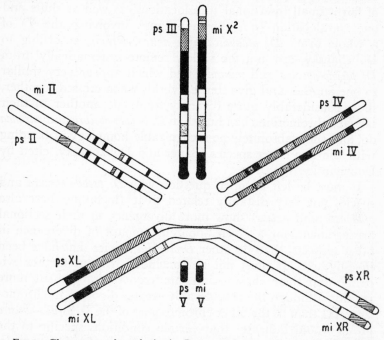

FIG. 3. Chromosome homologies in *D. pseudo-obscura* and *miranda* (after Dobzhansky and Tan, 1936).

Sections having the same arrangement of parts in the two species are shown in white, sections inverted with respect to each other are cross-hatched, translocated sections are stippled, and sections not showing recognizable homologies are black.

mutations affecting cross-fertility and crossability, and (2) that at the same time, as above suggested, the latter groups of species had undergone more change through selection (even though change not resulting in more obvious differences), in comparison with change through drift, than had the *pseudo-obscura* group.

But, whatever the explanation may be of these differences in the degree of sectional divergence as compared with divergence in other respects, there can be no doubt that the comparative work on chromosome banding has brought out the vast differences in the degrees of separation between different species of the same genus. Taken together, the results show that the evolutionary distance between two species like *D. melanogaster* and *pseudo-obscura*, which show no discernible correspondence of their banding (Dobzhansky and Tan, 1936), is so much greater than that between two other species, like *melanogaster* and *simulans*, as to be of a quite different order of magnitude from the latter, in terms of the number of mutational steps separating them. And this is true despite the fact that the two closer species themselves (crossable though they be) must differ by a very large number of steps indeed, far larger than most of the older 'mutationists' imagined.

11. *The Tracing of Phylogeny through Interlocked Rearrangements*

The very fact that the rearrangements are less abundant than gene-mutations helps to make them more individually identifiable and hence usable as diagnostic signs than are the multitude of overlapping gene-mutations. For this purpose the rearrangements have the additional advantage that many of those occurring in the same chromosome arm, especially those involving overlapping sections, cannot undergo recombination with one another by crossing-over. For in such cases, where a succession of them has occurred in the same arm, and individuals still exist representing the successive steps of accumulation of these sectional changes, the latter can be arranged in the precise order (branched or unbranched) in which they originally arose. It cannot, however, be inferred from such evidence alone in which direction, i.e. from which of the steps as a starting-point, the whole series of steps proceeded.

Taking advantage of this situation, Sturtevant and Dobzhansky have been able to construct a phylogenetic tree (Fig. 4), representing the course of evolutionary establishment of the rearrangements found in the third chromosome of *D. pseudo-obscura*. For all of these fulfilled the condition of not being able to recombine with those preceding or succeeding them, being inversions, nearly all of overlapping type. In this tree there is found to be just one meeting-point, common to the subspecies A and B, which must therefore represent a very old arrangement, which was ancestral to at least one of the two subspecies,

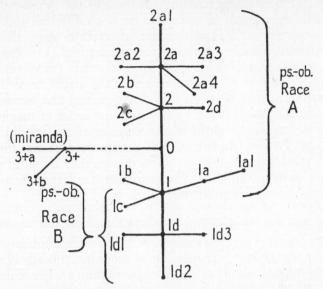

FIG. 4. Phylogenetic tree showing sequence of establishment of inversions in the third chromosome of *D. pseudo-obscura* (scheme after Sturtevant and Dobzhansky, 1936, but with more recent additions, and with notation of present author).

Each different number or number-letter combination represents a different chromosome configuration, differentiated from each of those next in line to it by a single rearrangement. In each case this rearrangement is unable to undergo recombination with that preceding or succeeding it—usually because it is an inversion, the region included in which overlaps that of the inversions next in sequence. Thus each rearrangement must remain unalterably locked in its place in the line. The point of origin of the tree is not known, but we deem it probably that denoted as 'o' (which is the only configuration that has not been found in unchanged form in some now-existing population). Configurations separated from the latter by one step are represented by single numbers (1 and 2). Additional steps away are designated by additional letters and numbers, assigned alternately. Thus this notation allows immediate recognition of relationships. Configuration 1 is shared by some individuals both of subspecies A and B; configurations shown below that of 1 on the diagram belong only to B, while those above 1 belong only to A. Names of configurations, as given by Sturtevant and Dobzhansky, are as follows:
o, 'Hypothetical A' (connexion with *miranda*); 1, Standard; 1a, Arrowhead; 1a1, Chiricahua II; 1b, Pike's peak; 1c, Sequoia I; 1d, Klamath; 1d1, Cowichan; 1d2, Wawona; 1d3, Sequoia II; 2, Santa Cruz; 2a, Tree Line; 2a1, Olympic; 2a2, Estes Park; 2a3, Oaxaca; 2a4, Hidalgo; 2b, Mammoth; 2c, Chiricahua I; 2d, Cuernavaca; 3+ denotes *miranda*, standard type, and 3+a and 3+b inversions found by Koller (unpub.). Type I is deemed probably ancestral by Dobzhansky.

although not necessarily to both. Removed from this by just one step is a configuration that no longer exists unaltered, but that represents the meeting-point of the line leading to or from *D. miranda* with the line of *D. pseudo-obscura*. As this separation is probably a still more ancient one than that between A and B, this point would seem to have a still higher probability of being the original one of this series, and we have therefore designated it as 'o'—no rearrangements, although it must itself have been derived by rearrangements from some still earlier condition. Taken together with the data on the geographical distribution of the different types (shown in Fig. 5, after Dobzhansky and Sturtevant), and with the data on their other characteristics, including especially data on rearrangements in other chromosomes, such studies constitute very valuable evidence concerning evolutionary histories.

Unfortunately, no group of actual species has yet been reported permitting the application of the above method, because in the relatively few groups of which the salivary chromosomes have so far been studied, either the amount of rearrangement was too little or the number of species was too small (two) to provide a sequence, or the amount of rearrangement was too great to allow analysis. In relatively few cases in *Drosophila* can interspecific hybrids be obtained, and in their absence an exact salivary chromosome comparison is so much more difficult that it interferes seriously with the homologizing of chromosomes that differ by several fair-sized sectional rearrangements, as, in the *pseudo-obscura* group, even species closely enough related to be crossable may do. When, added to this, the appearance of the banding has become altered by gene-mutations or minute rearrangements or both, the decipherment may be impossible by this cytological method.

12. *Comparisons of Chromosome Arms*

All the above results agree in showing the lesser frequency of establishment of transfers of sections from one arm to another (pericentric inversions and shifts, and translocations) than of rearrangements within the same arm. Evidence of the former kinds of rearrangements should also be obtainable by a comparative study of metaphase plates, for, where they were of moderate size, neither minute nor involving the transfer of a whole arm, they would usually add a visibly different amount of material than that subtracted and so would result in visible changes in the proportions of the arms, either of the same or of different chromosomes. Considering the far greater range of species available for such comparisons than for the salivary comparisons of inversions, it might have been expected that many such changes in proportion would have been observed. But such is not the case.

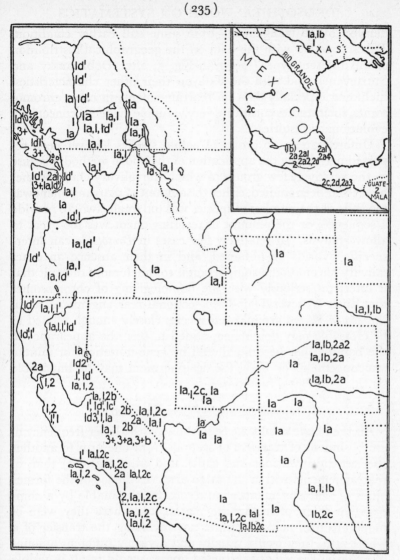

Fig. 5. Geographical distribution of third-chromosome types in *D. pseudo-obscura*, races A and B, and *miranda*, after Dobzhansky, 1937 and ex lit., Dobzhansky and Sturtevant, 1938, and (for *miranda*) Koller (personal communication), but with notation of types same as that of Fig. 4.

Race B types are here distinguished by a prime.

Thus, considering the chromosome configurations of Fig. 6,[1] based on mitotic metaphase plates which have been figured by Metz (1914 *et seq*.) and added to by Frolowa (1926) and others, we find that, omitting the more variable Y-chromosome, which represents mostly 'inert' chromatin, and the dot-like chromosome, only thirteen of the forty-two species of Drosophilinae investigated show striking differences from the rest (i.e. differences that were represented in these stages) in respect to the proportions of any of these major chromosome arms. Typically the size relations of these arms manifest an approximate equality. The twelve aberrant species consist of two pairs of species (of I and G types) and nine unique cases; some of them require pericentric inversions or shifts, others translocations, and others both processes, in explanation of their divergence. There are two other species (D and M) and also one of the above exceptional twelve (B) which have the peculiarity of showing no small chromosome—no doubt because of the union of its active material, by translocation, with that of one of the others. All of the other twenty-seven species fall into three apparent groups—A, F, and J—which, as Metz (1914) and Metz and Moses (1923) pointed out, differ visibly only by the substitution of one or two pairs of V's for two or four pairs of 'rods' (or vice versa) and can hence be most readily explained by assuming that entire chromosome arms have united or separated. As was shown by R. C. Lancefield and Metz (1921), different combinations of the arms may exist even within the same apparent group of species, since, although *melanogaster* and *willistoni* both have one rod and two V's, the X is the rod in the former, and is one of the V's (doubtless due, as they suggested, to the union of the usual X with a previously autosomal arm) in the latter. Similarly, Hughes (1938) has recently shown by direct salivary chromosome analysis that in (*virilis*) *americana*,

[1] Sturtevant, in a paper just published (1939, *Proc. Nat. Acad.* **25**. 1, 137–41) 'On the subdivision of the genus *Drosophila*', shows by an ingenious statistical study of the number of characters, apparently uncorrelated either through their developmental mechanism or through selection, which the species agree or differ in, that the whole genus is subdivisible into two large natural groups or sub-genera ('*Drosophila*' and '*Sophophora*'), each containing many species, and a third small sub-genus ('*Dasydrosophila*') containing but one species (*duncani*). We have added the superscript '1' in fig. 6 and in the legend to it to those species which Sturtevant has placed under the sub-genus *Drosophila*, and the superscript '2' to those which he has placed under *Sophophora*. For a few species these assignments are still doubtful.

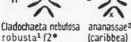
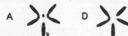

H — Cladochaeta nebulosa robusta¹ f2*

L — ananassae² (caribbea)

A — melanogaster², simulans², vibrissinae: 2b,1e,4 f1,2 f2, 1(?),and 4 of other genera.

D — immigrans f1

M — willistoni² f1

B — earlei f2

C (⇔J) — calloptera g Scaptomyza adusta

P — trivitata

F — virilis¹, etc. 5 f1 and 4 f2

J (⇔C) — pseudo-obscura² f2 miranda² f2

E — melanica¹ f2

K — affinis² f2

I — hydei¹ f2 repleta¹ f2

G — funebris¹ f1 hystrio

N — obscura² f2

O — "obscura-like"2 f2 (or indiv. var. of obscura?)

FIG. 6. Mitotic chromosomes of forty-one species of Drosophilinae, basically after Metz (1914) and Metz and Moses (1923), but schematized, reduced to the haploid female set, and extended so as to include later work (especially Frolowa, 1926, Frolowa and Astaurow, 1929).

The arrangement is, as in Metz's diagrams, intended to suggest *possible* modes of transformation, but has been somewhat revised, in the light of the more recent knowledge concerning the principles governing chromosome structure and rearrangement referred to in the above text. Capital letters are used to denote the cytological types (those to M, inclusive, having been assigned by Metz). Small letters denote the taxonomic subdivisions of *Drosophila* to which the species belong (as assigned by Sturtevant). Where 'X' is marked in figure, it has been identified as such, but only in those species which are named below the figure. For the cases of *americana* and *miranda*, in which the agreement with other species of the same apparent group is known to be only a formal one and the male is of a different type, see Fig. 7. In *ananassae* (L.), genetic evidence has been obtained by Kikkawa (1937) that the small V represents a combination of the dot-like chromosome with 'inert' material from the Y of other species. Lengths of arms shown are only roughly approximate, i.e. inequalities are represented only when they are considerable, so that small, or nearly compensating, translocational differences (such as distinguish *miranda* from *pseudo-obscura*) would not be detectable. Note that types 'C' and 'J' may be the same, though only in 'J' has the X been identified.

Species of type A: *Chymomyza amoena, C. procnemis*; *Microdrosophila dimidiata*; *Scaptomyza graminum*; *Drosophila*—group b: *bromeliae, florae*; group e: *buskii*¹; group f1: *melanogaster*², *nebulosa*², *quinaria*¹, *simulans*²; group f2: *americana*¹ (but see Fig. 7), *saltans*; *D. vibrissinae*.

Species of type F: *Drosophila*—group f1: *cardini*¹, *phalerata, similis, transversa*¹, *tripunctata*¹; group f2: *mulleri*¹, '*obscura-like*'² 1, *ramsdeni, virilis*.¹ *D. robusta*¹ resembles H, with an autosome reduced.

which belongs to the same apparent group as *melanogaster* but, like *willistoni*, has the X V-shaped, the two arms of the X are homologous, respectively, with the rod-like X and with one of the rod-like autosomes of *virilis*, and that the two arms of the other, autosomal V of *americana* are homologous with two of the other autosomal rods of *virilis* (see Fig. 7).

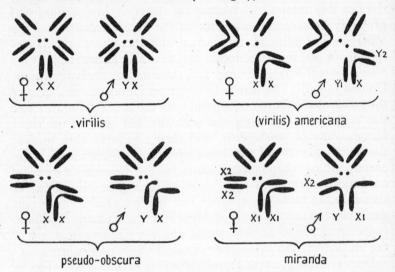

FIG. 7. Whole-arm differences between closely related species (*americana* after studies of Hughes and Spencer, *miranda* after studies of Dobzhansky, MacKnight, and Koller).

The figure of the *miranda* male has been schematized, as the homology of a part of the Y with X2 is not obvious from their positions, but has been disclosed by salivary chromosome analysis (MacKnight, 1937) and studies of their segregation (Koller, unpublished).

That the above stability in size of the arms is caused by the comparative infrequency with which large sectional interchanges between them become established is evidenced, not only by the rarity of such interchanges within populations and in the salivary comparisons of closely related species above referred to, but in the findings of genetics in regard to the genic composition of the arms even in widely different species. Thus Metz, D. E. and R. C. Lancefield and their co-workers (1918–23), early called attention to the fact that the existence in *pseudo-obscura*, *willistoni*, and *virilis* of several characteristic sex-linked mutants closely resembling those of the distantly related pair of species *melanogaster* and *simulans*—which latter, as found

by Sturtevant (1920, 1921, 1929) showed widespread parallelism with each other—must be more than a coincidence, even
when due allowance was made for Weinstein's (1920) demonstration that some of the resemblances must be spurious. In
addition, Metz, Lancefield *et al.* (1922 *et seq.*), and Koller (1932)
inferred that a part of the genetic map of the V-shaped X's of
the first two species, not containing the genes in question, was
probably homologous with one of the autosomal arms of the
other species, although the correct identification of this correspondence was first established by Crew and Lamy (1935),[1] for
pseudo-obscura, and confirmed and extended by their co-worker
Donald (1936). The latter investigators found the 'left' arm of
the *pseudo-obscura* X to correspond with the X of *melanogaster* and
the 'right' arm to correspond with the 'left' arm of the third
chromosome of *melanogaster*, and they also were able to find
the homologies of all the autosomes of *pseudo-obscura* with the
corresponding chromosome arms of the *melanogaster-simulans*
configuration through parallelism of their gene-mutations, as
shown in the table on p. 240. The linkage groups of mutant
genes worked out for *virilis* by Metz *et al.* (*op. cit.*) and by Chino
(1929 *et seq.*) have likewise made possible the homologizing of
the *virilis* with the *melanogaster-simulans* chromosome arms.

Despite these general correspondences of the arms taken as
wholes, it has almost from the beginning been evident from the
linkage map arrangements of those genes which were of more
nearly certain identifiability that there must be considerable
changes in gene sequence within the arms. This conclusion too
agrees with the studies on salivary chromosomes previously
referred to, which show some distinct differences in intra-arm
arrangement even between closely related species, and, between
more distant ones, such great differences that the homology
cannot be traced at all.

Summarizing the information on whole arms gained in the
above-mentioned genetic studies, and adding to it that gained
by the salivary chromosome comparisons of *pseudo-obscura* and
miranda, Sturtevant (1937) has made a table giving the homo-

---

[1] Owing to the fact that they did not use the customary terminology in desig-
nating the numbers and sides (right and left) of the chromosomes, it has sometimes
been mistakenly supposed that their identification was incorrect. In Donald's
paper, however, which has been generally accepted as correct, the same scheme
was presented, although in the orthodox terminology.

logies of the X-chromosome and autosomes of *melanogaster*, *simulans*, *pseudo-obscura*, *miranda*, and *virilis*, which we reproduce below, in slightly modified form and with the addition of the recent information gained by Hughes in his salivary chromosome comparisons of *virilis* and (*virilis*) *americana*. In this table *L* represents the 'left' and *R* the 'right' arm of any chromosome showing two distinct arms, and the roman numeral is that which has rather arbitrarily been assigned by geneticists to the chromosome as a whole.

Chromosome arm (notation ours)*	A	B	C	D	E	F
melanogaster and *simulans* . . .	X	II*L*	II*R*	III*L*	III*R*	IV
pseudo-obscura	X*L*	IV	III	X*R*	II	V
miranda	X*L*	IV	X2†	X*R*	II	V
virilis	X	IV	V	III	II	VI
(*virilis*) *americana*‡	X*L*				X*R*	IV

* Owing to the greater permanency of the arms than of the whole chromosomes, we are proposing the above notation for the arms, for use when chromosome homologies are in question. Chromosomes combining two whole arms can, when desired, be denoted by the two letters as, for instance, *BC* for the chromosome II of *melanogaster*. As the table shows, any system of numbering the whole chromosomes in sequence, as hitherto practised, must fail to indicate homologies.

† In the male of *miranda*, a homologue of X2 is attached to the partially 'inert' homologue of X*L*-X*R*, to form the Y (see Fig. 7).

‡ In *americana* two of the three arms *B*,*C*, and *D* are also attached together, with the third arm free, but it is not yet known which of the three are combined (see Fig. 7).

The reservation should here be made that the above homologies may—especially in view of the translocational differences separating two such closely related species as *pseudo-obscura* and *miranda*—turn out to be much less perfect than the above table seems to imply. Nevertheless, it may be that *pseudo-obscura* and its relatives are more than usually subject to the establishment of transfers of sections between arms, for reasons suggested in section 13. At any rate, the above series of facts can leave little doubt that in the Drosophilinae in general there is a considerable persistence of the individuality of arms, taken as wholes. Comparisons of *americana* with *virilis*, and of *pseudo-obscura* with *miranda*, indicate that whole-arm interchanges (including whole-arm unions and separations) may become established fairly readily, when we are thinking in such relatively large-scale terms of time and change as are represented by the transitions from one present-day species to another, even though such interchanges are rare as compared with para-centric inversions and hence are seldom encountered within species. Now since (1), unlike inversions, the number of possible types of whole-arm transfers (of type rods $\rightleftarrows$ V, or rod and V $\rightarrow$ V and rod)[1] is rather limited, but with the frequency of each given type considerably greater than that of some specific inversion on account of the readiness of breakage in the chromo-central region, and since (2) the different autosomal arms are indistinguishable (except in those cases where genetic or 'sali-vary' homologizing is feasible), visible differences in regard to the attachment of the arms to one another can hardly be regarded as in themselves very good indications of systematic affinities or remoteness. Evidently the species wander back and forth between one metaphase picture and another. Thus, species of both the two largest subdivisions of *Drosophila* (the first, or melanic, and the second, or paler, subdivision of Sturtevant's group 'f'), as well as other species, are to be found in both the cytological groups A and F, while comparatively few vary much beyond this range.[2]

If, however, it had happened that one of the relatively few unique types, representative of partial-arm transfer, had branched out to form a larger group, it would be expected that the members of the latter would tend to retain their distinctive arm proportions, and so would be more or less recognizable on metaphase examination. For to such cases the general prin-ciple applies—although it must be used with caution—that the existence of differences which are rare in their occurrence is usually indicative of remoteness of relationship, and that the degree of remoteness tends to vary with the number and rarity

---

[1] Genetic tests have shown that after exchanges of whole arms between two different V chromosomes (such as a change from the V's *AB* and *CD* to *AC* and *BD*) the resulting individuals, heterozygous for the new and the old types of V's, give a considerable number of aneuploid ('non-disjunctional') offspring. Hence such changes would be expected very seldom to become established at one jump. The same degree of interference with segregation would not be expected to apply in heterozygous individuals resulting from the change of two 'rods' to a V, or vice versa. Such cases are represented by the males of *americana* and *miranda*. Data are not yet on record to show the type of segregation for cases in which a V and a 'rod' of comparable size had exchanged one arm (as *AB* and *C* to *AC* and *B*), but it seems likely that the amount of aneuploid formation would not be nearly as great as in the case of an exchange between two V's.

[2] This holds also for Sturtevant's new divisions, which cut across the old.

of such differences. Unfortunately, however, the partial-arm exchanges in *Drosophila* seem to be too rare to be of considerable use in such a way, in the case of most of the species.

The transfer of material, whether a part or the whole of an arm, between an autosome and an X-chromosome, is subject to special limitations, and may hence be expected with far less frequency than other inter-arm exchanges. In the direction X to autosome, the difficulty is encountered that genes which, by their dosage difference, help to determine sex, are already widely distributed throughout an X-chromosome that has long existed as such (see the results of Dobzhansky and Schultz, 1931, 1934, of Patterson, 1931, Patterson, Stone, and Bedichek, 1935, 1937, and especially of Bedichek, 1938 and in press). Hence such a transfer, unless very small, will usually cause sterility. In addition, it will cause a lowering of viability, if not death, since the genes of the X-chromosome have become adjusted to having such dosage relations to one another (one to one) as normally exist in the X-chromosome, whereas the transfer of a part of the X to an autosome will cause those in this part to become diploid, in the male, while the rest remain haploid.

Transfers of the opposite kind, from an autosome to an X, will likewise cause a disturbance of the dosage relations of genes unless a whole chromosome or chromosome arm becomes a part of the X (or X-system), leaving its homologue to segregate with, or to become part of, the Y. In the latter case there will ensue, through 'drift', a gradual degeneration of genes in this new part of the Y-system (Muller, 1914, 1918), and, along with and following this, an adjustment of the genes in the new part of the X or X-system to their resulting difference in dosage in the two sexes—a phenomenon called 'dosage compensation' (Muller, 1932). As the latter adjustment would take a long time to complete, a genetic study of the effects of dosage differences, or of the associated phenomena of dominance, may give evidence of the given transfer from an autosome to an X having taken place in the phylogeny of a species (as indicated in recent unpublished studies of Crew, Lamy, Koller, and Muller on the *pseudo-obscura* group). And in such a case the inference in question may be drawn even in the absence of a species which in this respect represents the ancestral condition.

13. *The Variability in the Relative Degrees of Divergence of Different Kinds*

Despite our conclusion that, in *Drosophila*, intra-arm inversions constitute the chief form of sectional rearrangement, that whole-arm transfers ('rods' to V and vice versa) are considerably rarer, and partial-arm transfers of large sections the rarest of all, enough has been learned of the mechanisms by which such changes arise and are inherited to know that these rules of relative frequency would not retain their validity in all groups of organisms. A survey of comparative cytology confirms this. Thus for each group the main rules must be ascertained either empirically or through genetic knowledge. At the same time, however, the deeper principles of the mechanisms concerned, as found in the *Drosophila* work, remain valid and aid greatly in our arriving at such more special rules, and in our understanding of the causes and circumstances of the variation to which the latter are themselves subject.

So, for example, knowing how the method of formation of polar bodies in line with one another, as in *Drosophila* and many other animals, as well as most higher plants, results in the egg receiving the monocentric non-crossover chromatids, in individuals heterozygous for paracentric inversions, and so removes a potential hindrance to the spreading of such inversions in the population, we can see that in organisms not having this method of polar body formation (e.g. *Lilium* and some other monocotyledons) these inversions would (other things being equal) be much more hindered in their multiplication, and hence would occur far less frequently, either as intra- or inter-species differences, than in *Drosophila*.[1] Similarly, in all animals which, like mammals, have crossing-over occurring in the male, this polar body mechanism, being operative only in oögenesis, could not

---

[1] Evidence has, however, recently been found by Darlington (personal communication) in *Fritillaria*, which normally has the plane of the second meiotic division in the female germ-cells at an angle to that of the first, that the presence of a dicentric chromosome caused by crossing-over in a heterozygous inversion, with its resultant chromosome bridge between the nuclei of the first meiotic division, "mechanically" causes a deflexion of the plane of the second division so as to bring the latter division into line with the former one. Thus even here the egg receives the non-crossover chromatid, since the crossover chromatid initiates the very alignment which results in its final loss. It will be important to know how general such a mechanism is.

save the sperm from receiving the abnormal crossover chromatids that would be formed in spermatocytes heterozygous for paracentric inversions. Hence in such species, too, the spreading of these inversions must be hindered. On the other hand, in any organisms in which crossing-over failed to occur even in the female, or in which it was narrowly localized to given chromosome regions, not only paracentric but even pericentric inversions and shifts could survive well—provided only, in the species with localized crossing-over, that these inversions and shifts were wholly to one side of the region or regions of crossing-over.[1]

A different kind of effect would be noted in any animals in which, as in the plants *Oenothera* and *Datura*, terminal chromosome regions had a strong influence in determining the orientation of the homologues on the meiotic spindle. For here the segregation of these terminal chromosome regions from their homologues tends to remain regular (not resulting in aneuploid gametes) even when these regions have undergone mutual translocation, and so it is to be expected that the frequency of translocational differences, both intra- and inter-specific, would become much higher in such species than in *Drosophila*. Thus chromosome arms would not have nearly as strong a tendency to retain their identity in groups of organisms of the type in question.

The amount of chromocentral or 'inert' material present will also influence the frequency with which chromosome-changes of certain types occur. In organisms in which there is less such material near the centromeres, or in which it breaks less readily, there will less often be detachment or attachment of whole arms, while the presence of more of this material will have the opposite effect. Similar differences apply also to different chromosomes within the same species. In general, too, the existence in a species of large masses of chromatin of this kind—which, as in the case of the Y-chromosome, is readily mistaken for more 'active' chromatin, but is subject to far greater variation in size and shape without so much injury to the organism—will tend to confuse the picture of cytological variation. Likewise, in organisms in whose relatively recent history polyploidy

[1] See statement concerning probable case of this kind in Orthoptera, on pp. 226–7, which came to my attention after the above had been written.

or some other unusually large amount of duplication of chromatin has occurred, a much greater amount of further duplication or deficiency of the 'active regions' can be tolerated with
relative impunity.

In addition to sectional rearrangement, there is also the
possibility just referred to, that of polyploidy—i.e. increase in
the number of whole sets of chromosomes. This might truly
set up a new species at a single bound, as it does in some plants.
We have not hitherto discussed it here, however, because the
results in *Drosophila* have shown that it is to be expected only
with the greatest rarity in this group and, in general, in animals
having their sex determined by segregating sex-chromosomes
(Muller, 1925). The hindrances to establishment of polyploidy
in such cases lie chiefly in: (1) the fact that in triploids a relative
dosage of sex-determining genes like that in the heterozygous
sex (i.e. a dosage of sex-chromosomal to autosomal genes of
1:2) cannot exist; (2) that in triploids, the irregularities of
segregation lead to few normal progeny; and (3) that in tetraploids of heterozygous sex, were they to appear, the two like
sex-chromosomes of major value (X or Z) would tend to segregate from one another, with the resultant production of few or
no gametes having a normal ratio of X (or Z) chromosomes to
autosomes.

In some groups, however, special conditions might exist
which reduced the seriousness of the above difficulties. For
instance, there might be a greater range of dosage relations
compatible with the production of fertile individuals of the
heterozygous sex, or the direct step to tetraploidy, without
triploids as an intermediate stage, might occur oftener, and
some special mechanism, such as the presence of a single Y-
chromosome of double segregational strength, might send the
two like sex-chromosomes of major value to the same pole.
Such a group, perhaps, is that of the Hemiptera heteroptera, in
which Slack (unpublished) has obtained evidence indicating
that polyploidy has occurred independently a number of times.
And, as a result of polyploidy, there occur numerous changes
in the further evolutionary potentialities (see Muller, 1918),
which would lead to the formation of a different evolutionary
picture of gene and chromosome changes in any group that had
started on a polyploid basis, than that to be found ordinarily.

There are many other variable factors that can affect differentially the different types of divergence which a group of species exhibits. For example, both in cases where selection is so intensive that the frequency of mutation becomes a limiting factor in the rate of evolutionary change, and also in cases where there is so little selection that changes are mainly due to drift, an increase in the frequency of gene-mutation, without a corresponding increase in the frequency of sectional rearrangement, will lead to greater phenotypic divergence, in comparison with a given amount of cytological divergence, than in other groups. Since studies of the author (1928), of Plough (1935), and of Demerec (1936) have shown that some wild-type strains of *D. melanogaster* have a spontaneous gene-mutation frequency ten times as high as other strains, this effect might be very marked, provided sectional changes are not affected correspondingly (a question not yet answered).

Another genetic factor having an influence here is the extent to which sectional rearrangements exert a position effect and so affect the phenotype, for where the position effect is more marked the rearrangements must be more subject to natural selection and must accordingly have a different incidence of establishment, relative to other kinds of changes (whether a higher or lower incidence would depend upon the kind of character effects produced by the sectional changes). That marked differences in the incidence of the position effect do in fact exist is shown by the absence, in the records of investigations on plant material, of phenotypic changes attributable to this cause, although hundreds of newly arisen sectional rearrangements have been studied in maize alone.

Other important factors are those which determine the relative frequencies and the relative survival values (another term for natural selection) of the different types of phenotypic changes produced by mutation. The relative frequencies of dominants and recessives is also important. These matters in turn are bound up not only with the characteristics of the genetic apparatus as such, but also with the whole developmental mechanism, which tends to shunt the processes of development into certain lines, with the physiological mechanisms whereby given traits produce their further effects, and with all the ecolo ical relations that affect the value of given phenotypic structures or reactions. As these factors vary, then, so will the frequency of mutations of various types vary, and also the intensity of selection in various directions. It is this sort of bias to the evolutionary process which is referred to by Huxley (1936) in his term 'consequential evolution'.

Effects of the above kind are not necessarily obvious. It may be, for example, that a species has attained an optimal degree of development of all its obvious characters (when its mode of life, physiology, &c., are considered), yet selection may still be continuing on many more recondite characters, that may perhaps be expressible mainly in terms of chemistry. The latter selection, establishing in a sense equivalent yet chemically different mutations in parallel groups of organisms, may thereby cause these groups of organisms to become more and more cross-incompatible, as well as different, in, say, serological reactions, though allowing them long to remain alike in appearance and also in the more obvious details of their physiology and behaviour. Sooner or later, however, it is to be expected that some of the deeper-lying differences will so change the mode of expression of mutations, or the course of selection, as to issue in characters more conspicuous to the taxonomist.

Another condition which will favour the occurrence of changes of the former types (such as cross-incompatibility and cryptic chemical differentiation) is the existence of a considerable amount of drift (i.e. of accidental multiplication and decline of genes). Drift will, as previously mentioned, also favour the accumulation of sectional rearrangements and of any phenotypic changes that are relatively indifferent in their effects on survival. Now both the amount of drift itself, and also the efficacy of the processes of selection of mutations, and of favourable recombination of mutations, are greatly influenced by the conditions of breeding of the organisms concerned. Here there must be taken into account such factors as length of generation, number and variability in number of offspring per female and per male, reproductive behaviour, degree of randomness or specificity of determination of mating, amount of migration versus isolation, total numbers of local populations and of the whole species, and their variations in number, degree of inbreeding, &c. For example, species of low mobility the local groups of which tend to go through many 'bottle-necks', when the numbers are reduced to a few individuals, would tend to accumulate relatively many translocations and other rearrangements which, when heterozygous, lower productivity. We cannot digress to enter upon these matters here, but refer to them only to show how widely the biological conditions setting the stage for the processes of divergence may vary from one major group, or sometimes even from one minor group, to another one—a fact which Huxley justly emphasizes in his forthcoming work, *Evolution, the Modern Synthesis*.

In the light of the considerations set forth above, it is not surprising to find that even within the *Drosophila* group, among the species subjected to close scrutiny, the order of divergence is not entirely parallel. Thus, as Spencer points out (*ex litteris*), the pairs of closely related subspecies or species *pseudo-obscura A* and *B* (which we shall here designate as pair A), *pseudo-obscura* and *miranda* (which we shall call pair B), *melanogaster* and *simulans* (C), *virilis* and (*virilis*) *americana* (D), and *azteca* and *athabasca* (E) show the following seriations, when we place them in the order proceeding from the pairs showing most likeness (at the left) to those showing least likeness (at the right), in respect to each of the groups of characters mentioned below. (Those shown connected with an equality symbol may be taken as being of sensibly the same degree of likeness.)

Characters considered	Order of decreasing likeness of pairs of Drosophila groups (according to provisional judgement of Spencer)
Morphological and physiological characteristics . . .	A B E D C
Salivary chromosome structure (inversions, shifts, or translocations)	C A = D B E
Metaphase chromosome structure (whole-arm changes) . .	A = C = E B D
Hybrid fertility . . .	D A C = B = E
Psychology and sex-reactions .	A B E D C
Geographical distribution . .	C B A E D

If we assign ranks from 1 to 5 for the above, and then average them—omitting, however, the last criterion as being too doubtful in its significance—we obtain a kind of 'general likeness' seriation. This turns out to be as follows: A (of rank 1·5);

B = C = D = E (all of rank $3\cdot3 \pm 0\cdot1$). It will be seen from this result and from the table above that the amount of difference in seriation for different kinds of characters is considerable, but that, taking all the kinds of characters together, the members of all of these pairs have approximately the same degree of divergence from one another, except in the case of the admitted 'races' or subspecies of *pseudo-obscura*.

Similar sorts of results are obtained from the application of serological testing to different species of *Drosophila*, as recent work of Cumley's (1937 and in press) shows. On application, to a considerable number of different species, of the same kind of individual serological test—for instance, the determination of the highest degree of dilution of antiserum resulting in noticeable complement-fixation—results were obtained which, although more usually agreeing with the results of morphological comparison, were often at variance with the latter in some important cases. For example, on the complement-fixation test mentioned, as well as on another involving precipitation absorption, *D. hydei* gave results varying considerably from those of species seemingly related to it, but which were, curiously enough, not unlike the results from *D. melanogaster*.

On the other hand, when the results were combined from six different general classes of serological tests, applied in turn (in the form of about twelve separate tests) to just four different species—*melanogaster*, *caribbea*, *mulleri*, and *virilis*—the results agreed much better with those derived from previous taxonomic study. For the serological results thus obtained showed these four species to be grouped in two pairs, inasmuch as the differences between *melanogaster* and *caribbea* and also those between *mulleri* and *virilis* were considerably less than those between either of the first two and either of the last two species. A series of fourteen characters that had been considered as taxonomic differentia, when ranked and averaged, led to the same conclusion regarding the relative amounts of divergence of these four species from one another, again placing *melanogaster* and *caribbea* in one pair and *mulleri* and *virilis* in another. In fact, by both the morphological and the serological criteria, the two members of the first pair seemed about the same distance apart from one another as did the two members of the second pair from each other, while at the same time both members of the first pair appeared approximately equidistant from both members of the second pair.

It seems probable from these results and others that serological testing will afford another aid in classification when judiciously applied. In these tests much depends on how well the technique is controlled, by tests to determine the optimal proportions of the different constituents, the most favourable dilutions, &c. But it is evident from this and other results that no kind of serological test now known gives a reliable index of the number of mutations differentiating two species, or of their relative importance. And even when a series of the best-conducted tests are averaged together, it cannot be expected that the results will always agree with those from morphology, cytology, crossability, &c., when the latter do not even agree with each other.

14. *Towards the Further Understanding of Divergence*

What has been said above concerning the variability in the relative degrees of divergence of different kinds, as shown in a study of different series of organisms, implies, of course, that the various possible criteria of classification are all imperfect. There is no one royal yardstick, applicable to all types of organisms alike. And even if some kind of ideal of geneticists might be arrived at, and we were somehow enabled to estimate the relative numbers of mutational steps differentiating different types, the problem of how to evaluate the different kinds of mutation according to their importance for our classification would still be a major one, and one that would probably have to receive a different answer in the case of different groups. We have seen that, depending upon the conditions of variation and heredity, of breeding, of physiology, and of selection taken in its broadest sense, two related organisms will come to differ more in regard to one or another set of obvious characters, or more in regard to unseen chemical characters that were nevertheless adaptive, when considered in relation to those of the common ancestor, or more in regard to characters of relative indifference to survival. How much weight should be given to each set of these characters (supposing them to be determinable) in judging the 'mean' degree of separation of two given groups of organisms must then be decided largely by considerations of convenience, that will vary with the organisms in question. Thus, even our final decision, based on all possible criteria, will have no exact absolute meaning.

At the same time it must be recognized that all the organisms of any series considered must have been connected by a phylogenetic tree of definite form, and that one of the ultimate aims of the study of the series should be to throw light upon this tree. It is not, however, geometrically possible for any two- or even three-dimensional tree to depict accurately, not only the system of descent, but also the relative amounts of 'mean divergence' of all present-day parts of the tree from one another, for the directions which the divergence takes are multi-dimensional. Nevertheless, such graphic representations and simplifications are not merely of great aid but necessary for us in order to obtain even an inadequate grasp of the main features of the results.

The work on *Drosophila* has emphasized the fact that, for a proper understanding of the nature of the relationships in a given series of types, a knowledge not only of general principles but of the peculiarities of their genetics, breeding methods, ecology, and other biological characteristics is called for. The problems involved may, moreover, be attacked at different levels, with the employment of different proportions of analytical or empirical study, in arriving at facts of importance for the drawing of conclusions in systematics.

One half-way station, as it were, between the most analytical and the most empirical, which promises to give results of increasing significance in our understanding of the processes of divergence, is the study of genetic differences existing in and between populations of the same (and other, crossable) species. This field of study, for which *Drosophila* is very well suited, does not yet seem to have given more than a small proportion of the results that may be expected of it, although it seems at present in the process of rapid expansion. One of the kinds of results which it could give that would have a bearing on the processes of divergence is a set of values expressing the relative mutation-frequencies in different wild populations, under different conditions of inbreeding, of environment, &c. This can be obtained by the study of naturally occurring sex-linked lethals.

Another example of the significance of this type of study is the evaluation which it makes possible of the different degrees of inbreeding occurring in nature in different populations and under different conditions, and the correlation of these results with observations on mutation-rate and on divergence in respect to crossability and other characters. It has not been generally realized that the degree of inbreeding may be calculated from the existing abundance of autosomal *recessive* lethals, in populations in which the mutation frequency has been concomitantly determined through the above-mentioned studies of sex-linked lethals.[1] And by continuing a census of characteristics—including both rearrangements and gene-differences of positive, negative, and indifferent survival value—from place to place and year to year, a much more enlightening picture of the processes of drift, of selection, of divergence, and of mixing, should gradually take shape than that which we now have. For this study of what Timofeeff-Ressovsky has called 'micro-evolution' it would, as he proposes, be desirable to have an internationally organized, co-operating group, for the exchange of plans and materials as well as results.

For comparison with these results of 'populational' study, an extension of knowledge regarding the differences between closely related species or subspecies is highly desirable. Hitherto the smallness of the number of 'species' that had been found to be crossable at all, and the fact that all interspecific F_1 hybrids were sterile, seemed to stand in the way of such studies in *Drosophila*. But, following the finding of (*virilis*) *americana* and of the fact that its hybrids with *virilis* can be bred, Spencer has found another pair of species, this time of the *hydei* group, to be crossable at least as far as F_1. Moreover, Dobzhansky has recently obtained some hybrids from *pseudo-obscura* A with a race of *miranda* from Mt. Whitney, California, which have some degree of fertility. And according to Spencer's recent observations, it seems very probable that a more intensive study will presently reveal a number of whole groups of more or less crossable subspecies and species of *Drosophila*.

Even the results already at hand show the relativity of the species-concept in *Drosophila*—one of the groups in which species boundaries seemed formerly to be the most absolute and in

[1] The real difficulty here is that a very slight degree of dominance of a lethal increases its rate of elimination much more than does a rather high degree of inbreeding, and thus hinders the determination of the latter.

which morphological differentiation within the species, into geographical subspecies as ordinarily thought of, had seemed almost non-existent.[1] But now it is quite evident, for example, that the so-called 'races' of *D. pseudo-obscura* represent a kind of differentiation qualitatively like that distinguishing species, although the degree of this differentiation is not so marked as in the case of species in general. And *virilis* and (*virilis*) *americana*, though still giving F_1 hybrids capable of some reproduction, are in other respects quite good species. All this is, of course, only understandable in terms of a process of speciation which is going on, a process in which the same differences as at first distinguished individuals, become, *en masse*, by their accumulation with and without selection, the factors that separate the species and finally the groups of higher rank. In view of this, a knowledge of the way the process works—such as *Drosophila* of all forms is most suitable for giving us—is a *sine qua non* for a rational evaluation of the group differences empirically found.

It becomes, then, a matter of definition and of convenience, in any given series of cases, just where we decide to draw the line above which two groups will be distinguished as separate species, and below which they are denoted subspecies or races, since in nature there is no abrupt transition here. Nevertheless, this should not cause us to lose sight of the fact that, leaving aside transitional forms, the relation between two sets of individuals belonging to one well-knit species is qualitatively a quite different one from that between two sets of individuals of unquestionably separate (even though closely related) species. For in the former case an interchange of mutant genes and of rearrangements will eventually take place, among the descendants of these two sets of individuals, that will tend to result in the establishment of the better adapted combinations of the two, and in the elimination of those mutants which are mutually disharmonious, while in the latter case the spread of mutants

---

[1] Statistical studies on *pseudo-obscura* just published by Mather and Dobzhansky (1939, *Amer. Nat.*, **73**, 5–25) show that the individuals of different regions are after all distinguished in respect of quantitative characters. And although the curves for any given quantitative character overlap, as is so often the case for geographical races, nevertheless an individual can be identified as belonging to one or another geographical race with only 10% of error merely by measurement of a few of these quantitative characters. If more were taken into account, no doubt the identification could be made very accurate.

will occur quite separately in the two groups and regardless of any cross-incompatability, and thus will lead to an ever more pronounced divergence and physiological isolation. The inter-mingling in the former case constitutes a kind of influence of the two sets of individuals upon each other's progeny that is of great importance in their further evolution. And this influence is of a quite different type from that of mere competition which may occur in the latter case.

Thus the stage distinguished as 'speciation', even though it is not one that is usually abrupt in its origin, marks a distinction that is very real and significant, in those organisms in which amphimixis occurs. There is no other stage of divergence, either below or above it in rank, which, like it, involves the entrance of a qualitatively distinct factor, having a direct influence upon this process of divergence itself. In other words, what ranks of differentiation our terminology will assign, above or below this level, can only be decided by general considerations based on the apparent degree of difference existing. But whether specific rank is assigned should depend, theoretically, upon the probable answer to the qualitative question of whether the germ-plasms engage in a mixing that is effective in the sense described above. And while the taxonomist must, in practice, employ more practicable immediate criteria, nevertheless these do, on the whole, reflect the effects of speciation as defined in this more nearly functional, evolutionary sense. Often the answer to the question thus set is clear, but—unfortunately for the simplicity of use of our terminology—this qualitative differ-ence also has its quantitative aspects, and when the mixing becomes more or less likely to occur, or occurs with different degrees of ineffectiveness, it becomes a matter of convenience only whether or not the species rank should be assigned. Nor can we be much helped by a finely divided or sliding scale of terms here, for that only multiplies, by dividing them, the difficulties of drawing the verbal lines. At the same time, we cannot well cease to use the terminology of species in such cases, for it is necessary to have words to denote the groups we are referring to, and to know, at least to a rough approximation, how these groups stand in relation to that general level at which 'speciation' takes place.

In the face of this situation, then, although the attempt must still be made to have the terminology follow certain general standards, exactly which terms are used in these transitional cases becomes a matter of but minor importance. Seen to be not cut and dried, but in flux, the groups of organisms classified are not sufficiently set in their place by merely having a word assigned to them, but, for a truer understanding of their relationships, require a study of the forms, the pressures, the cross-currents, and the counter-influences of this process of flux of which their lives form both the means and the expression.

Résumé

The bearings of the *Drosophila* work on systematics have so far lain chiefly in the light this work has thrown on the nature of the processes whereby differentiation between groups of organisms takes place. There is evidence that species of *Drosophila*, as of other animals, very rarely originate at one bound, but originate by the accumulation of what were originally individual genetic differences. It has been found in *Drosophila* that the latter are virtually always Mendelian and chromosomal in nature and are of two major categories, the first and more important being gene-mutations, and the second being rearrangements of sections of chromosomes containing groups of genes. Both types arise by sudden steps, mutations, which are occasioned by chemical accidents of ultra-microscopic dimensions.

As this process does not permit a correlation between the kind of condition under which a mutation takes place and the kind of character-change caused by the mutation, most mutations are necessarily detrimental, and the direction of evolution, in so far as it is adaptive at all, must be determined by natural selection, choosing from among many different biological possibilities. In this process the 'small mutations', which are more numerous than the large ones, will more often take part, being less likely to be detrimental. In *Drosophila* exact analysis has shown that virtually all genetic individual differences are of this mutational, Mendelian, and chromosomal nature, even those which are less clear-cut and seem to show continuous variability, there being no genetic residuum due to other causes.

The differences due to gene-mutation, and also those due to sectional change, are, in *Drosophila*, found not only in the laboratory, but also in nature, any natural population being very heterozygous, especially for 'small mutations'. The numbers and kinds of mutants present fluctuate in a more or less random way in different regions and at different times, but there are also some adaptive local differences, which must have resulted from selection. The differences between races and even between species cannot only be matched, phenotypically, by these individual differences but, in those cases where analysis has been possible, have proved to be of fundamentally the same kind genetically. Most of the racial or specific differences found, whether in morphological characters or in physiological ones (such as cross-infertility), depend upon numerous gene-mutations, individually of small effect.

The non-crossability of different groups, or the comparative infertility or inviability of their hybrids, receives its explanation in the numerous mutations which cause infertility, sterility, or inviability when in one genetic combination and not another. When geographical or other isolation allows two populations to differentiate genetically, among the mutations differentiating them will be those which, while not reducing fertility in the genetic milieu in which they occur, will reduce it when in combination with the genotype of the other population. Thus a long period of non-mixing of two groups is inevitably attended by the origination of actual immiscibility, i.e. genetic isolation.

Displacements of chromosome-sections (gene-rearrangements) occur naturally far less frequently than gene-mutations, and exactly the same sectional change hardly ever occurs twice. Occasionally, however, a given sectional change may become more or less spread throughout a population. One factor influencing their spread lies in the fact that the rearrangements of the genes influence the functioning of those genes lying near the points of breakage and exchange of the chromosomes ('position effect'), thus giving effects similar to those of gene-mutations, which may be selected for or against. Another factor is that the rearranged section may no longer be able to undergo effective interchange (crossing-over) with the original section, and since it will then not accumulate the same recessive mutant genes as the latter it tends to give more vigorous hybrids (heterosis) unless it becomes too greatly multiplied. Being genetically isolated it may serve as a centre within the germ-plasm for the building up of a different genetic complex, which may, on occasion, give opportunity for the origination of a genetically different population. But in early stages its lack of interchangeability will militate against its evolvability.

The kinds of sectional changes that can differentiate species depend in the first place upon the kinds that can occur and survive. Rearrangements able to survive at all always involve a breakage of one or more chromosomes at at least two points, together with a union of the pieces so formed, by their broken ends, in a new order, leaving the originally free ends ('telo-meres') still free, and leaving one fibre attachment ('centro-mere') on each chromosome. But of the different types of translocations, inversions, &c., thus formed, only those can easily become spread in a population which, when in hetero-zygous combination with the normal type, do not lead to a reduction of fertility by the formation of inviable recombina-tions. In *Drosophila* this condition is only met by inversions confined to a given chromosome arm, and to a lesser extent by exchanges between virtually whole arms. Hence the former chiefly, and to a much lesser extent the latter, form the great bulk of the sectional differentiations within and between races and species of *Drosophila*. That other types occasionally occur also shows that, on rare occasions, the whole population may arise from a very few individuals. For, the smaller the popula-tion, the more chance would a rearrangement suffering from the temporary disadvantage in question have, to become multi-plied accidentally, despite this disadvantage, so as to become the predominant type in the group.

While the sectional differences between races and species are more easily studied than the differences caused by gene-mutations, they are far less numerous than the latter, and evolution and differentiation between groups could go on without them. However, they can afford a useful means for the tracing of phylogeny. The relative frequencies of the different kinds of sectional changes which will predominate in the evolution of different groups, and the relative frequencies of sectional rearrangements as a whole as compared with gene-mutations, will depend on various factors. Among these are those which influence the frequencies of mutations of different kinds, the amount of crossing-over, whether it is localized and whether it occurs in male, female, or both, the length of genera-tion, degree of inbreeding, amount of migration, amount of accidental differential multiplication of the individuals of the population, the intensity and character of the position effects, &c. The principles governing the operation of these factors are to some extent already known, so that deductions can be made regarding the types of differentiation occurring in different groups, in so far as these factors have been determined. How-ever, there remains a wide field for study here, and much may be learned from investigations of 'population genetics' and from genetic analyses of racial and specific differences.

Although all the work agrees in showing that speciation represents no absolute stage in evolution, but is gradually arrived at, and intergrades imperceptibly into racial differen-tiation beneath it and generic differentiation above, neverthe-less the concept represents a real stage, corresponding to some-thing of significance in nature, in so far as we may identify it with the stage at which effective intercrossing stops. For divergence goes on very differently, and much more freely, between groups that cannot cross than it does between those which can and do cross, and it is therefore justifiable and useful, even though difficult, to make the species distinction, if it is made in such a way as to correspond so far as possible with this stage of separation. At the same time it must be recognized that the species are in flux, and that an adequate understanding of their relationships can be arrived at only on the basis of an understanding of the relationships between the minor groups and even between the individuals, supplemented by the study of the differences found through observations on the systematics of the larger groups.

REFERENCES

ALTENBURG, E., and MULLER, H. J. (1920.) 'The Genetic Basis of Truncate Wing, an Inconstant and Modifiable Character in Drosophila.' Genetics, 5, 1–59.

BALKASCHINA, E. I., and ROMASCHOFF, D. D. (1935.) 'Genetische Struktur der Drosophila-Populationen. I. Swenigoroder (Moskauer Gub.) Popu-lationen von D. phalerata Eig., transversa Fall. und vibrissina Duda.' Biol. Zh. 4, 81–106. (Russ. with Germ. sum.)

BEDICHEK, S. (1938.) 'Sex Balance in the Progeny of Triploid Drosophila.' Address to Gen. Soc. Amer., September, 1938. Genetics, 24 (1939), 94–5.

BELGOVSKY, M. L., and MULLER, H. J. (1938.) 'Further Evidence of the Prevalence of Minute Rearrangement and Absence of Simple Breakage in and near Chromocentral Regions, and its Bearing on the Mechanisms of Mosaicism and Rearrangement.' (Abstr.) *Genetics*, **23**, 139–40.

BERG, R. L. (1937a.) 'Relative Frequency of Mutations in Different Chromosomes of *Drosophila melanogaster*. I. Lethal Mutations. II. Sterility Mutations.' *Genetics*, **22**, 225–40 and 241–8.

—— (1937b.) 'The Relative Roles of Stabilization and Redifferentiation of the Gene in the Evolution of the Hereditary Substance.' *Genetics*, **22**, 402–5.

—— and KOVALEV, A. (1937.) 'The Location of Sterility Mutations in the X-chromosome of *Drosophila melanogaster*.' MS. 6 pp.

BRIDGES, C. B. (1917.) 'Deficiency.' *Genetics*, **2**, 445–65.

—— (1919.) 'Duplications.' (Abstr.) *Anat. Rec.* **15**, 357.

—— (1923.) 'The Translocation of a Section of Chromosome II upon Chromosome III in *Drosophila*.' (Abstr.) *Anat. Rec.* **24**, 426.

—— (1935.) 'Salivary Chromosome Maps.' *J. Hered.* **26**, 60–4.

—— (1936.) 'The Bar "Gene" a Duplication.' *Science*, **83**, 210–11.

—— and MOHR, O. L. (1919.) 'The Inheritance of the Mutant Character "Vortex".' *Genetics*, **4**, 283–306.

CAROTHERS, E. E. (1917.) 'The Segregation and Recombination of Homologous Chromosomes as found in Two Genera of Acrididae (Orthoptera).' *J. Morphol.* **28**, 445–521.

CHINO, M. (1929.) 'Genetic Studies on the Japanese Stock of *Drosophila virilis*. Report 1.' (Japanese.) *Jap. J. Genet.* **4**, 117–31.

CREW, F. A. E., and LAMY, R. (1935.) 'Linkage Groups in *Drosophila pseudo-obscura*.' *J. Genet.* **30**, 15–29.

—— —— (1938.) 'Fertile Haploid Sectors by Partial Merogony in Mosaics of *Drosophila pseudo-obscura*.' *Nature*, **141**, 923.

CUMLEY, R. W. (1937.) 'Serology of *Drosophila*.' Address to Gen. Soc. Amer., Dec. 1937. (Abstr.) *Genetics*, **23**, 146 (1938).

DARLINGTON, C. D. (1932.) *Recent Advances in Cytology*, 1st edition. J. and A. Churchill, London. xviii + 559 pp.

—— (1937.) *Recent Advances in Cytology*, 2nd edition. xiii+671+16 pp.

DEMEREC, M. (1936.) 'A Mutability-Stimulating Factor in the Florida Stock of *Drosophila melanogaster*.' (Abstr.) *Genetics*, **22**, 190 (1937).

DOBZHANSKY, TH. (1933a.) 'Role of the Autosomes in the *Drosophila pseudo-obscura* Hybrids.' *Proc. Nat. Acad. Sci.* **13**, 950–3.

—— (1933b.) 'On the Sterility of the Inter-racial Hybrids in *Drosophila pseudo-obscura*.' *Proc. Nat. Acad. Sci.* **19**, 397–403.

—— (1934.) 'Studies on Hybrid Sterility I. Spermatogenesis in Pure and Hybrid *Drosophila pseudo-obscura*.' *Zeit. Zellforsch.* **21**, 169–223.

—— (1935a.) 'A Critique of the Species Concept in Biology.' *Philosophy of Science*, **2**, 344–55.

—— (1935b.) 'Maternal Effects as a Cause of the Difference between the Reciprocal Crosses in *Drosophila pseudo-obscura*.' *Proc. Nat. Acad. Sci.* **21**, 443–6.

—— (1935c.) 'The Y-chromosome of *Drosophila pseudo-obscura*.' *Genetics*, **20**, 366–76.

DOBZHANSKY, TH. (1935d.) 'Drosophila miranda, a New Species.' Genetics, 20, 377–91.

—— (1936a.) 'Position Effects of Genes.' Biol. Rev. 11, 364–84.

—— (1936b.) 'Studies on Hybrid Sterility. II. Localization of the Sterility Factors in Drosophila pseudo-obscura Hybrids.' Genetics, 21, 113–35.

—— (1937a.) 'Genetic Nature of Species Differences.' Amer. Nat. 71, 404–20.

—— (1937b.) Genetics and the Origin of Species. Columbia Univ. Press, N.Y. xvi + 364 pp.

—— (1937c.) 'Further Data on the Variation of the Y-chromosome in Drosophila pseudo-obscura.' Genetics, 22, 340–6.

—— (1937d.) 'Further data on Drosophila miranda and its Hybrids with Drosophila pseudo-obscura.' J. Genet. 34, 135–51.

—— (1938.) 'The Raw Materials of Evolution.' Sci. Mon. 46, 445–9.

—— and BOCHE, R. D. (1933.) 'Intersterile Races of Drosophila pseudo-obscura Frol.' Biol. Zbl. 53, 314–30.

—— and KOLLER, P. C. (1938.) 'An Experimental Study of Sexual Isolation in Drosophila. Biol. Zbl. 58, 589–607.

—— and QUEAL, M. L. (1938a.) 'Genetics of Natural Populations. I. Chromosome Variation in Populations of Drosophila pseudo-obscura inhabiting Isolated Mountain Ranges. Genetics, 23, 239–51.

—— —— (1938b.) 'Genetics of Natural Populations. II. Genic Variation in Populations of Drosophila pseudo-obscura inhabiting Isolated Mountain Ranges.' Genetics, 23, 463–84.

—— and SCHULTZ, J. (1931.) 'Evidence for Multiple Sex Factors in the X-chromosome of Drosophila melanogaster.' Proc. Nat. Acad. Sci. 17, 513–18.

—— —— (1934.) 'The Distribution of Sex Factors in the X-chromosome of Drosophila melanogaster. J. Genet. 28, 349–86.

—— —— (1935.) 'Further Data on Maternal Effects in Drosophila pseudo-obscura Hybrids.' Proc. Nat. Acad. Sci. 21, 566–70.

—— and STURTEVANT A. H. (1932.) 'Change in Dominance of Genes lying in Duplicating Fragments of Chromosomes.' Proc. 6th Int. Congr. of Genet., 2, 45–7.

—— —— (1938.) 'Inversions in the Chromosomes of Drosophila pseudo-obscura.' Genetics, 23, 28–64.

—— and TAN, C. C. (1936.) 'Studies on Hybrid Sterility. III. A Comparison of the Gene Arrangement in Two Species, Drosophila pseudo-obscura and Drosophila miranda.' Z. indukt. Abstamm.- Vererb.lehre, 72, 88–114.

DONALD, H. P. (1936.) 'On the Genetical Constitution of Drosophila pseudo-obscura, Race A.' J. Genet. 33, 103–22.

DUBININ, N. P. (1931.) 'Genetic-automatic Processes and their Significance in the Process of Organic Evolution.' (Russ.) J. exp. Biol. 7, 463–79.

—— (1936.) 'Experimental Alteration of the Number of Chromosome Pairs in Drosophila melanogaster.' Biol. Zh. 5, 833–50. (Russ. and Eng.)

——, HEPTNER, M. A., BESSMERTNAIA, S. F., GOLDAT, S. J., PANINA, K. A., POGESSIAN, E., SAPRIKINA, S. W., SIDOROV, B. N., FERRY, L. W., and ZUBINA, M. G. (1934.) 'Experimental Study of the Ecogenotypes of Drosophila melanogaster. First Part.' Biol. Zh. 3, 166–206. (Russ. with Eng. summary.)

Dubinin, N. P., Heptnfr, M. A., Demidova, Z. A., and Djachkova, L. I. (1936.) 'Genetic Constitution and Gene-dynamics of Wild Populations of *Drosophila melanogaster.*' *Biol. Zh.* **5**, 939–76. (Russ. and Eng.)

—— ——, Nikor, Z. S., Bessmertnaia, S. Z., Beliaieva, W. N., Demidova, Z. A., Krotkova, A. P., and Postnikova, E. D. (1934.) 'Experimental Study of the Ecogenotypes of *Drosophila melanogaster.* Second Part.' *Biol. Zh.* **3**, 207–15. (Russ. with Eng. summary.)

——, Romashov, D. D., Heptner, M. A., and Demidova, Z. A. (1937.) 'Aberrant Polymorphism in *Drosophila fasciata* Meig. (syn.-*melanogaster* Meig.) *Biol. Zh.* **6**, 311–54. (Russ. and Eng.)

—— and Sidorov, B. (1934.) 'Relation between the Effect of a Gene and its Position in the System.' *Biol. Zh.* **3**, 307–31. (Russ. with Eng. summary.) *Amer. Nat.* **68**, 377–80.

—— —— (1935.) 'The Position Effect of the Hairy Gene.' *Biol. Zh.* **4**, 555–68. (Russ. with Eng. summary.)

——, Sokolov, N. N., and Tiniakov, G. G. (1936.) 'Occurrence and Distribution of Chromosomal Aberrations in Nature.' *Nature*, **138**, 1035–6.

—— —— —— (1937.) 'Intraspecific Chromosome Variability.' *Biol. Zh.* **6**, 1007–54. (Russ. with Eng. summary.)

Duda, O. (1924*a*.) 'Beitrag zur Systematik der *Drosophiliden* unter besonderer Berücksichtigung der paläarktischen und orientalischen Arten (Dipteren).' *Arch. Naturgesch.* **90**, 172–234.

—— (1924*b*.) 'Revision der europäischen Arten der Gattung *Drosophila* Fallen (Dipteren).' *Ent. Medd.* **14**, 246–313.

—— (1925*a*.) 'Die costaricanischen *Drosophiliden* des ungarischen National-Museums zu Budapest.' *Ann. hist.-nat. Mus. Hung.* **22**, 149–229.

—— (1925*b*.) 'Die südamerikanischen *Drosophiliden* (Dipteren) unter Berücksichtigung auch der anderen neotropischen sowie der nearktischen Arten.' *Arch. Naturgesch.* **91**A (11/12); 1–228.

—— (1929.) 'Die Ausbeute der deutschen Chaco-Expedition. IX. *Drosophilidae.*' *Konowia*, **8**, 33–50.

Fisher, R. A. (1930.) *The Genetical Theory of Natural Selection.* Clarendon Press, Oxford. xiv+272 pp.

Ford, E. B. (1937.) 'Problems of Heredity in the Lepidoptera.' *Biol. Rev.* **12**, 461 (pp. 489–97).

Frolowa, S. (1926.) 'Normale und polyploide Chromosomengarnituren bei einigen Drosophila-Arten.' *Zeit. Zellforsch.* **3**, 682–94.

—— and Astaurow, B. L. (1929.) 'Die Chromosomengarnitur als systematisches Merkmal.' *Zeit. Zellforsch.* **10**, 201–13.

Gershenson, S. (1934.) 'Mutant Genes in a Wild Population of *Drosophila obscura* Fall.' *Amer. Nat.* **68**, 569–71.

Goldschmidt, R. (1937.) 'Spontaneous Chromatin Rearrangements and the Theory of the Gene.' *Proc. Nat. Acad.* **23**, 621–3.

—— (1938.) *Physiological Genetics.* New York and London: McGraw-Hill Book Co., Inc. ix+375 pp.

Gonzalez, B. M. (1923.) 'Experimental Studies on the Duration of Life. VIII. The Influence upon Duration of Life of Certain Mutant Genes of *Drosophila melanogaster.*' *Amer. Nat.* **57**, 289–325.

GORDON, C. (1935a.) 'An Experiment on a Released Population of *Drosophila melanogaster*.' *Amer. Nat.* **69**, 381.

—— (1935b.) 'An Analysis of Two Wild *Drosophila* Populations.' *Amer. Nat.* **69**, 381–2.

—— (1936.) 'The Frequency of Heterozygosis in Free-living Populations of *Drosophila melanogaster* and *Drosophila subobscura*.' *J. Genet.* **33**, 25–60.

GRÜNEBERG, H. (1937.) 'The Position Effect proved by Spontaneous Reinversion in *Drosophila melanogaster*.' *J. Genet.* **34**, 168–89.

HALDANE, J. B. S. (1922.) 'Sex-ratio and Unisexual Sterility in Hybrid Animals.' *J. Genet.* **12**, 101–9.

—— (1932.) *The Causes of Evolution.* Longmans, Green & Co., London. 235 pp.

HELWIG, E. R. (1929.) 'Chromosomal Variations correlated with Geographical Distribution in *Circotettix verruculatus* (Orthoptera). *J. Morphol.* **47**, 1–36.

HOLLINGSHEAD, L. (1930.) 'A Lethal Factor in Crepis effective only in Interspecific Hybrids.' *Genetics*, **15**, 114–40.

HORTON, I. H. (1938.) 'A Comparative Study of the Salivary Gland Chromosomes of *Drosophila melanogaster* and *D. simulans*.' Address to Gen. Soc. Amer., Dec. 1938. (Abstr.) *Genetics*, **24**, 75–6 (1939).

HUGHES, R. D. (1938.) 'The Chromosomes in the Hybrid between *Drosophila virilis virilis* and *Drosophila virilis americana* Spencer'. Address to Gen. Soc. Amer., Sept. 1938. (Abstr.) *Genetics*, **24**, 99 (1939).

HUXLEY, J. S. (1936.) 'Natural Selection and Evolutionary Progress.' *Rep. Brit. Ass.*, Sect. D., Presid. address. 15 pp.

—— (1939.) *Evolution, the Modern Synthesis.* (In press.)

KERKIS, J. (1933.) 'Development of Gonads in Hybrids between *Drosophila melanogaster* and *Drosophila simulans*.' *J. exp. Zool.* **66**, 477–509.

—— (1934.) 'Development of the Sexual Glands in Inter-racial Hybrids of *Drosophila pseudo-obscura*.' *C. R. Acad. Sci. U.R.S.S.* **3**, 640–5.

—— (1936.) 'Chromosome Configuration in Hybrids between *Drosophila melanogaster* and *Drosophila simulans*.' *Amer. Nat.* **70**, 81–6.

—— (1937.) 'The Causes of Imperfect Conjugation of Chromosomes in hybrids of *Drosophila simulans* and *melanogaster*.' *Bull. Acad. Sci. U.R.S.S.* 459–68. (Russ. with Eng. summary.)

—— (1938.) 'The Frequency of Mutations affecting Viability.' *Bull Acad. Sci. U.R.S.S.* 75–96. (Russ. and Eng.)

KIKKAWA, H. (1937.) 'The Inert Chromosomes of *Drosophila ananassae* Doleschall.' *Cytologia*, Fujii Jubilee Volume, 125–8.

—— (1938.) 'Studies on the Genetics and Cytology of *Drosophila ananassae*.' *Genetica*, **20**, 458–516.

KING, R. L. (1923.) 'Heteromorphic Homologous Chromosomes in Three Species of *Pseudotrimerotropis* (Orthoptera: Acrididae).' *J. Morphol.* **38**, 19–63.

KOLLER, P. C. (1931.) 'Genetic Studies of the Crosses of Two Races of *Drosophila obscura*.' *Magyar Biol. Kut. Int. Közl.* **4**, 580–600.

—— (1932a.) ' "Pointed", and the Constitution of the X-chromosome in *Drosophila obscura*.' *J. Genet.* **26**, 215–29.

KOLLER, P. C. (1932b.) 'Constitution of the X-chromosome in Drosophila obscura.' Nature, 129, 616.

—— (1932c.) 'The Relation of Fertility Factors to Crossing-over in the Drosophila obscura Hybrid.' Z. indukt. Abstamm.- Vererb.lehre, 60, 137–51.

—— (1934.) 'Spermatogenesis in Drosophila pseudo-obscura Frolowa. II. The Cytological Basis of Sterility in Hybrid Males of Races A and B.' Proc. roy. Soc. Edin. 54, 67–87.

—— (1935a.) 'Internal Mechanics of Chromosomes. IV. Salivary Gland Chromosomes of Drosophila.' Proc. roy. Soc. 118, 371–97.

—— (1935b.) 'Origin of Variations within Species.' Nature, 135, 69–70.

—— (1936.) 'Structural Hybridity in Drosophila pseudo-obscura.' J. Genet. 32, 79–102.

KOSSIKOV, K. V., and MULLER, H. J. (1935.) 'Invalidation of the Genetic Evidence for Branched Chromonemas.' J. Hered. 26, 305–17.

KOSSWIG, G. (1929.) 'Über die veränderte Wirkung von Farbgenen des Platypoecilus in der Gattungskreuzung mit Xiphophorus. Z. indukt. Abstamm.- Vererb.lehre. 50, 63–73.

KOZHEVNIKOV, B. Th. (1936.) 'Experimentally produced Karyotypical Isolation.' Biol. Zh. 5, 727–52. (Russ. and Eng.)

LANCEFIELD, D. E. (1922.) 'Linkage Relations of the Sex-linked Characters in Drosophila obscura.' Genetics, 7, 335–84.

—— (1925.) 'An Inter-racial Cross in Drosophila obscura producing Partially Fertile Hybrids.' (Abstr.) Anat. Rec. 31, 346.

—— (1929.) 'A Genetic Study of Crosses of Two Races or Physiological Species in Drosophila obscura.' Z. indukt. Abstamm.- u. Vererb.lehre, 52, 287–317.

LANCEFIELD, R. C., and METZ, C. W. (1921.) 'Non-disjunction and the Chromosome Relationships of Drosophila willistoni.' Proc. Nat. Acad. Sci. 7, 225–9.

—— —— (1922.) 'The Sex-linked Group of Mutant Characters in Drosophila willistoni.' Amer. Nat. 56, 211–41.

L'HÉRITIER, P., and TEISSIER, G. (1938.) 'Transmission héréditaire de la sensibilité au gaz carbonique chez la drosophile.' C. R. Acad. Sci. Paris, 206, 1683–5.

MACKNIGHT, R. H. 1937. 'Cytology of Drosophila miranda.' Address to Gen. Soc. Amer. (Abstr.) Genetics, 23, 158 (1938.)

METZ, C. W. (1914.) 'Chromosome Studies on the Diptera. I. A Preliminary Survey of Five Different Types of Chromosome Groups in the Genus Drosophila.' J. exp. Zool. 17, 45–59.

—— (1916a.) 'Chromosome Studies on the Diptera. II. The Paired Association of Chromosomes in the Diptera, and its Significance.' J. exp. Zool. 21, 213–79.

—— (1916b.) 'Chromosome Studies on the Diptera. III. Additional Types of Chromosome Groups in the Drosophilidae.' Amer. Nat. 50, 587–99.

—— (1920a.) 'The Arrangement of Genes in Drosophila virilis.' Proc. Nat. Acad. Sci. 6, 164–6.

—— (1920b.) 'Correspondence between Chromosome Number and Linkage Groups in Drosophila virilis.' Science, 51, 417–18.

METZ, C. W., and FERRY, R. M. (1923.) 'The Parallel Characters Cross-veinless and Vermilion in *Drosophila willistoni.*' *Amer. Nat.* **57**, 381–4.

—— and MOSES, M. S. (1923.) 'Chromosomes of *Drosophila*. Chromosome Relationships and Genetic Behaviour in the Genus *Drosophila*. I. A Comparison of the Chromosomes of Different Species of *Drosophila.*' *J. Hered.* **14**, 195–204.

—— —— and MASON, E. D. (1923.) 'Genetic Studies on *Drosophila virilis* with Considerations on the Genetics of Other Species of *Drosophila.*' *Carn. Inst. Wash. Publ.* **328**, 94 pp.

MOHR, O. L. (1919.) 'Character Changes caused by Mutation of an Entire Region of a Chromosome in *Drosophila.*' *Genetics*, **4**, 275–82.

—— (1923.) 'A Genetic and Cytological Analysis of a Section Deficiency involving Four Units of the X-chromosome in *Drosophila melanogaster.*' *Z. indukt. Abstamm.- Vererb.lehre*, **32**, 108–232.

MORGAN, T. H., BRIDGES, C. B., and STURTEVANT, A. H. (1925.) 'The Genetics of *Drosophila.*' *Bibliogr. genet.* **2**, 1–262.

—— STURTEVANT, A. H., MULLER, H. J., and BRIDGES, C. B. (1915.) *The Mechanism of Mendelian Heredity.* Holt & Co. xiii+262 pp.

MULLER, H. J. (1914.) 'A Gene for the Fourth Chromosome of *Drosophila.*' *J. exp. Zool.* **17**, 325–36.

—— (1916.) 'The Mechanism of Crossing-over.' *Amer. Nat.* **50**, 193–221, 284–305, 350–66, 421–34.

—— (1918.) 'Genetic Variability, Twin Hybrids and Constant Hybrids, in a Case of Balanced Lethal Factors.' *Genetics*, **3**, 422–99.

—— (1921.) 'Mutation.' Read before Int. Eug. Congr. at New York; publ. 1923 in *Eugenics, Genetics and the Family*, **1**, 106–12.

—— (1925.) 'Why Polyploidy is rarer in Animals than in Plants.' *Amer. Nat.* **59**, 346–53.

—— (1928*a.*) 'The Measurement of Gene Mutation Rate in *Drosophila*, its High Variability, and its Dependence upon Temperature.' *Genetics*, **13**, 279–357.

—— (1928*b.*) 'The Production of Mutations by X-rays.' *Proc. Nat. Acad. Sci.* **14**, 714–26.

—— (1930.) 'Radiation and Genetics.' *Amer. Nat.* **64**, 220–51.

—— (1932.) 'Further Studies on the Nature and Causes of Gene Mutations.' *Proc. 6th Int. Congr. Gen.* **1**, 213–55.

—— (1934.) 'Radiation-Genetics.' (Abstr.) *IV Int. Radiologenkongr.* **2**, 100–2.

—— (1935*a.*) 'The Origination of Chromatin Deficiencies as Minute Deletions subject to Insertion elsewhere.' *Genetica*, **17**, 237–52.

—— (1935*b.*) 'The Position Effect as Evidence of the Localization of the Immediate Products of Gene Activity. *15th Int. Physiological Congress*, Summaries of Communications, pp. 286–9.

—— (1935*c.*) 'The Status of the Mutation Theory in 1935.' Address at de Vries Memorial Meeting, Leningrad, Nov., 1935, publ. in part in *Priroda*, 1936, no. 6, pp. 40–50 (Russ.); and in full, 1938, in *Current Science* (Bangalore, India), Special Number (March), pp. 4–15.

—— (1937*a.*) 'The Biological Effects of Radiation, with especial reference to Mutation.' *Actualités Scient. et Indust.: Congrès de la Découverte*, **8**, 477–91.

MULLER, H. J. (1937*b*.) 'Reversibility in Evolution, considered from the Standpoint of Genetics.' Read at S.E.B. meeting, London, 21 Dec. 1937; *Biol. Rev.* **14**, 261–80 (1939).

—— (1938.) 'The Remaking of Chromosomes.' *Collecting Net*, **13**, 181–95, 198.

—— and PAINTER, T. S. (1932.) 'The Differentiation of the Sex Chromosomes of *Drosophila* into Genetically Active and Inert Regions.' *Z. indukt. Abstamm.- Vererb.lehre*, **62**, 316–65.

—— and PROKOFYEVA, A. A. (1934.) 'Continuity and Discontinuity of the Hereditary Material.' *C. R. Acad. Sci. U.R.S.S.* **4**, 74–83. (Russ. and Eng.)

—— —— (1935.) 'The Individual Gene in relation to the Chromomere and the Chromosome.' *Proc. Nat. Acad. Sci.* **21**, 16–26.

——, PROKOFYEVA-BELGOVSKAYA, and KOSSIKOV, K. V. (1936.) 'Unequal Crossing-over in the Bar Mutant as a Result of Duplication of a Minute Chromosome Section.' *C. R. Acad. Sci. U.R.S.S.*, N.S., **1** (**10**), 87–8.

——, PROKOFYEVA, A. A., and RAFFEL, D. (1934.) 'Apparent Gene Mutations due to the Position Effect of Minute Gene Rearrangements.' (Abstr.) *Rec. Genet. Soc. Amer.* **3**, 48–9. Republ. 1935, *Amer. Nat.* **69**, 72–3.

—— —— —— (1935.) 'Minute Intergenic Rearrangement as a Cause of Apparent "Gene Mutation".' *Nature*, **135**, 253–5.

——, PROKOFYEVA-BELGOVSKAYA, and RAFFEL, D. (1938.) 'The Absence of Transmissible Chromosome Fragments resulting from Simple Breakage, and their Simulation as a Result of Compound Breakage involving Chromocentral Regions.' (Abstr.) *Genetics*, **23**, 161.

—— and RAFFEL, D. (1937.) 'The Manifestation of the Position Effect in Three Inversions at the Scute Locus.' Address to Gen. Soc. Amer., Dec. 1937. Abstr. in *Genetics*, **23**, 160 (1938).

NEUHAUS, M. E. (1938.) 'A Cyto-genetic Study of the Y-chromosome in *Drosophila melanogaster.*' *Biol. Zh.* **7**, 335–58. (Russ. with Eng. summary.)

PAINTER, T. S. (1934.) 'A New Method for the Study of Chromosome Aberrations and the Plotting of Chromosome Maps in *Drosophila melanogaster.*' *Genetics*, **19**, 175–88.

PANSHIN, I. (1936.) 'New Evidence for the Position Effect Hypothesis.' *C. R. Acad. Sci. U.R.S.S.*, N.S., **4**, 85–8.

—— and KHVOSTOVA, W. W. (1938.) 'Experimental Proof of the Sub-terminal Position of the Attachment Point of the Spindle Fiber in Chromosome IV of *Drosophila melanogaster.*' *Biol. Zh.* **7**, 359–80. (Russ. with Eng. summary.)

PÄTAU, K. (1935.) 'Chromosomenmorphologie bei *Drosophila melanogaster* und *Drosophila simulans* und ihre genetische Bedeutung.' *Naturwiss.* **23**, 537–43.

PATTERSON, J. T. (1931.) 'The Production of Gynandromorphs in *Drosophila melanogaster* by X-rays.' *J. exp. Zool.* **60**, 173–211.

—— STONE, W., and BEDICHEK, S. (1935.) 'The Genetics of X-hyperploid Females.' *Genetics*, **20**, 259–79.

—— —— —— (1937.) 'Further Studies on X-chromosome Balance in *Drosophila.*' *Genetics*, **22**, 407–26.

PLOUGH, H. H., and HOLTHAUSEN, C. F. (1936.) 'A Case of High Mutation Frequency in *Drosophila* without Environmental Change.' Address to Gen. Soc. Amer., 1936. (Abstr.) *Genetics*, **22**, 203 (1937).

PRABHU, S. S. (1939.) 'Sterility Mutations in *Drosophila melanogaster*.' *J. Genet.* **38**, 177–91.

PROKOFYEVA-BELGOVSKAYA, A. A. (1937*a*.) 'Observations on the Structure of Chromosomes in the Salivary Glands of *Drosophila melanogaster*.' *Bull. Acad. Sci. U.R.S.S.* 393–426.

—— (1937*b*.) 'Inert Regions in the Distal Ends of Chromosomes of *Drosophila melanogaster*.' *Bull. Acad. Sci. U.R.S.S.* 719–24.

—— (1938.) 'The Inert Region in the Subterminal Part of the X-chromosome of *Drosophila melanogaster*.' *Bull. Acad. Sci. U.R.S.S.* 97–103.

RAFFEL, D. (1938.) 'A Genetic Analysis of Apparent Losses of the Distal End of the Scute-8 Chromosome.' Address to Gen. Soc. Amer., Sept. 1938. *Genetics*, **24**, 107 (1939).

SCHULTZ, J. (1933.) 'X-ray Effects on *Drosophila pseudo-obscura*.' *Genetics*, **18**, 284–91.

—— and DOBZHANSKY, TH. (1933.) 'Triploid Hybrids between *Drosophila melanogaster* and *Drosophila simulans*.' *J. exp. Zool.* **65**, 73–82.

—— —— (1934.) 'The Relation of a Dominant Eye Color in *Drosophila melanogaster* to the Associated Chromosome Rearrangement.' *Genetics*, **19**, 344–64.

SEREBROVSKY, A. S. (1929.) 'A General Scheme for the Origin of Mutations.' *Amer. Nat.* **63**, 374–8.

SPENCER W. P. (1937.) '*Drosophila virilis americana*, a New Subspecies.' Address to Gen. Soc. Amer., Dec. (Abstr.) *Genetics*, **23**, 169–70 (1938).

—— (1938.) 'On the Genetic Structure of *Drosophila hydei* Populations.' Address to Gen. Soc. Amer., Dec. (Abstr.) *Genetics*, **24**, 86–7 (1939).

SPETT, G. (1931.) 'Gibt es eine partielle sexuelle Isolation unter den Mutationen und der Grundform von *Drosophila melanogaster* Meig.?' *Z. indukt. Abstamm.- Vererb.lehre*, **60**, 63–83.

STURTEVANT, A. H. (1913.) 'The Linear Arrangement of Six Sex-linked Factors in *Drosophila*, as shown by their Mode of Association.' *J. exp. Zool.* **14**, 43–59.

—— (1915.) 'The Behaviour of the Chromosomes as studied through Linkage.' *Z. indukt. Abstamm.- Vererb.lehre*, **13**, 234–87.

—— (1918*a*.) 'An Analysis of the Effects of Selection. *Carn. Inst. Wash. Publ.* **264**, 68 pp.

—— (1918*b*.) 'A Synopsis of the Neartic Species of the Genus *Drosophila* (*sensu lato*).' *Bull. Amer. Mus. Nat. Hist.* **38**, 441–6.

—— (1919.) 'Inherited Linkage Variations in the Second Chromosome.' *Carn. Inst. Wash. Publ.* **278**, 305–41.

—— (1920–1.) 'Genetic Studies on *Drosophila simulans* I, II, III.' *Genetics*, **5**, 488–500; **6**, 43–64, 179–207.

—— (1921*a*.) 'A Case of Rearrangement of Genes in *Drosophila*.' *Proc. Nat. Acad. Sci.* **7**, 235–7.

—— (1921*b*.) 'The North American species of *Drosophila*.' *Carn. Inst. Wash. Publ.* **301**, 150 pp.

STURTEVANT, A. H. (1926.) 'A Crossover Reducer in *Drosophila melanogaster* due to Inversion of a Section of Third Chromosome.' *Biol. Zbl.* **46,** 697–702.

—— (1929.) 'The Genetics of *Drosophila simulans.*' *Carn. Inst. Wash. Publ.* **399,** 1–62.

—— (1931.) 'Known and Probable Inverted Sections of the Autosomes of *Drosophila melanogaster.*' *Carn. Inst. Wash. Publ.* **421,** 1–27.

—— (1937a.) 'Autosomal Lethals in Wild Populations of *Drosophila pseudo-obscura.*' *Biol. Bull.* **73,** 542–51.

—— (1937b.) 'The Homologies of the Chromosome Arms of Different Species of *Drosophila.*' Address to Gen. Soc. Amer., Dec. 1937. (Abstr.) *Genetics,* **23,** 173–4 (1938).

—— (1938.) 'Essays on Evolution. III. On the Origin of Interspecific Sterility.' *Quart. Rev. Biol.* **13,** 333–5.

—— and BEADLE, G. W. (1936.) 'The Relations of Inversions in the X-chromosome of *Drosophila melanogaster* to Crossing-over and Disjunction.' *Genetics,* **21,** 554–604.

—— and DOBZHANSKY, TH. (1936a.) 'Geographical Distribution and Cytology of "Sex Ratio" in *Drosophila pseudo-obscura.*' *Genetics,* **21,** 473–90.

—— —— (1936b.) 'Inversions in the Third Chromosome of Wild Races of *Drosophila pseudo-obscura,* and Their Use in the Study of the History of the Species.' *Proc. Nat. Acad. Sci.* **22,** 448–50.

—— —— (1937.) Observations on the Species related to *Drosophila affinis,* with Descriptions of Seven New Forms.' *Amer. Nat.* **70,** 574–84.

—— and MATHER, K. (1938.) 'The Interrelations of Inversions, Heterosis, and Recombination.' *Amer. Nat.* **72,** 447–52.

—— and PLUNKETT, C. R. (1926.) 'Sequence of Corresponding Third-chromosome Genes in *Drosophila melanogaster* and *Drosophila simulans.*' *Biol. Bull.* **50,** 56–60.

—— and TAN, C. C. (1937.) 'The Comparative Genetics of *Drosophila pseudo-obscura* and *D. melanogaster.*' *J. Genet.* **34,** 415–32.

TAN, C. C. (1935a.) 'Salivary Gland Chromosomes in *Drosophila pseudo-obscura.*' *Genetics,* **20,** 392–402.

—— (1935b.) 'Identification of the Salivary Gland Chromosomes in *Drosophila pseudo-obscura.*' *Proc. Nat. Acad. Sci.* **21,** 200–2.

TIMOFEEFF-RESSOVSKY, H. A., and TIMOFEEFF-RESSOVSKY, N. W. (1927.) 'Genetische Analyse einer freilebenden *Drosophila melanogaster*-Population.' *Roux Arch. Entw. Mech. Organ.* **109,** 70–109.

TIMOFEEFF-RESSOVSKY, N. W. (1927.) 'Studies on the Phenotypic Manifestation of Hereditary Factors. I. On the Phenotypic Manifestation of the Genovariation Radius incompletus in *Drosophila funebris.*' *Genetics,* **12,** 128–70.

—— (1934.) 'Über die Vitalität einiger Genmutationen und ihrer Kombinationen bei *Drosophila funebris* und ihre Abhängigkeit vom "genotypischen" und vom äusseren Milieu.' *Z. indukt. Abstamm.- Vererb.lehre,* **66,** 319–44.

—— (1935a.) 'Auslösung von Vitalitätsmutationen durch Roentgenbestrahlung bei *Drosophila melanogaster.*' *Nachr. Ges. Wiss. Göttingen, Biol.,* N.R. **1,** 163–80.

TIMOFEEFF-RESSOVSKY, N. W. (1935*b*.) 'Experimentelle Untersuchungen der erblichen Belastung von Populationen.' *Der Erbarzt,* **2,** 117–88.

—— (1935*c*.) 'Über geographische Temperaturrassen bei *Drosophila funebris.*' *Arch. Naturgesch.* **4,** 245–57.

—— (1936.) 'Qualitativer Vergleich der Mutabilität von *Drosophila funebris* und *D. melanogaster.*' *Z. indukt. Abstamm.- Vererb.lehre,* **71,** 276–80.

TSHETVERIKOV S. S. (1926.) 'On Some Factors of the Evolution Process from the Standpoint of Present-day Genetics.' *J. exp. Biol.* (Russ.), Ser. A, **2,** 1–54. (Russ. with Eng. summary, pp. 237–40.)

—— (1927.) 'Über die genetische Beschaffenheit wilder Populationen (Referat).' *Verh. d. V. int. Kongr. f. Vererb.,* Suppl. Bd. II d. *Z. indukt. Abstamm.- Vererb.lehre,* 1499–1500 (publ. 1928).

—— (1928.) 'The Experimental Solution of an Evolutionary Problem.' *Proc. 3rd. Congr. Russian Zool. Anat. and Hist.* 52–4. (Russ.)

WEINSTEIN, A. (1920.) 'Homologous Genes and Linear Linkage in *Drosophila virilis.*' *Proc. Nat. Acad. Sci.* **6,** 623–39.

WRIGHT, S. (1931.) 'Evolution in Mendelian Populations.' *Genetics,* **16,** 97–159.

—— (1932.) 'The Roles of Mutation, Inbreeding, Crossbreeding, and Selection in Evolution.' *Proc. 6th Int. Cong. Gen.* **1,** 356–66.

ZELENY, C. (1918.) 'Germinal Changes in the Bar-eyed Race of *Drosophila* during the Course of Selection for Facet Number.' *Proc. Ind. Acad. Sci.* **17,** 73–7.

—— (1922.) 'The Effect of Selection for Eye Facet Number in the White Bar-eye Race of *Drosophila melanogaster.*' *Genetics,* **7,** 1–115.

—— (1929.) 'The Problem of the Unit Hereditary Factor or Gene.' *Trans. Ill. Acad. Sci.* **21,** 72–3.

—— and MATTOON, E. W. (1915.) 'The Effect of Selection upon the "Bar-eyed" Mutant of *Drosophila.*' *J. exp. Zool.* **19,** 515–29.

PROBLEMS OF THE ORIGINS OF SPECIES

By LANCELOT HOGBEN

WE name assemblages as such for two reasons. One is discontinuity of pattern among living creatures. The other is that it is necessary to have a convenient card index of distinguishable types. The procedure we adopt in making it has little to do with experimental inquiry into the nature of hereditable variations; and there is no necessary reason for expecting a close connexion between categories of resemblance based on the architecture of the germ-cells and categories of resemblance appropriate to the practice of taxonomy. So it has always seemed to me a misfortune that Darwin called his best-known work *The Origin of Species*. The word 'species' has no single meaning. Hence there is no one problem of the origin of species. There are many problems of the origins of species.

Having said that there is no one problem of the origin of species, I shall not suggest that there are only two. At the same time, it is useful to distinguish two broad categories which belong to different social contexts in which the problems of species have been discussed. The naturalists of the eighteenth century, still largely immersed in the historic task of the herbalists, were predominantly preoccupied with differences between creatures living together within a comparatively restricted locality. Partly for this reason and partly because biology was still emerging from superstitious beliefs about metamorphoses, they were specially concerned to emphasize the fixity of species. In so far as they permitted themselves to speculate about origins their problem was how systematic units which are distinct as *breeding units* came to be so. In the period of rapid colonial expansion which followed Cook's voyages, the Napoleonic wars, and the subsequent introduction of steam navigation, the standpoint of the explorer-naturalist prevailed. Systematic units which the traveller-naturalist meets in different countries are *ipso facto* breeding units. What interests him is not how species come to be *distinct*, but how they come to be *distinguishable*, i.e. the various ways in which they differ.

Having drawn this distinction we need not prolong a barren

controversy about the various definitions of species. All we are
concerned with is whether a group of forms can be recognized
as a distinct unit which preserves its identity for reasons which
may be *extrinsic* or may be *intrinsic*. Since it is not the business
of the taxonomist to probe very deeply into what these reasons
are, there is no justification for supposing that the origin of
what the taxonomist distinguishes as a species constitutes a single
class of problems.

When biologists differ about evolution it is often because of
undue emphasis on either the *extrinsic* aspect or the *intrinsic*
aspect of species differentiation. Much apparent disagreement
about evolution among biologists is merely superficial. It arises
because some biologists are more interested in one aspect of
the evolutionary problem, others in another. Whether natural
selection furnishes a sufficient explanation of one is not an issue
about which most experimental biologists differ, and Darwin
himself never claimed that it provided an all-sufficient explanation of the other.

By the *extrinsic* problems of species differentiation I mean the
evolutionary issue as the traveller-naturalist sees it. To him
the *distinctness* of species is guaranteed by the topographical
barriers to their dispersal. What specially interests him is the
way in which the differences which distinguish them are related
to the circumstances of their distribution. Apart from the fact
that Darwin's belief in blending inheritance led him to entertain some views which do not harmonize with results of modern
genetical work, few biologists would deny that Darwin's conception of natural selection offers a satisfactory clue of species
differentiation in this sense.

To avoid misunderstanding let me here insist that Darwin
used the phrase to distinguish the action of *external* agencies
which favour the survival of individuals with particular hereditable characteristics. If a species inhabits a given area, the
spread of a mutant character will be determined by the distribution of external agencies propitious to its persistence or
otherwise. At different polar extremes of the same region,
climatic and vegetative circumstances will conspire to build
up different combinations of mutant characters. In course of
time the population becomes topographically dissociated.
Darwin believed, and said, that if this went on long enough

species isolated by the physical segmentation of the environment might become intersterile.

There was no direct evidence for this when Darwin wrote the *Origin*, and many of his opponents seized on the absence of evidence as a fatal objection to his theory. We have no difficulty in accepting it to-day. Intersterile stocks have arisen under experimental observation, and such work as that of Reade and Gordon on the Mexican Killifish shows us how a gene-substitution whose effect is merely ornamental in one gene-complex can be lethal when introduced to another. In his own time the supporters of Darwin's doctrine paid little attention to criticism of this sort. They were looking at the problems of species from a different angle. The fact that species may be biologically distinct units in experimental conditions as well as topographically distinct units in nature, is not the essence of the species problem from the standpoint of the traveller-naturalist. He encounters species in conditions which guarantee their separate existence, and the data of his problem are the differences by which they are distinguishable as such.

The taxonomist, who follows in his footsteps, has not the equipment to test whether dead specimens sent to museums from different localities belong to intersterile stocks. So the concept of species as a breeding unit has scant relevance to museum practice. The distinction between geographical varieties and true species is often arbitrary, especially when museum practice does not have to meet the requirements of horticultural importation. Thus a large number of species included in at least two genera of the Canidae produce fertile hybrids. In captivity interspecific and even intergeneric crosses of ducks, of pheasants, and of moths have also been found to produce fertile hybrids which illustrate the principle of segregation.

We can sometimes see this process of extrinsically determined species differentiation in its incipient stages. Thus each of the three interfertile races of the polymorphic species *Quercus robur* L. (*pedunculata*, *sessiliflora* and *lanuginosa*) has distinct local foci, although there is much overlapping. Sometimes also there is direct evidence for the survival value of characteristics which distinguish local races which are not sufficiently different to be placed in distinct species. Thus Cuénot cites experiments in which species of *Echium* from the Canaries grown side by side with a local French strain were killed by the first frost, which did not hurt the latter.

The physical segmentation of a population polarized in this way does not necessarily imply geographical isolation. A population may spread into different habitats so that different selective agencies operate according to the choice of host, of food, of dry, humid, cold, exposed, or shady conditions, and the prevalence of other animal species as prey. Cryptofauna, parasites, gall-forming and phytophagous animals illustrate this type of species differentiation, as do many related aquatic species which flourish at different levels of salinity, like *Cardium edule* Linn., *C. exiguum* Gmelin, and *C. ovale* Sowerby, or in stagnant, running, upland and lowland waters, like *Cambarus virilis* Hag., *C. immunis* Hag., *C. diogenes* Girard, and *C. monongalensis* Ortman. Polymorphic species of plants furnish examples of all stages in the process of separation. On the border-line of complete separation we find forms like *Dianthus deltoides* L. with solitary flowers, and *D. armeria* L. with a dense inflorescence. These two species are respectively confined to sandy uplands and loamy soil, so that their fertile hybrids are rarely found.

Thus the traveller-naturalist is fully entitled to extend his hypothesis over a much wider field of species differences, guaranteed in the formative stage of species differentiation by extrinsic separation. If all species which are clearly distinct entities were confined to a restricted habitat or locality, and if closely related species were never found living side by side, or were only found to do so in circumstances pointing to a previous separation, we should be entitled to accept the mathematical theory of natural selection as an all-inclusive hypothesis. We might then dismiss lightly Bateson's plea for the experimental study of species intersterility.

Needless to say, we might also be entitled to make reservations. Some of these have been frequently stated by naturalists. For instance, the alleged selective value of differences between closely allied species like the blue and the brown hare sometimes demands an effort of imagination, if not an act of faith. Apart from this, we are entitled to wonder whether it is not a little previous to assign an upper limit to mutation-rates unless we are assured that laboratory conditions reproduce all the conditions propitious to the transformation of genes in formative stages of species differentiation in nature. Up to a point, mathematical analysis of evolution is a healthy discipline, because it can at least tell us whether selection could *not* have produced observed structural differences when the conditions postulated by the hypothesis are fulfilled.[1] At the same time, we should not forget the highly arbitrary assumptions in any formal mathematical treatment of selection.

I do not wish to press these reservations. Without doubt natural selection is a very important, perhaps the all-important feature of species differentiation, so long as we are concerned with the class of problems discussed so far. What I am concerned to emphasize is that another class exists, and if its existence has often been overlooked by experimental geneticists it has never been denied by field-botanists. In contradistinction to the traveller-naturalist, the field-naturalist who stays at home is impressed by the fact that closely related species are often found side by side in nature. Circumstances sometimes suggest that they may have been selected for separate topographical situations or separate ecological units which have since coalesced. Often there is much to suggest that no such separation has occurred. When this is so, the fact that they do not interbreed is no longer a subsidiary issue.

Bateson's special contribution to post-Darwinian discussion of selection was the recognition of this class of problems. Though he sometimes chose his words *pour épater le bourgeois*, there is little doubt about his main reason for criticizing the mechanical view that all evolution is the interplay of mutation and mortality, or for emphasizing the need to study the intersterility of closely allied forms. As a field-naturalist, he was specially interested in the coexistence of closely allied species in the same habitats. *The Problems of Genetics* harps on this theme. To any one familiar with plant life the spectacle of different species of Potentilla, Geranium, Veronica, Ribes, and many other genera growing side by side is a commonplace. Cuénot points out that Darwin's theory met with more contemporary criticism from botanists than from zoologists, among whom the standpoint of the traveller-naturalist predominated at the time.

---

[1] Professor Haldane's suggestive treatment of phenomena supposed to support orthogenesis illustrates the use of such calculations.

A group of animals I once studied from the cytological standpoint provides a clear-cut illustration of the evolutionary problem from an alternative standpoint. Cameron recognizes about 67 species of gall-forming Cynipidae. Of these 54, or 81 per cent. of the total, infest a single plant species, the *oak*. As to the remaining 13 named species, 20 per cent. of them infest the rose. Those who are content with the simple mechanical view which reduces all evolution to the interplay of mutation and mortality are entitled to point out that all oak cynipids do not infect the same vegetative structures. While this is true, it is equally true that many do so, and, as far as I know, there is no noticeable preference of closely related species for a particular type of oak tree. It is common to find several kinds of galls on the same leaf. *Neuroterus lenticularis* (Olivier), *N. numismatis* (Four.), and the cherry-gall *Dryophanta scutellaris* (Olivier) are commonly found together on the same tree and on the same leaf of the same tree.

Analogous remarks apply to the inquiline species or guest-wasps of the same family. I do not believe that any naturalist familiar with the Cynipidae would seriously entertain the possibility that this great proliferation of species in one and the same ecological situation is compatible with selection for different habitats which have subsequently coalesced. On the other hand, the facts are not so difficult to explain if we take into account a species characteristic which does not and cannot yet enter into any formal mathematical treatment of evolution as a whole. All the gall-forming Cynipidae have an agamic generation, usually alternating with a spring or bisexual brood. The latter is sometimes eliminated so that the species is entirely parthenogenetic. This is true of the marble-gall *Cynips kollari* Hartig, of the moss-gall *Rhodites rosae* (Linn.), of at least four species of *Andricus*, and probably one of *Dryophanta*. The absence of sexual forms in five or six other species is more doubtful.

The possibilities of further variation in the descendants of an individual member of a species depend on two things, its own gene-complex and opportunities for interbreeding between its own progeny and individuals with ancestors endowed with a gene-complex different from its own. In so far as these opportunities are not restricted, selection will ensure that a particular gene-complex eventually becomes distinctive of a particular population. If the opportunities for interbreeding are restricted the spread of mutant genes is also restricted. Selection acting on different stocks may then produce a variety of different types in the same environment. Species-differentiation then proceeds as with widely different species in the same habitat, and *the condition of this does not lie in external nature*. It resides in the biological make-up of the type.

In contradistinction to the extrinsic aspect with which the theory of natural selection is concerned, the intrinsic aspect of evolution is concerned with characteristics of the biological make-up and habit of animals, in so far as they promote the possibility of species-differentiation in one and the same habitat. In a limited sense Darwin anticipated the need for a distinction of this kind by contrasting *natural* selection with *sexual* selection. Owing to gratuitous assumptions on which theories of sexual selection have been erected the latter has now been pushed into the background. The result is that the mathematical geneticists either claim for selection far more than Darwin did himself, or use the term in a totally different sense.

A certain class of mutant characteristics, of which the power of agamic reproduction is only one example, introduce new evolutionary potentialities which justify a new name. In the Hegelian terminology, which I rarely use, they illustrate the passing of quantity into quality. The mere fact of giving them a separate name directs attention to the need for researches which are otherwise liable to be neglected. Difference of opinion in this context is largely a matter of perspective. No one denies that one species (e.g. the black rat) may invade the territory of another (e.g. the brown rat). Likewise no one denies that speciation in one and the same environment does *sometimes* occur. What some zoologists—in contradistinction to most botanists—would maintain is that the evolution of different species in the same region is comparatively rare, so rare that the broad outlines of the evolutionary drama emerge with sufficient clarity, if we leave it out of account.

Here it seems to me is a vital difference between evolution as the traveller-naturalist or the zoologist trained in type morphology sees it and the evolutionary problems which concern the field-ecologist. If you are content to lump a stretch of moorland with its ericaceous flora, a chalk down with its varied assortment of blue butterflies, a coral reef, an oak infested with gall-flies, or a bat cave, as exceptional phenomena, or if you are prepared to argue that all the related species coexisting in these situations have been differentiated by selection for slight differences of habitat, it is permissible to hold that the origin of species is mainly determined by natural selection in Darwin's sense. If not, you have to include among the formative agencies of evolution, intrinsic biological circumstances which predetermine the subsequent operation of external selection for a particular combination of genes.

For instance, various chromosome mutations (polyploid, polysomic, and inversions) are associated with partial or total intersterility with respect to parent stock. In the more extreme case a mutation of this kind can survive only if the individual is capable of perpetuating itself. This it can do if it can reproduce by clones, as do so many denizens of a coral reef, if it is a hermaphrodite capable of self-fertilization, as are so many related polyploid species of flowering plants, or if it is parthenogenetic, as are some elementary species of *Hieracium* or some animals like aphids. If these or other (*vide infra*) conditions are not realized at the outset, selection is powerless to ensure the survival of the new type. In brief, selection is not the explanation of the formation of new species in this way. Although species capable of vegetative reproduction, parthenogenesis, and self-fertilizing hermaphroditism are rare among animals, they are not collectively negligible, and I shall draw attention to other, possibly more common, biological mechanisms which act in the same way.

Long ago, the frequent occurrence of very slight differentiation of forms, which preserve their identity as breeding-units while living side by side, compelled botanists to draw a somewhat arbitrary distinction between elementary species or *jordanons* and major species or *linneons*. In many cases the biological prerequisite of species-dichotomy without topographical or ecological isolation is fully understood. Thus the crucifer *Draba* (*Erophila*) *verna* L., with over 200 elementary species, of which it is possible to find as many as a dozen growing within an area of a few square yards, includes forms which are apogamous and others which are hermaphrodite and cleistogamous. Artificial crossing of the latter may give fertile hybrids which produce apogamous types from which new pure lines can be cultured. Others give sterile hybrids. Either way their separate identity as distinct breeding-units is guaranteed by the fact that self-fertilization is obligatory or fertilization is unnecessary. If obligatory self-fertilization occurs, mutants which are intersterile with respect to parent stock are privileged. Their survival is not compromised by the unlikelihood of finding a suitable partner. Cuénot says that the three over-lapping and very closely allied species *Viola arvensis* Murr., *V. nana* Godr., and *V. kitaibeliana* Roem. & Schult., include at least 5 intersterile races with 14, 16, 24, 36, and 48 chromosomes. Polysomy and polyploidy in this group is again associated with cleistogamy.

There is no need to catalogue the immense number of allied plant species which are polyploid in origin. Their existence is instructive for two reasons. The first is that chromosome-(as distinguished from gene-) mutation is often associated with very striking structural differentiation and with a high degree of intersterility with reference to parent stock; and chromosome-mutations thus furnish *an indisputable example of species-formation without the instrumentality of selection.* The second is that their frequent occurrence is associated with optional or obligatory self-fertilization or with apogamy. Hermaphroditism is the rule in flowering plants. Conversely, polyploidy, which is so common in Angiosperms, is very rare in Gymnosperms.

Obligatory self-fertilization is extremely rare in animals, and optional self-fertilization is not the rule among the small proportion of animals which are hermaphrodite. This may be why polyploid species are extremely rare in animals. The few indisputable examples occur in agamic species of Isopods and Branchiopods. Vandel has shown that there are 2 overlapping geographical races of *Trichoniscus provisorius* Racovitza, of which one is bisexual and has 16 chromosomes. In the other, which has 24 chromosomes, males are very rare. The parthenogenetic race of larger build is a typical triploid of the type common in flowering plants. In *Artemia salina* (Linn.) Gross has distinguished between diploid, tetraploid, and octoploid races. The diploid races may be bisexual or parthenogenetic. Tetraploid or octoploid races are only parthenogenetic.

The fact that parthenogenesis, like obligatory self-fertilization, is rare among animals does not mean that intrinsic species-dichotomy without differentiation is exceptional in animals. A mutant intersterile with respect to parent stock may produce a new race if it can bud off individuals of either sex. Such propagation by clones is very common among sedentary animals, of which the hydroid fauna of rock pools and the coral population of a reef provide examples of closely related species in the same habitat. Analogous to clone production is the phenomenon of polyembryony. This is extremely rare. The best-known examples occur in Gymnosperms, parasitic Hymenoptera, Cecidomyidae, and armadillos.

Two other mechanisms of intrinsic differentiation are less sharply distinguished from the interplay of natural selection. One is delimitation of sexual periodicity. The other is sexual discrimination.

When fertilization is external and vegetative reproduction does not occur, the first is the only method of establishing new species in the same habitat. If sexual congress takes place, mating may be restricted to particular times of the year. Intrinsic species-differentiation by variation of the mating season is easily confused with selection as usually defined. This is because minor species distinguished by their mating or flowering-seasons are often restricted in their habitats. For instance, the cowslip and primrose, placed by Linnaeus in the same species because their fertile hybrids are sometimes found where their ecological domains overlap, generally behave as distinct assemblages kept apart by two circumstances. One is the fact that primroses prefer the shade of the hedgerow or wood, while cowslips grow in open meadows. The other is that the flowering-season of the cowslip does not begin till that of the primrose is almost over. The shift in the time of flowering is almost sufficient to make the two forms clear-cut species, and their ecological distribution is almost discontinuous. Hence it is impossible to say whether the former is primary and the latter is secondary, or vice versa. The same remark may apply to a pair of species which are fully separated like the two moths *Eupithecia innotata* Hufn., which feeds on *Artemisia*, and *E. unedonata* Mab., which emerges much earlier, on *Arbutus*. By cooling the pupae of the *Arbutus* species, Dietze delayed emergence and produced fertile hybrids with the *Artemisia* species.

The seasonal character of the reproductive process in other

distinct or incipient species which are closely related is clearly antecedent to ecological or topographical disintegration of the external environment. Two slightly differentiated races of the 17-year Cicada (*Tibicen septemdecem* Linn.) probably belong here. Apart from the fact that the single brood of *Lysandra coridon* Poda emerges between the two broods of *Lysandra bellargos* Rott., there is no known obstacle to interbreeding between these two butterflies. When, as in many Lepidoptera, a sharp seasonal difference of mating accompanies a difference of food plant, the ecological isolation of the larval stage offers no obstacle to interbreeding, unless the plants themselves belong to different associations.

The need for ecological research into species-formation from this point of view is illustrated by a survey of Lo Bianco, who has tabulated pairs of species belonging to 37 genera of molluscs and 52 species of crustacea from the same area to ascertain how far their breeding-seasons overlap. In both classes he found that 21 ± 2 per cent. of the pairs examined had quite distinct times of spawning. In 63 per cent. the periods overlapped. In 15 ± 2 per cent. they were co-extensive. It would be instructive to take a limited region of this kind, compare the number of related species with and without association of the sexes, combined with or without clone production or parthenogenesis, and tabulate side by side with these figures the coincidence of seasonal reproductive activity.

Another type of intrinsic species-differentiation includes Darwin's sexual selection, and any other form of assortative (i.e. non-random) mating. The only analogous phenomenon in plants is the preference of insect species for flowers of one or another kind. Sexual discrimination is conditioned by the biological make-up of animal species in a variety of ways. It can only occur in species of which individuals of opposite sex associate in an act of coitus. This excludes all species which are agamic, all species which are sedentary like coelenterates or polyzoa, and a large proportion of mobile marine invertebrates such as echinoderms and polychaetes. It also presupposes a certain level of evolution in the receptive mechanism of behaviour. In gregarious species or species which live in small family groups it has greater potentialities, especially if sexual behaviour is conditioned by previous experience.

The important point about sexual discrimination, i.e. any kind of assortative mating, is that it increases enormously the chance that a new variation will be established as a pure line. Sexual discrimination may depend on structural differentiae common to both sexes. It has recently been shown that a definite preference of like for like exists when white-eyed mutants and wild-type individuals of *Drosophila* are bred together.

Differential virility in sexual congress is another type of assortative (i.e. non-random) mating illustrated by the partial barrier between the white mouse and the house mouse. The most obvious form of sexual discrimination involves selection for sex-limited characters. Of all groups in the animal kingdom, butterflies and birds provide the most prevalent illustrations of sexual dimorphism and therefore presumably of assortative mating for sex-limited characters. May it not be significant that these are the two pre-eminently successful groups equipped for aerial locomotion? The reproductive environment of an aerial—even less perhaps than that of an aquatic—organism is least susceptible to ecological or topographical isolation. So they should be least subject to natural selection, by which I mean what Darwin meant, and not the ambiguous usage of modern writers.[1] In spite of this, the great aerial groups contain an exceptionally large number of related species, and the association of closely related species, such as the blues or heaths among the Lepidoptera, in the same habitat is quite common, indeed specially striking, among them.

Contrariwise the bats, which do not exhibit extreme dimorphism of the sexes, provide a plausible illustration of species-differentiation without topographical or ecological isolation, and might therefore be cited to refute the suggestion implied in the preceding remarks. It is possible and not unlikely that another type of sexual discrimination may exist in the bat cave. The researches of Zuckerman indicate that mammals display a peculiar specialization of sexual discrimination associated with the development of the forebrain. For lack of a better term we may call it tuitional sexuality.

[1] The interplay of intrinsic and extrinsic aspects of evolution is illustrated by the possibility that a mutation affecting beak structure may favour the choice of a different diet, hence of a different situation as a meeting-place for similar individuals.

Tuitional sexuality in this context signifies the contribution of love-play between litter mates to the normal consummation of sexual habit. Its importance lies in favouring incest. Incest is a type of assortative mating which does not necessarily imply great dimorphism in the visible differentiae of the sexes; and it holds hitherto unexplored possibilities of promoting species-formation. For that reason our ignorance of the extent to which it prevails is regrettable. Fortunately it is also remediable. Analysis of wild populations for the frequency of homozygous dominants offers a straightforward, if laborious, method of ascertaining its prevalence.

The study of human inheritance draws attention to several relevant characteristics of close inbreeding. In general a rare recessive mutation (e.g. human albinism) occurs with relatively high frequency among the issue of consanguineous unions and it must also be *familial*, i.e. it occurs among several members of a fraternity whose parents do not exhibit the mutant character. When a single gene-substitution is involved the proportion of all recessives in a fraternity containing at least one recessive approaches a lower limit of 0·25. For litters of eight the appropriate figure is 0·277 and for litters of two it is 0·576. The study of rare recessive traits in human communities thus illustrates two principles. The first is that circumstances which encourage close inbreeding *in excess of what would occur in a system of random mating*[1] increase the frequency of recessive types. The second is that circumstances in which recessive types most commonly emerge are such that there is a *high probability of mating* inter se, *when little or no exogamy occurs, and the size of the family is small*.

The relevance of these considerations to the problem of species-formation is not far to seek. It is easy to imagine that a recessive type (*aa*) may be interfertile with its own kind and intersterile with parent stock (*Aa* or *AA*). Such intersterility may be relative or absolute, structural, biochemical, or behaviouristic. Statistics of human nuptiality would probably reveal many categories of relative intersterility based on 'preference', and animal genetics provides factual examples of size

[1] The frequency of inbreeding increases at low density in a system of random mating without affecting the frequency of recessives (cf. Dahlberg, *Proc. Roy. Soc. Edin.*, 1938).

differences which effectively constitute an absolute barrier to interbreeding in normal circumstances. In a system of random mating a rare mutation which is intersterile with parent stock, like any other rare mutation, has a negligibly small chance of mating with its kind and starting a pure line. When endogamy is obligatory this is not true. A rare and relatively viable recessive has a relatively *high* chance of mating with another of its kind and therefore of starting a pure line which will be a breeding-unit from its inception. In so far as recessive mutations may be relatively or absolutely intersterile with parent stock, endogamy therefore constitutes a new potential of species-formation in animals which produce few offspring at a time.

In so far as evolution involves different mechanisms of *species-dichotomy* or intrinsic species-differentiation (as opposed to species-differentiation dependent on extrinsic causes), how species originate involves different problems in plants and animals and different problems at different evolutionary levels in either of them. For instance, mosses and ferns have a higher potential of species-dichotomy than cross-pollinated flowering plants. In these phyla a single individual which is sexually incompatible with the parent stock produces a multiplicity of new sexual forms by spores. Hence it should not surprise us to find many fern or moss species growing together in the same habitat.

A mutant which will not produce offspring when mated back to parent stock, or, if it does so, will produce only sterile hybrids, can establish itself if one of various conditions is fulfilled. Of these, seven are as follows: (i) hermaphroditism combined with the possibility of self-fertilization, (ii) the existence of a separate spore-forming generation, (iii) parthenogenesis, (iv) production of individuals of either sex by clones from the same soma, (v) polyembryony, (vi) obligatory close-inbreeding, (vii) the occurrence of an epidemic of similar mutations at the same time. Restriction of the reproductive season and intense assortative mating in one form or another may also establish a partial species-barrier and enable species-differentiation to proceed by selection in the same environment from a different genic basis. Such a barrier may gradually become a complete obstacle to interbreeding in the environment, and all stages of this process can be illustrated in moths.

If evolution progresses with ecological separation, different inversions of chromosome segments, fusions, non-disjunctions, or fragmentations may occur in contiguous stocks, of which hybrids are less viable than their parents in the habitats where the latter thrive best. If this continues for some time, chromosome-mutations which do not militate against survival in competition with one parent stock may well do so with the other. Selection might then favour the separation of species into incompatible breeding-units. Thus selection would become the agent of new biological barriers to the interbreeding of species. This could only be true at a low level of ecological isolation permitting frequent hybridization to occur. On the other hand, species-differentiation associated with geographical isolation does not imply the slightest selective advantage for biological obstacles to interbreeding. This may be why very striking species-differences between localized species may coexist with complete inter-fertility.

One corollary of this is the futility of controversy about whether Man or the dog is polyphyletic in origin. Several local 'species' of the dog family, like races of mankind, are inter-fertile products of geographical specialization. In so far as extrinsic barriers separate them into distinct assemblages, they may be given taxonomic rank as species, and they remain so as long as the extrinsic barriers are there. So the taxonomic distinction is relative to a certain level of transport industry. In so far as this is so, the origin of dog species is less a problem of biology than a problem of economic history. The sterility of discussing the polyphyletic origin of man is analogous, and also illustrates how difficult it is to think clearly about matters which involve social preferences.

That the method of species-formation differs vastly at different levels of evolution is specially emphasized by a comparative study of the genetic architecture of animals and plants. One illustration has been given. Polyploid species are common among plants and very exceptional among animals. In some groups of animals the chromosome numbers vary little. Thus all the Urodeles recorded in Ethel Browne Harvey's monograph have twelve pairs of chromosomes with no striking sexual differentiation of an X-pair. Nearly all the species listed are geographically distinct. Apparently all primates have twenty-four pairs. Lepidoptera and birds are two groups in which the

chromosomes are numerous and highly variable. No attempt
so far as I know has been made to link up these variations in
the genetic architecture of species with the circumstances of
their occurrence in nature.

Perhaps the most striking feature revealed by the summaries
which have been published by Ethel Browne Harvey is the
occurrence of *formative* genera or species which show considerable variation in groups which are otherwise homogeneous.
Out of 13 families of Diptera, excluding the family to which the
genus *Drosophila* belongs, all the 20 recorded species of 9 families
have 12 chromosomes. In all, 24 species or 65 per cent. of the
37 listed, distributed among 21 genera and 13 families, have
this number. One family, the Culicidae, includes 4 species, all
of which have 6 chromosomes. This accounts for 28 species of
Diptera. The remaining 9 species, having 8, 10, 14, 16, and
18 chromosomes, occur in families which accommodate other
species having 12. Such uniformity is in striking contrast with
variability within the limits of the single genus *Drosophila* which
contains species with 6, 8, 10, or 12 chromosomes, the numbers
8 and 12 being modal. The Orthoptera listed by Ethel Browne
Harvey are also instructive from this standpoint. Fifty-six out
of 67 listed species of Acridiidae have 24 chromosomes. In the
Locustidae the numbers 24, 30, 32, 34, and 36 occur with no
noticeable modality. In the 6 families including, besides the
2 last-named, the Blattids, Gryllids, and earwigs, 62 out of
83 species have the number characteristic of the Acridiidae.
Closely allied homogeneous assemblages of the same phyletic
rank are thus found at every level of classification side by side
with assemblages of species or even—as in Coreid bugs—of
subspecies displaying great variability in the architecture of
the germ-cells.

In current text-books such differences are sometimes stated
to furnish an explanation for the existence of sterile hybrids.
For instance, it is often said that the common mule is sterile
because the chromosomes of the horse and donkey differ in
number and size. The problem of how they came to be
different is therefore shifted into the Miocene, where there is
no temptation to undertake the inconvenient task of solving
it. Similarly, a text-book explanation for the intersterility of
Drosophila melanogaster Meig. and *D. simulans* Sturt. is the existence

of a large inversion on the third chromosome. Presumably this is due to a succession of small inversions of the type which arise after X-radiation. Such inversions may be associated with partial intersterility which might become complete if several occurred successively. This may well have happened. The view that selection of *favourable* mutants furnishes an all-sufficient explanation of evolution does not help us to see why it should have happened.

We are thus left with a category of specific differences for which neither selection nor any of the mechanisms of intrinsic species-differentiation so far discussed offer a satisfactory explanation. In *Drosophila obscura* Fln., Lancefield has isolated two races which are intersterile in nature. They differ in the size of the Y-chromosome, overlap in their distribution, and are hardly distinguishable in other respects. How have they arisen? It seems to me that we can choose between two alternatives. If they are partially adapted to the habitat which they prefer in ways which we cannot distinguish, and if their hybrids were less adapted to either, at a stage when they were still interfertile, it is possible that selection contributed to their present condition. On that view the fact that the Y-chromosome of one race is twice as large as the Y-chromosome of the other is not the reason for their intersterility. If the true explanation lies in the known occurrence of chromosome-mutations, we require a subsidiary hypothesis.

X-radiation has made it possible for Stern to isolate intersterile races in *Drosophila melanogaster*. Presumably the possibility of doing so lies in the fact that this procedure enormously increases the mutation rate. Since *Drosophila* is not agamic nor necessarily incestuous, nor hermaphrodite, and is incapable of reproducing by clones, we should expect that chromosome-mutations which result in partial or complete intersterility with respect to parent stock would have no chance of surviving. Stern's work suggests an explanation for the occurrence of chromosome species of the type which Lancefield describes, if we grant that circumstances in nature from time to time result in a frequency of mutation with no other parallel in the experience of standardized laboratory cultures. If so, the circumstances responsible for mutation itself are more significant than the action of selection in producing species which differ in the architecture of the germ-cells. Bacon said that the subtlety of nature is many times greater than the subtleties of our reasoning powers. So I do not, and have never, suggested that this is the only possible explanation of the facts. I do insist that the mechanical view of evolution as the interplay between external selective agencies and mutation rate raised to the status of a universal physical constant in the mathematical formulation of the theory does not offer a better one.

REFERENCES

CUENOT, L. (1934). *L'Espèce*. Paris.

GROSS, F. (1932). 'Untersuchungen über die Polyploidie und die Variabilität bei *Artemia salina*.' *Naturwissenschaften*, **20**, 962–7.

HALDANE, J. B. S. (1932). *The Causes of Evolution*. London.

HARVEY, ETHEL BROWNE (1916 and 1920). 'A Review of the Chromosome Numbers of the Metazoa, Part 1. *J. Morph.* **28**, 1–63; Part 2, ibid. **34**, 1–67.

LANCEFIELD, D. E. (1929). 'A Genetic Study of Crosses of Two Races or Physiological Species of *Drosophila obscura*.' *Z. indukt. Abstamm.- Vererb. lehre*, **52**, 287–317.

LO BIANCO, S. (1909). Cited by Robson, *The Species Problem*, Edinburgh & London, 1928. 'Notizie biologiche riguardanti specialmente il periodo di maturità sessuale degli animali viventi nel Golfo di Napoli.' *Mitt. Zool. Sta. Neapel*, **19**, 513–761.

REED, H. D., and GORDON, M. (1931). 'The Morphology of Melanotic Overgrowths in Hybrids of Mexican Killifishes.' *Amer. J. Cancer*, **15**, 1524–46.

STERN, C. (1931). 'Zytologisch-genetische Untersuchungen als Beweise für die Morganische Theorie des Faktorenaustauschs.' *Biol. Zbl.* **51**, 547–87.

VANDEL, A. (1934). 'La Parthenogenèse géographique.' *Bull. biol.* **68**, 419–63.

GEOGRAPHICAL DIFFERENTIATION IN FRESH WATERS WITH SPECIAL REFERENCE TO FISH

By E. B. WORTHINGTON

Introduction

THIS chapter does not in any way pretend to be a summary of the present position in regard to geographical differentiation as a part of the mechanism of evolution. Its purpose is to put forward certain ideas and conclusions on the subject of evolution, which have come from the study of fresh waters by investigators in diverse parts of the world, most of the examples being drawn from parts of Great Britain and Africa with which I am personally familiar. Several books on geographical differentiation have been published in recent years, and among those in the English language the volume by Allee and Schmidt (1937) based on Hesse's *Tiergeographie auf oekologischer Grundlage* is perhaps the most satisfactory, in that it lays emphasis on the habitats occupied by animals in addition to describing what is usually understood by the term distribution. This volume is, however, concerned mainly with broad ecological principles; the authors have little to say concerning the actual process of speciation as correlated with geographical isolation. This comes from the study of what may be termed 'minor' systematics, a subject discussed especially by Rensch (1929). On the subject of fish, the group with which I am specially concerned, Carl L. Hubbs (1934) has given a useful guide to recent literature relating to variation. In surveying work on variational gradients which can be correlated with environmental conditions, he very rightly gives prominence to the extensive work on marine economic fish, especially the herring, to J. Schmidt's classical cases of *Zoarces* and the cod, and to work done in his own laboratory at Michigan. He points out that there is a tendency to new and improved methods in fish taxonomy, and emphasizes that 'systematic groups are populations, and must be investigated by population analysis'.

In the following discussion, the Neo-Mendelian standpoint,

which is emphasized by other contributors to the volume, is assumed in broad outlines. This assumption is not intended to commit me to unqualified agreement with Neo-Mendelism, nor to exclude the possibility of evolutionary factors on Lamarckian principles, as suggested by some of the evidence. The Mendelian standpoint is, however, definitely relevant to the issues raised, especially now that Sewall Wright (1931, &c.) has shown that in small isolated populations the Mendelian view will explain the rapid differentiation of non-adaptive characters.

Various examples mentioned below are suggestive as showing how the evolution of organisms has run parallel with the evolution of the isolated environments in which they live. This does not mean that the change of environment has *caused* the change in the organisms, but we can presume that new physical conditions have favoured some variants and have caused others to die out by a process of selection. According to Sewall Wright's postulates, accidental non-adaptive divergence must occur as well as any divergence which may have taken place as a result of adaptive processes. In this connexion it is an ascertained fact, empirically, that isolation does favour differentiation. This is well seen in many island forms which have diverged in isolation while their counterparts on the mainland have remained constant over wide areas, in spite of the greater diversity of environment. Many such examples are recorded in the literature, especially in the book by Rensch (1929) and the survey of the races of non-marine vertebrates of Europe (including freshwater fish) by Økland (1937). It must be remembered, however, that in the more diverse environment, e.g. the mainland as opposed to islands, there may be factors of biological importance acting as a brake to differentiation. One such factor, namely the influence of predators, has had attention drawn to it by Buxton (1935 and 1938) in his study of the isolated insect communities on the islands of the Pacific, and is emphasized below in connexion with the fresh waters of east and central Africa. Such environmental influences are my chief concern here, especially in so far as they allow variants to persist and to reproduce their kind. Therefore the evolution of the environment has to be considered in addition to that of the organisms.

Conclusions on this subject must obviously be based in large measure on taxonomic data, and the fish group is no exception in that long series of specimens from many types of environment are necessary before the mass of data on measurements, scale-counts, and the like can be seen in proper perspective. At the same time ecological conditions in the field must be appreciated fully, so the ideal arrangement for advance in this subject would be for the field ecologist to work out his own collections, and for the museum taxonomist to obtain his own material. Any value that this discussion may have arises from the fact that its author has dabbled both in the museum and the field.

When dealing with such a variable group as the freshwater fish the usual methods of taxonomy, by which species and sub-species are separated mainly on proportional measurements, often of comparatively few specimens, are open to many criticisms. No doubt fish taxonomists themselves are the first to recognize these shortcomings, but to demonstrate their importance some recent work from America on the white fishes belonging to the Coregonid family may be mentioned. In American glacial lakes there is a Coregonid of considerable economic importance, namely the cisco, *Leucichthys artedi* (Le Sueur). This species has many local races in isolated lakes, and W. N. Koelz (1931) put forward a somewhat elaborate systematization recognizing a number of subspecies more or less distinct in characters such as depth of body and length of head, eye, and fins in relation to length of body, the number of gill-rakers, and so forth. More recently R. Hile (1935) has examined large samples (1,548 specimens in all) of the species from four lakes, selected as types on the basis of their physical and biological characters. Statistical analysis of measurements of all these fish showed, firstly, that in the same population certain body-proportions change naturally with increase in size and age to produce differences greater than those which have been used in separating some of the subspecies. This finding invalidates much of the current systematics, but it does not reveal any new principle to most fish taxonomists, who quickly recognize those characters subject to differential (allometric) growth and make suitable allowances in comparing fish of different sizes. What is more disturbing in Hile's study is that he finds these and similar characters to vary not only with size but with rate of growth: thus in one environment, where factors such as food supply allow rapid growth, the fish

P P

have one set of ratios in their characters as compared with size, while in another, where growth is stunted, these ratios are different. It is easy to see how such an additional variable can provide pitfalls for the systematist, especially when dealing with a group so susceptible to environmental influences as the Coregonids (see also Huxley, 1932, chapter vii). No doubt similar extensive morphometry, if applied to Coregonids from elsewhere or to other groups of fish, would demonstrate many errors in current taxonomy, and this emphasizes again the great importance of coupling environmental studies with taxonomy.

Evolution of Organisms

The study of organic isolation has in recent years followed the example of so many other subjects and been divided into compartments. Thus it is now customary to refer to (1) geographical isolation as the prevention by physical barriers of intermixture and interbreeding; (2) ecological isolation as the effect of differences in habitat, though not in general environment; (3) reproductive isolation as the effect of all barriers to breeding caused by reproductive behaviour in general, changes of generative organs, incompatibility of gametes, &c.; (4) genetic isolation, which is concerned with changes in the chromosomal mechanism. The term 'physiological isolation' is used by some authors to cover (3) and (4) above, but is now often used, as by J. S. Huxley and W. H. Thorpe in the present volume, for special cases of ecological isolation such as the differentiation of physiological races of parasites or phytophagous insects, or other cases of restriction to particular habitats. These distinctions in nomenclature are convenient as an aid in defining the problems, but it would be a pity if the study of isolation in nature were to become so specialized that the general issues were obscured. Since this chapter is concerned with environmental influences, attention must be directed primarily to the first two categories of isolation, namely geographical (*sensu stricto*) and ecological.

Geographical barriers are clearly of much greater importance in fresh waters than in the sea, and it is hardly necessary to give examples of physical features which divide fresh waters one from another. It must, however, be emphasized that the several barriers to distribution in one drainage system vary very widely in their effectiveness in isolating different forms. The most simple case is a waterfall on a river which presents no serious obstacle to salmon, but is impassable, in the upstream direction, by trout and other fish. A more illuminating example is to be seen on the White Nile system, in the upper reaches of which there are two falls—the Ripon Falls separating Lake Victoria from Lake Kioga, a drop of only some 15 ft., broken in places, and the Murchison Falls, a vertical drop of 130 ft. or more, on the river joining Lake Kioga to Lake Albert. The Ripon Falls are impassable in the upward direction to small fish, but not to powerful swimmers. Hence, while there are a number of specific or subspecific distinctions between the fauna of Lake Kioga below and Lake Victoria above, these two lakes have faunas which are similar as far as genera and most of the species are concerned. The Murchison falls are obviously impassable to all fish in an upstream direction, and it seems that no fish attempting the descent could survive the shock, which is accentuated by a break in the falls near the foot where all the water dashes on to an exposed rock surface before plunging into the pool below. Hence many genera of Nile fish occur only in the river system below, and in only about three cases are the same species present above and below, in a fish fauna of some 50 species below and 120 above.[1]

Even the divisions of a continent into major watersheds need not be barriers to the distribution of all aquatic forms, because, apart from the chance distribution over watersheds, by eggs carried on birds' feet and so forth, many opposing drainage basins are connected at their headwaters by swamps which are passable in periods of flood. This occurs especially in regions where the peneplain type of topography is predominant. In warm climates a secondary ecological factor is of great importance, namely the depletion of oxygen in tropical swamps, as emphasized by Carter and Beadle (1930). To take a specific example from Africa, the major watershed between the Zambezi and Congo drainage basins runs along the political boundary between Northern Rhodesia and the Katanga division of the Belgian Congo. This boundary has proved particularly difficult to define on account of the nature of the country, which

---

[1] References to recent literature concerning this and other African examples are given in a paper by Worthington (1937).

tends during the wet seasons to become a series of interconnected swamps draining in both directions. Although the ecological conditions have not been examined on the spot, it is safe to assume by analogy from work in other parts of Africa that these swamps are deficient in oxygen and therefore passable only by those fish which are adapted for breathing atmospheric air. This is borne out by the facts of distribution, which demonstrate that the fish fauna of the Luapula River (Congo basin) is distinct specifically, and for the most part generically, from that of the Kafue River (Zambezi basin), except in the case of air-breathers in the genera *Spirobranchus*, *Protopterus*, and *Clarias*, of which the same species occur on either side of the watershed.

Another general feature emerges from a study of the African fish, that evolution proceeding separately in different drainage basins has led in many cases to an overlap of species. Thus the fish of a given river, say the Nile, are mostly divisible into a number of definite species. The same may be said of the Congo fish, but in certain cases, where closely related forms inhabit both these rivers, the species from the Nile does not match that from the Congo, the variability of a given character being distributed about a somewhat different mean. Sometimes it appears that one original species has persisted in one river since the time of isolation, while in another it has differentiated into two or more. This naturally leads to trouble in systematization, but it can be eased by treating each basin or isolated lake as an entity for taxonomic purposes. Bearing on the same problem these African waters provide good examples of clines (geoclines) as defined by Huxley (1938). One such is a group of cat-fish species in the genus *Clarias*, which are separable mainly on the shape of the band of vomerine teeth. They range from *C. lazera* Cuvier and Valenciennes which has a broad band of teeth and inhabits the northern part of Africa, through *C. mossambicus* Peters in the Lake Victoria and Tanganyika region, and *C. gariepinus* (Burchell) from the Zambezi to the Orange River, to *C. capensis* Cuv. and Val. which has a narrow interrupted band of vomerine teeth and lives only in Natal (see David, 1935). A somewhat different aspect of the problem concerns those fish, usually of small size, which do not travel far. Here the broadly ecological factor of sedentary habit interlocks with the geographical factor of mere distance to secure a relatively high degree of isolation for local populations. One such case in America, concerning a fish known in Illinois as the Johnny Darter, has been analysed by Thompson (1931), who found that the number of spines and fin-rays varied roughly as a function of the distance by water of one population from another. The different types are not arranged in a gradient, so this case cannot be regarded as a cline. The point emerges that the greater the water-distance between two populations, the more differentiation they are likely to show, irrespective of whether the ecological characters of the streams they inhabit are similar or not.

A classical example of the same sort in marine fish is provided by the investigations of Schmidt (1917) on *Zoarces viviparus* (Linn.). Here the effect of mere distance was found in populations from the open sea. Within the fjords, however, a cline effect operated, the genetically determined number of vertebrae and certain fin-rays decreasing with distance from the mouth of the fjord.

Passing now to ecological isolation, examples given above show that no sharp distinction divides it from geographical isolation. In any watershed, even where no geographical barriers exist, there are numerous ecological barriers which prevent mixture of faunas. Thus a typical British river can be divided into a series of overlapping zones, inhabited by trout, grayling, coarse fish such as roach, perch, tench, &c., in several subzones, and finally the estuarine zone with such fish as flounders living side by side with freshwater species. In such a case specific ecological requirements limit each fish to its particular zone.

The division of a drainage system into distinct environments finds its extreme in the presence of lakes and swamps where conditions of life are so different from those in flowing water. Certain species become adapted to lacustrine conditions and are thereby prevented from becoming widely distributed. Distinctions of habit are perhaps most obvious in feeding, and to illustrate the question at issue we may take one type of fish-food which is characteristic of lakes rather than rivers, namely the crustacea of the plankton. In every sizable lake except those entirely devoid of fish life, one or more species of fish feeds predominantly on these organisms. In British lakes trout very often fill this niche, but still more characteristic are the chars (*Salvelinus*) which are regarded by Tate Regan (1911) as belonging to a number of species, each isolated in one or more lakes. It should be noted that some of these so-called species are very like each other and would probably be designated as subspecies by many taxonomists. The history of the char's differentiation is clear because all the lake basins in question had a common origin during the Ice Age, when they were scooped out by glacial erosion. There is little doubt that soon after the Ice Age the British chars were all one species and were migratory in habit, descending for part of their time to the sea, as does the Arctic char to-day. But as the glaciers receded, the waters they inhabited became warmer and the cold-loving char became isolated in the deeper lakes. It seems likely that the temperature factor and competition with trout and other fish in the inshore regions, drove the char to the deep open waters, where the major source of fish-food is the plankton. Thus in Windermere it seems that they live during most of the summer in water below the thermocline, where the temperature does not exceed about 7° Centigrade, and come into the shallows only for a few days in winter to breed. That a change in feeding habits has taken place during isolation is indicated by the fact that the original migratory char, like the salmon, lived in rivers, where plankton is insignificant as a food-supply.

Another illuminating example of the effects of isolation brought about by this plankton-eating habit is shown in East Africa, where in nearly every lake some small fish species fills this habitat. It is usually the most abundant and ecologically the most important fish in the water, because, by feeding on the plankton, it converts the major food-resources into a form consumable by larger species. Typically this habitat is filled by members of the Cyprinid genus, *Engraulicypris*, of which there is a distinct species (or subspecies) in each of the lakes—Victoria, Tanganyika, Rudolf, Nyasa, and Rukwa. Clearly these all had a common origin and have come to differ during their period of isolation. Certain lakes do not contain this typically pelagic genus, and it is the adaptation of other forms to the pelagic habitat that offers the greatest interest. Thus in Lake Edward, which has a large expanse of open water and abundant zooplankton, the same niche is filled by a Cyprinodont, *Haplochilichthys pelagicus* Worthington. This species has forsaken the usual Cyprinodont habitat of shores and swamps to live a truly pelagic existence. Its morphology has changed so much in the process that it is one of the very few Cyprinodonts which can be identified at a glance—it is long and thin, has exceptionally small scales and a pronounced tail colouring. There is considerable evidence to show that this, and other instances of evolution in Lake Edward, have taken place entirely since the arid period which separated the two major pluvial periods of central Africa, and the conclusion is clear: that where a good niche exists, vacant for reasons of isolation, some species will fill it rapidly, even though considerable structural alterations are involved in the process.

Evolution of Environments

So far environments have been considered as differing in their degree of isolation one from another. The next question is how far the changes to which each environment is subject as time proceeds have influenced the evolution of organisms. This branch of the subject is not often emphasized as an integral part, perhaps an important cause, of specific differentiation of the type correlated with isolation. Freshwater environments are subject to change in many ways: the upper reaches of a river cut deeper and deeper into the substratum, the lower reaches usually become silted, and every lake, from the moment of its formation, is subject to changes which will ultimately lead to its extinction.

The details of such changes in so far as they effect plant and animal life have been worked out, perhaps more thoroughly than elsewhere, in the English Lake District. W. H. Pearsall (1921) and others have pointed out that, whereas all the lakes in the district were formed at the same time, by glacial erosion in the Ice Age, some have changed in the past 15,000 years or so very much more than others, the rate of change being controlled by the depth of the lake, the type of rock forming the drainage basin, the area which is drained into the lake, the extent of agricultural land (which is dependent on the nature of the rock), and, in recent years, the amount of sewage or other waste material which enters. Physical changes have been accompanied by biological changes, and the sedimentation of dead organisms, from the open water as well as from the inshore areas, have had great effect on speeding up evolution of the environment. Thus the lakes as they exist to-day can be arranged in a series of which the different members represent evolutionary stages, the so-called primitive lakes such as Wastwater and Ennerdale being at one end of the series, and the advanced lakes such as Windermere and Esthwaite at the other. From existing conditions the succession of plant and animal associations which must have inhabited each lake can be ascertained: every group of fresh-water organisms is involved, from the bacteria and algae to the fish. Taking the fish as the simplest example, the change has been from an association consisting of whitefish (*Coregonus*), char, and trout to one in which the coarse fish predominate, particularly perch and pike. As a whole the change is one involving an ever-increasing productivity, the water becoming progressively richer in nutritive salts, the plants and animals increasing in quantity, until finally the depth of water, always being reduced by silting, becomes a limiting factor.

The same type of succession has been recognized as applying to the glacial lakes of North America, where it has very rightly been used as a basis for the management of fisheries. Thus R. W. Eschmeyer (1936) points out that in the evolution of a glacial lake the rise in productivity throughout nearly all the sequence of changes renders the environment most suitable for the following succession of fish: cisco (*Leucichthys artedi*), trout (several species), perch (*Perca flavescens* Mitchill), northern pike (*Esox lucius* Linn.), small-mouthed bass (*Micropterus dolomieu* Lacepède), blue-gill (*Lepomis pallidus* Mitchill), large-mouthed bass (*M. salmoides* Lacepède), common sun-fish (*Eupomotis gibbosus* Linn.), bullhead (*Ameiurus nebulosus* Le Sueur).

If these glacial lakes of England or North America had been entirely isolated, we might have expected many of the original inhabitants to have adapted themselves to the changing conditions of life, and to have undergone physiological and structural change in the process—that is to say, the evolution of the fish and other organisms might have kept pace with the evolution of the environment. The fact that the whitefish and chars of some British lakes are taxonomically distinct suggests that this may have in fact occurred to some extent. But such evolution could not take place to any marked degree in wet countries intersected by rivers and streams, where the barriers to distribution are incomplete, because, as the environment changed, better-suited species from elsewhere found entry to the lakes and competed successfully with the original inhabitants.

To find the best examples of organic evolution keeping pace with physical change, we must look to dry climates, where lakes and rivers are widely separate, and offer the minimum opportunity for invasion from outside. An admirable example is present in East Africa, where Lake Rudolf, the northernmost of the rift valley lakes, lies isolated in a closed drainage basin. Evidence 'from high level beaches together with that from the fauna show that, during the African pluvial epoch, Lake Rudolf was very much larger than at present and overflowed its basin to the north-west, being connected to the White Nile by a river. At that time it is clear that the fish fauna was nearly the same as that of the Nile, and that the water was no more salt or alkaline than that of the majority of east African waters. Since then, that is to say during the past 15,000 years or so, the desiccation of that part of Africa caused the lake first to lose its outlet, thereby isolating the fauna completely, and subsequently to shrink in volume to such an extent that the environment has changed very markedly. Particularly is this so in the case of the dissolved salts, mainly sodium bicarbonate, so that now the alkalinity of Lake Rudolf is twenty times as great as that of most of the East African waters which flow to the Nile. During this process many of the Nile fishes which were isolated appear to have undergone considerable structural change, so that some have been regarded as distinct species, others as subspecies. It must be assumed that physiological adaptations to the changed chemical environment have taken place also, but these are far less easy to assess. Of course it cannot be claimed that the structural changes of Lake Rudolf fish have been caused by the environmental change, but the fact that they have taken place while the water has become progressively more alkaline is suggestive.

A similar case of organic evolution running parallel with environmental change may help to explain the presence of the thalassoid prosobranch molluscs in Lake Tanganyika, one of the most striking examples of isolated evolution in fresh waters. Lake Tanganyika has been in existence for a very long time, and at one stage of its history, during a mid-pleistocene period of pronounced aridity which separated the two major pluvial periods of central Africa, there is little doubt that its volume was greatly reduced, and the salts in solution became concentrated. Subsequently it returned to fresh water as a result of flooding in the second pluviation and the through flow of water has probably continued with little interruption up to the present day. There is reason to believe that the same period of aridity exterminated the fauna of the shallower lakes of East Africa by complete desiccation, and the fossil remains of the former inhabitants have been found in certain areas. In one case near Lake Edward, an extensive fossil gastropod fauna shows various stages in the ornamentation of the shells which is characteristic of the Tanganyika prosobranchs. Since these fossils near Lake Edward probably lived in water with a high concentration of salts, their describer, V. E. Fuchs (1936), was led to suggest that the factors leading to their evolution were similar to those in Tanganyika, and that the evolution of thalassoid Prosobranchs in Tanganyika was correlated with, perhaps caused by, a period of increasing salinity. Quite recently C. M. Yonge (1938) has once more drawn attention to the great interest of these forms, especially in regard to the evolution of their feeding methods.

Effect of Predators

The evolution of fish since pluvial times in central Africa is shown most strikingly by the fauna of those lakes which do not contain the bulk of Nile fish genera. This applies to the Victoria Nyanza and Lake Kioga, isolated by the Murchison Falls, and to Lakes Edward and George, isolated by falls and a succession of rapids on the Semliki River. As mentioned above, the region occupied by these lakes, representing the chief gathering ground for the White Nile, was probably dried up to a few pools of stagnant water during the great arid period which separated the two major pluviations. A few fish, such as the air-breathing lung-fish, cat-fish, and *Spirobranchus*, may have survived *in situ*, but the great bulk of the fish species which inhabit these lakes to-day must be descended from the few kinds which found access when the lakes refilled with water.

Most of these fish are representatives of the family Cichlidae, of which fifty-eight endemic species are known from Lakes Victoria and Kioga, and eighteen from Lakes Edward and George. In this family the evolutionary radiation which has taken place appears to be mainly of an adaptive kind: for example, in the single genus *Haplochromis* the long series of endemic forms in Lake Victoria ranges from some with small mouths and minute hair-like teeth for feeding on microscopic plants and animals, to others with large underhung jaws and large teeth for feeding on other fish. Among those species with habits intermediate between the two extremes one striking adaptation is for eating molluscs, the teeth of some species being large and flat-crowned for crushing shells. Similar though less striking adaptations have taken place among representatives of other families, one example having already been given above in another connexion, namely the pelagic Cyprinodont of Lake Edward. In spite of these obvious adaptive characters it would be unjustified to assume that all the evolution which has taken place to produce these endemic faunas is of an adaptive kind, because many of the species can be distinguished from each other only on such criteria as the size of scales in different parts of the body and the number of rays in the fins, characters on which it is difficult to place any adaptive significance.

This astonishing evolutionary radiation which has taken place in a relatively short time is all the more remarkable in that Lake Albert, in which lacustrine conditions have continued at least as long, has very few endemic species, and even the completely isolated Lake Rudolf has given rise to no radiation of forms in the least comparable. There seems little doubt that the reason for these differences lies in the presence or absence of large predators. Lakes Albert and Rudolf have large and active predator fish, the so-called Nile perch (*Lates*) and the tiger-fish (*Hydrocyon*); but in Lakes Victoria Edward, &c., the only large predators which either survived the desiccation or regained access subsequently are the relatively inactive lung-fish and cat-fish. Thus these upland lakes of eastern Africa provide very fine examples, firstly of geographical isolation in the strict sense, and secondly of ecological isolation: the few kinds of fish which regained access at the end of pluvial times found themselves in vast lakes almost devoid of fish-life but offering every kind of ecological niche. Variation of habits and of structure took place as generation after generation of fish took advantage of the many opportunities. During the process of adaptation from one habitat to another, such as from inshore to open water conditions, many imperfectly adapted intermediate forms must have appeared, their imperfections having reference to attack from predators. In normal conditions they would have stood little chance of survival, but in Lakes Victoria and Edward they escaped and were able to reproduce their kinds because the predators were not there to consume them. Meanwhile in the other lakes the same urge may have existed to vary habits and structure, but the predators have acted as a steadying influence: unless the variants slipped immediately into vacant and suitable niches, they had short lives. This factor in itself may account in large part for the more extreme variation which has taken place in those lakes without predators.

Lake Tanganyika is an exception to the rule that great radiation of small fish has only taken place in the absence of the active predators such as *Lates* and *Hydrocyon*. This is explicable, however, by the fact that here isolated conditions have continued for a very much longer period than in those lakes mentioned above. The fauna of Lake Nyasa, which likewise survived the arid period on account of the lake's great depth, bears out the contention regarding the stabilizing effect of predators. *Lates* and *Hydrocyon* are absent, their place being taken by much less vigorous predators, in the shape of species of *Barilius*, which have been evolved locally. The number of distinct species of Cichlid fish differentiated here by a purely local radiation has reached the high figure of 171 (Trewavas, 1935), nearly twice as many as in Lake Tanganyika.

In those lakes where the predators are important, these predators themselves have undergone differentiation of some interest. The Nile perch, *Lates*, in particular, has split in each lake into two forms, which are best regarded as subspecies rather than species because occasional specimens are somewhat intermediate in character and suggest that interbreeding sometimes takes place. In those lakes examined thoroughly from the ecological point of view, e.g. Albert and Rudolf, one form inhabits the shallow waters, and is extremely large, up to 200 lb. and more in weight, while the other, limited to the deeper parts, is much smaller, rarely exceeding 10 lb., and is distinguished by having a larger eye, smaller scales, &c. The same distinction in habitat may well characterize the two species of *Lates* in Lake Tanganyika and perhaps also the two large species of *Barilius* in Lake Nyasa.

Conclusion

The conclusions from the discussion above may be stated as follows. Firstly: where geographical isolation is complete or almost complete, as in the African examples but not in the British, it is accompanied in a high percentage of cases by some degree of differentiation. This degree, however, depends very largely on the group of organisms considered: thus representatives of some families of fish such as the Cichlidae seem to differentiate wherever they are isolated in favourable environments, whereas others, the lung-fish being an extreme example, show no disposition to do so. Secondly: the differentiation of species or subspecies has a much deeper significance if it can be associated with change in the environment. Thirdly: in a group capable of rapid differentiation, the environmental conditions are all-important in determining the amount of differentiation which can take place. Of these conditions, two are specially important—the existence of numerous unoccupied ecological niches, and the absence of predators.

Assuming such favourable conditions, the speed at which differentiation proceeds must depend on the time taken to pass through each generation, to allow variations to come into being. In general it can be assumed that animals such as fish, which have no mechanism for maintaining a constant body-temperature, have a higher rate of metabolism in a warm environment than a cold one. Consequently the growth and rate of reproduction of fish must be greater in the tropics than in temperate climates. There appear to be very few data on this effect, but if we presume, for the sake of argument, that among fish of similar size and capacity for differentiation a generation is passed through twice as quickly in the tropics, it is obvious that changes in structure noticeable from the taxonomic point of view should appear in half the time. Looked at from this point of view, it is less surprising that many endemic species and subspecies of fish have come into being in the African lakes during and since the pluvial epoch, while in temperate regions the same lapse of time has produced relatively little differentiation. Thus it is to the tropics that we should look for information on the rate at which evolution proceeds in aquatic forms.

I am much indebted to Dr. J. S. Huxley for helpful suggestions and criticism in the preparation of this chapter.

REFERENCES

Buxton, P. A. (1935). *Insects of Samoa.* Brit. Museum Publ.

—— (1938). 'The formation of species in Samoa, &c.' *Proc. Linn. Soc.* **150**, 264–7.

Carter, G. S., and Beadle, L. C. (1930). 'The Fauna of the Swamps of the Paraguayan Chaco in relation to its Environment.' *J. Linn. Soc. Zool.* **37**, 205–58.

David, L. (1935). 'Die Entwicklung der Clariiden und ihre Verbreitung.' *Rev. Zoo. Bot. Afric.* **28**, 77–147.

Eschmeyer, R. W. (1936). 'Essential Considerations for Fish Management in Lakes.' *Proc. North American Wildlife Conf.* 332–9.

Fuchs, V. E. (1936). 'Extinct Pleistocene Mollusca from Lake Edward, Uganda, and their bearing on the Tanganyika Problem.' *J. Linn. Soc. Zool.* **40**, 93–106.

Hesse, R., Allee, W. C., and Schmidt, K. P. (1937). *Ecological Animal Geography.* London.

Hile, R. (1936). 'Summary of Investigations on the Morphometry of the Cisco, *Leucichthys artedi* in the Lakes of the North-eastern Highlands, Wisconsin.' *Pap. Mich. Acad. Sci., Arts & Letters*, **21** (1935), 619–34.

Hubbs, C. L. (1934). 'Racial and Individual Variation in Animals, especially Fishes.' *American Naturalist*, **68**, 115–28.

Huxley, J. S. (1932). *Problems of Relative Growth.* London.

—— (1938). 'Clines: an Auxiliary Taxonomic Principle.' *Nature*, **142**, 219.

Koelz, W. N. (1931). 'The Coregonid Fishes of North-eastern America.' *Pap. Mich. Acad. Sci., Arts & Letters*, **13** (1930), 303–32.

Økland, F. (1937). 'Die geographischen Rassen der extramarinen Wirbeltiere Europas.' *Zoogeographica*, **3**, 389–484.

Pearsall, W. H. (1921). 'The Development of Vegetation in English Lakes, considered in relation to the general Evolution of Glacial Lakes and Rock Basins.' *Proc. Roy. Soc. B.* **92**, 259–84.

Regan, C. T. (1911). *British Freshwater Fishes.* London.

Rensch, B. (1929). *Das Prinzip geographischer Rassenkreise.* Berlin.

Schmidt, J. (1918). 'Racial Studies in Fishes, I.' *J. Genet.* **7**, 105.

Thompson, D. H. (1931). 'Variation in Fishes as a Function of Distance.' *Trans. Illinois State Acad. Sci.* **23**, 276–81.

Trewavas, E. (1935). 'The Cichlid fishes of Lake Nyasa.' *Ann. Mag. Nat. Hist.* ser. 10, **16**, 65–118.

Worthington, E. B. (1937). 'On the Evolution of Fish in the Great Lakes of Africa.' *Int. Rev. d. ges. Hydrobiol. u. Hydrogr.* **35**, 304–17.

Wright, Sewall (1931). 'Evolution in Mendelian Populations.' *Genetics*, **16**, 97–159.

Yonge, C. M. (1938). 'The Prosobranchs of Lake Tanganyika.' *Nature*, **142**, 464–6.

THE PROBLEM OF CLOSELY RELATED SPECIES LIVING IN THE SAME AREA

By C. DIVER

THE increasing importance of linking up the advances in taxonomy, ecology, and genetics is becoming daily more obvious, if for no other reasons than that each discipline may effectively help the others and that a number of major problems require a joint and concerted attack. The extreme specialization of modern science has raised formidable barriers of terminology and outlook. If these are to be removed, a just appreciation is required of the limitations and difficulties under which each branch is working, and a simple statement of the principal factors that form their common background.

The systematist and ecologist are primarily concerned with the organism as a whole; but the geneticist made no progress till he learnt to analyse the phenotypic complex into its component parts, each representing a particular characteristic which could be separately studied. The startlingly rapid success of this analytical method has led to a maze of technical terms that mean little or nothing to his neighbours on the other side of the party wall; and this concentration on the particulate aspect has sometimes made it difficult to appreciate the value of a more generalized outlook.

The aim of taxonomy is more than the mere pigeon-holing of different organisms on some convenient but completely arbitrary system of card-indexing. It seeks to establish relationships, and to determine what degree of dissimilarity is consistent with placing two individuals within the same species. Starting with the type specimen, the taxonomist draws a circle round it and says that if an individual does not conform with the range of variation lying within this circle it does not belong to this species. We need not be concerned here whether the taxonomic hierarchy erected on these specific units is a correct representation of phylogenetic relationships or not; or with the fact that the conception of a species is not the same in all groups. Whatever definition may be adopted, it is common ground at least in sexual organisms that all individuals within a species are potentially,[1] though not always practically, capable of fertile union, and that there is an interchange of germ-plasm perpetually taking place within a species—sometimes even between different species. The relationship established by the taxonomist is, in fact, genetic.

These taxonomic assemblages are in nature distributed as populations over a geographical area; and it is the business of the ecologist to determine, among other things, the structure of these populations and their inter-relationships with neighbouring populations and other assemblages. By this means he can demonstrate the practical extent to which the basic material of heredity is distributed. Here the respective fields of the ecologist and geneticist fuse so completely that it is impossible to proceed safely without a practical knowledge not only of both these disciplines but also of the working limits already set by the taxonomist. Further, ecological data are of systematic importance because differences in ecological distribution may be the practical expression of physiological variation.

It is still an open question, even among geneticists, whether the small genetic differences which are the regular material of intraspecific genetic analysis are the blocks with which interspecific and generic differences can be built up. But there can, surely, be no doubt that it is the change and interchange of the component units of the germ-plasm and their reactions both with each other and the external environment which determine the phenotypic differences with which the taxonomist and ecologist must work. For these units it is convenient to use the term 'gene' in its broadest sense without begging the question whether some effects are controlled by cytoplasmic (e.g. plastids) rather than chromosomal units. It is for the cyto-geneticist to determine the structure of the germ-cell and to attempt to relate particular phenotypic expressions with particular expressions of this general structure. During this work he has obtained, and will continue to obtain, results that have fundamental bearings on the work of the taxonomist (e.g. cryptic species, incipient sterility barriers).

In the vast majority of cases the taxonomist is compelled to delimit his species from dead material; that is, he must rely

[1] This does not apply to what may be called supra-species, in which extreme forms may be incapable of interbreeding though all intermediates are found.

solely on morphological characters supplemented by distributional data often of the sketchiest nature. The fields of developmental, physiological, ecological, bionomic, cytogenetic, and biochemical variability are usually closed to him. The impressive fact is not that the taxonomic positions of some rare species are in doubt, nor that in some cases of extreme complexity (e.g. *Rubus*, *Taraxacum*) his assemblages are too small or too large, but that working under severe limitations he achieves such an extremely close approximation to the facts of nature. The skilled naturalist, dealing with living material, usually separates the closest species by the indefinable resultant of many small differences in habit, movement, ecological tolerance, general behaviour, and appearance—which together give a far clearer indication of specific difference than can be obtained from the dead specimen; but it is extremely seldom that the study of this widely increased field of variability indicates divisions which have not already been recognized on purely morphological grounds. The obvious conclusion is that, although morphological variability is only a part of the whole field of variability, there is very little variation in the rest of the field that is not correlated with some morphological change, however slight. This is the ray of hope that lights the way of the paleontologist.

Argument between systematic 'splitters' and 'lumpers' is not infrequently due to this enforced concentration on morphological aspects; and it is in such cases that the additional evidence of the ecologist and geneticist may well help to settle the question. It may be thought that such arguments are trivialities; but this is not so. The study of evolution is the study of variability in all its aspects, and the differentiation of discrete assemblages is the central problem. The cases that naturally attract the 'splitter' are those where differentiation is in process of taking place (geographical races, subspecies, incipient species) or has relatively recently been achieved (closely related species) but may have escaped recognition. These largely overlapping circles of variation are among the best contemporary material we may hope to obtain, and such conclusions as may be drawn from them must also be considered in the light of paleontological findings. For the paleontologist, in so far as he can obtain a good series, is able to see the circles of the contemporary taxonomist as three-dimensional, irregular, and possibly branching cylinders along which, if he is lucky, he can trace the trend of morphological change but can hardly say in any particular cylinder where one 'species' ends and another begins. To him the contemporary species-concept is only applicable to the cross-section made at a particular horizon.

The purpose of this chapter is not to consider the species-concept nor the wide problem of incipient and closely related species generally; but those special cases, which may be found in any group, where closely related species live together. These cases present one of the most interesting problems in evolutionary mechanics. So many misconceptions are liable to arise in discussions on this subject owing to the concentration of different workers on different aspects that it may be well to state the precise meaning attached in this context to the phrase 'closely related species living in the same area'. The term 'species' is used here in the purely practical sense to mean a taxonomically recognizable assemblage of individuals which are sufficiently similar in most of their attributes to suggest that successful interbreeding could freely take place between them; but are sufficiently (and demonstrably) differentiated in some of their attributes from all the individuals of any other assemblage with which they could reasonably come into direct contact (the case of geographically widely separated races or species does not concern us) to render effective cross-breeding improbable or rare. This definition is admittedly more generally applicable to animals than to plants; since in some groups of plants, within which effective cross-breeding is not rare, populations are produced which, though the end-terms have the appearance of separable species, are so intergraded as almost to defy taxonomic division.

Two or more such species may reasonably be said to be closely related when they are morphologically so similar as to make the allocation of a particular specimen to one species or the other difficult except for an expert; and when there are no grounds for supposing that this close similarity is due to convergence rather than recent divergence. The decision on morphological grounds is strengthened when an equally close similarity in habit, ecology, distribution, and general behaviour is also displayed. By 'living in the same area' is meant that populations of each species may occur in the same places at the same time (though the periods of sexual maturity may not always synchronize) and in the same type of habitat, often forming mixed populations in which individuals of two or more such species freely intermingle. From this it follows that such species will display a very considerable overlap in both their geographical and ecological ranges.

The theoretical possibilities that might cause specific divergence have been dealt with in other chapters. The main object of this chapter is to set out a few facts and from them to indicate which of the various possible systems is most likely to be in operation in the cases considered. The obvious working unit is the natural population. It is therefore of primary importance to know both generally and specifically how the populations which together make up the species are distributed in nature and what is their structure.

The general phenotypic expression of a given population is determined by the following factors: (1) the proportions in which different genes are present, or the gene-frequency; (2) the ecological plasticity of the species, or the degree to which particular external environmental factors may modify the phenotypic expression of the hereditary factors; (3) the mutation-rate including the reverse mutation-rate; (4) the differential survival and reproduction rates, or the rate at which changes in the gene-frequency are brought about by positive or negative selective forces or by the cumulative effects of random elimination; (5) the randomness of mating; (6) the amount of germinal interchange, whether as gametes or zygotes, that takes place between this and other populations of the species, which may conveniently be referred to as the gametic and zygotic migration rates, including both emigration and immigration.

It is difficult to measure accurately in nature the effects of some of these factors; but in certain species which display obvious clean-cut genetic variations (e.g. *Helix* (*Cepaea*)) the frequency of certain genes can be directly and easily determined by observation, and thus in such cases, by carefully controlled sampling, it is possible to estimate the amount of intrapopulation random mating. Further, it is relatively simple, though laborious, to determine the amount of individual movement, at least between neighbouring populations and in those species that lend themselves to individual marking. All the above factors relate to what may be called the breeding-structure of a population; but before proper attempts can be made to measure their respective influences it is necessary to know what a population is, and how the populations of a species are distributed; in other words, what may be called the distributional structure of a specific assemblage.

The distributional structure of a given species can be stated generally if the following questions, among others, are answered. How much actual discontinuity (apart from occasional voluntary and involuntary wanderers) is there between populations? What is the range of variation in numerical size of different populations at the same time? What is the degree of annual or periodic fluctuation in numerical size? What relationship is there between numerical size and area of occupation, i.e. density? What are the maximum and minimum densities possible in a unit area? What is the amount of normal individual movement? How much population movement takes place? How are new populations founded? How much involuntary dispersal is there?

Information is steadily accumulating that will ultimately answer some of these questions. Mass migration has received attention from many workers in different groups. The recent work of Hardy and Milne (1937) throws much new light on involuntary dispersal by air currents. Elton (e.g. 1924) and others have effectively concentrated on the factors concerned with cyclical fluctuations in animal numbers. But curiously little attention seems to have been directed to determining, what for our purposes is the vital question, what is the natural unit of population, and how are these units spatially distributed? Much of the theoretical work on evolutionary mechanics seems to have been based on the conception that the effective population unit was extremely large and might even be species-wide. A preliminary examination of *Sphagnum* populations made many years ago showed me that, though in certain conditions large continuous populations exist, much of the lowland distribution is in quite small discontinuous units often widely separated. A somewhat similar but more detailed inquiry was later undertaken into two species of snail, *Cepaea nemoralis* (L.) and *C. hortensis* (Müll.). In these species widely continuous populations reaching millions or even hundreds of thousands are difficult to come by, and quite small sharply discontinuous colonies which may be counted in hundreds, or even tens, are the general rule. In the two really large populations of *C. nemoralis* that have been examined it is most doubtful whether the apparent continuity is in fact real, and probable, for reasons which will be given later, that they are a congeries of a large number of quite small breeding units. Anderson (1936), working on certain species of *Iris*, found a similar distribution. Indeed, these facts are well known to all field collectors, though their significance does not seem to have been fully appreciated.

The cases quoted above are characterized by the fact that in each the distribution was examined of a few species over a relatively large area. When the detailed ecological survey of South Haven Peninsula, in Dorset, was begun in 1932 the reverse process was attempted. The distribution of a large number of species representing many different groups of plants and animals over a small area (2 miles long and covering about 750 acres) is here being examined by methods which have been described elsewhere (Diver and Good, 1934, and Diver, 1938*a*). From this inquiry there emerges the salient fact that the large majority of non-marine species are distributed in quite small discrete colonies—small both in numbers and in area of occupation—between which there is often no evidence of any even thinly scattered permanent or resident population; and that even in such a small area the number of these separate populations may be quite considerable.

It is indeed obvious to any one who looks no farther than at the distribution of the more conspicuous species of plants in any bit of country that, though a few ecologically dominant species, e.g. *Calluna* on heaths, may display really large continuous populations covering a great number of square miles, most species are distributed in a definitely patchy manner. But this patchiness may not always be as sharply discontinuous as it looks at first sight. A thin line of continuity may be provided through a few scattered and inconspicuous individuals. For instance, *Calluna* may just subsist very sparsely in habitats that superficially appear quite unsuitable, and where the plants would probably be overlooked unless a yard to yard survey was carried out. The methods adopted on South Haven Peninsula render the chances of such omissions, at least in the case of an immobile and relatively conspicuous organism, remote. Admittedly, on large land-masses where the disruptive effects of human interference are negligible or absent the size of continuously dominant populations may sometimes be enormously increased; but such species and such areas of uniform physical conditions are the exceptions rather than the rule, and the effect of man is only one among many types of interference.

It may be argued that this discontinuity is to be expected in organisms, like plants, which are incapable of individual movement and must depend entirely on involuntary dispersal, or even in snails, but that animals possessed of considerable powers of movement would not be so distributed. The facts derived from our survey do not support this guess. The larger dragon-flies have strong powers of flight—sufficient at least to enable them to cover long distances in migratory swarms, but the areas occupied by populations of breeding adults can be delimited. These, of course, from a racial or evolutionary point of view are the effective populations. A small population of the migratory species *Sympetrum fonscolombii* Selys appeared on South Haven Peninsula in the summer of 1933. Though large tracts of the peninsula provide suitable hawking territory for, and are in fact occupied by, other species of *Sympetrum*, of which *S. striolatum* Charp. is by far the commonest, *S. fonscolombii* was only found closely restricted to the margins of one part of Little Sea. The juxtaposition of the several vegetational types occurring within the area of occupation is not, in fact, repeated on the peninsula, but appears to be similar to that described for another such population elsewhere. If, as is possible, this population contained only males, and since there is no reason to suppose that *fonscolombii* is any more particular than any other related species what small insects it eats, this close localization may be mere conservatism of habit. *S. striolatum* is a species so common that within an area as small as the peninsula it would readily be said that it occurs everywhere. A detailed survey reveals that this is not strictly true even for this species, of which the field diaries contain over 700 locus-habitat-date records. Certain areas are outside its population limits, which means not only that individuals do not hawk there regularly but that wanderers visit or pass over these places so infrequently as never to have been seen there.

It does not seem to be generally appreciated what an extensive part is played by fine changes in the plant-carpet in controlling animal distribution (Diver, 1938*a*), or that this control is exercised far beyond those species which are directly limited to particular plant species for feeding or egg-laying purposes or secondarily limited as predators of such species. The mere fact that the plant-carpet presents an irregular mosaic, made up by the intermingling or overlapping of numerous discrete populations of different species, of necessity imposes a colonial structure upon the distribution of the vast majority of animals, if not on all. Obviously this is not the only factor. The naturalist does not expect, nor does he find, that those animal species which, for instance, tolerate the conditions in an almost pure *Calluna* heath necessarily have population limits coextensive with those of the *Calluna* population. Leaving out of account purely accidental factors affecting dispersal, there come into play many other fine shades of difference which are sufficient to break up the continuity of the animal population but have no effect on the distribution of the plant. These differences may be due to the behaviour of the plant itself. At some spots, even within a pure stand, a collection of individual plants will be more luxuriant and densely spaced than at others, so producing a mosaic of differences in the micro-climatic conditions at the soil surface which are of extreme importance to some small ground-living species.

In large, highly developed species of animals, which are perhaps least affected by any changes in the plant-carpet, the colonial structure may appear extremely loose or even non-existent; but this effect is partly a product of the great increase in scale relative to human ideas of distance. Further, it is in such cases that the so-called herd instinct not infrequently comes into operation, the results of which, in fact, secure that a unit of population does not become so dispersed as to render the chances of meetings between mature individuals of opposite sex too remote for racial safety.

The fact that these conditions, which result in breaking up specific assemblages into a great number of numerically small, discrete population units, are so widespread has a highly important bearing on evolutionary mechanics (Wright, 1939). In such a distributional structure it is most unsafe to assume any wide degree of random mating. In those few cases where some evidence is available (e.g. *Cepaea*) there is obviously a large amount of inbreeding; and in a great many populations the migration rate must be extremely low. The need for carefully planned attempts to measure this in a few selected cases is pressing. The problem almost seems not one of why local races are formed but rather why such differentiation is not proceeding more prevalently and at a faster rate than it apparently is.

There is in this aspect of the problem an interesting difference between the majority of higher plants and those animals which have a reasonable control over their movements. Cross-pollination is entirely a matter of chance, and it is conceivably possible that wind-borne pollen, or that transported by a few species of individually wide-ranging insects, may be effectively distributed not only to neighbouring populations but over relatively long distances. If this is so, such direct gametic gene-flow is a factor that must be added to the zygotic migration rate based on the chance transference of seeds. Matings between animals proceed on very different principles (I have seen a snail soliciting all comers until it achieved its object). It is a suggestive fact that the formation of races seems most pronounced in those animals which are least liable to involuntary dispersal (Diver, 1938b), not only mammals and birds (for quantitative data see Rensch, 1933) but in the more powerful insects (e.g. *Bombus*).

It is against this type of background that the facts relating to the following examples of closely related species must be considered. The only selection exercised in choosing them is that they are confined to those species of which I have had reasonable personal experience in the field and that I have tried to include cases from different groups of organisms rather than several from the same group.

The Genus Syrphus (*Syrphidae, Diptera*).

Among the hover-flies (Syrphidae) several good cases could be given; but the simplest is that of three species of the genus *Syrphus* (at one time considered doubtfully distinct), *S. torvus* Ost.-Sack., *S. ribesii* L., *S. vitripennis* Meig. Verrall (1901) placed *torvus* at a little distance from the other two because of its hairy eyes, but admitted that for some time he was unable to separate males of *ribesii* and *vitripennis* with any certainty until he recognized one stable character—a difference in the colour of the minute hairs at the apex of the hind femora (the females differ in the colouring of the hind femora). Lundbeck (1916) treats them as three very nearly related but good species. Though, apart from the characters already mentioned, there are several small differences of the 'statistical' type (i.e. a character 'usually' present in one species but 'usually' absent in the other), none appears to have any adaptive significance. In body-length *torvus* (9·5–13 mm.) and *ribesii* (8·5–13 mm.) are much the same, but *vitripennis* (7·5–11·5 mm.) is usually a little smaller.

The geographical range given by Lundbeck suggests a slightly contracting series with *torvus* the most wide-ranging but including the ranges of the other two, and *vitripennis* the least but apparently not passing outside the range of *ribesii*:

S. *torvus:* all Europe to northern Sweden, Finland, Greenland to L. 70° N., N. America.

S. *ribesii:* all Europe to northernmost Sweden, Finland, Iceland, N. America.

S. *vitripennis:* all Europe to northern Sweden, Finland.

Curiously, *torvus* appears to be less common in this country and in Denmark than the other two, both of which are about equally common.

The general ecological statements given by Verrall and Lundbeck can be summarized by saying that all three species occur widespread in woods, gardens, fields, and other habitats, but that *vitripennis* is commoner in gardens than *ribesii*. The data so far obtained from South Haven Peninsula, considering only major loci and broad habitat types, may be tabulated.

Broad habitats occupied	Woods and clumps	Turfy areas often with Pteris	Marshes and damp scrub	Heathy areas	Totals
Total major loci occupied by 1 or more spp. . . .	14	10	8	3	35
Loci occupied by . . .					
torvus	3	1	1	..	5
ribesii	11	6	3	1	21
vitripennis	11	7	5	2	25

Though it is possible that fine shades of difference may be revealed when a more detailed range of tolerance is worked out for each of the two common species (the limited range of *torvus* is due to the fact that only five individuals have been seen), these figures certainly do not suggest gross differences in habitat preference.

The period during which adults are on the wing also shows a general similarity. The earliest and latest dates are given below from Verrall, representing general British collecting, Lundbeck Danish, and South Haven Peninsula (S.H.P.).

	S. torvus	S. ribesii	S. vitripennis
Verrall . .	22 June–31 Aug.	13 June– 9 Sept.	22 Apr.–13 Sept.
Lundbeck . .	12 May–11 Oct.	26 Apr.–18 Oct.	16 May– 8 Sept.
S.H.P. . .	5 Apr.– 6 Sept.	15 Apr.–26 Sept.	20 May–15 Oct.

I have also elsewhere taken the two latter species visiting ivy bloom together as late as 17 October. This extensive time distribution of adults, through six or seven months, together with Lundbeck's scattered information about larvae, suggests that there is more than one generation a year. There is thus every opportunity for sexually mature individuals to come into frequent contact, and it is well known that they do so. But our survey records reveal an interesting difference between the two common species in the time of maximum abundance. If the locus-date records (the same minor loci are not infrequently visited at different seasons) are summarized by months, they give comparative figures for the number of times the presence of the species was recorded in any loci (these figures do not relate to the number of individuals seen at any given spots).

Month . . .	4	5	6	7	8	9	10	Total
S. ribesii . . .	4	17	19	5	9	2	..	56
S. vitripennis . .	..	4	2	1	18	24	1	50

And it is seen that 71 per cent. of the *ribesii* records were made *before* July while 86 per cent. of the *vitripennis* records fall *after* July. The South Haven populations are not extensive and the loci often have to be worked rapidly; even so, all three species have once been taken simultaneously at one spot and two species together twice. But a fairer measure of their chances of meeting in this area is given by the percentage of the thirty-five inhabited major loci in which at one time or another more than one species has been recorded. All three species have occurred in 9 per cent., two in 31 per cent., while in the remaining 60 per cent. only one species has been recorded.

In view of these facts it is not perhaps surprising that none of the morphological differences appear to have any adaptive significance, and the most likely theoretical cause of divergence would seem to be small inherited differences leading to barriers the growth of which may well have been fostered by a distribution in small discontinuous populations such as Wright (1939) has shown leads to random differentiation.

The Genus Crambus *(Crambidae, Lepidoptera).*

Among the grass-moths of the genus *Crambus* there are several groups of species showing marked superficial resemblances. Three morphologically close British species will serve as an example, *C. uliginosellus* Zell., *C. sylvellus* Hübn. (= *adipellus* Tr.), and *C. pascuellus* L. The 'key' character which Meyrick (1927) gives to differentiate *uliginosellus* and *pascuellus* is that the hindwings of the former are 'whitish' and the latter 'grey'; but this is a purely quantitative difference very difficult to apply in practice. In fact, the three species in this respect form a series leading from the rather whiter wings of *uliginosellus*, of which Meyrick in his description says 'whitish, towards apex suffused grey', through *pascuellus* which he describes as 'grey, more whitish dorsally', to the rather more grey hindwing of *sylvellus*. Apart from the fact that *uliginosellus* (18–23 mm.) is usually smaller than the other two (23–26 mm. and 22–26 mm. respectively), the only safe characters are the position (in relation to the costa, termen, and second line), size, and shape of the white median longitudinal streak on the forewings. This, with slight differences in the shapes of the forewings and a few insignificant markings, is due to fine changes in *proportions*—a difference frequently observable between close species.

The geographical ranges given by Meyrick are:

C. uliginosellus: S. England to Hereford and Norfolk; C. Europe, Asia Minor.

C. sylvellus: Surrey to Dorset and Norfolk; Killarney; N. and C. Europe.

C. pascuellus: Britain to the Shetlands, Ireland; Europe to E. Siberia.

Thus, the first two species have a considerable overlap, and *pascuellus* not only completely covers both their ranges but extends far outside them. Both the first two species are very local in this country, but are usually plentiful where they occur; whereas *pascuellus* is common and widely distributed.

Ecologically the three species show a similar relationship. The first two appear to have a narrow range of habitats that they will tolerate (tolerance-range), finding their optimum in bogs. Here *pascuellus* is also a regular inhabitant (and the three species quite frequently live together), but it extends freely into damp heath habitats and is equally at home in turfy areas characterized by tufts of *Juncus*. It can also tolerate drier conditions and I have even taken it in my small London garden. Within the South Haven survey area there is only one permanent population of *uliginosellus* and *sylvellus*, where in fact all three species live together (Spur Bog). Beyond this another small population of *sylvellus*, not at present existing, has been reported from a site loosely describable as freshwater-marsh; while *uliginosellus* has been recorded, but only in ones and twos, from seven other freshwater-marsh habitats. A number of small discrete populations of *pascuellus* are well scattered over the many damp or marshy loci. Outside the survey area I have examined several moss-bogs where all three species live together.

The flying dates given by Meyrick are June and July for *uliginosellus* and *pascuellus*, and June–August for *sylvellus*. At South Haven the outside dates are for *uliginosellus* 10 June–13 Sept., *sylvellus* 3 July–27 Aug., *pascuellus* 7 June–29 Aug. The locus-date records are distributed as follows:

Month	6	7	8	9	Totals
C. uliginosellus . . .	5	5	2	1	13
C. sylvellus . . .	..	3	10	..	13
C. pascuellus . . .	67	76	10	..	153

A sample of the Spur Bog population made by G. I. Crawford on 15 June 1933, out of 12 to 15 Crambids seen during twenty minutes, gave 6 *pascuellus*, 3 *uliginosellus*. On the same day a sample of 20 from another bog off the survey area gave 9 *pascuellus*, 10 *uliginosellus*. In that year *sylvellus* was first recorded on 16 July, and on 19 August was plentiful (which means a flying population of perhaps 100) and the other two species were not on the wing. On 29 June 1935 the Spur Bog population was noted as *uliginosellus* plentiful, *pascuellus* occasional, *sylvellus* not yet flying. In 1932-3-4-5 the maximum population of *sylvellus* was on the wing in the first half of August, i.e. at a time when the adult populations of the other two species had practically disappeared.

The general relationships between these three species are very similar to those of the three species of *Syrphus*, and there is an equal absence of adaptive characters. Though all three species can be taken on the wing at the same time, there is a rather sharp time-barrier between *sylvellus* and the other two, which may have played some part in differentiating it; but even this does not exist between *uliginosellus* and *pascuellus*. One explanation (though not the only one) which is possible on the evidence is that the two former species may have split from the wide-ranging *pascuellus*, or its prototype, as the result of random differentiation in small, locally isolated, populations. Once this process has proceeded far enough to erect barriers to out-crossing, the new groups can spread without being swamped.

The Genera Myrmica and Lasius (*Formicidae, Hymenoptera*).

The social ants present a very different problem with their nest-populations, the careful restriction of mating to a few chosen days of which detailed records are difficult to come by, and our ignorance of the degree of cross-mating that may take place between different nests. But there is no doubt about the closeness of many groups of species.

There are six British forms of the genus *Myrmica* which have been considered by some authors to be subspecies of *rubra* L. but by others as good, though closely allied, species (Donisthorpe, 1927). Three of these species, M. *ruginodis* Nyl., M. *sulcinodis* Nyl., and M. *scabrinodis* Nyl. (together with its variety *sabuleti* Meinert), have been found on South Haven Peninsula during the examination of 984 locus-habitats. They display interesting differences in their ecological ranges of tolerance which, taken in conjunction with their morphological and other small differences, lend further support to their distinctness. M. *sulcinodis* appears to be confined to two small centres of population occupying a few acres of damp heath; the number of nests cannot be large, some half-dozen have in fact been found. Excluding typical *sabuleti* which cannot be dealt with effectively in brief, *ruginodis* and *scabrinodis* are about equally common, having been recorded from 161 and 152 locus-habitats respectively. Their fine ecological differences cannot be fully treated here. Though both occupy freshwater-marsh habitats to about the same limited extent, *ruginodis* prefers the shade effects of taller vegetation and damp places, while *scabrinodis* prefers shorter vegetation and on the whole drier places. The following preliminary figures will illustrate this. Out of the 161 records for *ruginodis*, 27 per cent. are from deciduous wood, or put the other way, the species is present in 47 per cent. of the 93 locus-habitats classed as deciduous wood. Only one record for *scabrinodis* has so far been made from this habitat type, and that was from a bank on a wood margin. Of the 76 locus-habitats classed generally as scrub, 38 per cent. are occupied by *ruginodis* and only 8 per cent. by *scabrinodis*. The presence of a bracken canopy over heathy or turfy habitats makes them more suitable for *ruginodis* than *scabrinodis*. The former does not nest in marram dunes; the latter does, though very sparsely. There is a sharp contrast in the occupation of salt-marsh; *ruginodis* is absent from the 93 locus-habitats examined, while *scabrinodis* occupies 27 per cent. of them (16 per cent. of its 152 records).

The two species may nest within a few feet of each other; and the marriage flights of all three are stated (Donisthorpe) to occur mainly in August and September. Since nests of all three species can be found less than 100 yards apart, there is no doubt that the sexes could intermingle if the flights synchronized. The geographical ranges given by Donisthorpe of all three species show great similarity and may be summarized as the British Isles, north and central Europe to east Siberia; but *scabrinodis* is reported from Turkestan and has varieties in North America, while *sulcinodis* occupies mainly the northern part of this area, becoming a mountain species farther south; *ruginodis* equally becomes a mountain species to the south of its wider European range.

In the genus *Lasius* Fabricius (= *Acanthomyops* Mayr., the name used by Donisthorpe) *L. niger* L. and *L. alienus* Först. are an interesting pair. The latter has generally been considered to be a race or subspecies of the former, and comparative ecological studies may help to settle its taxonomic status. The morphological differences visible in dead material, both in the workers and the sex forms, are very slight, being practically confined to the presence or absence of a few small outstanding hairs on the scape of the antennae and on the tibiae; but in living material the differences in general behaviour and appearance are far more striking, and in the majority of cases the two species can be safely separated in the field by a competent worker without microscopic examination (though to avoid possible arguments ecological records should be supported by specimens).

The geographical ranges given by Donisthorpe show *niger* as the wider-ranging species, covering probably the whole of the *alienus* range: *niger* whole of Europe, Siberia, Caucasus, Turkestan, China, Japan, North Africa, Madeira, varieties in North America; *alienus* Europe widely (though apparently less common in north than *niger*), Siberia, Caucasus, Turkestan, and from north-west Himalayas up to 9,000 feet. The swarming dates of both species apparently have an extensive overlap but those of the latter tend to begin and end a little later.

The fine ecological preferences suggested by the South Haven Peninsula survey show a more striking divergence. Of the total 984 minor locus-habitats examined, *niger* was present in 435, or 44 per cent., showing a remarkably wide tolerance-range— nests being recorded from dry tufts of *Psamma* (*Ammophila*) on the dunes as well as from wet *Sphagnum* and frequently in standing or fallen dead trees. It is well represented in all the eight major habitat types, being found in 68 per cent. of the 25 sand-dune locus-habitats, in between 52–45 per cent. of salt-marsh (93), scrub (76), damp heath (142), grass and turf (135), and deciduous wood (93); while in dry heath (337), from which the largest number of the *niger* records, 29 per cent., comes, it occupies 37 per cent., and in freshwater-marsh (83) 34 per cent. On the other hand, *alienus* is closely restricted, 135 (81 per cent.) of its 167 recorded locus-habitats being on dry heath. It has been recorded from 13 damp heath sites and 12 turfy sites (mostly on the roadside). In five places it was foraging in salt-marsh, but it does not nest in such habitats, and in two cases nests were recorded from scrub loci, but both were on the margins of dry heath. In sand-dune, freshwater-marsh, and woodland it is absent.

It is in the occupation of dry heath habitats that the most interesting difference between these species is to be seen. South Haven Peninsula is partly composed of Eocene Bagshot beds, and partly of recent blown-sand (Diver, 1933) of which the older ridges are now mainly covered by various aspects of *Calluna* heath. Though *niger* occupies 37 per cent. of the total dry heath loci and *alienus* 40 per cent., the two species are not often in the same locus. The former is largely confined to the Bagshot heaths and the latter mainly to the recent blown-sand, there being some very pretty, sharp changeovers within a few feet where blown-sand gives way to exposed Bagshots. There are, however, some small populations of *alienus* among the *niger* populations on bits of the dry Bagshot heaths, and it looks as if *alienus* had a pronounced nesting preference for a particular type of soil structure. In the small damp heath dips of the blown-sand ridges there are similar enclaves of *niger*, and again nests of the two species may be only a few feet apart. A form morphologically intermediate between these two species has been described, *alieno-niger* Först. This also occurs rarely on the peninsula and it is equally intermediate in general behaviour and ecology. We have so far about six records of intermediates, all of which occurred within the blown-sand area of dense *alienus* occupation, but only in the very narrow intermediate zones, a yard or two wide, between the damper spots occupied by more or less isolated *niger* nests. The ecological facts support the specific distinctness of the two main forms, which may possibly have differentiated in relation to habitat. The intermediates naturally suggest occasional crossing, but conclusions at this stage would be quite premature.

In these cases it seems possible that factors leading to fine ecological isolation may have played some part in species differentiation; but the whole question of race-formation and speciation in the *Formicidae* needs careful and special consideration.

The Genus Juncus (*Juncaceae*).

Similar cases could be taken from a number of plant genera including other species in this genus; but since the peculiarities of speciation in plants cannot be discussed here, one simple example must suffice.

Some botanists have considered the common rush, *J. communis* Mey., to be one species containing two intergrading forms; but by others this aggregate has been separated into two species *J. conglomeratus* L. and *J. effusus* L. The differences are small, involving habit, shape of capsule, and degree of striation of the stem (see Butcher and Strudwick, 1930), but in the South Haven material I have not seen intergrading forms. I am informed that *conglomeratus* has a narrower range of tolerance than *effusus* and is more frequent on acid than basic soils, while the latter seems almost indifferent; both are frequent on the acid soils of the peninsula, but *effusus* (414) occurs in about twice as many locus-habitats as *conglomeratus* (210). The full analysis of these species has not yet been made, but of the 210 loci containing *conglomeratus* at least 89 per cent. also contain *effusus*; that is, *conglomeratus* very seldom occurs alone; *effusus*, on the other hand, occurs alone in 55 per cent. of its recorded loci. So closely may they intermingle that on one occasion it was necessary to dig up a tuft to demonstrate (to a botanist) that the two species were not growing from the same root-stock. The general impression gained is that *effusus* not only more readily tolerates flooding but in contrast is a far more successful colonist of the recovery phase (after burning) of damp heath habitats; while *conglomeratus* is most obvious on the very slightly rising zones that border a 'slack' where *Myrica gale* L. is also often present.

The facts suggest that some genetic isolation may have been the main cause of separation in this type of case.

The Genus Sphaerophoria (*Syrphidae, Diptera*).

This genus of some ten palearctic species has four representatives in Europe, all of which occur on South Haven Peninsula. Lundbeck (1916) states that taxonomically the genus has given trouble because of the amount of intraspecific variation and a tendency to form local races. *S. loewii* Zett., which is readily distinguished from the others, appears to be really rare every-

T t

where, being taken only in ones and twos. I have only traced
four British specimens of which three were taken on South
Haven Peninsula in two adjacent loci in different years. From
what little is known of its habitats its tolerance-range appears
to be very limited. *S. flavicauda* Zett. is local to rare but has
several named varieties. Its tolerance is rather wider, with a
possible optimum in salt-marsh, where three out of the four
South Haven records were taken in company with the next two
species. The closest pair is *S. scripta* L. and *S. menthastri* L., both
of which are common; they differ in several small points, none
of which appears to be adaptive. In *scripta*, which is slightly
the larger, the male abdomen is rather longer than the wings
(in *menthastri* both are about the same length); the scutellum
is normally yellow-haired (as opposed to black-haired in *menthastri*, but there is a yellow-haired form); apart from the male
genitalia which show distinctive differences, the only stable
character present in both sexes appears to be a difference in
the distribution of the minute hairs on the hind femora. Many
'species' have in the past been made of the races and varieties
of each of these two on the basis of variations in abdominal
markings and leg-colour, and some four or five named varietal
forms of each are still retained.

The geographical ranges given by Lundbeck again suggest
a partially contracting series in which the least widespread
species are included within the joint range of the other two,
but *menthastri* extends farther east than *scripta* though it does
not go so far north.

    S. scripta: all Europe to N. Sweden, Finland, Iceland, Green-
        land, N. America, down to Egypt, the Canaries, Madeira.
    S. menthastri: all Europe to N. Sweden, Finland, Siberia,
        Japan, N. America, the Canaries.
    S. flavicauda: N. and C. Europe from mid-Sweden to Austria,
        Hungary, also recorded from Italy, Spain.
    S. loewii: N. and C. Europe from mid-Sweden to Austria.

Ecologically there is little to choose between the first two;
about 50 per cent. of the records of each are from the various
types of freshwater-marsh and about 10 per cent. from salt-
marsh, some 15 per cent. from grassy loci, and both occur
occasionally in damp and dry heath, in scrubby areas (but
not woodland proper), and on dune. Both species were flying

together in well over half the loci from which *menthastri* was recorded and in others *scripta* was later recorded as present.

The flying records show a wide overlap, the first and last dates being:

	S. loewii	S. flavicauda	S. scripta	S. menthastri
Verrall . . .	..	7 May to 12 Aug.	3 May to 3 Sept.	18 May to 31 Aug.
Lundbeck . .	20 May to 10 July	July	14 May to 14 Sept.	15 May to 8 Sept.
S.H.P.	26 Aug. to 1 Sept.	9 June to 26 Aug.	29 Apr. to 25 Sept.	21 May to 13 Sept.

The distribution of the S.H.P. records through the months gives the following table:

Month . .	4	5	6	7	8	9	Totals
scripta . .	1	9	6	73	124	66	279
menthastri .	..	7	2	32	37	3	81

which shows that though *scripta* has been recorded at the end of April, *menthastri* is slightly the earlier species. The adult populations are often quite small. A small discrete patch of *Juncus* and turf was swept on 23 July under optimum flying conditions and apparently cleared of its population; the count gave *scripta* 8 ♂♂ and 9 ♀♀, *menthastri* 10 ♂♂ and 3 ♀♀.

The similarity of these two species in every aspect, including their parallel variations, is very close, and one can only suppose that their differentiation has been brought about by isolation, of which small barriers interfering with mating or fertility seem the most likely main cause.

The Genus Cepaea (*Helicidae, Mollusca Pulmonata*).

The two British species of the genus *Cepaea* are very closely related. Both show a wide range of parallel variation in which, however, there are statistical differences, e.g. the lip of the shell in *C. hortensis* (Müll.) is usually white while that of *C. nemoralis* (L.) is usually pigmented. Since the lip colour has often been taken as a ready means of distinguishing the two, white-lipped *nemoralis* have sometimes been ascribed to *hortensis*, and no doubt vice versa. The only safe diagnostic characters lie in the genitalia (particularly in the shape of the

dagger-like 'dart' used in courtship), and in the general proportions of the shell.

The geographical ranges (Taylor, 1914, and Økland, 1925)
overlap very extensively, covering central Europe though possibly not extending far into Russia; but *hortensis* goes farther
north, including the British Isles to the Shetlands, some way
up the coast of Norway, the Faroes, Iceland, and north-east
North America, and not so far south, occupying only a part of
Spain and not crossing the Alps into Italy; while *nemoralis* does
not reach the north of Scotland, or beyond the southern end of
Scandinavia, nor does it occur in North America except where
introduced, but it reaches the south of Spain and almost to the
south end of Italy. A quite distinct larger race of *nemoralis*
occurs in the extreme west of Ireland and at least in the
Pyrenees. Both species, including the Pyrenean race, show the
same overlapping distribution in Pleistocene times, and *hortensis*
has been recorded from the Pleistocene in North America (Dall,
1910). Though both are probably much older, Mr. Kennard
informs me that he considers the allocation of the few specimens
he has seen from before the Pleistocene cannot be regarded as
certain.

Between 1920 and 1929, with the help of a number of workers,
451 separate colonies containing one or both species were
sampled. These colonies have been drawn from all the major
divisions of England and include a few from Wales, Scotland,
Ireland, and continental Europe. Of these, 74, or 16·4 per
cent., contained a mixture of both species living together, in
240 *hortensis* was alone, and *nemoralis* was alone in 137. With two
exceptions colonies were mostly sampled on the principle of
taking every visible adult throughout the area of occupation.

From the 314 colonies containing *hortensis* 24,753 shells were
obtained, giving an average of about 79 per population. One
more or less continuous population that was very fully worked
yielded about 2,000 living snails; only five others yielded above
500. If it be assumed that the samples include no more than
one-quarter of the adult population, it is clear that the average
discrete population is still quite small, and some populations can
certainly be counted in tens. Populations are often strung out in
lines along hedgerows or banks, and from the distribution of
known genes it seems that germinal interchange between the

two ends is extremely restricted. For instance, in a population continuously occupying a 45-yard strip, brown shells were present in all sub-samples for 25 yards, forming 2·3 per cent. of a sample of 653, but absent from the next two samples (10 yards each), which totalled 552 and 346 respectively.

In *nemoralis*, though some colonies may be extremely small and the individuals sparse, the average population size is somewhat larger, and really large areas of population do occur. Two such loci were examined, at Bundoran in Ireland and Berrow in Somerset, both on dunes, by taking random samples of small areas. At Bundoran 25,835 shells in 44 samples were collected, of which 16,473 were living adults, the rest being shells from which the animals had been eaten by birds or mice, unbroken dead, and young; while at Berrow a total of 19,521 was taken in 56 samples, of which 10,447 were living adults. It seems probable that the former population ran into seven figures and the latter into six; but it was equally clear, both from the distribution of the living snails and from an examination of gene-frequencies, that such populations are really a number of quite small though more or less adjacent subpopulations. This was particularly well seen at Berrow, where the subpopulation units were often the 20–40 snails living in a single tuft of *Iris foetidissima* L. from which they emerge to feed and mate on the surrounding short turf, the degree of direct out-mating depending presumably on the distances between neighbouring occupied tufts. Excluding the 45,356 snails from these two exceptionally large populations and 9,480 from the three other samples (each exceeding 2,000) from areas not worked by myself, there are left 27,154 snails from 204 colonies giving a mean sample of 133, or nearly twice the size of the *hortensis* figure.

Another method of arriving at a closer estimate of population size is the collection of all shells after some occupied area (e.g. a patch of bramble or gorse scrub) has been burnt. Two such populations of *nemoralis* can be given from the South Haven records: (*a*) 88 individuals of which only 4 were large young (the very small young would partly be destroyed and were not looked for); (*b*) 157 including 25 large young, mixed with a population of 21 adults and 7 young of *Helix aspersa* Müll.

There is a considerable overlap in the ecological tolerance

of the two species, but with some interesting differences. In rural England the optimum conditions for *hortensis* colonies seem to be found in road-banks topped by well-kept hedges, while *nemoralis*, though it may also occur here, tolerates coarser vegetation and rather less disturbed habitats; it also occupies woods more freely than *hortensis*. On sandhills in England *nemoralis* alone seems to occur (though at Berrow *hortensis* occupies the roadside hedge just landward of the *nemoralis* dune population); but towards its northern limits in Scotland *hortensis* may be found with it and the latter continues northward to occupy dunes after *nemoralis* has dropped out (Boycott, 1934).

Both species live for several years and are sexually active from early summer to autumn. They can be made to cross, though with considerable difficulty, and A. W. Stelfox (unpublished) has successfully reared the hybrids for several generations. Natural hybrids have been claimed, but if they occur they are undoubtedly rare. There is no indication that the different colour and band forms confer any advantage, nor that the interspecific differences are in any way adaptive.

Given that the sexually active individuals of two animal species can normally come into contact, there are still three possible barriers which must be broken through before a successful cross can be achieved. The first of these to be tested is 'psychological'; small differences in *courtship* behaviour not only may fail to produce the required response but may even act as a direct deterrent. The second is the mechanical difficulty of actual *mating* that may arise from differences in genital structure. Lastly, there is the genetic barrier of differences in chromosome structure, &c., which interferes with *fertility*. A close examination of a large number of courtships of both these species shows slight differences in behaviour which are in part correlated with the differences in the jaw and in the shape of the dart. Courtships between the two species have also been observed, and the slightly smaller *hortensis* seems to find the more ponderous and rather fiercer advances of *nemoralis* disconcerting; further, *hortensis* usually parries the smaller curved dart of its own species while the straight dart of *nemoralis* normally wounds. One such courtship was abruptly terminated by *hortensis* at this stage. If the courtship barrier is broken (which I suspect is a very rare event), there seems to be no effective mating barrier;

but such evidence as is available indicates considerable genetic difficulties (e.g. Lang, 1908).

Many factors may have been brought to bear through a long period of time on the slow building up of the distinctness of these two species—a distinctness that even yet is not so absolute as entirely to preclude the possibility of germinal interchange by hybridization. The fairly marked ecological differences that obtain to-day may have been even more effective before Pleistocene times in isolating widely scattered small populations. The present distribution suggests that the interference of man has provided habitats which should favour an increase in the number of *hortensis* colonies. The courtship barrier, which is now probably an effective agent in maintaining specific separation, is not the product of a single genetic change. Though the range of variation is strikingly parallel, there are marked differences between the two species in the frequencies of parallel forms. In British populations, at any rate, *hortensis* forms smaller colonies but is less variable than *nemoralis*. There may well be differences in comparable mutation-rates. Random differentiation should be favoured by their population-structure, and one might reasonably suppose that it has been a prominent factor in producing this split.

If the few facts that are known about the unselected cases given above are considered dispassionately, it seems that selective forces and adaptive values have played little direct part in these specific differentiations; nor is there any evidence to suggest that geographical isolation, which obviously plays a large part in different circumstances, has been operative here, though the possibility is by no means excluded. The most probable general cause is random differentiation in small partially isolated populations which Wright (1939) shows in chap. 5 to be statistically possible. Though in the large number of cases of the type considered here natural selection is perhaps quite ineffective as a single mechanism to split two species from a common stock, it would be fantastic to generalize from this and to say that it therefore plays no part in the slow secular change by which one species becomes another, or that it cannot be an effective cause of species-differentiation in different circumstances. The truth seems to be that speciation and evolution are brought about in different ways in different cases, that a number of different factors may be brought into play, and that the importance of the role of each will vary with the particular circumstances.

REFERENCES

ANDERSON, EDGAR (1936). 'The Species Problem in Iris.' *Annals Missouri Botanical Garden*, **23**, 457–509.

BOYCOTT, A. E. (1934). 'The Habitats of Land Mollusca in Britain.' *J. Ecol.* **22**, 1–38.

BUTCHER, R. W., and STRUDWICK, F. E. (1930). *Further Illustrations of British Plants*. Ashford, Kent.

DALL, W. H. (1910). *Harriman Alaska Expedition*, **13**, 'Mollusca'. Smithsonian Institution.

DIVER, C. (1929). 'Fossil Records of Mendelian Mutants.' *Nature*, **124**, 183.

—— (1933). 'The Physiography of South Haven Peninsula, Studland Heath, Dorset.' *Geogr. J.* **81**, 404–27.

—— (1936). 'The Problem of Closely-related Species and the Distribution of their Populations.' *Proc. Roy. Soc. B*, **121**, 62–5.

—— (1938*a*). 'The Plant-carpet in relation to Animal Distribution.' *Proc. Linn. Soc.*, Session 150, 124–35.

—— (1938*b*). 'The Distribution of Natural Populations.' *Proc. Zool. Soc.*, *C*, **108**, 61–2.

—— and GOOD, R.d'O. (1934). 'Contributions towards a Survey of the Plants and Animals of South Haven Peninsula, Studland Heath, Dorset. —IV. General Scheme of the Survey.' *J. Anim. Ecol.* **3**, 129–32.

DONISTHORPE, H. St. J. K. (1927). *British Ants*. London.

ELTON, C. S. (1924). 'Periodic Fluctuations in the Numbers of Animals: Their Causes and Effects.' *Brit. J. Exp. Biol.* **2**, 119–63.

HARDY, A. C., and MILNE, P. S. (1937). 'Insect Drift on the North Sea.' *Nature*, **139**, 510.

LANG, A. (1908). 'Über die Bastarde von *Helix hortensis* Müller und *Helix nemoralis* L.' *Festschr. Univ. Jena*. Jena.

LUNDBECK, W. (1916). *Diptera Danica*, pt. V. London.

MEYRICK, E. (1927). *A Revised Handbook of British Lepidoptera*. London.

ØKLAND, F. (1925). *Die Verbreitung der Landgastropoden Norwegens*. Oslo.

RENSCH, B. (1933). 'Zoologische Systematik und Artbildungsproblem.' *Verh. Deutsch. Zool. Ges.* (1933), 19–83.

TAYLOR, J. W. (1914). *Monograph of the Land and Freshwater Mollusca of the British Isles*, **3**. Leeds.

VERRALL, G. H. (1901). *British Flies*, **8**. London.

WRIGHT, SEWALL (1939). 'The Statistical consequences of Mendelian heredity in relation to speciation.' In *The New Systematics*, ed. J. S. Huxley, Oxford.

ECOLOGICAL ASPECTS OF PLANT TAXONOMY

By E. J. SALISBURY

THE ecologist is concerned with the study of the causal relations respecting the presence of particular species in particular places. Any such study presupposes an exact knowledge of the precise nature of the systematic aggregates that are involved, otherwise there is inevitable obscurity and confusion of issues. The ecologist is thus dependent upon the taxonomist for the discrimination, from the morphological point of view, of the material with which he deals.

There is, in addition, the direct contribution which the ecologist can make towards the sum total of the characters that distinguish the taxonomic units, and these ecological criteria may for certain organisms constitute their salient diagnostic features. There are, for example, a number of pairs of species which though approximating closely to one another when considered from the purely morphological point of view are markedly differentiated in their ecological requirements. In assessing the status that must be accorded such units the physiological features would appear to be more important than the structural.

A striking instance in the British flora is furnished by the two species *Galium saxatile* L. and *Galium sylvestre* Poll. Morphologically these species resemble one another very closely, though there is a difference in the leaf-form, and the fruit of *G. saxatile* is tuberculate whereas that of *G. sylvestre* is nearly smooth. But though, like many other species which have definite habitat preferences, both can, in the absence of competition, be grown on a variety of soils, in nature *G. sylvestre* is almost confined to very calcareous soils whereas *G. saxatile* is a feature of soils poor in bases (Tansley, 1917).

Under the name *Gentiana acaulis* L. two different plants were for long confused, owing to their general similarity of habit and flower-structure. Of these one has a corolla tube with green spots within, and there is an abrupt insertion of the calyx teeth. This plant is known as *Gentiana excisa* Koch. The other, known as *Gentiana clusii* Perr. et Song., has a corolla tube devoid of

U u

green spots and the sinus between the calyx teeth is V-shaped. The distinguishing morphological features are thus comparatively slight, and both species can be regarded as occupying the same niche in the Alpine pasture community. But whereas *G. excisa* is a feature of clayey non-calcareous soils, *G. clusii* is associated with soils which are rich in lime. Similarly we have *Rhododendron hirsutum* L. and *Rhododendron ferrugineum* L., *Achillea atrata* and *Achillea moschata* Jacq., *Anemone alpina* L. and *Anemone sulphurea* L. The ash of *Gentiana clusii* was found by Popovici (1934) to contain about 28 per cent. of CaO as compared with 10·4 per cent. to 15·9 per cent. CaO in the ash of *G. excisa*, whilst the ash of the calcicole *Anemone alpina* contained rather less calcium than that of the calcifuge *A. sulphurea* growing in the same soil.

The relations of calcicole and calcifuge species to their respective habitats would thus seem not to be a simple question of calcium requirement, but would appear to be of a very complex character (cf. Salisbury, 1920). Though the factors involved may vary in respect to the species concerned, the physiological preferences, commonly accentuated by competition, bring about a more or less marked isolation that diminishes if it does not actually prevent any possibility of hybridization. So, too, the continental species *Veronica spicata* L. differs but little morphologically from its oceanic counterpart *Veronica hybrida* L., but their climatic preferences are markedly distinct.

Hybrids between members of such vicarious pairs would appear to be unusual and in nature are sufficiently rare not to blur the distributional limits of the parent species. The writer (Salisbury, 1916, 1918) showed that in the semi-natural woodlands of Hertfordshire *Quercus robur* L. occurs naturally on the heavy calcareous soils of the clay-with-flints, whilst *Quercus sessiliflora* Salisb. is the native oak on the equally heavy London clay and also on light types of soil similarly deficient in carbonates and exchangeable bases. Where, as at Symonds Hyde near Hatfield or Haugh Wood in Herefordshire, part of the woodland is on soil favourable to the one species and part on soil favourable to the other, hybrid oaks are frequent along the zone where the two types of soil meet. At Symonds Hyde, Cox's Wood, situated upon clay-with-flints with a thin covering of loamy glacial drift, contains the two species in almost equal proportions together with hybrids. In Haugh Wood, where part occupies soil derived from Mayhill sandstone and part soil derived from the Wenlock limestone, the transition zone is more abrupt and hybrids are confined to a narrow belt of woodland. Though we might hesitate to grant specific rank to types whose morphological distinctions are slight, if these were alone involved, the ecological characters and resultant areas of distribution provide additional criteria for their separation.

The contact of ecologist and taxonomist is a very close one, for not only does the former find floristic composition to be one of the diagnostic features of the diverse types of community that he studies, but the exact determination of the constituent units is the more essential, by reason, on the one hand, of the diverse reactions of the smaller aggregates of which the Linneon is composed, and, on the other, the range of phenotypic expression that the habitat may induce in or impose upon a given genotype.

But the point of view from which the taxonomic units are considered is necessarily different. The systematist naturally lays particular stress upon those characters which are visible and upon those in particular which are relatively stable. To the ecologist, on the other hand, the physiological characters, some of which may have no visible manifestations, are fundamentally the most important, whilst the visible features of external morphology and internal structure are for him mainly significant in so far as they represent, or are concomitants of, the physiological or biological equipment of the species concerned that affects its relations to the habitat conditions, either physical or biotic.

The ecologist tends, for instance, to stress the vegetative resemblances between the succulent Euphorbias and their Cactaceous homoeomorphs, whereas the taxonomist stresses the great diversity in the structure of their reproductive organs. The ecologist thinks of these plants rather as occupying the same or similar niches in the economy of nature, the taxonomist rather as representatives of widely separated families. This difference of emphasis inevitably means that the ecologist is more frequently concerned with those characters which are variable and least reliable as indices of affinity, and, moreover, often only revealed as a result of experimental inquiry. The taxonomist desires characters which are visible and which are preferably not susceptible to modification by environmental conditions, and such are liable to be features that have less survival-value and less ecological importance.

The term 'ecotype' suggested by Turesson would appear to be useful as a designation for subspecific segregates of which the salient characteristics are ecological rather than morphological, but the use of 'ecophene' which he proposes apparently as an equivalent for the familiar term 'ecad' would seem a quite unnecessary addition to terminology. The fact that morphological response is often of such a nature as to render the individual better fitted for the special conditions in which it grows makes it the more necessary to establish, by means of experimental taxonomic cultures and genetical study, whether the characteristics of a taxonomic aggregate in a particular community are genotypically or phenotypically distinct from its representatives in other types of vegetation. Both phenotypic and genotypic variations may, in a sense, be held to represent a type of plasticity, but whilst plasticity in the germ-plasm may be essential to survival of the race, plasticity in phenotypic response may perhaps be more important for the survival of the individual.

It is a familiar fact that most plants which have the potentiality of developing hairs, sunken stomata, thick cuticle, spines, &c., do so to a more marked degree the greater the aridity of the habitat in which they develop. Whether that aridity be produced by climatic factors such as deficiency of rainfall or high rates of evaporation, by edaphic factors such as excessive porosity of the soil and lack of water-retention, or by biological factors such as poor root-development, or, as more usually obtains, from the combination of all three, the result, in plastic species, is normally to bring about morphological and anatomical changes which tend towards water-economy. Conversely, under conditions of high humidity the potentially hairy species may become glabrous. *Ulex europaeus* L., for example, loses its spiny character and the juvenile type of trifoliate leaf-form may persist in place of the leaf-spines which normally characterize the adult. Since the response usually results in rendering the plant better suited to the extreme conditions, it follows that such plasticity tends to increase the diversity of habitats that the species can tolerate and to extend its potential geographical range. But many species also include varieties which differ in similar respects to ecads, though often these hereditary types may be more pronounced than those imposed by the environmental conditions. A striking example of such an hereditary variation is afforded by the aquatic Speedwell *Veronica scutellata* L. Normally this occurs as a submerged aquatic in shallow water with completely glabrous foliage. If established plants be exposed by a fall in the water-level they will survive on the mud and develop ecads with leaves of thicker texture and a more pronounced cuticle. There is, however, a strikingly distinct variety known as *Veronica scutellata* var. *villosa* Schum. which is densely hairy and which I have found flourishing in comparatively arid situations at the upper margin of exposed mud where the ecad of the type could not long survive.

Some species, such as *Stellaria media* L., though embracing various strains, are morphologically relatively stable under a diversity of habitat conditions. If, however, we are concerned with such a species as *Plantago coronopus* L., we find that one and the same genotype is capable of exhibiting a very wide range of external form depending upon the habitat conditions. The so-called type of our sandy heaths has pinnately lobed leaves which are hairy, forming rosettes usually about 20 cm. in diameter whilst the inflorescences are many-flowered cylindrical spikes. For many years there has been known a so-called variety *pygmaea* Lange that grows at the edge of brackish dune slacks and other similar slightly halophytic situations. This type has, in its extreme form, fleshy linear leaves which are quite entire or with only vestigial teeth to represent the lobes of the type, whilst the surface may be completely glabrous. The rosettes are often not more than 2 cm. in diameter, whilst the inflorescences are very few-flowered and almost capitate in form. So striking is the difference that a distinguished continental taxonomist once mistook this plant for *Litorella lacustris*. Actually by cultivating this remarkable form in favourable conditions in garden soil I was able to show that the 'variety' *pygmaea* changed into the normal type and was in fact no hereditary variety but an ecad of a rather extreme type.

The xeromorphic ecad and the xeromorphic variety alike have their biological importance, and the same is true also of the hygromorphic equivalent.[1] Both extend the potential range of the species, but whereas plasticity renders the species capable of adjustment to fluctuating conditions, the 'adaptive' variety is usually more fitted for extreme conditions that are relatively permanent and stable.

If a species be both plastic and variable there is likely to be an extension of range without isolation, and we shall tend to accord a lower status to the varieties than when in the absence of plasticity the type and variety tend to occupy different habitats and distinct areas. Put in another way, plasticity tends to lead to continuity of occupation over a wide range of habitat conditions, whereas hereditary differences, which are often more extreme, may lead to discontinuity. In the one case the value of geographical distribution as a taxonomic character is low, whereas in the other its value may be high.

The degree to which we subdivide the species or recognize by our nomenclature the differences between individuals must ultimately be a matter of convenience. One often hears protests against those systematists whose intensive studies lead them to extreme segregation. One can hold no brief for those who merely make two species grow where one grew before, when it is a mere segregation that is divorced from any appreciation of the value of the synthetic approach and pays no regard to either utility or convenience. Nevertheless, it cannot be too strongly emphasized that whereas the larger aggregates represented by the Linneons may have little value for the floristic study of plant communities, their taxonomic segregates may be highly characteristic of different vegetation-types or of phases in the plant succession. A few examples from our own flora will suffice to show the ecological importance of such segregates.

The annual British species of *Salicornia* grouped under the Linneon *Salicornia herbacea* L.agg., afford a striking example of an aggregate species of which the component critical segregates are not only ecologically specialized as shown by their spatial distribution, but exhibit also a serial range of morphological characters that suggests a definite sequence of evolution. To appreciate this it will be necessary to refer to the perennial

---

[1] E.g. the shade ecads of the grass *Dactylis glomerata* are according to Turesson paralleled by an hereditary shade variety, namely *Dactylis glomerata* var. *lobata*.

species, of which *Salicornia perennis* Miller is the sole British representative. Throughout the genus the inflorescence is analogous to that of the Labiatae in that it consists of a raceme of partial inflorescences arising in the axils of decussately arranged leaves, each partial inflorescence being a modified dichasial cyme. But whereas the dichasial cymes or verticill-asters of the Labiatae exhibit pedicels bearing the individual flowers, here in the Salicornias the flowers of the dichasia are sessile and embedded in the fleshy axis formed by the coalescent bracts of the spike.

In some foreign species of perennial *Salicornia* the partial inflorescences may consist of more than three equal-sized flowers, but in the British *S. perennis* there are only three flowers of almost equal size, the order of flowering, namely the central flower followed by the two lateral, witnessing to the fact that the group is in fact a reduced dichasial cyme. Amongst the annual species, *Salicornia dolichostachya* Moss alone shows a similar dichasium with lateral flowers nearly equal in size to the central, which latter completely separates the former. It would seem natural to regard those species in which the dichasia evince further reduction as being derived types, and it is there-fore of interest to note that the pioneer phanerogamic species of the salt-marsh succession in this country is usually *S. dolicho-stachya*. At a slightly later stage in salt-marsh development, representing a higher level and in consequence less frequent and less prolonged tidal inundation, *Salicornia herbacea* L. sensu stricto is often the dominant species found on the more muddy types of salt-marsh, or *Salicornia ramosissima* Woods where the conditions are more sandy. In both these species the lateral flowers of the dichasia are appreciably smaller than the central ones and rarely one or other lateral may be absent or incom-pletely formed. At a still higher level on the marsh may be found the critical *Salicornia gracillima* Moss, in which the lateral flowers are still smaller relative to the central one. Character-istic of the highest parts of the marsh—where exposure during intertidal periods may be prolonged and osmotic extremes, of high salinity due to evaporation or low salinity due to dilution by rainwater may occur—there may be found *Salicornia dis-articulata* Moss, a species in which the lateral flowers are absent as a normal feature.

Morphologically and ecologically the erect *S. dolichostachya*, *S. ramosissima*, and *S. disarticulata* have their prostrate counterparts. Thus the annual species of this genus form a series in which the critical segregates have an ecological significance that is entirely lost if we consider them as an aggregate.

A parallel illustration of the association of habitat-differences with the segregates of a Linneon is afforded by *Limonium* (*Statice*) *vulgare* Mill. sensu amplo. Of these *Limonium rariflora* O. Kuntze appears normally at the lowest levels, often in association with *Aster tripolium* L., and though characteristic of the early phases of salt-marsh succession sometimes persists to the intermediate stages. *L. vulgare* Mill. sensu stricto is the characteristic species of these latter, whilst the variety *pyramidale* is particularly a plant of the higher levels and later stages of the succession.

Each plant community comprises a floristic assemblage which includes species that are generally distributed in many types of vegetation, and others, the selective species, which show a preference, either by virtue of their differential frequency or their relative abundance or both, for a particular type of community. There are also the so-called characteristic species which are found in one community and rarely or not at all in other vegetation units. Each has its value for synecological diagnosis and each may have an importance in determining the biotic conditions of the environment according to its abundance. But any such value is clearly dependent upon the accurate determination of the taxonomic units concerned, and it is quite irrelevant to their ecological importance whether such units be regarded as varieties, subspecies, or species. It is, however, of paramount importance in assessing the ecological significance of any taxonomic aggregate whether any plasticity exhibited be that of the individuals or of the race.

Progress in floristic ecology is thus in no small measure dependent on cultural experiments that have for their object the determination of genotypic constitution and of phenotypic response.

One of the most important assets of the plant's equipment for its struggle to survive is the height to which it can attain compatible with a capacity to form an adequate canopy of foliage (cf. Salisbury, 1929). The higher a plant can grow and still have a sufficient surplus of material to develop its leaves to normal size, the greater the probable variety of competitors it can overshadow. The etiolated plant of deep shade may, it is true, attain unusual stature, but at the sacrifice of its photosynthetic area and thus also of its competitive efficiency. Thus strains which differ in respect to height alone may have a biological importance that would justify their ecological distinction, although to the purely morphological systematist their differentiation might appear unwarranted. Thus the polyploids with their normally larger size may have a survival value greater than the diploids from which they are derived, whilst the rarity of haploids may in part at least be a concomitant of their reduced dimensions. The tall and dwarf strains may, however, each alike have their niche to fill just as prostrate and erect types of *Salicornia* have each their particular zone or area of the salt-marsh where they tend to predominate.

Or again, the dwarf races of the late-fruiting *Caucalis arvensis*[1] Huds. and *Aethusa cynapium* L. play a significant role as weeds in the stubble-fields in autumn, whence the taller strains have been eliminated by a process of unconscious artificial selection, since the reaping machine beheads them before the maturation of their fruits. So, too, depth of rooting which has been shown to vary between strain and strain may determine drought-resistance or survival from potential 'frost-lifting'. Such instances, which might be considerably extended, serve to emphasize the fact that the ecologist who is concerned, not with the mere description of communities but with their causal relations, may require a subdivision of the major taxonomic units that have little significance or value from the point of view of comparative morphology with which the professional systematist is most frequently concerned.

Ecology is very largely the study of the differential effects of the environment upon organisms, and as such the sense of values respecting morphological features becomes shifted; and whereas the systematist concerned with relationships between organisms rightly regards the more conservative reproductive structures of flower and fruit as of greatest significance, it is, as we have already emphasized, to differences in the physiological equipment manifest in the more variable morphology of vegetative parts that the ecologist must often look for those clues

---

[1] *C. infesta* Curt.=*C. arvensis* Huds.

X X

which will help to explain the subtle relationship between organism and habitat.

The geneticist who studies wild species in the protected conditions of the breeding-ground often finds a variation far wider than that which the species appears to exhibit in a wild state, probably resuscitating many of Nature's *rejectamenta*. It is, indeed, not without significance that species of open habitats where competition is least severe often display a variety of races that is in marked contrast with the comparative uniformity of those which occupy 'closed' communities where competition is severe. If this be generally true, then it is likely that diversities in the one may be more significant than those in the other.

Moreover, the morphological taxonomist is usually concerned rather with the adult conditions, whereas the ecologist is frequently forced to recognize that differences in the juvenile state may be as important, or even more so, than those of maturity.

Even in one and the same partial habitat we encounter diversity of leaf-form that it is difficult to believe can bear any direct relation to competitive success. Yet it may well be that these adult distinctions are necessary concomitants of features more subtle that have an ecological importance for the species concerned.

If we assess plant maturity by the production of flowers we find that the period of its inception may vary within wide limits according to the conditions of competition. A plant of *Trollius europaeus* raised from seed in a garden may mature in a single season and actually bear viable seed in the first year. Grown in a dense community, however, subject to the rigours of competition, it has been shown that the juvenile state of this species may extend over a period of seven years (Linkola 1935). But in addition to such individual plasticity we have races which differ in respect to the period of maturation, a fact which may well affect their survival capacity in different environments. Such biological races may require ecological recognition like the early- and late-flowering ecotypes of Turesson (1925), yet we can scarcely expect the taxonomist to burden his already heavy nomenclature with the provision for our requirements.

The question naturally arises as to whether additional nomenclature is necessary to meet the needs of the ecologist. It is clearly in the best interests of biology as a whole that any elaboration of nomenclature necessitated by advance in any of its branches should, if possible, be of such a character as to enlarge the basis of existing systems rather than to supplant them in any degree. Subdivision within the framework of existing taxonomic categories—though a hard saying to those who desire novelty for its own sake—has obvious and important advantages which only real necessity should force us to relinquish.

If the use of the term 'variety' were always strictly adhered to for categories in which the morphological distinctions were of a minor character but which were genetically different, and the term ecad or *forma* confined to those not distinguished by hereditary differences, the term 'ecotype' for hereditary types of which the distinctions are ecological rather than morphological, the multiplication of types within these categories should, I think, suffice for most if not all the ecologist's present needs. In saying this one recognizes the difficulty which sometimes obtains in assessing the status of an aggregate. Clearly no series of segregates can be grown under all possible combinations of environmental conditions, and without the omniscience which such cultures would confer the potentialities of any strain or strains we study must necessarily be of a more or less putative character. But the recognition of these limitations to our ascertained knowledge need not deter us from tentative if reasonable assumptions. A provisional term for infraspecific categories of which the hereditary or non-hereditary character of the differences is as yet unknown would be of considerable value. Perhaps the terms 'putative ecad', 'putative variety', &c., and their abbreviations p.e., p.v., might serve this end.

The foregoing brief consideration of the relation between morphological units and ecological requirements has served to emphasize not only that there must be close co-operation between the ecologist and the taxonomist, but that the former cannot be too meticulous in his recognition of the units with which he deals, the more so that, as we have seen, his requirements may demand a segregation of types that are distinguished far more by their physiological characteristics than by their morphological features.

REFERENCES

LINKOLA, K. (1935). 'Über die Dauer und Jahresklassenverhältnisse des Jugendstadiums bei einigen Wiesenstauden.' *Acta Forestalia Fennica*, **42**, 1–56.

POPOVICI, N. (1934). *Étude chimique de la calcicolie et calcifugie de quelques espèces végétales.* Thesis No. 943. University of Geneva, pp. 1–80.

SALISBURY, E. J. (1916). 'The Oak-Hornbeam Wood of Hertfordshire, Parts I and II.' *J. Ecology*, **4**, 83–116.

—— (1918). 'The Oak-Hornbeam Wood of Hertfordshire, Parts III and IV.' *J. Ecology*, **6**, 14–52.

—— (1920). 'The Significance of the Calcicolous Habit.' *J. Ecology*, **8**, 212–15.

—— (1929). 'The Biological Equipment of Species in relation to Competition.' *J. Ecology*, **17**, 197–222.

TANSLEY, A. G. (1917). 'On the Competition between *Galium saxatile* L. and *Galium sylvestre* Poll.' *J. Ecology*, **5**, 155–72.

TURESSON, G. (1922). 'The Genotypical Response of the Plant Species to Habitat and Climate.' *Hereditas*, **3**, 211–350.

—— (1925). 'The Plant Species in relation to Habitat and Climate.' *Hereditas*, **6**, 147–236.

—— (1931). 'The Geographical Distribution of the Alpine Ecotypes of some Eurasiatic Plants.' *Hereditas*, **15**, 329–46.

ECOLOGY AND THE FUTURE OF SYSTEMATICS

By w. h. thorpe

THE term 'ecology', including as it should in the widest sense
the relation of the organism to its whole environment, has of
late tended to usurp the older terms 'Natural History' and
'Bionomics'. This, in so far as it means that the study of natural
history is becoming more exact and quantitative, is all to the
good, although a glance through some of the journals devoted
to ecological studies does not always give this impression.
There is a good deal of incomplete and casual observation
which, although worth recording and perhaps ultimately of
real importance, scarcely deserves to be dignified by the term
'ecology'.

Ecology is conveniently divided into two sections which it has
become the fashion to call, after Schröter (1896, 1902), 'Synecology' and 'Autecology'. The term 'synecology' has become
particularly connected with the concept of an association of
plants or animals as forming in some sense an organic whole,
but involves also the subsidiary ideas of succession and climax.
This type of ecology has in itself had relatively little direct effect
on the studies of systematists beyond giving them a great deal
of identification work and taking much valuable time and
energy which might in many cases have been more usefully
employed. Its effect on the ardent and youthful naturalist is,
however, very salutary in that he comes to realize more quickly
than in any other way the immense complexities of even an
apparently simple environment and the enormous numbers of
species present even in the most restricted areas. If he himself
undertakes, as he must do if he is ever to have a real understanding of ecological problems, the task of getting to know the
species of one or two of the groups which he comes across, his
attitude to the systematist, which will probably at first be one
of benevolent condescension, will rapidly change. At the com-
mencement of his investigations he, like most of us at that stage,
will think but lightly of identifying a number of specimens
belonging to several different groups in the course of an evening

and will perhaps wonder why the real expert is so cautious. But this phase will soon pass and before long, particularly if he happens to be working with one of the more obscure groups of insects rich in species, he will find himself beginning to marvel that any one ever succeeds in separating and identifying anything unless it be by adopting the simple plan of discarding intermediates!

But there is no sharp line of demarcation between the two branches of ecology, and synecology will sooner or later in the course of any investigation merge into autecology and vice versa. And the influence of autecology on the work of the systematist is already profound. Moreover, it is only beginning. This is inevitable because, after all, autecology is merely an exact study of the relation of the individual species with its environment in all its aspects and over its whole range. In this sense, indeed, ecology comprises all investigations concerning the animal as a whole and therefore is fundamental to and includes the whole of applied biology—marine, freshwater, agricultural, veterinary, and medical.

It should hardly be necessary to stress the fact that although many species are distinguished by more or less sharply defined structural characters in the adult, they are in fact equally characterized by biological and physiological peculiarities at every stage in the life-history. The taxonomist in his task of classifying and reducing to order a host of individuals has naturally based his descriptions on structural characters merely for convenience when dealing with collections in the museum. This investigation of structure is, of course, not without interest, but small physiological characters are often extremely important biologically, whereas small structural characters are in many cases merely by-products, as it were, of very doubtful adaptive value. Indeed, one may perhaps define the modern conception of a species as a population of individuals prevented from interbreeding with all other populations by physiological differences (in the widest sense) whether or no structural differences are also present. A species is thus regarded as that stage in evolution at which physiological isolating mechanisms become virtually complete. The crux of the whole matter is that the present methods of taxonomic investigation often fail to separate groups which biologically and ecologically are clearly distinct, and which on every biological ground should be classified as distinct species. In some cases the difficulties encountered by systematists may be due to lack of precision in the examination of structural characters. In such instances it is always possible that further investigations will reveal the importance of structures hitherto overlooked and will provide 'good' characters for their separation. In others minute structural characters will have to be treated statistically and tests for correlation undertaken, or else 'characters' sought for in the larval stages. In yet others it may prove necessary to study internal anatomy in more detail. Indeed, in certain groups, e.g. Turbellaria and Nemerteans, owing to the lack of structural features on the surface, internal characters have long been used for separating species, many of which can only be identified by means of section-cutting. But however great the perfection to which the study of the structural characters of species may be brought, there seems no doubt that finally in certain cases no satisfactory structural differences will be discoverable, and it will be then essential to distinguish some perfectly good species on biological grounds alone. The question whether it will prove necessary to invent a new systematic category for such cases can wait for the present. But it would seem that some modification of nomenclature will ultimately be necessary to avoid confusion.

Perhaps the most important way in which exact ecological work has affected systematics is in the evidence it has supplied for the frequency of biological differentiation within populations hitherto regarded as single species. In other words, modern ecology has demonstrated the frequency of what have been defined as 'biological' or 'physiological' races, and it is to this aspect of the subject that the writer proposes to devote the greater part of this chapter.

In 1930 he published a summary of the knowledge of biological races in insects and allied groups up to that date. It is neither necessary nor desirable to repeat what was there set forth, and examples quoted here will be drawn almost entirely from work published since that time. Even so, owing to exigencies of space, only the more striking examples will be referred to and many interesting cases must be passed over. The examples will be concerned mainly with insects, since this group has been more attentively studied than many others and since, owing to the enormous number of species known, the problem of finding adequate characters for systematic work is particularly acute.

But before coming to the subject of biological races proper one must deal briefly with the subject of geographical races, particularly those geographical races in which biological differentiation is markedly developed. The ordinary geographical races which show clearly well-defined structural or colour differences in different parts of their range do not present any particular problem; progress in their study is generally a matter of more exact observations of minute characters, often involving the employment of statistical technique. Moreover, there is already a terminology in the form of trinomials employed for this type of variation, and in many groups of birds in particular the description and classification of geographical races is very far advanced. For a summary of this subject so far as non-marine vertebrata of Europe is concerned the valuable paper by Økland (1937) should be consulted. But there are many cases now known in which the biological characters of geographical races are far more striking than the structural or pigmentary characters, so that the presence or absence of overlapping distribution provides the only line of division between the categories of biological and geographical races. It will be seen, of course, from the definition given above that there is no suggestion that, merely because two geographical races are easily separated, they should be considered as species; only if it is shown that, when brought into the same area, their physiological mechanisms interfere with cross-breeding are there any real grounds for specific separation. Geographical isolation in itself is on a different plane from any type of physiological isolation.

A very curious example of biological differentiation in different geographical areas is provided by the work of Promptoff (1930). This worker showed that chaffinches (*Fringilla coelebs* Linn.) in southern Russia can be divided up, solely on the basis of variation in song, into well-defined populations each confined to a given area. These differences appear not to be wholly hereditary but to some extent at any rate to be handed on from parent to offspring by force of example, the young learning their song from that of their parents and of other adult individuals in the same neighbourhood. That isolation of this sort can persist is probably due to the fact that, although migration takes place, there is a strong tendency to return to the same restricted locality for the breeding season which is, of course, the song period. Although in this case no structural characters are involved, ornithologists will call to mind many examples of closely related species and subspecies in which the song is by far the most prominent distinguishing character, e.g. warblers of the genus *Phylloscopus*, the wood-pewees *Myiochanes* (Taverner, 1926), the meadowlark *Sturnella magna* (Linn.) (Chapman, 1900), and the subspecies of the pipit *Anthus spinoletta* (Linn.) and the wagtail *Motacilla flava* (Linn.).

Another remarkable case is provided by the work of Krumbiegel (1932), who made a detailed comparison of the physiological characters of European races of the ground-beetle *Carabus nemoralis* Müll. with those of well-defined species of the same genus. He investigated the optimum and limiting temperature in an apparatus which provided a temperature-gradient; he studied also the phototropic responses, and he investigated the activity of the different forms by a self-recording 'hypnometer'. In all these respects he found significant differences between species and in nearly all cases between geographical races. While morphologically these races are extremely similar, there being no doubt that they all come from the single structural species *C. nemoralis*, the physiological differences between them are often as great as those between species. Krumbiegel also finds that striking parallelisms can be worked out between physiological and structural characters. Thus differences in phototropism can be correlated with slight racial differences in the structure of the eyes. Responses to temperature-gradients also show correlation with the climatic conditions under which the race is found, and the activity curves, together with the phototropic responses, also indicate whether a given race is nocturnal or diurnal. These, then, are instances of races which, although they can be easily defined by the usual methods of systematics, also have important biological characters which appear to be of survival value. Krumbiegel's paper should be consulted for references to similar cases, less thoroughly investigated, in other groups; and there is also the monumental work of Goldschmidt (1934) on the races of *Lymantria dispar* L. which is too well known to need recounting here.

It is when we come to consider the populations of animals living in the same area and yet clearly separable by biological characters, with or without minute structural differences, that the problem of species definition becomes acute. That there are many cases of complete biological or ecological separation is becoming increasingly clear, and it is proposed first to give a few examples where, while ecological separation seems more or less complete, practically no structural differences have yet been found. One of the most striking of these concerns the cricket *Nemobius fasciatus* De Geer. Earlier work described in the previous review had shown that this species is split up into races doubtfully distinguishable morphologically and inhabiting different ecological niches, though easily separable by song. Fulton (1933) has since crossed examples of these races, and found that crossing in captivity results in a song of intermediate frequency, a type of song which is never heard in nature even in localities where the two races overlap, and experiments showed that this intermediate type of song is not due to incomplete dominance of any one Mendelian factor, but is more like what would be expected from the interaction of several factors. All evidence points to the fact that these forms are more distinct physiologically than morphologically and that interbreeding seldom or never takes place under natural conditions. K. B. Lal (1934) has published a very interesting account of two races of the Homopteron *Psylla mali* Schmidt, a species which is known in England as the apple-sucker and attacks apple and hawthorn. The adults appear identical except for size, although there are slight differences between the nymphs, and on these grounds the insects from hawthorn had been—quite rightly from a biological viewpoint—separated under the name *Psylla peregrina* Först. Lal found that it was not possible to induce cross-breeding in captivity, nor was it possible to obtain oviposition on the host plant of the other race. The interesting point in connexion with these two forms is that certain Chalcid and Proctotrypid parasites attack the hawthorn race but the apple race is free from them. How far this is an expression of physiological differences between the races, or whether it is to be explained on the ground of the unsuitability of the environment of the apple form for the parasites, is not known. Such ecological restriction of insect parasites to a certain portion of their host population is by no means uncommon. Very close indeed to this instance comes that of the blueberry maggot, a recent account of which is given by Lathrop and Nickels (1931). Earlier work had made it virtually certain that the so-called blueberry maggot was merely a specialized race of the apple maggot, *Rhagoletis pomonella* Walsh. This conclusion has been amply upheld by the work of subsequent investigators, and owing to its economic importance this is an animal which has been very intensively studied. It is extremely difficult to rear the blueberry form on apple and vice versa, but the reasons for this difficulty are not thoroughly understood. Although there is constant difference in size, no structural characters can be found; yet from an ecological viewpoint the forms appear absolutely distinct. It appears difficult, though by no means impossible, to secure cross-matings between the different host-plant races in the laboratory, and the crosses which have been made seem viable (Pickett, 1937).

The differences in the parasitism of the two races of *Psylla* mentioned above recalls the work of Emerson (1935) on the termite *Nasutitermes guayanae* (Holmgren) in British Guiana. Emerson has shown that this species can be divided into two groups according to the termitophile fauna. One group always harbours four species of Aleocharine (Staphylinid) beetles, while nests of the other group always contain two other species. Although the evidence is not conclusive, this difference is regarded by the above author as evidence of subtle biological differences between the colonies of termites. The sexual forms of the termites show no differences whatever, but soldiers do show a bi-modal variation in head-length which coincides with the differences in the termitophile population. This appears to be the first record of intraspecific biological differentiation in this group. More surprising is the work of H. H. Storey (1932), who showed that the leaf-hopper *Cicadulina mbila* Nandé comprises two different races which can be distinguished only by the differences in their ability to transmit the virus of 'streak disease' to maize. One race can transmit the virus easily, while for the other this is quite impossible. Storey was unable to find any morphological differences whatever, and he showed that the ability to transmit disease is inherited as a sex-linked dominant. It seems that this difference is dependent on the inability of the virus to penetrate the gut wall in the case of one of the forms, since, if the wall is mechanically punctured, the insect becomes ndowed with the same powers as a vector which the other form possesses.

The presence of a diapause is a character which is frequently present quite irrespective of any structural differentiation; it may be inherited as a Mendelian character, and it is of great importance in the separation of two races in view of the fact that it may entirely prevent cross-breeding. Decoppet, for instance (1920), insists that the three- or four-year life-cycle of *Melolontha* does not depend on climatic conditions but that there are two races of the insects each with its fixed cycle. Similarly, Heller (1926) finds that the hawk-moth *Celerio euphorbiae* Linn. provides an instance of a species some individuals of which undergo an obligatory diapause while others develop without any period of quiescence. It should perhaps be mentioned that the work of Decoppet has been strong.y criticized by Zweigelt (1928) and must as yet be considered as not proven. Perhaps the best known work in this line is that of the very able investigator Timofeeff-Ressovsky (1933), who compared the survival powers of strains of the fruit-fly *Drosophila funebris* Fab. of different geographical origin. The geographical races in this, as in other species of *Drosophila*, are morphologically identical. For this reason a peculiar technique had to be employed. A number of eggs of a given strain of *Drosophila funebris* was placed with the same number of eggs of *D. melanogaster* Meig. in a culture-bottle with a standard quantity of food. The quantity of food was intentionally made insufficient for the optimum development of all the larvae that hatched from both lots of eggs. Owing partly to the crowding and partly to the scarcity of food a number of the larvae died, and consequently the number of adult flies that hatched in each bottle was well below the maximum. By counting the numbers of the two species that had hatched, it was possible to obtain an estimate of the relative viability of the two species under the conditions of the experiment. In different cultures, different strains of *D. funebris* were thus compared with the same strain of *D. melanogaster*, so that their viability could be expressed in percentages of the latter. The data disclose characteristic differences in the behaviour of the strains of *D.*

funebris. Thus at 15° C. strains from Mediterranean countries are inferior to *D. melanogaster*, while the strains of central and northern Russia are almost as viable as that species. On the other hand, at 29° C. the strains from southern Russia suffer less than others. As a result of a large number of experiments it was shown that at 15° C. the viability of the strains from the Mediterranean region is consistently lower and that of the strains from Russia consistently higher than that of the strains from western, central, and northern Europe, and the author shows that these characters are very closely correlated with the climatic conditions of the countries of origin.

Similarly, *D. pseudo-obscura* Frolowa has been divided by Dobzhansky (1937) into two races. Race A is found in the Rocky Mountains and Mexico and on the coasts of San Francisco Bay: race B is restricted to the Pacific coasts of the United States and Canada and to the Sierra Nevada and Cascade Mountains. Thus, although the two overlap, the distribution region of race B is characterized by a mild, and that of race A by a hot, summer. Dobzhansky has shown that there is a relation between the fecundity of the different strains and the temperature. This is very suggestive in connexion with the geographical distribution of the two forms. Race A reaches maximum productivity sooner after hatching from the pupa than does race B. The productivity of race A remains higher than that of race B throughout the lifetime, and this accounts for a greater total egg-production. At lower temperatures (19° and 14°) race B reaches the peak of productivity later than race A but retains it much longer, and from this and other observations it is obvious that the optimum temperature for egg-production is lower in race B than in race A. Here is a case of well-marked biological differences which apparently remain distinct even where the forms overlap. The isolation here appears to be of genetical type (see also discussion in Sturtevant, 1938).

To take a similar instance from among the vertebrates, one may mention the very interesting experiments of Dice (1931) on the species and races of the mouse *Peromyscus*. Although the species are not as a rule inter-fertile under laboratory conditions, the sub-species (geographical races) of the same species can be crossed and produce offspring. In this connexion it is remarkable that some races occur in the same geographical region without either producing intermediates or losing their distinctness. Dice has made a study of two races of *P. maniculatus* (Wagner), the distribution areas of which overlap in the State of Michigan. He finds that one of these forms lives almost exclusively in forests and the other on lake beaches. Two other races of the same species occur together in Montana, and in this case it has been reported by Murie that one of them is confined to forests and the other to prairie habitats, and this again prevents crossing. In contrast to the *Drosophila* mentioned above, these races of mice show well-defined differences in colour and size and therefore do not present any special problem to the systematist. It would not be difficult to find similar instances among insects. Take, for example, the case of the Hymenopterous genus *Trichogramma*, which lives as a parasite in the eggs of a great variety of Lepidoptera. The forms of *Trichogramma* coming from different parts of the United States of America are characterized by slight colour-differences accompanied by differences in temperature optimum and therefore in length of life-cycle. Though primarily geographical races, there is much overlapping. To distinguish these forms satisfactorily the only method appears to be to rear them at a constant temperature on the same species of host egg. When this is done differences in length of life-cycle and in colour are immediately apparent. Otherwise, colour is not reliable as a distinguishing character, since it varies considerably according to the temperature at which the rearing is conducted. It is not to be wondered at that the systematics of *Trichogramma* are in fearful confusion. Indeed, Peterson (1930 *a* and *b*), one of the authorities on the genus, is reduced to speaking of one form as 'the species which has distinctly lemon-yellow females during the warm part of the active season'! For further details the works of Marchal (1936), Flanders (1931), Harland and Atteck (1933), and Salt (1937) should be consulted. Another group of Hymenoptera in which similar phenomena are manifest is the Cynipidae. The studies of Kinsey (1929, 1936), have shown that many races of the genus *Cynips* are distinguishable solely by means of differences in the type of gall produced. For the rather special case of the Aphids the works of Mordwilko (1935) and Zweigelt (1928, 1931) should be consulted.

In the previous review some examples were given of poecilogony, a term coined by Giard to connote the phenomenon of species being inseparable as adults but distinguishable in one or other of the earlier developmental stages. The importance of a study of the immature stages of insects as a means of separating otherwise very closely-allied races and species has been greatly emphasized in recent years by the work of Hackett & Missiroli (1935), and others, on the forms of malaria mosquitoes. It was long ago noticed that in some localities malaria is widespread, whereas in other districts it is rare, even though *Anopheles maculipennis* Meigen is equally common in both areas. Subsequent work has in fact revealed that *A. maculipennis* is split up into a number of races, the distribution of which overlaps. These races have very well-marked differences in behaviour, although there is no structural difference to be observed in the adult apart from some rather unreliable variations in the shape of a single spine on the male genitalia. In the larval form some structural differences are present, but they are very slight indeed, consisting merely of differences in the number of branches on certain of the body-hairs, and are only of value when treated on a statistical basis. It is the average number which provides the clue to the form which is present. When, however, eggs are examined, well-defined and easily observed differences are seen. These involve the pattern on the egg itself and the structure of the egg-float, and it has been shown that these are a sure index of the habits of the adult. On these characters *A. maculipennis* can be satisfactorily subdivided and there are now eight or nine races known, of which at least six are well established by biometric, genetic, and physiological tests as well as by field studies on bionomic characters. The first of these six races is *melanoon* Hackett. Its eggs are black or spotted and the float large and smooth. This is a form particularly associated with rice-growing. It is not a malaria carrier, and so its biology has as yet been relatively little studied. Secondly, there is *messeae* Falleroni, the eggs of which exhibit a checkered pattern on a grey ground with dark bars; the floats in this case are large and rough. This is a race which predominates in continental areas, particularly northern Europe. It prefers cool, fresh-standing water. It will not mate in confinement. It hibernates in cold shelters, it does not take blood, but lives on the fat-body reserves throughout the cold period of the year. It occurs throughout eastern Europe from Stockholm to Italy and the Balkans. Although perfectly capable of transmitting malarial parasites it is not seriously regarded as a vector of the disease since its habits take it to cattle rather than to man. The third race of *A. maculipennis*, *typicus*, is also of little importance as a malaria carrier and does not feed on man at all if other sources of food are available. Its eggs have two heavy black transverse bars on a bright grey field, with large rough floats. It breeds in fresh, pure, usually running water, and hibernates completely during the winter. It is with certain curious exceptions a mountain species, and is the least domesticated of all the races, never having been bred in captivity.

Number four, *atroparvus* van Thiel, has the egg dappled, and the floats are small and smooth. It is an inhabitant of northern Europe, is absent in the Balkans, and is occasionally a source of mild endemic malaria. It breeds in cool waters of slight to moderate salinity, and is very different from the last species in that it will mate readily in small cages and the males do not display the swarming habit. It tends to occupy warm places for hibernation, taking occasional meals of blood during the winter.

Number five, *labranchiae* Falleroni, is a form with pale broad eggs and very small rough floats. It inhabits warm brackish and salt marshes and is found chiefly in southern Europe. It is interesting to note that it will breed in fresh water. It has been suggested that this happens only when it is relieved of the competition of other races. In view of its distribution it has, as might be expected, only a short and imperfect hibernation period, and it will bite man under a great variety of conditions. For these reasons it is always a dangerous malaria carrier.

Finally, there is *elutus* Edwards, usually accepted as a distinct species. It has an egg devoid of pattern and lacking floats. It breeds in shallow standing water open to the sun with much aquatic vegetation. It is the race most tolerant to salt, although in Palestine it appears to have lost this tolerance and to be primarily a fresh-water form. It is confined to the Mediterranean region and is always associated with intense malaria. It is primarily a feeder on human blood and persistently enters bedrooms even when an abundance of other food is available close at hand.

It will be seen that, although the structural differences in these cases are so trivial that, considered alone, no systematist would regard them as warranting a specific separation, yet the biological differences with which they are associated are profound and of the very greatest importance in public health. That these forms remained constant even when present in the same area appeared probable early on in the intensive study of *A. maculipennis*. The mere fact of the differences in habitat and feeding preferences might, of course, be sufficient to render cross-breeding very rare. As a matter of fact, recent work by De Buck, Schoute, and Swellengrebel (1934) has revealed that there is a very considerable degree of physiological incompatibility between the different races. In some cases crossing cannot be obtained under experimental conditions, in others, although crossing is obtained, the eggs are often sterile or the larvae die without hatching or at a very early stage after hatching. In the *atroparvus-elutus* cross larvae die at a more advanced stage, while in a *typicus-atroparvus* cross the eggs of the F_1 generation produce healthy but sterile insects. In other crosses some of the females may be normal but all the males are sterile. In the most favourable cross which has yet been obtained all the females but only a part of the males are fertile.

Recent work (see Hackett, 1937 *a* and *b*) has shown that other widespread species of the genus *Anopheles* are made up of complexes similar to that of the *maculipennis* group, and the experiments of Tate and Vincent (1936) on similar races of the gnat, *Culex pipiens* Linn., indicate that biological characters similar to those which differentiated the races of *Anopheles*, and which also occur in *Culex*, are hereditary.[1] Much further work would, however, be necessary to establish the exact Mendelian behaviour of the various characters. In his earlier review the author referred at some length to the bearing of the study of such races on problems of the inheritance of acquired characters. He pointed out that although the existence of such forms showing apparently adaptive characters in nature make a Lamarckian explanation superficially attractive, yet

---

[1] It is interesting that many species of the malaria parasite itself also show signs of being split into races physiologically distinct, and that in all probability here as elsewhere the species will be defined on genetic terms according to their powers of hybridization within the invertebrate host (Manwell, 1936).

none of the examples so far studied and none of the experiments so far carried out gives any convincing demonstration of its occurrence. This is a subject which is really outside the scope of the present article, but it may be said that no work that has since been carried out either on the natural occurrence or the experimental production of biological races in insects has given conclusive evidence of any Lamarckian effect. While the work of Sladden (1934, 1935) on the transference of the induced ivy-feeding habit in the stick-insect *Carausius morosus* Br. W., seems to point very strongly in the direction of the inheritance of acquired characters, one must still feel caution in accepting the results until an explanation is forthcoming of the fact that even 'control' insects show a slight increase in their ability to eat ivy and in their preference for it.[1]

Quite apart, however, from any question of induced hereditary effect is the isolation which may be brought about by that type of host-selection which results from an olfactory conditioning in the larval stage of insects. As has already been pointed out by Thorpe and Jones (1937), a conditioning mechanism of this sort may well be responsible for many of the factors usually grouped under the 'Hopkins Host-selection Principle', and would thus do away with the necessity of any Lamarckian explanation such as the earlier writers on the subject regarded as more or less inevitable. Thorpe and Jones were able to show that the Ichneumonid *Nemeritis canescens* (Gravenhorst), normally a parasite of the larva of the meal-moth *Ephestia kühniella* Zell., displays a significant change in its olfactory responses when reared on the small wax-moth *Achroia grisella* Zell. Whereas the insects reared on the normal host show absolutely no response to the odour of *Achroia* when they encounter it in the air-stream of an olfactometer, those which have been reared on *Achroia*, or which have

---

[1] Since the above was written a further paper has appeared: Sladden, D. E. and Hewer, H. R. (1938), '*Transference of Induced Food Habit from Parent to Offspring*,' Proc. Roy. Soc. (*B*) *126*, 30–44. It is shown that the increased ability to eat ivy shown by the 'control' privet stock is largely a function of the time of year, this annual rhythm being absent from the ivy-fed stock. The latter shows a significantly greater ivy-preference throughout the year than does the former and it seems that the experiments can be regarded as satisfactory evidence of the hereditary transference of induced habit. So far these results stand alone and in any case the genetic basis for such changes must remain unknown until the work can be repeated with a sexually-reproducing form.

been exposed to close contact with it immediately after emergence from the pupa, are significantly attracted. It was concluded from this result that while *Nemeritis* has an inherited oviposition response to *Ephestia* larvae, an additional response to the odour of *Achroia*—a response which is entirely lacking in normal insects—can be induced by contact with this unusual host. While this does not produce any diminution in the ability of the insect to respond to *Ephestia* when no other attraction is present, it does result in the development of an entirely new response to *Achroia*. It has since been shown by the present writer (1938) that the susceptibility of *Nemeritis* to conditioning in the larval stage is apparently due to a tendency to become responsive to an olfactory stimulus characteristic of a generally favourable environment and that this tendency manifests itself equally in the adult stage. It results in a kind of 'becoming aware' of a new odour as a result of which a slight positive attraction to it is developed. As has already been pointed out, the theoretical importance of such a conditioning effect is that it will tend to split a population into groups attached to particular hosts or particular food-plants, and thus will of itself tend to prevent cross-breeding. It will, in other words, provide a non-hereditary ecological barrier which may serve as the first stage in evolutionary divergence, tending to aid the establishment of a new variety in exactly the same way as do geographical barriers.

This is hardly the place to discuss in detail the subject of isolating mechanisms, and physiological isolation is being dealt with by Professor Hogben in another chapter. It is perhaps the most important problem facing the modern geneticist interested in evolutionary problems, and it has hitherto been neglected in a most unaccountable manner. Dobzhansky, who has an excellent chapter on the subject in his book *Genetics and the Origin of Species*, refers to the 'appallingly insufficient attention that the problem of isolation has received in genetics'; and, after stating that there is probably a great variety of isolating mechanisms at work in nature, says that the mode of origin of these mechanisms remains a puzzle. He quotes Bonnier (1924 and 1927) as an example of a group of investigators who are inclined to believe that known genetic principles are insufficient to account for it. The origin of intraspecific mating preferences is one of the most difficult and most puzzling aspects of this subject of physiological isolation. Here more than almost anywhere else in this particular field is careful experiment required. Evidence that biological races do exhibit the phenomenon of preferential mating was brought forward by Thorpe (1928) in the case of races of the moth *Hyponomeuta padella* Zell., and by Lancefield (1929) and Dobzhansky (1937) for forms of *Drosophila pseudo-obscura* Frol.

Finally the question presents itself: Has recent ecological work thrown any light on the problem of the definition of the category of the genus?

Richards and Robson (1926) have pointed out that the characters used by systematists to distinguish species are often extremely trivial and show as a rule no indication of having any adaptive value. It might appear at first sight that a natural line of separation between the species on the one hand and the genus and higher categories of taxonomy on the other might be provided on this basis. Could not a genus be regarded as a group of individuals distinguished by the possession of a common structural adaptation? No doubt every worker on the systematics of all but the lowest animal phyla will be able to think of examples in his own particular group of genera restricted to very well-defined environments and distinguished by characters which seem obviously adaptive. But it appears to the writer that, although it is true that the species is a real entity while the genus is not, we cannot really say that specific characters are in any way of less adaptive importance than are generic.[1] Any difference is, in our opinion, merely due to the fact that the really fundamental characteristics of species are minute physiological ones and these, of necessity, have been neglected by taxonomists. The differences between genera are also, it is true, fundamentally biological, but, being larger and more thoroughly established, they have become more generally associated with structural characters which are also adaptive and which have been of use to systematists. The line dividing a geographical subspecies of animal, or any other infra-specific category, from a species is fundamentally different from that separating the cate-

---

[1] In some groups of mammals, birds, and insects even subspecific structural and pigmentary characters appear to be adaptive (e.g. mice of the genus *Peromyscus*, the desert larks *Ammomanes*, and certain of the races of *Carabus nemoralis* referred to above).

gory species from the category genus, not in any degree of adaptation but in the fact that the separation of the species may be defined as that stage in the evolutionary process at which physiological and ecological isolating mechanisms have become effectively established (Dobzhansky). There is thus, as was early emphasized by Bateson, a clear distinction (restricted of course to organisms with sexual reproduction) between the categories of geographical races and true species which has no counterpart in the separation of the species from the genus. To this extent the genus is artificial whereas the species is a natural entity.[1]

It seems then impossible at present to formulate any definition of a genus which would stand any chance of being acceptable to workers in all groups. For practical reasons the genus, to be a convenient category in taxonomy, must in general be neither too large nor too small. Any attempt to define a genus as that stage at which obviously adaptive structural characters are developed (Muir, 1928), while perhaps in line with the practice of those taxonomists who deal with certain groups of vertebrate animals, would result in inconveniently large genera in most other groups. Indeed, in the Protozoa and in many classes of insects a genus so defined might include a whole series of families as at present accepted. It seems far better to admit frankly that the category is purely artificial and leave it at that. This being so, there is, from the practical point of view, much to be said for the use of subgenera or other equivalent subdivision. Such intermediate groupings obviate the inconvenience of unduly large genera and on the other hand help to do away with that *reductio ad absurdum* the monotypic genus. For a more detailed discussion of the significance of the higher categories the reader is referred to the excellent paper of Kinsey (1936). Although this author's nomenclature and certain of his theoretical conclusions may be open to criticism it will be admitted

---

[1] It is true that the work of Raistrick and his colleagues (1931–8) has shown that genera of fungi such as *Fusarium* and *Helminthosporium* are as sharply characterized on biochemical grounds as they are on morphological, and that in other genera (though not in *Fusarium*) the species and strains are equally well differentiated chemically, there being many complex organic acids and nitrogenous substances known only from a single species of mould fungi. But the whole concept of species and genera is so different in the lower fungi from what it is in a sexually-reproducing metazoan that one cannot argue from one to the other, for where reproduction is asexual or parthenogenetic, species in the usual sense do not exist.

that there are few taxonomic studies based on a more comprehensive collection of material and data.

Conclusion

It seems, then, that the tendency of recent ecological and biological work generally has been to show that there exist in many phyla[1] (see Thorpe, 1930) groups of individuals which are undoubtedly distinct species in every sense except the accepted morphological one; they may be perfectly isolated from other populations present in the same region by ecological barriers, including different food habits and different time of emergence from egg or pupa which result in the impossibility of crossing. Coupled with this type of barrier there may be disinclination for cross-mating based on psychological factors, with the result that natural crosses are either excessively rare or entirely absent, while in the extreme cases—for instance, the races of *Anopheles maculipennis*—there may be physiological inability to cross even though there appears to be no valid structural dissimilarity in the mature animal.

How, then, is the work of the taxonomist which, after all, is primarily that of finding adequate and convenient handles for taking hold of these physiologically distinct groups of individuals, to be developed in order to keep pace with the advances on the biological side?

In the opinion of the writer the answer is that, just as the experimental biologist has adopted the most advanced technique of physics, chemistry, and mathematics to advance his investigations, so the taxonomist must be prepared to adopt any and every line of attack in the study of the species-problem. The fact that taxonomic work in the past has in many cases been so strongly vindicated by subsequent biological investigation, while it reflects the greatest credit on the ability—or rather genius—of the best taxonomists, does not absolve him from adopting new methods. But to enable this development to take place the museum of the future, great though recent improvements have been, will have to be a very different place from that of the present day.

[1] It seems probable that future work will show the phenomenon to be present in all phyla. Up to the present not all groups have been studied with sufficient intensity.

To the present writer it seems that, particularly in dealing with insects, the primary requirements for the development of a really adequate taxonomy are as follows:

1. All specialists should have facilities for studying their group in the field. Only with the aid of long experience in the field as well as in the museum can a really first-class systematist be developed.

2. Properly equipped biological laboratories should be attached to each museum department so that material of certain particularly plastic and difficult groups can be reared under properly controlled conditions.

3. Where this is impossible, as in certain types of marine and fresh-water biology especially, the museum should work in as close association as possible with a laboratory where the necessary facilities can be obtained, and provision should be made for interchange of staff.

4. Facilities for the adequate preservation of the early stages of animals should be made. This is particularly urgent in the case of insects and is perhaps the first need of present-day entomological museums.

5. Facilities should be provided for securing and recording exact measurements of the structure of a large series in the case of difficult species and it should be possible to have these adequately treated by modern statistical methods.

6. Finally, secretarial and other help should be available for the preservation of the fullest and most exact data for all specimens in a convenient form.

The complaint is sometimes heard that taxonomic work no longer attracts the best type of student. There is undoubtedly some truth in this. Universities are often blamed, and with some justification. University teachers have tended too often in the past to speak contemptuously of the man who spends his time counting hairs or drawing bristles, as if biology as a whole could possibly advance when the essential work of systematics is allowed to lag behind. It is true that much of the work encountered in the course of drawing up a really adequate description of a group of species is laborious in the extreme. If it becomes divorced from all other aspects of the study of the animal it may amount to drudgery of the most depressing kind. If, on the other hand, it is properly related with methods of experimental biology and ecology, there is no work of greater interest and importance. But the fault is not entirely that of the universities, it is perhaps even more that of museum conditions. These have sufficed up to the present, and facilities and conditions of work have improved enormously of recent years. But there will have to be still more changes if the taxonomist, notably the insect taxonomist, of the future is to prove equal to his task. Admirable though it is, it is not enough that there should be close co-operation between the taxonomist, on the one hand, and the ecologist, physiologist, geneticist, and statistician, on the other. While the man with a flair for taxonomy will probably—both of desire and of necessity—remain primarily a museum worker in the present sense of the term, it is essential that he should have a broad training to be able to evaluate all the evidence bearing on the species-problem as it concerns his particular group, and that he should have the facilities, as and when required, to undertake field and laboratory research from a taxonomic viewpoint. The more the present-day concept of a species becomes understood, the more essential will co-operation between the workers in different fields become for the proper study of systematics in its wide sense. The line of demarcation between taxonomy and other forms of biological research will become far less distinct than it now is. To many this may sound a depressing conclusion. If this is the position what chance is there for the relatively untrained amateur to do useful work? The answer is 'comparatively little if his work is private and unco-ordinated'. At present much amateur work is of little value because of this lack of co-ordination and because the problems tackled are incapable of solution with the time and technique available. But that there is a vast amount of biological work of real value that can be well undertaken by amateur naturalists is already being shown by such bodies as The Association for the Study of Systematics in Relation to General Biology, The British Trust for Ornithology, and The Society for British Entomology. It should be the function of such organizations, acting through the medium of local natural history societies, to direct the enthusiasm and ability of amateurs into the right channels. If this is done much valuable work may be accomplished. It will perhaps not be long before really critical systematics in certain groups will have to be the concern of teams of workers rather than of individuals. A similar tendency has long been manifested in the sciences of experimental physics and biochemistry. An admirable example is the work of Raistrick and his colleagues (1931–8) on the forms of *Aspergillus* and other mould fungi which, incidentally, has on biochemical grounds vindicated in an astonishing way the previous conclusions of the morphologist and systematist. The museum worker whose primary function, apart from the arrangement of educational exhibits, is the reduction to order of natural objects, should be equipped so that every line of approach can be followed up. This may seem a counsel of perfection. The ideal museum, with its biological laboratories and its specialized workers in many branches, may seem at present far beyond practical politics. But unless, by some method or another, the resources of the museum worker are augmented so as to enable him to achieve the precision and refinement of work necessitated by the rapidly increasing rate of ecological and bionomical investigation, the gap between the requirements of the practical entomologist and zoologist and the abilities of the taxonomist will become ever greater. Without some such advance many branches of zoological work, particularly in applied biology, will be hindered and eventually brought to a standstill. But if the development does take place taxonomy will resume its rightful position as one of the most fundamental and important branches of biological work, and systems of classification will become an accurate index of the knowledge of animals obtained by all the varied techniques of biology.

REFERENCES

BONNIER, G. (1924). 'Contributions to the Knowledge of Intra- and Interspecific Relationships in *Drosophila*.' *Acta Zool.* **5**, 1.

—— (1927). 'Species-differences and Gene-differences.' *Hereditas*, **9**, 137.

CHAPMAN, F. M. (1900). 'A Study of the genus *Sturnella*.' *Bull. Amer. Mus. Nat. Hist.* **13**, 297.

DE BUCK, A., SCHOUTE, E., and SWELLENGREBEL, N. H. (1934). 'Crossbreeding Experiments with Dutch and Foreign Races of *Anopheles maculipennis*.' *Riv. Malariol.* **13**, 237.

DECOPPET, M. (1920). *Le Hanneton.* Lausanne.

DICE, L. C. (1931). 'The Occurrence of Two Subspecies of the Same Species in the Same Area.' *J. Mammal.* **12**, 210.

DOBZHANSKY, T. (1935). *Philosophy of Science*, **2**, 344.

—— (1937). *Genetics and the Origin of Species.* New York.

EMERSON, A. E. (1935). 'Termitophile Distribution and Quantitative Characters as Indicators of Physiological Speciation, &c.' *Ann. ent. Soc. Amer.* **28**, 369.

FLANDERS, S. E. (1931). 'The Temperature Relationships of *Trichogramma minutum* as a Basis for Racial Segregation.' *Hilgardia*, **5**, 395.

FULTON, B. B. (1933). 'Inheritance of Song in Hybrids of Two Subspecies of *Nemobius fasciatus* (Orthoptera). *Ann. ent. Soc. Amer.* **26**, 368.

GOLDSCHMIDT, R.: many publications, especially: (1932). 'Untersuchungen zur Genetik der geographischen Variation. V. Analyse der Überwinterungszeit als Anpassungscharakter.' *Arch. Entw. Mech.* **126**, 674; (1933). 'Untersuchungen zur Genetik, &c., VI. Die geographische Variation der Entwicklungsgeschwindigkeit und des Grössenwachstums.' Ibid. **130**, 266.

HACKETT, L. W., and MISSIROLI, A. (1935). 'The Varieties of *Anopheles maculipennis* and their relation to the Distribution of Malaria in Europe.' *Riv. Malariol.* **14**, 45.

HACKETT, L. W. (1937a). *Malaria in Europe: an Ecological Study.* London.

—— (1937b). 'Recent Additions to our Knowledge of *Anopheles maculipennis* Races.' *Bull. Health Organ. League of Nations*, **6**, 1.

HARLAND, S. C., and ATTECK, O. M. (1933). 'Breeding Experiments with Biological Races of *Trichogramma minutum* in the West Indies.' *Z. ind. Abst. Vererb.* **64**, 54.

HELLER, J. (1926). 'Chemische Untersuchungen über die Metamorphose der Insekten. III. Ueber die «subitane» und «latente» Entwicklung.' *Biochem. Z.* **169**, 208.

—— (1930). 'Sauerstoffverbrauch der Schmetterlingspuppen in Abhängigkeit von der Temperatur.' *Z. vergl. Physiol.* **11**, 448.

KINSEY, A. C. (1929). 'The gall-wasp Genus *Cynips*. A Study in the Origin of Species.' *Indiana Univ. Stud.* **84**, **85**, and **86**.

—— (1936). 'The Origin of Higher Categories in *Cynips*.' *Indiana Univ. Pub. Sci. Ser.* **41**.

KRUMBIEGEL, I. (1932). 'Untersuchungen über physiologische Rassenbildung.' *Zool. Jahrb. Syst.* **63**, 183.

LAL, K. B. (1934). '*Psyllia peregrina* Först., the Hawthorn Race of the Apple Sucker, *P. mali* Schmidt.' *Ann. Appl. Biol.* **21**, 641.

—— (1934). 'Insect Parasites of Psyllidae.' *Parasitology*, **26**, 325.

LANCEFIELD, D. E. (1929). 'A Genetic Study of Crosses of Two Races or Physiological Species of *Drosophila obscura*.' *Z. ind. Abst. Vererb.* **52**, 287.

LATHROP, P. H., and NICKELS, C. B. (1931). 'The Blueberry Maggot from an Ecological Viewpoint.' *Ann. ent. Soc. Amer.* **24**, 260.

LUND, H. O. (1934). 'Some Temperature and Humidity Relations of two Races of *Trichogramma minutum*.' Ibid. **27**, 324.

MANWELL, R. D. (1936). 'The Problem of Species, with special reference to the Malaria Parasites.' *Ann. Trop. Med. Parasit.* **30**, 435.

MARCHAL, P. (1936). 'Recherches sur la biologie et le développement des Hyménoptères parasites, Les Trichogrammes.' *Ann. Epiphyt. phytogen.* **2**, 447.

MORDVILKO, A. (1935). 'Die Blattläuse mit unvollständigem Generations-zyklus und ihre Entstehung.' *Ergebn. Zool.* **8**, 36.

MUIR, F. (1928a). 'Some Remarks on Function as a Base for Classification and its Relationship to Form.' *Proc. Hawaii entom. Soc.* **7**, 135.

—— (1928b). 'The Role of Function in Taxonomy, &c.' *Trans. 4th internat. Congr. Entom.* **2**, 600.

MURIE, A. (1933). 'The Ecological Relationship of Two Subspecies of *Peromyscus* in the Glacier Park Region, Montana.' *Occ. Pap. Mus. Zool. Mich.* **270**, 1.

ØKLAND, F. (1937). 'Die geographischen Rassen der extramarinen Wir-beltiere Europas.' *Zoogeographica*, **3**, 389.

PETERSON, A. (1930a). 'How may Species of Trichogramma occur in North America?' *J. N.Y. ent. Soc.* **38**, 1.

—— (1930b). 'A Biological Study of *Trichogramma minutum* Riley as an Egg Parasite of the Oriental Fruit Moth.' *U.S. Dep. Agr. Tech. Bull.* **215**.

PICKETT, A. D. (1937). 'Studies on the Genus *Rhagoletis* (Trypetidae), &c.' *Canad. J. Res.* **15**, 53.

PROMPTOFF, A. (1930). 'Die geographische Variabilität des Buchfinken-schlags (*Fringilla coelebs* L.), &c.' *Biol. Zbl.* **50**, 478.

RAISTRICK, H. (1938). 'Certain Aspects of the Bio-chemistry of the Lower Fungi (Molds.).' *Egebn. Enzymforsch*, **7**, 316.

—— et al. (1931). 'Studies in the Bio-chemistry of Micro-organisms.' *Phil. Trans. Roy. Soc.* (*B*), **220**, 1 (see esp. Part III, pp. 27–54).

—— (1931–8). *Biochem. J.*, many papers.

RICHARDS, O. W., and ROBSON, G. C. (1926). 'The Species Problem and Evolution.' *Nature*, **117**, 345 and 382.

ROBSON, G. C., and RICHARDS, O. W. (1936). *The Variation of Animals in Nature*. London.

SALT, G. (1937). 'The Egg-parasite of *Sialis lutaria*: A study of the Influence of the Host upon a Dimorphic Parasite.' *Parasitology*, **29**, 539.

SCHRÖTER, C., and KIRCHNER, O. (1896 and 1902). *Vegetation des Bodensees*, Parts I and II. London.

SLADDEN, D. E. (1934, 1935). 'Transference of Induced Food-habit from Parent to Offspring,' Parts I and II. *Proc. Roy. Soc.* (*B*), **114**, 441, and **119**, 31.

STOREY, H. H. (1932). 'The Inheritance by an Insect Vector of the Ability to transmit a Plant Virus.' Ibid. **112**, 46.

STURTEVANT, A. H. (1938). 'On the Origin of Interspecific Sterility.' *Q. rev. Biol.* **13**, 333.

TATE, P., and VINCENT, M. (1936). 'The Biology of Autogenous and Anautogenous Races of *Culex pipiens* L., &c.' *Parasitology*, **28**, 115.

TAVERNER, P. A. (1926). 'Birds of Western Canada.' *Mus. Bull. Victoria Mem. Mus.* **41**.

THORPE, W. H. (1928). 'Biological Races in *Hyponomeuta padella* L.' *J. Linn. Soc.* (*Zool.*), **36**, 621.

—— (1930). 'Biological Races in Insects and Allied Groups.' *Biol. Rev.* **5**, 177.

—— (1938). 'Further Experiments on Olfactory Conditioning in a Para-sitic Insect.' *Proc. Roy. Soc.* (*B*), **126**, 370.

THORPE, W. H., and JONES, F. G. W. (1937). 'Olfactory Conditioning in a Parasitic Insect and its Relation to the Problem of Host Selection.' Ibid. **124,** 56.

TIMOFEEFF-RESSOVSKY, N. W. (1933). 'Über die relative Vitalität von *Drosophila melanogaster* Meigen und *D. funebris* Fabricius, &c.' *Arch. Naturgesch.* (N.F.), **2,** 285.

—— (1935). 'Über geographische Temperaturrassen bei *Drosophila funebris* F.' Ibid. **4,** 245.

ZWEIGELT, F. (1928). 'Der Maikäfer.' *Monogr. angew. Ent.* **9.**

—— (1931). 'Blattlausgallen.' Ibid. **11.**

EMBRYOLOGY AND TAXONOMY

By G. R. DE BEER[1]

ALL biologists are familiar with von Baer's dilemma, quoted by Darwin: 'In my possession are two little embryos in spirit, whose names I have omitted to attach, and at present I am quite unable to say to what class they belong. They may be lizards or small birds, or very young mammalia, so complete is the similarity in the mode of formation of the head and trunk in these animals.' It was, of course, on the basis of experiences such as this that von Baer was led to formulate his famous principle that 'embryos of different members of the same group are more alike than their adults, and that the resemblances are greater the younger the embryos examined', as Sedgwick (1894) has epitomized it.

The bearing of von Baer's generalization on systematics was also seen by Sedgwick, for it might mean 'that whereas the differences between the adults are large and important differences of class value, the differences between the embryos are slighter and unimportant, and of less than class value'. If von Baer's principle were of universal or even of general application, it is clear that the outlook for the possible contributions which embryology might make to minor taxonomy would be unpromising, although its importance in establishing affinities between large groups (e.g. annelids and molluscs, which have a trochophore larva) may be great. Embryology enabled Baur (1864) to recognize the molluscan nature of *Entoconcha* from its veliger, and Thompson (1836) to establish the systematic position of *Sacculina* from its cypris larva. Embryological studies can often supply evidence of affinity in a general way between groups, but can only rarely provide material for the establishment of divergences between small groups.

However, with the progress of embryology and increasing familiarity with embryonic and larval material, it becomes

[1] The writer wishes to acknowledge the help he has received in suggestions from Dr. J. S. Huxley, Mr. E. B. Ford, and Mr. J. A. Moy-Thomas, and in connexion with entomological literature from Prof. G. D. Hale Carpenter and Dr. B. M. Hobby. In regard to some points concerning allometric growth he has had the privilege of consulting Professor R. A. Fisher and Professor J. B. S. Haldane.

more and more clear, as Sedgwick (1894) was among the first to show, that (in his words) 'a species is distinct and distinguishable from its allies from the very earliest stages all through the development, although these embryonic differences do not necessarily implicate the same organs as do the adult differences'. In whatever way the 'value' of class differences may be determined, it must be held to apply to the whole life-history of an organism, and not merely to a time-section through it.

While it is the usual condition to find that the child is father to the man in the more general aspects of his structure, it can sometimes be shown that important peculiarities of an adult are directly traceable to particular developmental events. The characteristic torsion of the gastropod molluscs is the result of an episode in early development, as Garstang (1928) has stressed; the rosy lips of adult man are probably a consequence of an infantile adaptation to prolonged lactation, as Devaux (1933) has suggested; the bodily proportions of many forms are the result of particular local growth-rates during development (see p. 378), as Huxley (1932) has amply demonstrated. But even if the important systematic differences of the adult are imperfectly or incompletely developed in the young, this would provide no justification for degrading the value of these differences from that of one systematic group to that of another of lower rank. The principle enunciated by von Baer is merely a rough formulation, without detailed analysis, of the phenomena of development as presented by most organisms; and there are no grounds for the view that an organism as it develops passes through systematic categories of differing 'values', or of differing degrees of estrangement from organisms of other groups.

These considerations do not, however, conflict with the fact that there are, occasionally, marked similarities between young forms not exhibited by their adults, largely because the differentiations which characterize the adults have not yet appeared. This is especially the case with groups which possess characteristic larval forms. For a considerable time the study of this question was obscured and obstructed by the desire to see in larval forms the adult form of the ancestors, as the theory of recapitulation in its Haeckelian sense, now generally abandoned, tried to make out. On the contrary, it is now accepted that the various larvae, trochophore, veliger, pilidium, nauplius, pluteus, &c., represent adaptive modifications to a pelagic habit of life, fulfilling the function of securing the dispersal of the species. It is a corollary of such adaptations that the better the larva is suited for its mode of life, the greater will be the difference between it and its adult, and the more violent will be the metamorphosis by which the adult is produced. But although it can in many cases be shown that these larval forms could not represent the adult ancestral forms, this does not detract from their value as evidence of affinity between the organisms which possess any particular type. Thus, annelids are related to molluscs because of their trochophore larva; the tornaria larva of *Balanoglossus* relates it to Echinoderms. In the same way, the phenomenon of spiral cleavage exhibited by Polyclad Turbellaria, Nemertinea, Polychaeta, and Mollusca may be regarded as having been inherited from a common ancestor, but itself gives no information as to what that ancestor was like. A pretty indication of the common descent of Scaphopod Mollusca and Polychaeta is provided by the fact that the method of cleavage, with formation of a polar lobe containing the organ-forming substances for the apical organ and the post-trochal region, is identical in *Dentalium* and in *Sabellaria*, as Wilson (1904) and Hatt (1932) have shown. Their common ancestor may not actually have possessed a polar lobe, but they must have inherited from it the prerequisite conditions for its development.

From the point of view of evolutionary studies, something very valuable is gained by the grouping together of the above-mentioned phyla and classes which possess the method of spiral cleavage; and it is satisfactory that reptiles, birds, and mammals agree in the possession (though not necessarily in the method of formation) of an amnion by their embryos; the structure of the placenta has enabled Hill (1932) to make a valuable contribution to the phylogeny of primates. On the other hand, there are many cases in which developmental phenomena by themselves have proved a very insecure foundation upon which to build systematic categories, as a consideration of a few examples will reveal.

The idea of classifying Insecta according as to whether they undergo metamorphosis or not can be traced back to Swammerdam (1669) and Ray (1710), while Leach (1817) introduced the terms Ametabolia and Metabolia. Since then there have been numerous other attempts, for an account of which the reader is referred to Handlirsch (1908). But such a subdivision of the class in no way reflects the structural resemblances between the adults of the various orders, and is clearly artificial. The same is true of Latreille's (1825) classification of Urodela into Caducibranchiata and Perennibranchiata. Here it can be demonstrated beyond question that neoteny and the retention of larval characters has occurred independently in each of the five orders of the sub-class: in Cryptobranchoidea, *Cryptobranchus alleghaniensis* (Daudin); in Amblystomoidea, *Amblystoma tigrinum* (Green); in Salamandroidea, *Amphiuma means* Garden and *Typhlomolge rathbuni* Stejneger; in Proteidae, *Necturus maculatus* Rafin. and *Proteus anguineus* Laur.; and in Sirenoidea, *Siren lacertina* L.

Attempts to base systematic groups of high rank on developmental phenomena may, therefore, present serious dangers. As to groups of lesser rank, as will be seen below, the value of embryological studies to systematics lies not so much in the establishment of groups on this or that larval character, as in the recognition that groups of different rank vary in the extent of the discrepancies that they may show when classified according to adult or larval characters.

A study of the relations between development and systematics must therefore consider the difficult problems presented by those cases in which the larval forms of groups of related organisms lend themselves to schemes of classification which disagree with schemes on which the adults are classified.

The condition most usually found is that in which differences between the adults of related groups are reflected in corresponding but lesser differences between their larval or youthful forms. This simple condition, in which classification-schemes built upon adult and larval characters would coincide, is, however, by no means universal, and Weismann (1876) considered the possibilities of larval and adult classification-schemes being 'congruent' and 'incongruent'. The problem has been reinvestigated by van Emden (1929), who has shown that many situations are possible. The first is the congruent condition: group-definitions based on larval and on adult characters coincide. The last is the incongruent condition: classification based on larval structure is at odds with that based on adult structure. Between these extremes, however, there are other possibilities, including cases in which indistinguishable or very similar larvae give rise to different adult types, and others in which distinguishable larvae give rise to very similar adult types. It will be useful, then, to consider in turn the conditions of: I, congruence; II, adult divergence; III, larval divergence; and IV, incongruence; and to find examples for each of these, as van Emden has done, in respect of: a, species of a genus (or closely related genera); b, subspecies of a species; and c, mutants. (The last category in van Emden's work is 'varieties', but it is preferable to restrict attention to varieties whose genetic basis has been established.) It must be remembered that in spite of the importance of the problem, little is known of the time at which genes exert their effects during development. Haldane (1932) has proposed a very useful classification of genes from this point of view.

I.a. The congruent condition is the most usual. It is necessary to bear in mind the fact that in all these cases, which follow von Baer's principle of progressive specialization during development, the differences between young forms will be less marked than between adults, though nevertheless of specific value. An example given by van Emden is that of *Carabus clathratus* L., *C. granulatus* L., and *C. cancellatus* Illig., in which, although very similar, differences of specific value are found between larvae as well as between the adult beetles.

I.b. Less common is the congruence between larval and adult characters in subspecies of a species. *Haliplus fulvus* F. has a Pyrenean subspecies *carlitensis* Rég. the larva of which is also distinguishable by a difference of subspecific value in mandible form.

I.c. The occurrence of mutations which visibly affect both larva and adult is rare. This, as Ford (1937) has pointed out, is to be expected, as larval and adult organisms usually possess different habits of life entailing different adaptive requirements. An example is that of *Colias philodice* Godt. in which the larva and the eye of the butterfly are grass-green in colour owing to the presence of chlorophyll-α and xanthophyll. A recessive mutation studied by Gerould (1921) inhibits the extraction of xanthophyll from the food and results in blue-green larvae and imagines with eyes of similar colour. Another mutation has been discovered which reddens the xanthophyll pigments, so that larvae and imaginal eyes are olive-green.

II.a. Examples of different species in which the larval forms are apparently indistinguishable or very similar are not common. Some are provided by *Bematistes macarista* (E. M. Sharpe) and *B. poggei* Dewitz, where the larvae are 'of identically the same appearance' as described by Hale Carpenter (1912), who also observed great similarity between the larvae of *Acraea alciope* Hew. and *A. humilis* E. M. Sharpe, and between those of *Acraea terpsichore* L. and *A. alicia* E. M. Sharpe. Other examples are supplied by species of *Chironomus* as described by Lenz (1926). *Smerinthus populi* L. and *S. ocellata* L. provide a case where the larvae are much more similar than the adults, and, among Anura, Boulenger (1908) could find only a trivial colour-difference between the tadpoles of *Megalophrys montana* Kuhl, and those of *M. parva* Boulenger.

II.b. *Pieris napi bryoniae* O. has been regarded as a subspecies of *Pieris napi*, and its larva is similar to that of the type. However, Muller (1933) has produced evidence tending to show that *bryoniae* is a distinct species of *Pieris*, in which case this example should be included under II.a. Boulenger (1891) was unable to find any differences wherewith to distinguish between the tadpoles of the various races of *Rana esculenta* L. which he had diagnosed.

II.c. A great number of mutant genes affect the adult and not the larva, and so fall into this category. For examples, the reader is referred to monographs such as that of Morgan, Bridges, and Sturtevant (1925) on the genetics of *Drosophila*.

III.a. Cases in which young forms of different species differ widely while their adults are very similar, are hard to find. Sedgwick (1894) states that he was long in doubt whether *Peripatus capensis* Grube and *P. balfouri* Sedgwick were distinct species until he studied their development; for while the adults differ in trivial characters, the ovum of *P. capensis* is 0·6 mm. long and the embryo contracts and shortens when touched, but the ovum of *P. balfouri* is 0·4 mm. long and the embryo when touched coils into a spiral. The best example of this category is, however, that of the moths *Acronycta tridens* Schiff. and *A. psi* L. So similar are the adults of these species that South (1908) states: 'I am unable to indicate any character that will serve to distinguish between this moth [*A. tridens*] and the Grey Dagger [*A. psi*].' In fact the distinction as based on the genitalia is given by Pierce (1909) and amounts practically to little more than the bifurcation of the clasper in the male in *psi* and its trifurcation in *tridens*. But the larva of *tridens* has a white stripe with orange spots down the back and a blunt black hump on the fourth ring, whereas that of *psi* has a yellowish stripe and a slender tall hump on the fourth ring which is easily distinguishable.

Among Amphibia, Annandale (1917) has shown that two closely allied species of frog, *Rana tigrina* Daudin and *R. cancrivora* Gravenhorst, have tadpoles which differ widely in their buccal armature. Other examples in which the larvae differ more than the adults are provided by *Rana jerboa* Günther and *R. whiteheadi* Boulenger, described by Boulenger (1893), and by *Rana beddomei* Günther and *R. semipalmata* Boulenger, described by Annandale (1918). Lastly, there are those cases like *Salamandra salamandra* [L.], and *S. atra* Laurenti, in which related and similar adults differ in their development, which is in one case of the larval and in the other of the embryonic type.

III.b. Of subspecies of a species in which the larval forms differ more than the adults, an example given by van Emden (1929) is *Acronycta auricoma* F., the larva of which has yellowish-red tubercles on each ring, while that of subspecies *alpina* Frr. has the tubercles a brilliant white. According to Lenz (1926), *Chironomus salinarius* Kieff has two larval forms differing in the degree of reduction of the gills. Schmidt (1934) has described a remarkable developmental dimorphism in the Nemertine *Lineus gesserensis-ruber* O. F. Müll. It has long been known that this species develops by means of an embryo of the Desor type; the eggs, 0·5 mm. in diameter, are laid, six in a soft-membraned capsule, in flexible masses of spawn. All eggs develop into inert embryos with small blastopore and thick epidermis. But occasionally spawn is found in sausage-shaped masses of capsules with thick membranes, each containing about fifteen eggs 0·25 mm. in diameter. Only 30 per cent. of these eggs develop, into very mobile embryos with thin epidermis and large blastopores which engulf the other eggs. The adult *Lineus* shows colour variations ranging from red to green, and Schmidt observed that red or reddish adults laid eggs which developed solely according to the newly discovered type, while green or greenish adults laid eggs which developed along the lines of the Desor type.

III.c. Several examples are given by Cockayne (1928) of larval variation in insects, and by Ford (1937) of larval mutants. The larva of *Lasiocampa quercus* var. *sicula* Stgr. has red fur; that of var. *meridionalis* Tutt has white fur; the difference is due to a single pair of genes. In *Lymantria dispar* L. Goldschmidt (1924) found that a single pair of genes is responsible for the fact that the larvae of Eurasian races are dark, while those of south-west Japan are light in colour. Races of *Lymantria* may also differ in the number of moults which they undergo, without affecting size at pupation, and Goldschmidt (1933) has produced evidence to show that moulting is controlled by a system of three multiple allelomorphs. Many mutant genes of *Bombyx mori* belong here.

IV. Incongruence of classification based on larval and adult characters provides problems of great interest. Van Emden (1929) cites the case of *Smerinthus ocellata*, whose adult resembles that of *Calasymbolus excaecata* (Abb. and Smith), while its larva resembles that of *S. populi* and differs considerably in colour from that of *C. excaecata*. In this case, a classification based on adults would group *ocellata* with *excaecata*, while a classification based on larvae would dissociate them and group *ocellata* with *populi*.

For the practical purposes of taxonomy the adult scheme of classification is usually regarded as the more important, though it is not always easy to see how the larval scheme is to be brought into line with it. This has, however, been attempted for the apparently incongruent species of *Carabus* by Bengtsson (1927). While it is clear, as Noble (1925-6) has shown for Amphibia and Mortensen (1921) for Echinoderms, that group-characteristics can be recognized in the larvae of the majority of groups as characterized by adult structure, exceptions occur which transcend the classification widely. The remarkable case of the Echinoidea and their plutei has been studied by von Ubisch (1933). The structure of the skeleton of the four-armed pluteus is practically identical in *Sphaerechinus granularis* A.Ag. and *Echinocyamus pusillus* Gray, although the families (Strongylocentrotidae and Fibulariidae) to which they belong are in different sub-classes (Regularia Ectobranchiata and Irregularia). Similarly, the four-armed pluteus of *Arbacia lixula* (L.) (sub-order Arbacina) is practically indistinguishable from that of *Strongylocentrotus franciscanus* A.Ag. (sub-order Echinina); and the eight-armed pluteus of *Arbacia punctulata* Gray is very similar to that of *Echinocardium cordatum* Penn.

On the other hand, the plutei of *Lytechinus variegatus* Lamk. and of *L. verruculatus* Ltk. differ markedly, owing to the trellis-work of the postoral arms and the aboral 'basket' of the latter. Mortensen (1921) is even inclined to create a separate genus for *verruculatus*.

The incongruent distribution of the characters of the plutei has been interpreted by von Ubisch (1933) on morphogenetic grounds.[1] There is evidence in the larva of a gradient of skeleton-forming activity, with its high point at the vegetative pole. Skeletal pieces near the vegetative pole of the larva tend to be more complex in structure, to show trellis-work instead of simple rods, and to be massive instead of slender. Alterations in intensity of the skeleton-forming gradient might occur for reasons totally unconnected with common descent, and might occur independently in different groups. This would go far to explain the similarities between distantly related and the differences between closely related plutei.

A crude case of incongruence is provided by the Ophiuroidea, for whereas their adult structure relates them much more closely to the Asteroidea than to the Echinoidea, the ophiopluteus larva bears a closer resemblance to the echinopluteus than to the brachiolaria. Such resemblance is, however, spurious and due to the adaptive needs of flotation.

Having now considered the various modes of congruence and incongruence between larval and adult characters, it remains to see whether conclusions may be drawn of importance from the point of view of systematics. It will have been noted that in all the categories the material chosen for the demonstration of examples, whether nemertine, insect, echinoderm, or amphibian, is uniformly characterized by extensive metamorphosis. This is, of course, a necessary condition for the emphasizing of larval structures, which in forms with direct development are harder to differentiate. It must also be remembered that such

[1] For somewhat similar cases in plants, see Thoday, D., 1939, ' Interpretation of Plant Structure,' *Nature, 144,* 571.

conclusions as can be drawn are subject to the manner in which the species and subspecies in question have been defined by the systematists. Nevertheless, the following points emerge and are probably valid. As pointed out by van Emden (1929), in respect of possibilities of incongruence, the species agrees in general with the lesser systematic categories of subspecies and mutant, and all three differ from the family and higher ranks of classification. The genus appears to occupy an intermediate position in this respect. It may be presumed that divergence of genetic value usually affects both young and adult types. Further, it is to be noticed that the systematic unit in which the limits as defined by larval and adult characters coincide most frequently is the species; i.e. in the preceding analysis, category I.a is commoner than I.b or I.c. In other words, when the whole life-cycle is taken into consideration, the species has more clearly defined limits than the subspecies or the mutant. Conversely, it can be seen that the systematic unit in which the categories other than congruence are most rarely found is again the species; categories II.c and III.c are much commoner than II.a or III.a. In other words, larval convergence, larval divergence, and incongruence are most frequently found in subspecies and mutants. The unit which systematists call the species appears, therefore, to be in a slightly different position as compared with the subspecies and the mutant. This conclusion is not only of interest and importance in itself, but it also suggests a reason for the difference between the species and the lower categories. For during the time that the differences between mutants and subspecies have widened into the value of interspecific differences, the now distinct species, ceasing to resemble one another sufficiently closely in either larval or adult state, no longer fall into any other category of the preceding analysis than I.a.

These matters can be profitably expressed in the form of a table (p. 375).

Attention may now be turned to another aspect of the relations between embryology and taxonomy, namely the question whether there is a connexion between the time of appearance in ontogeny of an evolutionary novelty and the ultimate systematic value of the new type. So long as the Haeckelian theory of recapitulation held sway, such a question could not arise, for it was regarded as axiomatic that evolutionary novelties contributing to phylogeny could only be introduced at the end of the life-histories, to be pressed into earlier and earlier stages of

	a. *Species of a Genus*	b. *Subspecies*	c. *Mutants*
I. Congruence	Most species	*Haliplus fulvus* and var. *carlitensis*	*Colias philodice*
II. Adult divergence	*Bematistes macarista* and *poggei* *Acraea alciope* and *humilis* *Acraea terpsichore* and *alicia* *Chironomus* spp. *Smerinthus populi* and *ocellata* *Megalophrys montana* and *parva*	*Pieris napi* and var. *bryoniae* *Rana esculenta*	Most mutants
III. Larval divergence	*Peripatus capensis* and *balfouri* *Acronycta tridens* and *psi* *Rana tigrina* and *cancrivora* *Rana jerboa* and *whiteheadi* *Rana beddomei* and *semipalmata*	*Acronycta auricoma* and var. *alpina* *Chironomus salinarius* *Lineus gesserensis-ruber*	*Lasiocampa quercus* vars. *sicula* and *meridionalis* *Bombyx mori* *Lymantria dispar* and many larval variations not yet genetically analysed
IV. Incongruence	*Smerinthus ocellata* and *populi*, *Calasymbolus excaecata* *Carabus* spp. *Sphaerechinus granularis* and *Echinocyamus pusillus* *Arbacia lixula* and *Strongylocentrotus franciscanus* *Lytechinus variegatus* and *verruculatus*		

ontogenetic development with progressive phylogenetic advance. Novelties appearing during development, termed caenogenetic by Haeckel, were regarded as without significance for phylogeny.

But the theory of recapitulation, in this sense of abbreviated and accelerated repetition of phylogeny, is now discredited and generally abandoned, thanks to a number of workers, among whom it will suffice to mention Garstang (1922). It is now clearly recognized that evolutionary novelties may make their appearance in any stage of the life-history, and may in subsequent generations become retarded, accelerated, or retain the same position in the time-scale of the ontogeny. In other words, it is just as possible that the adult descendant may resemble the ancestral embryo as that the embryo of the descendant may resemble the ancestral adult. The former possibility appears to be much the more important, and since it accounts for the dropping out from the life-history of the descendant of the adult characters of the ancestor, this condition may be known as 'anti-recapitulation'. It was pointed out by de Beer (1930) that the phylogenetic effects of largest systematic importance seem to be associated with evolutionary novelties which have either made their first appearance and exerted their main effects in early stages of ontogeny (cases of 'caenogenesis' or 'deviation'), or which have resulted in the retention of juvenile characters in the adult (cases of 'neoteny').

As an example of caenogenesis may be mentioned the embryonic membranes which distinguish the three highest classes of Chordata from the remainder as the Amniota. An example of deviation is provided by the sudden twist which gastropod larvae undergo and which, when it first occurred, was the starting-point of what was to become the whole class. To neoteny may be ascribed the origin of Chordata from organisms resembling echinoderm larvae, or of Insecta from the larvae of some myriapod-like forms. It is to be noted that in the last three cases there has been the production of a new type of adult organization, endowed with high potential for further evolution, and this process has been termed 'paedomorphosis'.

On the other hand, evolutionary novelties which exert their main effects at later stages of the life-histories (cases of adult variation and 'acceleration') are less likely to produce large changes and may be supposed to give rise to mutants, subspecies, species, and genera; such evolution is characterized by ever-increasing specialization and progressive loss of the potential for further evolution. This process is referred to as 'gerontomorphosis'. The study of ontogeny to find the stage of development at which the difference between types first becomes manifest, has been termed 'phenogenetics' by Haecker (1925): a field which appears to be of great promise.

It is concluded that, as evolution proceeds, paedomorphosis is succeeded by gerontomorphosis which actualizes the further evolutionary potentialities opened up by paedomorphosis and exhausts them. The group then lingers or becomes extinct unless a new bout of paedomorphosis supervenes. It is of interest to note that palaeontologists, among whom may be mentioned Wedekind (1920) and Beurlen (1930), have on independent grounds come to the same conclusion regarding the occurrence of alternate bouts of 'large' and 'small' evolution. Schindewolf (1937) has also recognized the correlation between early ontogenetic appearance of the evolutionary novelty and systematic importance of the resulting new type.

A point of view in many ways similar to that outlined above has been developed by Sewertzow (1931). He recognizes large changes of general adaptive significance which do not restrict the possibilities of life of the type, and which he terms 'aromorphosis'. Examples are the evolution of the brain and heart in early Chordata, of jaws and fins in Gnathostomata, of lungs in Tetrapoda. On the other side there are the changes which lead to a progressive restriction of mode of life and specialization, which Sewertzow calls 'idio-adaptation'. As to the time in ontogeny when the evolutionary novelties may arise, Sewertzow has shown that it may be early (cases of 'archallaxis'), or in the middle (cases of 'deviation'), or at the end of development (cases of 'anaboly'). He concludes that major novelties arise by archallaxis, while anaboly leads to the modification and specialization of organs and structures already present.

The importance of these matters in connexion with the present discussion is that the *ultimate* systematic value of the new group formed is correlated with the time in ontogeny at which the variation made its effects manifest. Thus, when the larva of an ancestral untorted mollusc underwent its torsion (it would seem to have been sudden, for there are no intermediate stages of torsion; to-day it takes about two minutes in *Acmœa*) it provided a new type which was destined to become a class, out of which all Gastropoda have become differentiated.

The idea that groups of potentially higher systematic value

are formed rapidly during paedomorphic phases of evolution, and subsequently become split into groups of progressively restricted systematic value during gerontomorphic evolution, finds support in Matthew's (1927) study of the early history of the mammals. At the beginning of the Tertiary period, many orders of mammals are already present, but they are represented by few types and are not yet diversified into the numerous families and genera which exist now. In other words, evolution had not proceeded very far in producing what Osborn (1902) called the 'adaptive radiation' of the mammals.

A comparative study of embryos and adults of ancestors and descendants is thus able to support systematics in the view that there have been origins of phyla, classes, and orders, as well as origins of species, and to suggest a reason why some new types have lent themselves better than others to the formation of the groups of higher rank. But since the systematist is mainly concerned with the making of new species, and other groups of low rank, and evolution is slow, the prognosis of the ultimate systematic importance of a new type will necessarily be of academic rather than practical interest.

The study of the relative growth-rates of parts of organisms, or allometric (previously: heterogonic) growth, has a bearing of the greatest importance on systematics. To appreciate this fact it will be convenient to give a brief account of the essential principles underlying the phenomenon of allometry. The easiest method of approach is to consider first the special case of isometric growth and to imagine two magnitudes such as the size of an organ and the total size of the body, growing at the same rates (relatively to their size), and therefore maintaining a constant proportion between them. If the organ is denoted by y and the body by x, this state of affairs can be expressed by saying that y is proportional to x, or $y \propto x$. Now introducing the possibility of exponential powers, since $x^1 = x$, the same expression can be written $y \propto x^\alpha$ where $\alpha = 1$. In all cases of proportion, the sign 'equals' can be substituted for 'is proportional to' by introducing a figure which denotes how great y is when $x = 1$. The expression then becomes $y = bx^\alpha$, and b is the constant of proportion, which can be calculated from the fact that $b = y/x^{\alpha}$. The value of b will depend on the units of measurement employed; that of α does not.

Now if α remains equal to 1, the two magnitudes will always bear the same proportion to one another, and the growth of the organ or part is said to be isometric. But observation and measurement of relative growth-rates of parts and wholes of the most widespread material among plants and animals has shown that organs or parts not only frequently grow relatively faster (or slower) than the wholes, but that this relative difference of growth-rate is constant over long periods of time during development and adult life. In other words, the value of α in these cases is either greater or smaller than 1, and the growth is said to be positively or negatively allometric. The value of α is the relative growth-rate and is known as the growth-constant. For examples of cases of allometric growth the reader is referred to the interesting studies by Huxley (1924, 1932), to whom more than to any one is due the recognition of the significance and importance of these phenomena. It is to be noted that the law of allometric growth applies not only to the magnitudes of organs and parts but also to quantities of chemical substances present at different stages of development, as Teissier (1931) and Needham (1934) have shown, and to changes in the rate of oxygen consumption, as shown by Atlas (1938). It is clearly of fundamental importance.

One more point remains to be mentioned in connexion with the allometric growth formula. Introducing logarithms, it can be written $\log y = \log b + \alpha \log x$. The advantage of this notation is that, when plotted in the form of a graph, the data of a case of allometric growth give a straight line. The angle made between this line and the axis of x determines the value of α, so that the tangent of this angle is equal to α. It will be noticed that when the angle is $45°$, the tangent is 1, and the growth is isometric, which is merely a special case of allometric growth. (For terminology, see Huxley & Teissier, 1936.)

It must also be noted that the value of α can change at certain times of the life-history and continue constant in its new value for a considerable or at least appreciable length of time. It will therefore be realized that the relative size of an allometric organ or part is dependent on the values of b and of α, and on the time of onset of changes in the value of α.

From the point of view of systematics, the first important fact to notice is that in a species which possesses allometric organs the proportions of the form, i.e. the 'shape' of the species, change with the total size. No definition of such a species can therefore rest on any specification of proportions of allometric organs or parts relatively to the whole. Further, in the majority of forms there is no fixed limit of growth, so that if such species have allometric organs, they possess no fixed or definitive adult form.

But while there is in such cases inconstancy of *form*, there is constancy of *form-change*, and this, measured by the value of the growth-constant α, is also a specific character.

Other lines of work have shown that rates of production of substances in the body are under the control of genes. Ford and Huxley's (1929) demonstration of the control of the speed of formation and deposition of melanin in the eyes of *Gammarus chevreuxi* Sexton, may be taken as an example. There it has been found that the rapid or slow darkening of an otherwise red eye is dependent on the rate of melanin deposition, which in turn is controlled by a few pairs of genes. Since growth must be regarded as the result of the activity of some growth-promoting substance, and the quantity of such substance must presumably be under the control of similar 'rate-genes', there is every reason to believe that the characteristic growth-constants of a species are inherited under rigorous genetic control.

These facts can now be used to test the validity of the distinction between different systematic groups. Attention may therefore be turned to comparisons between the growth-phenomena of different alleged races of a species, or even different species.

First may be considered cases in which the values of b and α are constant, but the total size attained by the organisms differs. *Cervus elaphus* L. (the red deer) in Scotland seldom exceeds 125 kg. in weight or 12 points on the antlers. In the Carpathians, the stags may reach 250 kg. in weight and have 25 points on the antlers. Huxley (1931a) has shown that the antlers grow in such a way that the final size which they reach in relation to the body in each year is allometric ($b = 0.00162$, α $= 1.6$). The difference in body-size may to some slight extent be due to genetic differences, but these cannot be important since Scottish deer introduced into New Zealand grow almost as big as their Carpathian relatives. Therefore this particular type of difference between the Scottish and Carpathian deer involves little genetic difference, although it is customary to separate them as geographical varieties or subspecies.

The phenomenon of developmental polymorphism as exhibited by certain insects (organisms with a fixed definite size) may profitably be considered here. In the stagbeetle *Cyclommatus tarandus* (Thunb.) the mandibles of the males not only vary in relative size, but also in the number and disposition of 'teeth' carried on them, to such an extent that five types ('prionodont', 'amphiodont', 'telodont', 'mesodont', 'mesamphiodont') have been distinguished by coleopterists. It will have been noticed in the case of stags' antlers that large antlers are not only quantitatively different from the small ones in size, but qualitatively different in shape in possessing more points. The shape seems to be correlated with size in some manner. There appears to be no doubt that the same is true of the mandibles of *Cyclommatus*, and Huxley (1931*b*) has shown that as the mandibles are markedly allometric ($b = 0\cdot01$, $\alpha = 1\cdot97$), the different types have no genetic basis at all, and are merely the effects of allometric growth following upon the attainment of different final body-sizes by the organisms. (On the other hand, there are also cases of beetles—*Eurytrachelus gypaëtus* Casts. and *E. purpurascens* Snell.—where, as Paulian (1936) has shown, polymorphism is due to genetic differences).

Cases may now be considered in which races of a species differ in one or both of the constants in the allometric growth formula, or in the time of onset of change. Examples of these have been given by Teissier (1936).

First, there is the possibility that the value of α may remain unchanged, but b may vary. This is found in *Littorina sitchana* Phil. from Asodokoro and Yunoshima, studied by Nomura (1926). The length and height of the shell differ so that if the former is regarded as x and the latter as y in the allometric formula, the value of α is found to be $0\cdot74$ in both races, but the value of b is 7 per cent. smaller in the Yunoshima than in the Asodokoro race. Nothing is as yet known as to whether the difference in the value of b is genotypic or phenotypic in this case. This question would require experiments either of breeding or of transference of individuals from one locality to the other.

Identity of the growth-constant α need not invariably imply identity of species, for the possibility may occur that the initial size differs in two forms and in such a case the whole scale of the phenomena will be altered. A good example of this is provided by Teissier's (1937) studies on the growth of *Maia squinado* (Herbst) and *M. verrucosa* M. Edw. In both species the growth of the propus of the male claw relatively to the length of the carapace is allometric; the value of the growth-constant α is 1·93 in both cases. But *squinado* is absolutely larger than *verrucosa*, and while in the former the propus reaches 75 per cent. of the carapace-length at a carapace-length of 180 mm., this proportion is attained in the latter at a carapace-length of 90 mm. A difference of absolute size is thus an important feature of the difference between these two species. The genetic control of size is, of course, well known in countless examples of animals and plants. It would be interesting to study the growth-constants of other cases in which speciation has apparently resulted from size-differences (e.g. *Necturus m. maculatus* (Rafin.) and the diminutive *N. m. lewisi* Brimley, or *Bufo peltacephalus* Dum. and Bibr. and the diminutive *B. dunni* Barbour).

That differences in the value of *b* can rest on a genotypic basis is proved by experiments of Sinnott and Kaiser (1934) on the shapes of the gourd *Cucurbita pepo* L. The differences between the 'disk', 'sphere', and 'elongate' types of fruit are already apparent in the earliest primordia, thus showing that the growth-constants (i.e. the values of α) are already fixed; the variation is in the value of *b*, and the genetic behaviour of these types proves that they are controlled by two pairs of genes.

Next may be considered cases in which local races of a species have the same values for α but differ in the time of onset of changes in those values. Chevais (1937) has analysed a case of this nature in *Corophium volutator* (Pallas). The second antenna of this amphipod crustacean shows an allometry which at Roscoff is slightly positive in the young ($b = 0·406$, $\alpha = 1·36$), and in males which have reached a length of 4·5 mm. becomes accentuated ($b = 0·14$, $\alpha = 2·07$), while in females it becomes negative ($b = 0·739$, $\alpha = 0·91$).

In a population of *Corophium* from Wimereux, the values of *b* and of α in the young are the same as in the young of the Roscoff population, and the values of α for adult males and females also correspond exactly. But the time of onset of these changed values of α is delayed until the time when the body-length is 6 mm. The values of b for adult males and females (0·03 and 0·597 respectively) of the Wimereux race consequently differ from those of the Roscoff race.

There is nothing to show in this case whether the difference in time of onset of the changed rate of growth is phenotypically or genotypically determined. But cases are known in which the moment of onset of a reaction is under genetic control. Examples are provided by *Gammarus chevreuxi* in which Ford and Huxley (1929) showed that there are genes controlling the time of onset of deposition of melanin in the eyes as well as others controlling its rate.

Passing now to cases in which the growth-constant α varies in different races, an example is provided by *Haliotis gigantea* Chemmitz, studied by Sasaki (1926). The growth of the transverse diameter of the shell of this form relatively to the longitudinal diameter shows an allometry with the growth-constant α equal to 1·05 for individuals of the type species, and of 0·84 for individuals of the race *discus* Reeve. Another example is found in the Essex race of *Corophium volutator* (see above), where the values of α (1·57 for young forms, 2·23 for adult males, 1·05 for adult females) differ from those found in the Roscoff and Wimereux races, being larger in each case.

Here, again, it is unknown whether the differences in the values of α are due to genetic or environmental change. That the value of α can be controlled genetically is known from the case of *Capsicum annuum* L. where genes have been found by Sinnott and Kaiser (1934) to control the shape of the fruit by determining the growth-constant, for the ovary of the pepper flower is spherical, and the difference between the spherical and elongated types of fruit only becomes manifest shortly after flowering.

The discovery that a local population had an aberrant value of α and that it was under genetic control would be good evidence that the population in question formed a distinct subspecies. Conversely, the fact that the growth-constants of a reputed race or species conformed to those of another race or species might throw doubt on the validity of the distinction.

Chevais (1937) has found that the growth-constants of *Corophium arenarium* Crawford, from Leigh-on-Sea, are much closer to those of *C. volutator* from Roscoff than to those of *C. arenarium* from Roscoff. These facts raise doubts, also shared by Crawford (1937), as to whether *C. arenarium* is anything more than a subspecies of *C. volutator*.[1]

Reference must now be made to the so-called rule of Lameere (1904) or of Geoffrey Smith (1906). Briefly, this is the observation that when related species have homologous allometric organs, those organs are often of a relative size that varies, within limits, with the absolute body-size of the species, just as occurs among individuals of a species with an allometric organ. This interspecific allometry is, however, usually less exact than the allometry within the different species, and its quantitative value is different. Many examples of this phenomenon are cited by Champy (1924). A good series is that presented by the beetles *Golofa porteri* Hope, *G. imperialis* Thoms., and *G. eacus* Burmeister. Another example is that of the Cervidae, where in general the head-ornament is relatively smaller in absolutely smaller species.

These facts mean that variation in body-size between species is accompanied by an effect on the allometric organ of the same nature as that consequent upon variation in body-size within a species. In this connexion a fact of great interest has been noted by Huxley (1932), namely, that where homologous allometric organs are found conforming to the phenomenon of Lameere, it is clear that the relative size of the allometric structure is automatically determined and consequential on the body-size, and has not been selected for adaptive value. This fact will be particularly appreciated by systematists. On the other hand, selection is often active in keeping down the size of positively allometric organs and structures, as examples cited by Champy (1924) show, constituting exceptions to the phenomenon of Lameere. A disharmony in size of copulatory organs, for example, would be disastrous to the species. Where selection is unable, so to speak, to disconnect the growth-rates of an allometric organ and of the body, as was probably the case with the Irish elk, the species faces the danger of extinction.

[1] See also Reeve, E.C.R. 'A statistical analysis of subspecific differences within the genus Tamendua (Xenarthra).' *Proc. Zool. Soc.*, in press.

Attention may now be turned to one of the most remarkable phenomena connected with allometry. It was noticed by Dubois (1897) that the weight of the cerebral hemispheres as compared with that of the body in adult mammals of the same sex in groups of different, *yet related*, species obeyed a formula equivalent to $y = bx^\alpha$, and that the value of α was in all cases approximately 0·56. Lapique and Girard (1905) established the same relations for the brain in birds, as did Dubois (1913) in reptiles and fishes; the value of α remaining approximately equal to 0·56.

The problem has been reinvestigated by Brummelkamp (1937, 1939), who has shown that this growth-constant of value 0·56 is applicable (within each family or group) to 94 species of mammals distributed among a dozen families, to 26 species of birds falling into 6 groups, to 9 species of reptiles falling into 2 groups, and, with less precision, to some species of Amphibia and fish.

Brummelkamp claims to have brought out the additional remarkable fact that, in all these cases, the value of the constant of proportion b as calculated for the different groups of species, varies from group to group by a simple multiple of $\sqrt{2}$. Also, isolated species may differ from the bulk of related species in the same way. Thus in mammals, taking the value of log b for *Homo sapiens* as standard, that for *Pan vetus* and *Hylobates leuciscus* is lower by 3 log $\sqrt{2}$; that for *Gorilla gorilla*, *Simia satyrus*, *Hylobates syndactylus* and *H. lar* is 4 log $\sqrt{2}$ lower; that for *Canis lupus*, *C. nubilus*, *C. domesticus*, *C. aureus*, *C. vulpes*, *C. zerda*, and *Hyaena striata* is 6 log $\sqrt{2}$ lower. Among the Ungulates, the same value for b applies to *Camelus dromedarius mehari*, *Giraffa camelopardalis*, *Equus caballus*, *Alces americanus*, *Oryx beisa*, *Antilope caäma*, *Cervus porcinus*, &c.; the value of b for *Bos taurus*, *Phacochoerus africanus*, and *Tapirus indicus* is log $\sqrt{2}$ lower; that for *Tragulus javanicus* and *Hippopotamus amphibius* is 2 log $\sqrt{2}$ lower; that for *Sus scrofa* is 3 log $\sqrt{2}$ lower; on the other hand, for *Elephas indicus* the value of log b is 3 log $\sqrt{2}$ higher, and for *Cervus muntjac* it is 2 log $\sqrt{2}$ higher.

The allometric growth formula for cerebral hemispheres relatively to body-weight may therefore be written:

$$v = b(\sqrt{2})^k x^\alpha$$

where k is a whole number or zero.

3 D

Expressed in another way, it can be said that if the value of the constant of proportion b for *Homo sapiens* is taken as b_H, then the following values for b can in a general way be ascribed to the following groups: Anthropomorpha, $\frac{1}{4} b_H$; Canidae, Bovidae, Cervidae, $\frac{1}{8} b_H$; Tragulidae, Viverridae, Leporidae, Dipodidae, $\frac{1}{16} b_H$; Talpidae, Muridae, $\frac{1}{32} b_H$; Microchiroptera, $\frac{1}{64} b_H$.

The term 'cephalization-constant' has been applied by Dubois to the constant of proportion b, since it is concerned with the degree of cerebral development over and above that which is consequential on the allometric growth-constant α. It indicates relatively how much more brain one species has than another after allowing for differences in body-size and relative brain-size. The value of b may therefore be held in some measure as a rough guide to the degree of cerebral development and as a very rough approximation to the mental powers of an organism. A list of mammalian species classified in order of their cephalization-constants is given by Anthony (1928).

The constancy of the value of α when measuring cerebral hemisphere-size and body-size *from one species to another* is remarkable enough. But equally important is the fact, discovered simultaneously by Dubois (1898) and Lapique (1898), that the value of α when measuring cerebral hemisphere-size and body-size of large and small adult individuals *of one and the same species* is also constant, but with a much lower value, approximating to 0·26. This fact has been established for *Homo sapiens*, *Canis familiaris*, *Felis domesticus*, *Equus caballus*, *Ovis aries*, *Lepus cuniculus*, *Talpa europaea*, *Gallus domesticus*, and *Rana catesbeyana* (references in Brummelkamp, 1937).

The value of α thus shows a difference between the extent of intraspecific and interspecific variability, which will be referred to again below. Dubois has given the terms 'phylogenetic constant' and 'ontogenetic constant of individual variability' to the interspecific and intraspecific values of α, approximating respectively to 0·56 and 0·26. In this connexion it should be noted that the brain appears to be peculiarly favourable material for the study of this phenomenon. In the case of the dimensions of face-length y relatively to total skull-length in horses, Robb (1935) has shown that the value of α in the expression $y = 0·3x^{1·23}$ holds good for interspecific as well as intraspecific variation.

An additional point of interest is the fact that the value of the 'ontogenetic constant' is lower in domestic species (*circ.* 0·22) than in wild species, and the same is true of the 'cephalization-constant'. It would appear, as suggested by Huxley (1932), that the artificial selection practised by man in intensifying intraspecific variation in body-size has produced less change in brain-size than is apparently brought about by natural selection working on wild forms.

By way of explanation of the value of the 'ontogenetic' constant, Dubois (1918) has calculated that the volume of fully developed and homologous neurons (cell-bodies) in the cerebral hemispheres varies allometrically to the body-weight with a growth-constant equal to 0·27. It follows, since this value is so close to that of the 'ontogenetic constant', that the differences in size of the cerebral hemispheres within one and the same species will be largely accounted for by differences in volume of a definite number of cells. On the other hand, the differences in size of the cerebral hemispheres between one species and another require differences in number as well as in the volume of the cells of which they are composed.

According to Brummelkamp, the value of the 'ontogenetic constant' was assessed too highly by Dubois, and should be in the neighbourhood of 0·22. On the other hand, the value of the growth-constant for the size of the cell-bodies of neurons relatively to body-size comes out at about 0·3 from Brummelkamp's investigations This value is of great interest, since it indicates that the volume of the neuron varies roughly as the cube root of body-size; in other words, the volume of the neuron varies with the linear dimensions of the body The linear is, of course, the dimension with which the growth of axons is most closely concerned. The volume of the cell-body of a given neuron would thus vary with the length of the axon.

No explanation is forthcoming of the value (0·56) of the 'phylogenetic constant' of interspecific variability, although it may be connected with some surface-volume relation. As to why the constant of proportion should vary by integral multiples of √2, possible explanations have been advanced by Dubois and by Brummelkamp. For Dubois (1923) the reason for the integral nature of the difference between the value of *b* in different groups of species is to be found in the assumption that all the cells of the cerebral hemispheres undergo one or more extra general cell-divisions. Brummelkamp (1937) has found that the total nuclear volume of neurons contained in cylinders of unit cross-sectional area taken right through the cerebral cortex varies from species to species by multiples of $\sqrt{2}$ where the multiple is a whole number or zero. He also cites numerous other cases (liver cells, testis interstitial cells, carcinoma cells) where in those cases in which nuclear volume varies it does so proportionately to a whole-number multiple of $\sqrt{2}$. The significance of this relation is, however, still obscure and deserves further study.

The fact remains that this remarkable study of the relation of brain-size (the cerebral hemispheres represent a fraction of the entire brain that can be calculated with considerable accuracy) to body-size, which Dubois has called the theory of cephalization, opens up a field of great importance from many points of view, and particularly that of systematics. More observations will, of course, be required before the constancy of the 'ontogenetic constant' for intraspecific variability and of the 'phylogenetic constant' for interspecific variability can be regarded as definitely established. This constancy seems already to have been demonstrated, however, for a sufficient number of cases, for it to be well worth taking into consideration in assessing the nature of variability. Studies must also be made of earlier stages of development to determine the value of the allometric growth-constant of the cerebral hemispheres during those stages, and to find out the relation between this constant (or constants) and the 'ontogenetic' and 'phylogenetic' constants.

As an example of the way in which these facts may turn out to be of use in the estimation of the 'value' (i.e. interspecific or intraspecific) of variability and in the study of evolution, Dubois (1923) mentions the case of the polecat, *Putorius putorius*. The variability of cerebral hemisphere-size and body-size in this form has an allometric growth-constant of the value of 0·42, which is roughly midway between the values of the intraspecific 'ontogenetic' constant 0·26 and the interspecific 'phylogenetic' constant 0·56. Can it be that this form shows a transition from intraspecific to interspecific variability?

Again, the fact that related groups of species tend to differ from one another in respect of simple multiples of $\sqrt{2}$ in the constant of proportion raises the question whether there may not here be a method of determining whether problematical forms fit on to one or other of the known values of $b, \times 1, 2$, or other integer. It would, for example, be interesting to know the value of b for Cetacea, Sirenia, Tubulidentata, Tarsioidea, Chrysochloroidea, Marsupialia, and Monotremata.

Lastly, arising out of these matters, there is a point concerning the relative dimensions of the skull, which are often used for descriptive and diagnostic purposes. Kappers (1927) pointed out that, among individuals of one and the same species, the smaller the absolute body-size the more pronounced the brachycephaly and brachencephaly; the larger the absolute body-size the more pronounced the dolichocephaly and dolichencephaly. These facts receive their explanation from the studies on the intraspecific variability of brain-size and body-size. For since the value of the allometric growth-constant of the brain (better, cerebral hemispheres) is low (0·26), the growth of the brain is negatively allometric. Therefore at small body-size the brain is relatively large, and its accommodation in the skull is accompanied by the tendency towards the assumption on the part of the latter of the more geometrically economical form of the sphere: the brain becomes brachencephalic and the skull brachicephalic. On the other hand, at large body-size the brain is relatively small, there is no difficulty in its accommodation within the skull, and there is no necessity for the approximation to spherical form: the brain therefore is dolichencephalic and the skull dolichocephalic.

Now, therefore, when a distinction between two alleged races is based on differences of proportions of skull dimensions accompanied by differences in body-size, there is a strong suspicion that these differences are simply the result of the effect on skull-form of the intraspecific brain growth-constant. For instance, the common stoat *Mustela erminea stabilis* Barrett-Hamilton, is said to have skull-lengths varying from 48·8 to 52·4 mm., and skull-widths ranging from 28·4 to 30 mm. (average ratio 0·57) The Jura stoat *M.e.ricinae* Miller, is smaller in general size, and its skulls vary in length between 47 and 50 mm, and in width between 28·4 and 31·2 mm. (average ratio 0·61). This is just what would be expected according to the argument developed above, and it will at any rate be clear that differences in skull proportions such as these are not by themselves trustworthy indices of systematic differences. As Huxley (1932) has pointed out, variations in certain dimensions in the skull of Man must be treated with similar caution, for they may only represent the effects of allometry of skull-growth in different dimensions at varying total body-sizes.

REFERENCES

ANNANDALE, N. (1917). 'Zoological Results of a Tour in the Far East. Batrachia.' *Mem. As. Soc. Bengal*, **6**, 115.

—— (1918). 'Some Undescribed Tadpoles from the Hills of Southern India.' *Rec. Ind. Mus.* **15**, 18.

ANTHONY, R. (1928). *Anatomie comparée du cerveau.* Paris.

ATLAS, M. (1938). 'The Rate of Oxygen Consumption of Frogs during Embryonic Development and Growth.' *Physiol. Zool.* **11**, 278.

BAUR, A. (1864). 'Beiträge zur Naturgeschichte der Synapta digitata.' *Verh. k. leop.-carol. Akad. Nat.-forsch.* **31**, (3).

DE BEER, G. R. (1936). *Embryology and Evolution.* Oxford.

BENGTSSON, S. (1927). 'Die Larven der Nordischen Arten von Carabus L.' *Lunds Univ. Årsskr.* **24**, 1.

BEURLEN, K. (1930). 'Vergleichende Stammesgeschichte, Grundlagen, Methoden, Probleme unter besonderer Berücksichtigung der höheren Krebse.' *Fortschr. Geol. Paläont.* **8**, (26) 317.

BOULENGER, G. A. (1891). 'A Contribution to the Knowledge of the Races of *Rana esculenta* and their Geographical Distribution.' *Proc. zool. Soc. Lond.* 374, 593.

—— (1893). 'Description of new reptiles and Batrachians obtained in Borneo by Mr. A. Everett and Mr. C. Hose.' Ibid. 522.

—— (1908). 'A Revision of the Oriental Pelobatid Batrachians (genus *Megalophrys*).' Ibid. 407.

BRUMMELKAMP, R. (1938). *Normale en abnormale hersengroei in verband met de cephalisatieleer.* Proefschrift, Amsterdam.

—— (1939a). 'Das sprungweise Wachstum der Kernmasse.' *Acta neerl. Morph.* **2**, 177.

—— (1939b). 'Das Wachstum der Gehirnmasse mit kleinen cephalisierenden Sprüngen.' Ibid. **2**, 188.

CHAMPY, C. (1924). *Sexualité et hormones.* Paris.

CHEVAIS, S. (1937). 'Croissance et races locales de Corophium volutator.' *Trav. Stat. biol. Roscoff*, (15).

COCKAYNE, E. A. (1928). 'Annual Address. Larval variation.' *Proc. S. Lond. ent. nat. Hist. Soc.* 55.

CRAWFORD, G. I. (1937). 'A Review of the Amphipod genus *Corophium* with Notes on the British Species.' *J. mar. biol. Assoc.* **21**, 589.

DEVAUX, E. (1933). *Trois problèmes.* Paris.

DUBOIS, E. (1897). 'De verhouding van het gewicht der hersenen tot de groote van het lichaam bij de Zoogdieren.' *Verh. Akad. Wet. Amst.* 5, no. 10.

—— (1898). 'Ueber die Abhängigkeit des Hirngewichtes von der Körpergrösse beim Menschen.' *Arch. Anthrop. Braunschw.* 25, 423.

—— (1913). 'On the Relation between the Quantity of Brain and the Size of the Body in Vertebrates.' *Verh. Akad. Wet. Amst.* 16, 651.

—— (1918). 'On the Relations between the Quantities of the Brain, the Neurone and its Parts, and the Size of the Body.' Ibid. 20, 1328.

—— (1923). 'Phylogenetic and Ontogenetic Increase of the Volume of the Brain in Vertebrata.' Ibid. 25, 230.

VAN EMDEN, F. (1929). 'Ueber den Speciesbegriff vom Standpunkt der Larvensystematik aus.' *3. Wandersamm. deutsch. Entomol.* 47.

FORD, E. B. (1937). 'Problems of Heredity in the Lepidoptera.' *Biol. Rev.* 12, 461.

—— and HUXLEY, J. S. (1927). 'Mendelian Genes and Rates of Development in *Gammarus chevreuxi*.' *Brit. J. exp. Biol.* 5, 112.

—— —— (1929). 'Genetic Rate-factors in *Gammarus*.' *Arch. Entw.Mech. Org.* 117, 67.

GARSTANG, W. (1922). 'The Theory of Recapitulation: a Critical Restatement of the Biogenetic Law.' *J. Linn. Soc. Lond. (Zool.)* 35, 81.

—— (1928). 'The Origin and Evolution of Larval Forms.' *Rep. Brit. Ass. Adv. Sci. D.*

GEROULD, J. H. (1921). 'Blue-green Caterpillars: the Origin and Etiology of a Mutation in Hemolymph Color in *Colias (Eurymus) philodice*.' *J. exp. Zool.* 34, 385.

GOLDSCHMIDT, R. (1924). 'Untersuchungen zur Genetik der geographischen Variation. I.' *Arch. Entw.Mech. Org.* 101, 92.

—— (1933). 'Untersuchungen zur Genetik der geographischen Variation. VII.' Ibid. 130, 266.

HAECKER, V. (1925). 'Aufgaben und Ergebnisse der Phänogenetik.' *Bibl. Genet.* 1, 93.

HALDANE, J. B. S. (1932). 'The time of Action of Genes and its Bearing on Some Evolutionary Problems.' *Amer. Nat.* 66, 5.

HALE CARPENTER, G. D. (1912). 'Synaposematic Resemblance between Acraeine Larvae.' *Trans. ent. Soc. Lond.* 702.

HANDLIRSCH, A. (1908). *Die fossilen Insekten.* Leipzig.

HATT, P. (1932). 'Essais expérimentaux sur les localisations germinales dans l'œuf d'un annélide *(Sabellaria alveolata* L.).' *Arch. Anat. micr. Paris,* 28, 81.

HILL, J. P. (1932). 'The Developmental History of the Primates.' *Philos. Trans. B,* 221, 45.

HUXLEY, J. S. (1924). 'Constant Differential Growth-ratios and their Significance.' *Nature, Lond.* 114, 895.

—— (1931a). 'The Relative Size of Antlers in Deer.' *Proc. zool. Soc. Lond.* 819.

—— (1931b). 'Relative Growth of Mandibles in Stag Beetles.' *J. Linn. Soc. Lond. (Zool.)* 37, 675.

HUXLEY, J. S. (1932). *Problems of Relative Growth.* London.

HUXLEY, J. S. and TEISSIER, G. (1936) 'Terminology of relative growth.' Nature, *137*, 780.

KAPPERS, C. U. A. (1927). 'The Influence of the Cephalization Coefficient and Body Sizes upon the Forms of the Fore Brain in Mammals.' *Proc. K. Akad. Wet. Amst.* **31**, 65.

LAMEERE, A. (1904). 'L'Évolution des ornements sexuels.' *Bull. Acad. Belg.* 1337.

LAPIQUE, L. (1898). 'Sur la relation du poids de l'encéphale au poids du corps.' *C. R. Soc. Biol. Paris* (Ser. 10), **5**, 62.

—— and GIRAUD, P. (1905). 'Poids de l'encéphale en fonction du poids du corps chez les oiseaux.' *C. R. Acad. Sci. Paris*, **140**, 1057.

LATREILLE, P. A. (1825). *Familles naturelles du règne animal.* Paris.

LEACH, W. E. (1817). *The Zoological Miscellany.* London, **3**, 57.

LENZ, F. (1926). 'Die Chironomiden-Metamorphose in ihrer Bedeutung für die Systematik.' *Ent. Mitt.* **15**, 440; 'Die Larve der mycetophilide *Gnoriste apicalis* Mg. als Quellbewohner.' Ibid. **16**, 18.

MATTHEW, W. D. (1927). 'The Evolution of the Mammals in the Eocene.' *Proc. zool. Soc. Lond.* 947.

MORGAN, T. H., BRIDGES, C., and STURTEVANT, A. H. (1925). 'The Genetics of Drosophila.' *Bibl. Genet.* **2**.

MORTENSEN, T. (1921). *Studies of the Development and Larval forms of Echinoderms.* Copenhagen.

MÜLLER, L. (1933). 'Pieris bryoniae O. und napi L.' *Int. ent. Z.* **27**, 93.

NEEDHAM, J. (1934). 'Chemical Heterogony and the Ground Plan of Animal Growth.' *Biol. Rev.* **9**, 79.

NOBLE, G. K. (1925). 'An Outline of the Relation of Ontogeny to Phylogeny within the Amphibia. I and II.' *Amer. Mus. Nov.* nos. 165, 166.

—— (1926). 'The Importance of Larval Characters in the Classification of South African Salientia.' Ibid. no. 237.

NOMURA, E. (1926). 'Further Studies on the Applicability of $a=kb^x$ in expressing the Growth Relations in Molluscan Shells.' *Sci. Rep. Tohoku imp. Univ.* **2**, 63.

OSBORN, H. F. (1902). 'The Law of Adaptive Radiation.' *Amer. Nat.* **34**, 353.

PAULIAN, R. (1936). 'Sur la nature génétique de certains cas de polymorphisme chez les mâles de Lucanides.' *Proc. zool. Soc. Lond.* 751.

RAY, J. (1710). *History of Insects.*

ROBB, R. C. (1935). 'A Study of Mutations in Evolution, I and II.' *J. Genetics*, **31**, 39.

SASAKI, K. (1926). 'On the Growth Relations in Earshells.' *Sci. Rep. Tohoku imp. Univ.* **2**, 197.

SCHINDEWOLF, O. H. (1937). 'Beobachtungen und Gedanken zur Descendenzlehre.' *Acta Biotheor.* **3**, 195.

SCHMIDT, G. A. (1934). 'Ein zweiter Entwicklungstypus von Lineus gesserensis-ruber O. F. Mull.' *Zool. Jahrb. Abt. Anat. Ont.* **58**, 607.

SEDGWICK, A. (1894). 'On the Law of Development commonly known as Von Baer's Law; and on the Significance of Ancestral Rudiments in Embryonic Development.' *Quart. J. micr. Sci.* **36**, 35.

SEWERTZOW, A. N. (1931). *Morphologische Gesetzmässigkeiten der Evolution.* Jena.

SINNOTT, E. W., and KAISER, S. (1934). 'Two Types of Genetic Control over the Development of Shape.' *Bull. Torrey bot. Cl.* **61**, 1.

SMITH, G. W. (1906). 'High and Low Dimorphism, with an account of certain Tanaidae of the Bay of Naples.' *Mitt. zool. Sta. Neapel,* **17**, 312.

SOUTH, R. (1908). *Moths of the British Isles.* London.

SWAMMERDAM, J. (1669). *Algemeene Verhandeling van bloedloose diertjens.* Utrecht.

TEISSIER, G. (1931). 'Recherches morphologiques et physiologiques sur la croissance des insectes.' *Trav. Sta. biol. Roscoff,* **9**, 29.

—— (1936). 'Croissance comparée des formes locales d'une même espèce.' *Mém. Mus. roy. Hist. Nat. Belg. 2ᵉ Sér.* 629.

—— (1937). 'Comparaison biométrique de deux espèces du genre Maia (Crustacés Brachyoures).' *C. R. Acad. Sci. Paris,* **204**, 67.

THOMPSON, J. V. (1836). 'Natural History and Metamorphosis of *Sacculina carcini.*' *Ent. Mag.* **3**, 452.

VON UBISCH, L. (1933). 'Untersuchungen über Formbildung. III. Ein vorwiegend speculativer Beitrag zur Frage der Entstehung und systematischen Bedeutung der Seeigelplutei.' *Arch. Entw.Mech. Org.* **127**, 216.

WEDEKIND, R. (1920). 'Ueber Virenzperioden (Blüteperioden).' *Sitz.Ber. Ges. Beförd. ges. Naturw. Marburg,* 18.

WEISMANN, A. (1876). *Studien zur Descendenz-Theorie,* **2**, Leipzig.

WILSON, E. B. (1904). 'Experimental Studies on Germinal Localization, I. The Germ Regions in the Egg of Dentalium.' *J. exp. Zool.* **1**, 1.

PALAEONTOLOGY AND THE TAXONOMIC PROBLEM

By W. J. ARKELL and J. A. MOY-THOMAS

'Darwin gave us a new conception, but, being a wise man, did not attempt to base a new system upon it. Ernst Haeckel, however, with the enthusiasm and imagination of a poet, and with a poet's license, started us well on the road to a Phylogenetic System. Along this road we have progressed with more and more certainty in proportion as we have taken shorter steps with securer foothold. But the further we penetrate the mists of our ignorance, the more do we recognize that our new system is quite incompatible with any of the older systems; and we begin to wonder whether it can really serve that practical purpose which every classification must serve if it is to justify its existence. Some of us therefore are impelled to put to the modern systematist the old question "*Quo vadis?*" ' (Bather, 1927*a*, p. 96).

PALAEONTOLOGICAL classification, like all classification, must primarily be useful. It should provide a practical means by which fossils can be identified and compared. Since geologists date the strata by the contained fossils, it is essential to their science that they should be able readily to identify the fossils. The method of classification now used by the majority of palaeontologists is the phylogenetic one, in which fossils are arranged as nearly as possible in accordance with the supposed course of their evolution. Thus classification has come to aim, not only at providing an easy means of recognizing fossils, but also at giving a summary of existing knowledge of phylogeny. It is because these dual objects frequently tend to produce conflicting results that the problems of taxonomy have arisen. Some writers, such as Bather (1927*b*), have expressed doubt whether phylogeny is really the best basis for a classification, and others (Bremekampe, 1931) have denied that it can usefully be considered at all.

The unit in all classification is the 'species', expressed in the second term of the name as constructed on the binomial system. Tate Regan (1926) aptly defines a species as 'a community or number of related communities, whose distinctive morphological characters are in the opinion of a competent systematist sufficiently definite to entitle it, or them, to a specific name'. In palaeontology the species can legitimately be thought of, more briefly, as 'a practical and convenient unit by which fossils are distinguished'.

The question 'What constitutes a species?', always so trouble-some to the neontologist, hardly concerns the palaeontologist, since the more he learns of phylogeny the more arbitrary must be the distinctions he draws between his species. He is, in fact, torn between two irreconcilable endeavours; for as a phylogenist he strives to reveal closer and closer relationships, while as a systematist he must point out differences and divide up his material into units bearing distinct names.

The palaeontologist, therefore, is concerned nowadays not so much with the concept of the species as with the concept of the phylogeny. It is part of the palaeontologist's business to unravel phylogeny by the study of fossils; but he can only arrive at an approximation to the truth, for he has only a fraction of the material to work on, the hard parts which alone have been preserved by fossilization. At the best of times his results are hypothetical and more or less subjective, and it may be questioned whether such results form a suitable foundation on which to build a classification and a nomenclature. Experts seldom agree on matters of phylogeny, especially the details. The work of one author is always liable to be swept away by another, and with it goes the classification and the nomenclature. The baffling changes of nomenclature that result from this cause are all too familiar.

Any classification, whether phylogenetic or morphological, is bound to suffer from inequalities due to the human factor. It is a composite edifice, planned, built up, and added to by architects and labourers of very different outlook, skill, and taste. Somehow their contributions have to be reconciled, and the best in each has to be preserved for the common good of the whole. The museum specialist wishes to trace out every side branch in the tree of life, to detect and label every subtle deviation from the norm; the university teacher and the field geologist seek merely a simple classification that shall be easy to use. An example of the pass to which this antithesis between the two points of view can bring us is to be seen in the classification of the fossil brachiopods. Modern monographs on these shells introduce a classification (and corresponding nomenclature) based on minute internal differences which can only be detected by the use of a difficult technique. The relationships revealed by this technique are highly interesting; but it is questionable whether they are such as ought to be expressed in the classification and nomenclature which must be used by all. The consequence of so doing is already a cleavage between the specialist on the one hand and the teacher and geologist on the other, who perforce employ two nomenclatures. Names that cannot be applied are useless and will never gain currency. They remain enshrined in the monographs, which, proportionately as they are loaded with them, will remain unread. Meanwhile old names like *Rhynchonella* and *Terebratula* continue to serve their purpose, and become more firmly entrenched as the world despairs of correctly adopting any substitutes.

Apart from this, there remains always with us a constant source of difficulty and unevenness, the difference between the 'lumpers', who tend to see the resemblances between organisms, and the 'splitters', who are always on the look out for differences. The results are often very misleading. If, for example, the Jurassic members of a group are worked out by a 'lumper' and the Cretaceous members by a 'splitter', the resulting genera and species will not be proportional to the relative diversity of the group in the two formations. Since the number of genera and species is to a great extent the only guide the non-expert has to the relative radiation and significance of the group at different times, it is highly important that some attempt at standardization be made. Zuckerman (1931) has pointed out how different our ideas of the evolution of man would be if, in distinguishing Neanderthal from modern man, the same values were attributed to the characters used as is customary in distinguishing *Pithecanthropus*, *Sinanthropus*, and *Eoanthropus*.

The major problems of palaeontological taxonomy may be summarized by saying that a phylogenetic and a practical classification are frequently incompatible, and that lack of uniformity in scale and unity of purpose introduce further confusions. It is the object of this essay to examine the extent to which the phylogenetic system may be useful, and how the problems due to the human element may be overcome.

The first of these difficulties faces, in particular, the student of ammonites at an early stage of his investigations. Schindewolf (1928) has shown in detail that a number of lineages of ammonoidea can be traced up through the Devonian rocks, all undergoing more or less parallel evolution. They may be classified in two ways: either 'vertically', making the genera correspond with the lineages, along which the successive forms are marked by parallel species, or 'horizontally', making the genera correspond with successive grades irrespective of the lineages.

When new forms are being investigated the systematist is free to choose the basis of his classification and a phylogenetic or vertical system may be the best to introduce. Or when a group is well known but has been kept under one generic name because considered too difficult for subdivision until very recent years, a 'planned' phylogenetic system may still be introduced, as Brinkmann (1929) has attempted for the ammonite genus *Kosmoceras*, using four subgenera to correspond with four supposed lineages. The chief objection to the 'vertical' system in such cases is the uncertainty of recognizing true lineages. As George has said (1933, p. 113), always 'In the last resort it is possible to deny the suggested phylogenies: they are not absolutely established, nor ever can be.' One of the present writers after studying the Kosmocerates finds it impossible to accept some of the lineages postulated by Brinkmann and consequently finds it necessary to regroup the subgenera. Schindewolf came to the conclusion that a horizontal subdivision of his Devonian ammonoids was the only practicable one.

When well-known and long-established genera are under investigation and have to be classified, there is no freedom of choice, because under the Rules generic names have to be accepted as they were introduced. The only alternative to an arbitrary horizontal classification would be a complete recasting of the nomenclature, a procedure not warranted by the premises. As a concrete instance may be cited the ammonite family Cadoceratidae, often regarded as two successive families Cadoceratidae and Cardioceratidae, which flourished in Callovian, Oxfordian, and Lower Kimeridgian times. This family (or families) comprises principally the well-known genera *Cadoceras*, *Quenstedtoceras*, *Cardioceras*, and *Amoeboceras*, which have a clearly defined time-sequence, as follows:

Cadoceras . . .	Kellaways Beds and basal Oxford Clay.
Quenstedtoceras . .	Upper Oxford Clay.
Cardioceras . .	Corallian Beds.
Amoeboceras . .	Upper Corallian Beds and Lower Kimeridge Clay.

Each genus embraces many different forms, all characterized, however, by an unmistakable rib habit and keel formation which as a rule serve to distinguish at a glance a member of one genus from one of another. The four genera as so understood are of great value to stratigraphy, for they are well known to all geologists who have studied Mesozoic rocks, and it is merely a rule of thumb to identify the formation if species of these genera occur. It is unthinkable that a *Quenstedtoceras* should appear in rocks of the age of the Corallian Beds, or a *Cardioceras* in the Kimeridge Clay, or an *Amoeboceras* in the Kellaways Beds or Oxford Clay.

Nevertheless, each of these genera includes forms which differ more widely from one another in some respects than from corresponding species in the other genera. Within each genus it is possible to distinguish smaller groups, which are best classed as subgenera, and for these Buckman has supplied ample generic names. For instance, *Quenstedtoceras* and *Cardioceras* embrace the following more or less well-defined subgenera:

Quenstedtoceras:	Cardioceras:
Quenstedtoceras sensu stricto.	Cardioceras sensu stricto.
Eboraciceras.	Vertebriceras.
Bourkelamberticeras.	Scarburgiceras.
Prorsiceras.	Cawtoniceras.
Pavloviceras.	Scoticardioceras.
Weissermeliceras.	Plasmatoceras.

As knowledge advances, it is becoming increasingly probable that each subgenus of *Cardioceras* evolved from a different subgenus of *Quenstedtoceras*, either known or still undiscovered. The earliest *Cardioceras* in English deposits, the genotype of *Scarburgiceras*, is indistinguishable until the later stages of its development from the last representatives of the latest subgenus of *Quenstedtoceras*, namely, *Pavloviceras*. There is greater 'true' affinity between *Pavloviceras* and *Scarburgiceras* than between either and its companion subgenera; yet *Pavloviceras* is obviously a *Quenstedtoceras*, and *Scarburgiceras* when full grown can only be classed as a *Cardioceras*.

If all the subgenera could be linked up in this way with any confidence there might be a strong case for reclassifying vertically. But the affinities of the other subgenera are by no means so obvious. *Vertebriceras* may have arisen from

Quenstedtoceras sensu stricto (= *Vertumniceras*, synonym) or from *Prorsiceras*, but beyond that probably no specialist would at present venture.

Hence, *if the essential purpose of a nomenclature is to be fulfilled*, we can only leave the four successive broad genera as they are, separated in a horizontal sense. At the same time it should be stressed that the essential purpose of a nomenclature is *not* fulfilled by the alternative adopted by Buckman and his followers, of raising all the small groups to full generic rank, so that no generic name implies affinity with any other. This method is an escape from responsibility, for it leaves the onus of shaping the higher groupings to the next worker. The multitudes of genera have eventually to be marshalled into families, which then correspond with the old genera, and neither knowledge nor theory is advanced by the manœuvre. The only result is that palaeontology is encumbered by a new crop of meaningless generic names.

An interesting converse to the ammonite groupings just discussed is provided by the British Jurassic corals. At each horizon on which corals occur commonly the same range of growth-forms is represented: simple, dendroid, massive. On these growth-forms were founded the old genera, which therefore ran vertically and were considered to be lineages. The genera were as follows:

Simple corals	*Montlivaltia.*
Dendroid corals . . .	*Thecosmilia.*
Massive corals ⎰ cerioid corals . .	*Isastraea.*
⎱ thamnastraeoid corals .	*Thamnasteria.*
⎱ cribrimorph corals .	*Microsolena.*

Recent opinion has swung round to the view that these are not true genera. Lang (1938, p. 154) writes that he has no doubt 'that the species included in these genera in the Aalenian beds are more nearly related to each other than they are to the Bajocian or Bathonian forms, and the Bajocian forms are more nearly related to each other than they are to the Aalenian or Bathonian forms'. He regards the assemblage of forms at each horizon as a lineage showing a trend towards compaction of corallites, and each growth-form (old genus) as a grade of evolution.

The changes of nomenclature necessitated by acceptance of

this hypothesis would be revolutionary. But Dr. Lang recognizes the practical utility of the old genera and he suggests that the names should be retained as 'genomorphic names' written within braces after the true genus. He defines genomorph as a 'morphological term and applicable to corresponding grades in parallel, similarly trending lineages', and 'the genomorphic name as replacing the term genus in those supposed genera which have been found to be but aggregates of more distantly related species, but species which have reached the same morphological grade'. 'Finally', he says, 'it is convenient to use the term genomorph to cover both the genomorphic form itself and the genomorphic name; just as the word genus is used to cover both the group of species and the name.'

Before accepting such a recasting of the nomenclature it is desirable to examine very critically the premises involved, and we do not think that this case survives the test. The assemblage of corals at each horizon cannot represent a lineage nor exhibit a trend, for its members were contemporaneous. The old genera lived side by side in the same coral reef, just as do the analogous generic forms at the present day. The impression that they are more closely related to one another than to their counterparts in earlier or later assemblages is founded mainly on the fact that at any one horizon there is a small number of gradations between each of the generic forms and its neighbours next in the series from simple to cribrimorph. Thus, as Dr. Lang states, 'within the single Corallian species, *Thamnasteria arachnoides* (Parkinson), are included cerioid, astraeoid, and thamnastraeoid forms, showing gradation along the trend of compaction of corallites'.

But there are other possible explanations of this phenomenon. It might be caused by interbreeding between adjacent lineages (old genera), or by an innate tendency in each lineage to throw off variations resembling the most closely allied lineages on each side, possibly as a form of throw-back to the time when the lineages were first undergoing differentiation and the growth-forms had not become so stereotyped. We simply do not know the true explanation. We are in the position of an observer who for the first time becomes aware of black and white men and half-castes in the United States: from the half-castes he might infer that the negro and white populations are more closely related to each other than to their negro and white forebears in

Africa and Europe, or that there is a trend from black to white or vice versa.

Among living corals, which repeat the Jurassic Hexacoral growth-forms with remarkable fidelity, the branching forms give rise to branching, the massive to massive, and in a succession of Pleistocene to living reefs the constituent genera maintain approximately the same relative numbers, exhibiting no tendency towards predominance of massive forms with the passage of time.

It seems to us more probable that likewise in the successive Jurassic coral reefs the dendroid *Thecosmiliae* were in the main ancestors of the *Thecosmiliae*, the cerioid *Isastraeae* of the *Isastraeae*, and so on, while all the time there was a certain amount of intercrossing between adjacent terms in the series simple to cribrimorph and the whole assemblage evolved more or less in the same direction, thus giving a 'family likeness' to the whole at any given moment of time. If this be admitted, then the old genera form the best basis for a phylogenetic classification.

Dr. Lang, in a correspondence which we have had with him on this subject, states that he would not advocate rearranging the nomenclature until there is certainty as to the lineages; a view in which we heartily concur.

A somewhat different problem is presented by long-ranging lineages or species-groups such as the lamellibranch group of *Oxytoma inequivalve* (J. Sowerby) (Fig. 1), originally described from the Middle Lias and the Kellaways Beds, the Middle Lias example being the type. It is not particularly common at either of these horizons, but in the Lower Lias and Oxford Clay and Corallian Beds shells of the same group, which some consider conspecific, are abundant, and the total range is from the Rhaetic Beds to the Chalk.

When as many specimens as possible from the Lower Lias are compared with as many as possible from the Oxford Clay, there is seen to be a marked difference in the norm. The Oxford Clay norm has a much longer and more excavated posterior wing, which is separated from the body of the shell by a valley, not developed in the Lias shells, and the valley and posterior part of the wing are unornamented, whereas in the Lias shells radial ribs are ubiquitous. Moreover, in the Oxford Clay specimens the ribs are more definitely differentiated into three orders, primary, secondary, and tertiary (see Fig. 1).

The form characteristic of the English Oxford Clay is also the dominant form in the equivalent beds in central Russia, and the typical English Lower Lias form is characteristic of the same beds in many countries. But it has often been pointed out that here and there varieties turn up at all horizons which combine the features of the norms at several different horizons. For instance, the norm in the English Corallian Beds is more like the Oxford Clay norm in the length and depth of excavation of its posterior wing and the presence of the dividing valley, and in the differentiation of its ribbing, but it resembles the Liassic norm in its larger size and the fact that the radial valley and posterior part of the wing are ornamented. At other horizons there are also variations in the size of the byssal notch and general shape of the shell.

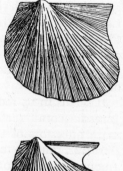

FIG. 1. Sketches of left valves of the *Oxytoma inequivalve* group. Above, form characteristic of the Lower Lias; below, form characteristic of the Upper Oxford Clay (aff. *expansa* Phillips).

Now it is purely a matter of choice how we express these facts in our nomenclature. The sole prerequisite is that the result should be as nearly as possible in scale with the rest of the system used. Several authors who have discussed the matter (L. Waagen, 1901; Gillet, 1924) have concluded that all the *Oxytoma inequivalve* group belongs to one species and should bear one specific name. The dozen or so other specific names already extant they therefore abolished, or used only as varietal names. Other authors have protested (Cossmann, Arkell; see Arkell, 1929–37, pp. 190, xvii). No other lamellibranch of commonly accepted specific status is known to have nearly such a long range, and the fact remains that the norm at various horizons differs enough to warrant a different name and to enable the rocks to be dated within broad limits in the absence of other fossils. As a palaeontologist of great experience said in 1887, 'A name given to a shell is simply a means of conveying a concrete idea of what is meant, and this purpose is not gained if we unite too many and different forms under one name' (W. Waagen, 1887). The result of L. Waagen's procedure is almost as much out of scale with commonly accepted lamellibranch classification as is Heinz's procedure (1932) (in the opposite direction) with *Inoceramus* (see below, p. 406).

Gradual change of the norm with continual giving off of numerous varieties in several characters is easier to deal with in a consistent classification than persistence or gradual change of a stable stock which repeatedly gives off variations in the same direction. An instance of the latter kind is the Mesozoic *Ostrea*, which by incoiling of the left umbo in the plane at right angles to the valve-margins gives rise to *Gryphaea* and by coiling of both umbones in the same plane as the valve-margins gives rise to *Exogyra*. There can be no doubt these changes have taken place several times in geological history; yet *Gryphaea* and *Exogyra* have been treated for over a century as homogeneous genera. The ideal classification in theory would recognize each lineage by a generic name, or still better subgeneric, keeping the genus *Ostrea* for all, and would express the grade of evolution in each lineage by the third term, corresponding in position with the specific name, but the same for all lineages. Thus the common form usually known as *Ostrea (Gryphaea) dilatata* J. Sowerby, or simply *Gryphaea dilatata*, would become *Ostrea (Dilatata) gryphaea*, and its Cretaceous equivalent known as *Pycnodonta corrugata* (Say) would become *Ostrea (Corrugata) gryphaea*. (See Arkell, 1934.)

Recasting of the nomenclature on these lines, however, is incompatible with adherence to the International Rules. Perhaps it is as well that this is so, for two reasons. In the first place, because it is only very rarely that the evidence is so clear as in *Gryphaea* and *Exogyra*, and there may be many other genera that are equally polyphyletic but the evidence is lacking and perhaps never will be found. Secondly, the philosophical grounds for such a change are not really so sound as they appear at first sight. It is purely the time-element in the repeated evolution of *Gryphaea* and *Exogyra* that is disturbing. If the same forms had evolved independently in different parts of the world at the same time, or so nearly at the same time as to be inseparable stratigraphically, they would unhesitatingly be referred to one genus. In any case, they are all descended from the same stock and so are not strictly speaking so polyphyletic as, for instance, the genera *Cardioceras* and *Amoeboceras*, referred to above. Purists who wish to express every subtlety of phylogenetic theory in their classification may surmount the difficulty by using the names *Gryphaea* and *Exogyra* as genomorphs, writing such species as *Gryphaea dilatata* in the form advocated by Dr. Lang for certain corals, *Ostrea (Gryphaea) dilatata*.

Once more, therefore, the conclusion is that we can only retain a system of classification and of nomenclature that shall perform its chief function of being useful if we broaden its philosophical basis and recognize that it must assimilate categories of different meaning and different value in different groups. This should not deter us from striving after as near an approach to uniformity as we can achieve, and from eschewing such extreme departures as Heinz's *Inoceramus* systematics (p. 406). But any System that can be devised is of necessity so artificial and so far from coinciding with Nature, that there is no reason for crippling ourselves with rules and restrictions which would rob the existing System of its useful elasticity.

Therefore, since palaeontological classification is intended to be practical, no useful purpose is served by complicating it with detailed phylogenies, which are often of little interest save for demonstrating convergence. The rules of nomenclature are now so well established and in such general use, that any radical change would only be a calamity. Their application, however, needs common sense and sense of proportion. Every systematist who makes new genera and species holds a position of responsibility, which cannot be overstressed. The most important question for a worker to ask himself, when erecting genera and species, is why he is doing so. He must remember that he is catering for the specialist and general geologist alike, and that any new addition should aim at clarifying the existing condition and not obscuring it. Despite the 'International Rules of Nomenclature', which lay down only the fundamental rules and recommendations for systematists, the irresponsibility of workers, often due to ignorance of the history and uses of classification, leads to entirely unnecessary complications. Many palaeontological systematists believe that it is sufficient to have read the rules and know the laws to plunge headlong into an orgy of new names.

Every new genus and species should fit as nearly as possible into a uniform scale of values. Perfect uniformity is obviously unattainable, but an approximation to it should always be aimed at in any group. Examples of flagrant disregard of this rule are Buckman's innumerable genera made by splitting up contemporary species of the single good Liassic ammonite genus *Dactylioceras*, and by Heinz's pulverization of the Cretaceous lamellibranch genus *Inoceramus* (1932). Out of what was originally a single genus *Inoceramus*, Heinz created a whole systematic hierarchy, comprising 2 families, 24 subfamilies, 63 genera, and 27 subgenera; and even so he did not take the Jurassic forms into account. Against this procedure Stolley (1936) has entered a timely protest. While not denying that the wealth of material on which Heinz worked (about 20,000 specimens) may justify minute subdivision, he points out that this should be carried out downwards in the scale, starting with the genus *Inoceramus* and proceeding through subgenera to groups and sections. All the advantages of minute subdivisions can thus be achieved without disturbance to the whole classification of Mollusca.

Similar is the impossible situation produced by erecting new genera on single more or less unidentifiable fragments such as fish scales. Brotzen (1935) has made 4 genera and 59 species on single Acanthodian scales, some of which are even doubtfully Acanthodian. The erection of these genera and species is valueless. Many of them are almost certainly synonymous with known forms, but it can hardly be considered worth while to find out.

Endless unnecessary complication is caused by not pitching the scale of the classification in such a way that the familiar genera of the literature of the last century or more remain as genera, so that they can still be used for faunal lists and records, while the new subdivisions become subgenera and need not be mentioned for all practical purposes. The new subdivisions can never be final. Each reviser will continue to regroup, but this will have no ill effects so long as each change is not reflected in the binomial nomenclature. There is no difference in principle between retaining familiar and long-established generic names for use, and relegating them to subfamilies or families, replacing them by unfamiliar new genera, but there is an enormous difference in practical results. Works in which all familiar genera are replaced by new ones are wellnigh unintelligible, and no scientific gain accrues. All that is achieved is a false appearance of exactness and deep learning.

Another point often overlooked is that it is essential to take *all* characters into account, but when giving, as has to be done, more weight to some characters than to others, to exercise reasonable judgement, and to select the same kind of characters in related groups.

An example of artificial classification arising from the unreasonable selection of one character to the exclusion of others is afforded by Buckman's (1909–30) classification of the ammonoids grouped as Perisphinctids. In this, minute details of relative lobe-lengths in the septal sutures were made the basis of a series of new genera, regardless of the fact that relative lobe-lengths change during ontogeny, and regardless of profound differences of whorl-shape and ribbing. (See Arkell, 1935, Introduction.)

It should be realized that even within a single group the value of species or genera is necessarily often very different, owing to the fact that they are based on different characters in different families or genera. For instance, it is possible for the palaeontologist to make more species in the lamellibranch genera *Pecten* and *Trigonia*, which possess ribs and scales and tubercles, than in Myacea, which usually lack them; but it would not be true to say in consequence that the Pectinidae or Trigoniidae are necessarily larger families than the Pleuromyidae.

In deciding upon what forms are to be considered species, it is essential to try to detect characters which change in time, and to distinguish them from analogous characters in other groups which are stable and therefore useless. Such plastic characters are the ribs and scales of the Pectens, which make many of them useful stratigraphically, as opposed to the stable though similar ribs and scales of *Oxytoma* and *Pseudomonotis*. It is important that characters which vary only vertically should be distinguished, even though they may be more subtle and elusive, from those which vary horizontally. A good example is afforded by the *Trigoniae* of the Corallian Beds (Arkell, 1929, Introduction). The choice may lie between, say, a dozen species of no value stratigraphically and two species which can be used as zonal indices, each possessing a dozen parallel variations.

Further, an unnecessary element of artificiality is introduced if authors split up big genera simply because they contain a larger number of species than some other genera and may look 'unbalanced'. Inequality is an essential characteristic of all groups of the hierarchy, and a classification should reflect this inequality faithfully. To talk of a genus being 'unwieldy' and therefore in need of splitting is either nonsense or dishonest, the latter when it is made the excuse for introducing new genera to immortalize the author's name.

To bestow new names (specific or generic or subgeneric) simply because of a difference in stratigraphical horizon is obviously unsound. Incredible as it may seem, this has been done extensively in the past, even in large works published by reputable societies (e.g. Rollier, 1912–17). It should be borne in mind that stratigraphy claims to identify the strata by the contained fossils; therefore stratigraphers who give new names to fossils because they occur in different strata are cutting away the foundations of their science.

Needless confusion is also caused by giving new names to the figures of previous authors unless the whole group is being revised and the specimens can be handled and refigured. If the specimens have been previously figured only in drawings, a new name should never be based upon them without providing a new photograph. Nothing is gained by sprinkling often irrelevant text with *nomina nova*, based on doubtful or even unrecognizable figures of other authors, and an infinity of trouble is caused to later workers, owing to the rule of priority. It should be remarked that a *nom. nov.* is meaningless by itself, and that since its author has to append to it the reference to the figure on which it is based, it is itself redundant.

It is time palaeontologists built up a body of public opinion which should discourage the '*nom. nov.* man' by making him feel the pest that he is. To this end two papers by Dr. Rudolf Richter have done valuable work and should be read by all palaeontologists (Richter, 1929, 1930).

It is impossible to over-estimate the value of Bather's writings on systematics, and as a further tribute to him we will end by quoting his words once more: 'A name once published is irrevoc-

able, a permanent addition to the labour of future investigators.
Let us beware of adding needlessly to the burden of posterity.'

REFERENCES

ARKELL, W. J. (1929–37). 'A Monograph of British Corallian Lamelli-branchia.' *Palaeontographical Soc. London.*

―― (1934). 'The Oysters of the Fuller's Earth; and on the Evolution and Nomenclature of the Upper Jurassic Catinulas and Gryphaeas.' *Proc. Cotteswold Nat. Field Club*, **25**, 21.

―― (1935). 'A Monograph of the Ammonites of the English Corallian Beds.' *Palaeontographical Soc. London.*

BATHER, F. A. (1927*a*). 'Quo vadis? A question from a Palaeontologist to the Systematist.' *C. R. Xe Congrès Internat. de Zoologie*, p. 95.

―― (1927*b*). 'Biological Classification: Past and Future.' *Quart. J. geol. Soc.* **83**, p. lxii.

―― (1928). 'The Shifting Diagnosis.' *Palaeobiologica*, **1**, 51.

BREMEKAMPE, C. E. B. (1931). 'The Principles of Taxonomy and the Theory of Evolution.' *Pamph. South African Biol. Soc. 4*,

BRINKMANN, R. (1929). 'Statistisch-biostratigraphische Untersuchungen an mitteljurassischen Ammoniten über Artbegriff und Stammesentwicklung.' *Abh. Gesellsch. Wiss. Göttingen. M.-P. Kl. N.F.* **13**, 3. (See also essay-review in *Geol. Mag.* 1931, **68**, 373.)

BROTZEN, F. (1934). 'Erster Nachweis von Unterdevon im Ostseegebiet durch Konglomeratgeschiebe mit Fischresten. 2. Paläontologie.' *Zs. Geschiebeforsch.* 10. Hft. p. 1.

BUCKMAN, S. S. (1909–30). *Type Ammonites.* London.

GEORGE, T. N. (1933). 'Palingenesis and Palaeontology.' *Biol. Rev.* **8**, 107.

GILLET, S. (1924). 'Remarques sur le Rameau d'*Avicula Oxytoma inaequivalvis* Sow.' *Bull. Soc. géol. France*, ser. 4, **23**, 450.

HEINZ, R. (1932). 'Aus der neuen Systematik der Inoceramen.' *Mitteil. a. d. Mineralog.-Geolog. Staatsinstitut, Hamburg*, Hft. 13.

LANG, W. D. (1938). 'Some further considerations on trends in corals.' *Proc. geol. Assoc.* **49**, 148.

REGAN, C. TATE (1926). 'Organic Evolution.' *Rep. Brit. Ass.* Southampton, 1925.

RICHTER, R. (1929). 'Nomenklatur und Nomenklatur.' *Senckenbergiana*, **11**, 380.

―― (1930). 'Nomenklatur und Ethik: der Fall Embrik Strand.' Ibid. **12**, 304.

ROLLIER, L. (1912–17). 'Fossiles nouveaux ou peu connus des terrains secondaires du Jura et des contrées environnantes.' *Mém. Soc. pal. Suisse*, **37–42**.

SCHINDEWOLF, O. H. (1928). 'Prinzipienfragen der biologischen Systematik.' *Pal. Zeit.* **9**, 122.

―― (1936). '*Paläontologie, Entwicklungslehre und Genetik.*' Borntraeger, Berlin.

STOLLEY, E. (1936). 'Grundsätzliches zur palaeontologischen Systematik. I. Die Inoceramen-Systematik von R. Heinz.' *28. Jahresber. Niedersächs. geol. Vereins zu Hannover.*

WAAGEN, L. (1901). 'Der Formenkreis des *Oxytoma inaequivalve* Sowerby.' *Jahrb. der k.-k. Geolog. Reichsanst., Wien,* **51**, 1.

WAAGEN, W. (1887). 'Salt Range Fossils.' *Pal. Indica,* 1887, p. 276.

ZUCKERMAN, S. (1931). 'Sinanthropus and other Fossil Men. Their Relations to Each Other and Modern Types.' *Eugenics Rev.* **24**, no. 4, p. 273.

TAXONOMIC PROBLEMS IN FUNGI

By J. RAMSBOTTOM

THE suggestion that there is a 'new systematics' is surely without foundation. The aim of taxonomy has always been twofold—the identification of organisms, and their arrangement in a systematic manner to show their affinities. The fact that as biological knowledge progresses its results are gradually absorbed by taxonomy, and that this often causes different methods to be adopted in classification, is merely a continuation of traditional procedure. It is not the purpose of this chapter to deal with the philosophical basis of what may be regarded as a natural system, but to give a summary of various aspects of mycology which may have a bearing on general principles. It may be pointed out, however, that botanical taxonomy should not be judged wholly by herbarium methods, which are obviously inevitably confined; and further that for practical purposes a system that is convenient rather than philosophical has to be adopted.

A detailed consideration of the numerous aspects of mycology which in some way or other affect modern ideas about the nature of species and the philosophical basis of classification, would occupy a space comparable with that needed for a similar consideration of phanerogams. Though the problems are of essentially the same nature, the methods which have to be adopted in the attempts to solve them are necessarily different.

One major difference is that the nuclei of most fungi are so small that little assistance can be gained from cytology. Further, the fact that hybridization appears to be extremely rare prevents our looking in that direction for any suggestion of a partial solution of the problems. It would seem very unlikely that polyploidy, even if it exists, could be observed, and there is little hope of such clues as are given, for example, by the American species of *Tradescantia* or by *Galeopsis tetrahit*.

Because they do not possess chlorophyll, fungi are either saprophytic or parasitic. It is possible to grow most saprophytes and a considerable proportion of parasites in pure culture, the chief exceptions being the Erysiphales and the Rusts. By changing the constitution of culture-media and the physical conditions of growth it is possible to alter greatly the appearance of many fungi. If the chemical and physical conditions of growth remained constant a clearer idea of the relation between the various factors and the induced changes in the fungi could be obtained, but although occasionally claims have been made that a definite relation exists, it must be remembered that the very fact of growth immediately alters the conditions; it is also to be noted that the previous history of a fungus in culture, or the presence of contaminations, may affect its growth.

In a general way identification of fungi depends upon colour, and the development, size, and shape of various structures, particularly the spores, which serve for reproducing the fungus. Spore is a general term, and the two types asexual and sexual (i.e. formed as a result of fertilization or its equivalent) have to be clearly distinguished. Formerly there were a number of terms in general use for asexual spores and following Vuillemin, there is a tendency to revive some of these and to add to their number in order to define their method of formation.

Any given fungus may have a sexual stage (Phycomycete, Ascomycete, or Basidiomycete) and, in addition, one or more asexual stages. A species includes all these stages. Thus *Uncinula necator* has *Oidium tuckeri* as its conidial stage, *Eurotium herbariorum* has *Aspergillus glaucus*, whereas when it was known from the first that the two stages belonged to the same life-cycle the asexual and sexual stages were not given separate names as, for example, in *Penicillium*. But thousands of fungi are known only in the asexual stage; they constitute the large and economically important group called Fungi Imperfecti. The genera and species here are theoretically only form-genera and form-species; they represent only a part of a life-cycle, and it is usually assumed in text-books that the perfect form exists and only awaits discovery or recognition. It is a comforting belief, but has little foundation. Doubtless very many connexions remain to be revealed and many suggested connexions only require proof, but probably no systematist would subscribe to it as a principle.

When these conidial stages are grown in single-spore cultures it is more usual than not that the cultures can be sorted into a number of strains which remain constant. The strains differ in several ways—character of colony, colour, measurements, and chemical reactions, and, if parasitic, in their degree of parasitism. Sometimes only a few strains are obtained, but with prolonged search, occasionally, as in *Botrytis cinerea*, over a hundred have been isolated. How are these strains to be regarded? Most mycologists treat them as pure lines within a given species. They grade round centres and for the most part show sufficiently well-marked gaps between these centres.

It has to be borne in mind that growth from a spore to spore-production is usually a matter of days rather than weeks, and that conditions can be controlled in a manner which is impossible with flowering plants; transplant experiments in mycology are a daily practice. Even under natural conditions we can envisage such a fungus repeating itself very frequently within a year. If it is affected in any way by environmental conditions there is no possibility of a reorganization following a sexual progress; to all intents and purposes the asexual stage arising from a spore of the original fruit-body is and remains a unit with the possibility of carrying on any change brought about in any way. This has important theoretical consequences and may be of some significance in accounting for specialization of parasites.

Saltation

When fungi are grown in culture it is not unusual for a portion of the colony to take on a totally different appearance. This resulting strain is known as a Mutant, Saltant, Variant, or Modification; in ring-worm fungi the phenomenon has been called Pleomorphism.[1] Much investigation has been carried out on this subject in the last thirty years and many different types have been described, and attempts made to classify them. Saltation has been assumed to have occurred in spores when a single spore has given rise to one or more variants. Usually it is assumed to have taken place in the mycelium as it manifests itself mostly as a sector in a Petri-dish colony. The sector is usually fan- or wedge-shaped, there may be one or more, and

---

[1] This is a wrong usage. Pleomorphism is the term for the occurrence of more than one independent form in the life-cycle of a species.

The term Saltant is adopted here as having no implied necessary relation to similar phenomena in other groups.

the proportion between sector and parent is variable. All sectors, however, do not give rise to saltants: some give a mixture of saltant and parent growing side by side and others, known as 'false sectors', give rise only to the parent and sometimes are due to the depth of the medium. Marked saltations have been described where inocula of spores or of mycelium taken from different parts of the parent consistently behaved differently from each other. The occurrence of saltation is often related to the age of a culture though most frequent in the youngest hyphae. Sometimes it occurs or becomes observable only at a high temperature.

The same saltant may always be produced by a given species, or a number may be produced in series with sometimes omission of an intermediate stage, or the change may be reversible, as is common in species of *Stemphylium*, which give *Alternaria* as a saltant which reverts to *Stemphylium*. Supplementary strains are sometimes produced which will form abundance of spores along the line of contact with the parent. Ever-saltating strains have been described where the change occurs at a definite age and in every cultural generation. Further, a different strain may develop from different minor branches of the same hypha or even from contiguous fragments of the same hypha when isolated, though not showing in culture. Various chemical and physical factors often bring about saltations—chemicals, temperature, radiation—but no definite relation between them exists; some fungi readily react to any of these stimuli by producing saltants, some resist the action of one or more, while others cannot be induced to saltate.

The morphological range is often so great that a single saltation will give what would be considered as a new species. Leonian (1926) described five mutants of *Phytophthora omnivora* so unlike each other that no one would take them to be members of the same species when grown under identical conditions. Even 'generic' changes have been recorded in some Fungi Imperfecti. Colour changes are most frequent and have been described even in Rusts. There are often differences in virulence of parasitism in pathogenetic fungi when the virulence is measured by pure-strain hosts.

The phenomena outlined above are difficult to fit into taxonomic categories. We have numerous strains which, judging from the fact that a binary name is always used for the whole, we may regard as constituting a recognizable species. When spores are sown in a culture-medium a change often occurs in a portion of the colony. If this change was always of the same nature or even had a time-period some scheme might be devised by which one could take account of their occurrence. But so varied are they that classification of the changes themselves have been suggested usually on pure assumption of different modifications of cell-structure. Assuming for the moment that these changes which are brought about in characters used in classification are sometimes of taxonomic significance, in other words that what are essentially different varieties arise spontaneously, can we seek here for an explanation of the occurrence of some at least of Fungi Imperfecti? If we assume that originally all such conidial forms were part of the life-cycle of fungi with sexual spores, can we suppose that some such saltation might alter heterothallic strains so that they can no longer fuse, or even throw a homothallic fungus out of its stride either by failure to produce the perfect form or by causing the two stages to become independent? (See p. 418.)

It is probable that many species of fungi have arisen by marked rather than by gradual changes, for it is difficult to imagine how competitive selection and gradual change could account for the facts. This is not the place to discuss this. The point is whether the marked changes seen in pure culture are changes of the nature which would give a clue as to how species might originate. It may be well here to interpolate the suggestion that pure culture conditions are very similar to those of horticulture—the organism is given every encouragement to grow and is protected from competition. It seems safe to assume that what occurs frequently in these circumstances occurs at least occasionally under what are usually called natural conditions. From the accounts of some of the saltations and from a knowledge of some hundreds of fungi in culture I am of the opinion that some of the changes are definitely of this kind.

Dual Phenomenon

Recent investigations by Hansen and R. E. Smith (1935) have shown that the whole of the past work must be revised and further that the species problem in Fungi Imperfecti is complicated in an unexpected manner. Hansen's latest paper (1938) gives a clear account of what he calls the 'dual phenomenon'.

When certain Fungi Imperfecti are grown from single spores and several successive single-spore series are carried out, three culture-types may be distinguished, one mainly mycelial in character producing comparatively few or no conidia, M; another producing conidia in relatively great abundance and usually less aerial mycelium, C; a third, intermediate in type, MC. It is found that M always gives rise to M type only, C always to C type, and MC to all three types. When M and C are grown in mixed cultures they combine, presumably by anastomosis, and produce the MC type which in single-spore analysis again gives rise to all three types. The homotypes do not always differ in the same way. Thus there is slight difference in the amount of aerial mycelium in the two types in *Verticillium alboatrum* though conidial production is very different. *Phoma terrestris* is of especial interest; the M and MC types produce pycnidia typical of *Phoma*, whereas the pycnidia of C type have beaks frequently several times as long as the diameter of the pycnidium; further, the mycelium of the two homotypes is markedly different in structure. From experiments so far made the three types may differ in pathogenic virulence, e.g. that of *Phoma terrestris* on onion-roots decreases from M through MC to C.

Fungi with multinucleate conidia usually give rise to several culturally distinct MC types that vary in appearance from being almost like M to almost like C. The difference in appearance is apparently correlated with the proportion of M and C nuclei they possess. In *Botrytis cinerea* the number of nuclei varies directly with the volume of the conidium; in conidia $8 \times 12\mu$ there are 7 and in conidia $12 \times 15\mu$ there are 19. As many as five consecutive single-spore series are sometimes required to bring out both homotypes. In *Phoma terrestris*, which has binucleate conidia, there is only one MC type and all three types invariably occur in the first series of single-spore cultures. In *Verticillium alboatrum*, with mainly uninucleate conidia, many cultures usually have to be made before the MC type appears, presumably in binucleate conidia.

Extensive single-spore culturing of conidia gave large numbers of culturally distinct 'geographical and ecological races'. Thus

300 isolations of *Botrytis cinerea* gave 123 distinct strains, 180 of *Verticillium alboatrum* gave 37. Of the 123 races of *B. cinerea* 68 were dual, and 21 of the 37 races of *V. alboatrum*. Three races of *Ascochyta pisi* and 28 races of *Phoma terrestris* were all dual. The universality of the phenomenon suggests that the nuclei determine the cultural, morphological, and physiological characters of the types. Thus a plurinucleate conidium is really a group of individuals and cannot give rise to a genetically pure culture unless all the nuclei it contains are genetically identical. No fungus investigated has more than two homotypes, which suggests that the dual phenomenon is not an expression of genetic instability but that duality is normal for these fungi. It is of interest to note that of thirty conidial isolations from several species of perfect fungi none was found to be dual.

The occurrence of this dual phenomenon doubtless accounts for many of the results obtained in experiments on saltations, though it seems impossible that it can account for all; but it is obvious that the whole question of saltation needs critical scrutiny. Further, the fact that the few conidial stages of perfect forms that have been analysed do not show the phenomenon suggests interesting theoretical possibilities. Is duality an attempt to replace sex-phenomena in strains which have lost their power of fusing or producing sexual stages? A disturbing fact is that the two homotypes may be so different, as in *Phoma terrestris*, that they would be placed in different form-genera, the C-type pycnidia in this species being totally unlike *Phoma*.

Separation of homotypes takes place in nature, and we have to face the fact that usually there is sufficient difference in cultural characteristics for them to be regarded as different species. Theoretically, it is possible for such isolated homotypes to undergo variation with a splitting of the original dual species.

Heterothallism and Homothallism

The dual phenomenon has much in common with the phenomenon of heterothallism, discovered by Blakeslee (1904) in the Mucorineae, and recorded since in all groups of fungi. Briefly, the facts in Mucorineae are that if a single spore is germinated some species will produce both asexual and sexual

stages, whereas others produce only asexual spores and two
different strains of mycelium are necessary for the formation of
sexual stages; the first type of fungus is called homothallic, the
second type heterothallic, the strains being designated (+) and
(—). Usually there is little difficulty in recognizing an asexual
stage in Mucorineae or even in Phycomycetes generally; as a
matter of fact, the asexual stage is usually used in defining both
genera and species. In other groups it is usually only by
analogy that a form-genus can be attributed to a perfect stage
in the absence of proof of genetic connexion. Thousands of
Fungi Imperfecti remain with no known sexual stage. The difficulty from a taxonomic standpoint is how to deal with these
forms. Many of them are of economic importance and it is
necessary to have some system of identifying them. The artificial system propounded by Saccardo (1889) is generally used,
but it is merely a convenience and has no logical basis. The
method proposed by Vuillemin (1910) relates various genera
by taking note of the method of spore-formation, but still deals
solely with the asexual stages.

It seems likely that many of these forms are (+) and (—)
strains of heterothallic species. Several species are known where
the conidial stage is common and the perfect stage extremely
rare, e.g. *Apiocrea* (*Sepedonium*) *chrysosperma*—so frequent on
Boletus and *Paxillus*. Presumably such species are heterothallic.
It requires only a step to have wholly unattached asexual stages
—no matter how the absence of the fusion is brought about.
But it is probable that modification of asexual stages occurs, as
for example by saltation, and if there is no straightening out
by a sexual process, any changes presumably are readily cumulative, and eventually a fusion would be impossible. Similarly,
some species which are parasitic probably develop along with
their hosts, which would account for a gradual change with
similar results: for parasites the host is the most important factor
of the environment. The large number of species of *Ramularia*
on Umbelliferae may probably be accounted for in some such
way. No investigation along this line appears to have been
carried out; it should be possible here so to group the forms as to
suggest their probable affinities.

Even where a sexual stage exists we see something of the same
progress in separation through parasitism. Certain genera of

Peronosporaceae have been studied biometrically from this point of view. The best-known work is that of Gäumann (1923) on *Peronospora*. *Peronospora parasitica*, which occurs on Crucifers, he divides into 54 species, arranged in 15 types.

A biometrical study of the conidia showed that each species differs slightly from the others, but the oogonia and oospores are indistinguishable. It is not possible to separate the species on morphological characters alone—a given species can only be placed in the 'collective species' *P. parasitica*—and the only constant and indisputable way of distinguishing them is by a determination of the physiological selection of host-plants. The logical practical treatment is to regard the collective species as being composed of a number of subspecies each including specialized forms. The theoretical point appears to be that we have a variable species becoming split up into smaller units by specialization in parasitism, or the production of a number of slightly different though constant forms by adaptation to new hosts at some period in their evolutionary history. Similar facts are known in other groups.

The consideration of the theoretical consequences of heterothallism also includes several other aspects of the problems under survey. There is still discussion about whether it is to be regarded as an expression of sex or of self-incompatibility. Whatever the correct interpretation, facts are rapidly being accumulated which are of importance in the study of the species problem.

Hyphal Anastomosis and Hybridity

When studying the enormous array of species with their range of variation, which is sometimes very great, there is the inclination to conclude that the multiplicity of appearances with the difficulty of interpretation must be due to some form of 'hybridity'. But so far as we know the origin of new forms in this way is unusual in asexual strains. The anastomosing of fungal hyphae of different species and even genera, heterocaryosis and subsequent variations have been postulated, but little convincing evidence of their occurrence has been given and, where careful experiments have been made and fusions obtained, no new strains or variants have as a rule arisen. Hansen and R. E. Smith (1935), however, after obtaining *Botrytis allii* and *B. ricini* in genetically pure cultures, attempted to combine the two by thoroughly mixing small amounts of conidia and mycelium of each in malted agar and using this for inoculating further media; they found that in 20 cultures 5 were strikingly different from either species, the remaining 15 appearing to be identical with one or other of the species. Twenty subcultures were made from one of the new forms, and all again were totally different from either species. Three types were segregated which were distinct enough to be regarded as new varieties or even new species, and they remained constant through a series of five single-spore cultures. This production of stable new homotypes suggests a possible way by which some of the differences in asexual types arose. It should be pointed out that the authors did not consider the evidence for physical fusion entirely satisfactory. Presumably here we are dealing with something analogous to grafting such as that carried out on *Phycomyces nitens* by Burgeff (1914), who was able to synthesize a neutral strain by inserting the tip of a (−) hypha into the cut end of a (+), so producing a mechanical mixture of the cell-contents.

In his work on heterothallism in the Mucorineae, Blakeslee was able to correlate the (+) and (−) strains of different genera and species by noting abortive attempts at fusion (imperfect hybridization). Since then many races in different species have been crossed and hybrids obtained between species or varieties in *Mucor* and *Phycomyces*.

Possibly the most detailed study on fungus hybrids is that on the Pyrenomycete *Neurospora*. Fertile hybrids were obtained by Dodge (1928) between different species and the progeny characterized. These results cannot be summarized in detail, the main point being that the production of hybrids is possible.

Uredineae (Rust Fungi) probably provide more problems than any other group of fungi, and those in taxonomy are amongst the most interesting, though some are difficult to appreciate without a detailed knowledge of life-histories. The first noteworthy point is the number of different types of spores which may have a place in the life-cycle—uredospore, teleutospore, sporidium, aecidiospore, and pycnidiospore (spermatium)—though not all species have the full complement. Theoretically, it is possible for any of these spore-forms to occur independently, but it is usual to assume that an isolated uredospore has a genetically attached teleutospore and that isolated pycnidia, if they exist, are not recognizable as such.

Phylogenetic Classification

Rusts lend themselves to a consideration of phylogenetic classification. The more general view now is that the primitive type of rusts had all types of spore (macrocyclic) rather than a single spore of the teleutospore or teleuto-aecidiospore type possibly accompanied by pycnidia (microcyclic). Further, it is now thought likely that the primitive Rusts were heteroecious, having alternate, unrelated hosts for different parts of the life-cycle.

Heteroecism is frequent in the Rust fungi; elsewhere it is known only in two species of the Discomycete *Sclerotinia*. Parasitism must have developed at an early stage in their phylogenetic history, as all known Rusts are obligate parasites, occurring on ferns and flowering plants only. The parasites must have developed along with the hosts, being influenced together with them by general environmental conditions and modified by any change in the host. (The fact that the percentage of heteroecious rusts is higher on ferns, gymnosperms, and the more primitive flowering plants is one of the reasons for assuming that this habit is the original one.) Heteroecism is a special form of parasitism and is presumably related to the need for a different supply of nutriment at a certain stage of growth, a rhythmic impulse from change of host; autoecious macrocyclic species presumably obtain the necessary impetus by a change in the quality or concentration of nutriment in the same host. The usual assumption that the length of the life-cycle is invariably fixed is erroneous, it having been shown that several species have a composite or unstable life-history (*Puccinia podophylli*). It is probably more true to assume that the presence of any spore-form other than the teleutospore is more or less an adaptation to internal or external conditions.

There is a strict parasitism—so close that host-plants are sometimes recognized from the Rust, as when Klebahn (1904) established the identity of a species of willow by its reaction to *Melampsora ribesii-purpurea*. It is now well known that certain Rusts, either of similar or of different life-histories, occurring on related hosts, show a close resemblance in morphological characters, a phenomenon called correlation. The most familiar type is the close resemblance existing between some macrocyclic species of *Puccinia* and *Uromyces*, where the hosts are the same, or nearly related; the only structural difference between the two species is in the teleutospores—whether they are continuous or uniseptate. It seems obvious that one species was derived from the other, and that the two, though now placed for convenience in different genera, are more closely related than either is to any third species. Correlation where the teleutospore of a microcyclic species shows close morphological similarity with the teleutospore of a macrocyclic heteroecious species is of considerable interest. Here the aecidia occur on the same host as the teleutospores of the corresponding microform. This type of correlation was first pointed out by Dietel (1887), who remarked on the close similarity of the teleutospore of *Puccinia mesneriani* on *Rhamnus* to that of the heteroecious *P. coronata* which has its aecidium on *Rhamnus*. Though morphological similarity does not necessarily imply phylogenetic relation, it is generally agreed that correlated species in Rusts are genetically related; Tranzschel (1904) was able to suggest relationships by its aid. There has been a tendency to subdivide genera on the basis of the length of the life-cycle, and even to erect these divisions to the rank of genera. Obviously, if this is done, we end in a purely artificial arrangement, for we disregard the fact that the length of a life-cycle may be shortened by the omission of one or more stages.

Although it may be said that Rusts are constant, there are variable and intergrading forms which as a rule occur on hosts which are similarly variable: e.g. *Phragmidium* on *Rosa* and *Melampsora* on *Salix*. The *Phragmidium* species on *Rosa* are macrocyclic forms with caeomoid aecidia. Three microcyclic forms also occur on *Rosa* which show a similar distribution of mycelia and the same general habit and manner of development of their aecidia. One, *Uromyces* (*Ameris*) *rosicola*, has one-celled teleutospores; the second, *Puccinia* (*Teloconia*) *rosae*, has two-celled teleutospores; while the third, *Phragmidium devastatrix*, has teleutospores with several cells: Jackson (1931) suggests that these three species, now placed in three different genera, have developed from the haploid generation of macrocyclic *Phragmidium* species. It is suggested that the variable number of cells in the teleutospore may be interpreted as variations from the many-celled *Phragmidium* type which have developed in the process of simplification to microcyclic forms, and presumably indicates that *Phragmidium* originated from an ancestral type which possessed two-celled teleutospores.

The genus *Endophyllum*, characterized by an aecidium-like structure producing spores which germinate as teleutospores, has puzzled mycologists. By some it has been considered as a primitive type, but comparative study suggests that it is derived from the haploid generation of macrocyclic forms, and, in temperate regions, from heteroecious species of *Uromyces* and *Puccinia*. It is apparent that if this is so, the different species of *Endophyllum* are not closely related to one another. *Kunkelia nitens*, which has a caeoma-like structure, but is otherwise like *Endophyllum*, is presumably a microcyclic form of *Gymnoconia interstitialis*; detailed study has shown that not one but several microcyclic forms of this species exist.

It is to American uredinologists that we owe most of the information we have which may eventually lead to a grouping of genera and species in a manner showing relationship. The present systems are easy of application, but at their best lead only to certainty of identification.

Specialized Parasitism

Perhaps in no other group of fungi has specialized parasitism been so closely studied. Its existence was recognized by Schroeter (1879), though de Bary (1879) had stated that the difference between the aecidial forms of *Chrysomyxa ledi* and *C. rhododendri* is 'more biologic than morphologic'. It is to Eriksson (1894), however, that we owe the first clear knowledge of the pathogenic differences between forms of the same species. Thus as the result of a long series of cultures he divided *Puccinia graminis* into two species, *P. graminis* Pers. emend. with aecidia on barberry and *P. phlei-pratensis* Erikss. & Henn. of which the aecidia were unknown. *P. graminis* was then divided into six forms *agrostis*, *airae*, *avenae*, *poae*, *secalis*, and *tritici*, according to the differential hosts. Since that time an enormous amount of investigation has been carried out. To take only the one form *P. graminis* f. *tritici*, Stakman and Levine (1922) by using 12 species and varieties of *Triticum* separated 37 'physiologic forms', a number which has now been about doubled. According to Stakman (1929):

'the constancy in the behavior of the physiologic forms of *P. graminis trictici* is quite remarkable. There are, of course, fluctuations in the degree of infection, depending on the environmental conditions under which the rust develops. But these fluctuations are no greater than, possibly not so great as, those in the morphologic characters of fungi grown under different environmental conditions. The determination of physiologic forms is quite as definite and precise as is the determination of morphologic species. The high degree of parasitic specificity of forms for species and varieties of higher plants also is noteworthy. Physiologic forms of the rust fungi are as definite and constant entities as are the species and varieties of host plants on which they grow.'

It should be pointed out that *Puccinia graminis* develops its aecidia on a few species of *Berberis* and *Mahonia*, while its uredospores and teleutospores occur on 98 species of 35 genera of Poaceae in North America alone. Presumably we should be safe in supposing that the species comprises at least a thousand specialized forms, strains, or whichever of the many terms is preferred.

The specialized forms of *P. graminis* are usually tested on pure lines of grasses. It has been shown, however, that the strains remain distinct on barberry and so are able to persist and multiply. Formerly, principally through the work of Ward (1902), it was considered possible to train a strain to parasitize a host previously immune to it, by growing it first on a bridging species: the results were obtained presumably by unwittingly using a mixture of strains. From the evidence we have it seems clear that the strains are constant except for occasional saltations; colour-changes are not infrequent, but changes in pathogenicity seem rare. It is probable that these strains may have arisen partly by hybridization. Craigie (1927) demonstrated heterothallism in rusts—which had been postulated by several previous workers—the four spores of the promycelium being two (+) and two (−). The pycnidiospores are comparable with the oidia of some Basidiomycetes and are 'unisexual and produce unisexual mycelia'. One of the species he worked with was *Puccinia graminis*. Immediately attempts were made to produce crosses both between different races and between different forms. In the progeny of two different races of *P. graminis tritici*, for example, of 126 cultures in F_2 all were identified as one or other of known forms. Crosses made between *P. graminis tritici* and *P. graminis secalis* and *P. graminis agrostis* gave several new physiological forms, many of which proved to be heterozygous.

We are thus left with rather a confused state of affairs but with a suggestion that we are approaching some possible explanation. But was *Puccinia graminis* originally a very variable species which became divided up into an almost indefinite number of forms and strains, or is it these forms and strains that constitute the species?

Hybridity in Smuts

The Ustilaginales (Smuts) lend themselves to laboratory investigation better than do the Rusts, and as they are important pathogenic fungi, have been much studied. It is established that the young chlamydospore is binucleate and that later the nuclei fuse. The association of the two nuclei to initiate the binucleate stage is reported to take place at different points in the life-cycle according to the species and the conditions of growth. When the mature chlamydospore puts out a promy-celium the fusion nucleus divides several times and nuclei pass into the sporidia. The cytological evidence for meiosis is meagre, and some results of cultivation on artificial media have been interpreted as indicating that it may be delayed until the third or fourth division of the fusion nucleus. Kniep (1919) showed that in *Ustilago violacea* monosporidial cultures can be arranged in two groups and that fusion occurs only between members of opposite groups. This simple type of hetero-thallism is now known in about fifteen species of *Ustilago*. Next he tried to cross the appropriate strains of different species (1926). He found that sporidia from chlamydospores with reticulate walls would cross, as also those from smooth or echinu-late spores, but he was unable to obtain fusion between sporidia from the two different groups. Usually there is no observable difference between the $(+)$ and $(-)$ strains, but occasionally there is marked physiological difference in cultural characters. Later investigators have found that an echinulate wall is dominant over a smooth one with a simple $3:1$ relation (e.g.

Ustilago hordei × *U. medians*, *U. avenae* × *U. levis*), but sporidia from some crosses are largely non-viable. Holton (1933), working with what he considered a buff-coloured mutant of *U. levis* (the change in the colour-factor being assumed to occur at meiosis), found that brown was dominant to hyaline with a simple segregation.

Tilletia tritici has been crossed with *T. levis* and echinulation of the spore-wall was again dominant together with the 'fishy' smell of *T. tritici* due to the presence of trimethylamine.

Not only species but also genera have been crossed. Thus Tyler and Shumway (1935) have crossed *Sorosporium reilianum* and *Sphacelotheca sorghi* and obtained a hybrid intermediate in both spore and sorus characters, and Vaheedudden (1938) obtained a fertile hybrid between *Sorosporium reilianum* and *Sphacelotheca cruenta* with a promycelium and sporidia in F_1 larger than those of either parent. Cultural characters and pathogenicity also appear to follow Mendelian segregation in several of the species investigated.

Certain species, e.g. *Ustilago heufleri* and *Entyloma calendulae*, are able to complete their life-cycle in culture-media, and the haploid and diploid mycelia of many species will grow quite readily, though occasionally the diploid mycelium is unstable. The Smuts are therefore not so restricted in their parasitism as are Rusts, and in some species sporidia are unable to infect a host-plant, the diploid stage alone being able to accomplish this. The results obtained in the distribution of sex-factors in the promycelium are not far enough advanced for any generalities. The main point is that there is the possibility of hybridity and its consequences.

As elsewhere, there are results which are confusing, a large number of these arising from the study of *Ustilago zeae*. On germination of the chlamydospore there are four sexual phases. Stakman and his collaborators (1933), from a single mono-sporidial unisexual line, obtained 162 distinct lines which arose as sectors in colonies of the original line and its variant derivations. Fourteen of these lines were cultured for five years on artificial media and persisted so definitely as to justify the conclusion that each constituted a distinct biotype, from which new biotypes, however, may arise by sectoring. The fact that some of the variant lines produced no sectors for about three years, when several distinct ones appeared, from which new lines were isolated, was regarded as supporting the idea that sectoring results from mutation rather than delayed segregation, although delayed segregation may sometimes occur. The biotypes may differ from each other not only in factors for cultural characters but also for sex and pathogenicity. There appear to be limitless possibilities, and only the accumulation of accurate and carefully analysed data can provide the clue to a correct and general interpretation. It is essential that in such work the subculture should be monosporidial rather than by mass transfers.

The point should not be overlooked that the reason for the abundance of results, many apparently inconsistent, in *Ustilago zeae* may be that because of its economic importance it has been most studied; it may, or may not, be more complicated than the majority of species. Is such a species as *Ustilago zeae* splitting up into the constituent strains, or are the saltations something new?

Morphological Classification

The remaining Basidiomycetes are for the main part the toadstools, bracket fungi, fairy clubs, and such like, most of them saprophytic. Comparatively few of them have been grown in pure culture, and of these only a small percentage have produced even rudimentary fruit-bodies.

The Friesian system (Fries, 1874) is the basis of our modern arrangement of Basidiomycetes; there have been considerable modifications introduced by various systematists but no fundamental changes. In all except the resupinate fungi, where the structure has necessitated an extensive use of the microscope similar to that in Phycomycetes and Hyphomycetes, the species-concept is much as it was sixty-five years ago. Fries's descriptions of Agarics, moreover, were so sound that little attempt has been made to do more than tinker with his classification.

On account of the labour involved in acquiring a knowledge of these fungi, together with the academic tradition that they were unworthy of study, little attention was paid to them by scientific botanists except in France, until the discovery of heterothallism in *Coprinus* by Bensaude (1918). Since that time a good deal of research has been carried out on the problem and some of the results have their value in taxonomy. Various theories have been put forward to explain tetrapolar and bipolar 'sexuality' (and the 'multipolar sexuality' consequent upon the existence of different sets of incompatibility factors in 'geographical races'). Without considering these it may be pointed out that the oidia which may be present on uninucleate mycelia are not to be confused with sex-organs: like those which occur on binucleate mycelia, they are accessory spores, presumably with dispersal as their function.

It has been possible to obtain, in culture, fusion between the appropriate mycelia of a few different species, but apparently no fruit-body so far has been obtained; however, as it is notoriously difficult to obtain these except in a few genera, failure probably has no significance.

Most observers seem to be satisfied that a species is heterothallic and that mycelial fusions have occurred if they can find the small buckle-shaped structures connecting contiguous cells of the hyphae (clamp connexions) first shown by Bensaude (1918) to be the means by which nuclei become associated. It is commonly assumed that clamps are the indubitable sign of a binucleate condition and that their absence is conclusive of a uninucleate mycelium or of homothallism. Clamps vary greatly in their abundance and situation and are used in the diagnosis of some of the resupinate fungi. They are, moreover, not all of the standard pattern so frequently figured; for example *Coniophora puteana*, one of the common fungi causing rots of structural timber, is diagnosed in its mycelial condition by its characteristic whorled clamps.

It is a point of interest that a haploid mycelium sometimes produces a fruit-body. Sometimes these are sterile—occasionally sterile fruit-bodies are found wild—or they may produce a few spores all of one sex, as in *Schizophyllum commune* and *Coprinus* species; Hanna (1928) grew *Coprinus lagopus* in haploid mycelium for ten generations. It may further be noted that occasionally, after a considerable time in culture, a uninucleate mycelium may become binucleate. Though it is possibly not open to question that morphology is the standard by which we judge affinities, it must be based on something more than just external form for it to have taxonomic value; one may even regard cytology as being to a considerable extent micromorphology. Many of the old generic characters in Agaricaceae are, however, of the crudest, and consequently some of the genera in most fungus floras are very heterogeneous. Within recent years there has been a tendency to divide the old genera more and more both on the method of development and on microscopic structure. The old primary divisions based on spore-colour are no longer regarded as anything more than a convenience, it being realized that genera differing in the colour of their spores may have many characters in common.

The investigations of Fayod (1889) and Patouillard (1900) form the foundation of a newer method, and the numerous scattered results of more recent investigations when synthesized would give a clearer outline of a natural classification. It may be well here to emphasize that it is not possible for a systematist to adopt a system as a working tool until it has been set out in detail—a phylogenetic tree, even when carefully drawn, is useless for his purpose. Saccardo's *Sylloge Fungorum* (1882–1931), which gives descriptions of all species published up to 1920, is by far the most valuable mycological work to the taxonomist, though probably no one regards Saccardo's system of classification as other than one of convenience.

It is only by a clearer understanding of species that generic and family characters can be more correctly assessed. Spore-colour in Agaricaceae has been taken note of for well over a century, but it is only comparatively recently that other spore-characters have been noted. Attention was next given to spore-size. On the whole it may be said that the size and shape of spores are remarkably constant in any given species, but that measurements should be made in three dimensions on spores which have just been shot off the basidia; dried specimens may give small or abnormal spores.

Though four spores are the normal complement to a basidium, occasionally fungi with two-spored basidia are found. These have been described as distinct varieties, species, or even genera, e.g. *Godfrinia* which was characterized by a uninucleate subhymenium. Cytological investigation has shown that the bispored condition may arise by the spores receiving two nuclei as in *Naucoria semiorbicularis* and *Mycena metata*, while in others, as in *Hygrophorus virgineus* and *Mycena megaspora*, it arises parthenogenetically. The spore-size in a bispored form is generally much larger than that of the normal type.

The possibility of some kind of mechanical mixing of mycelia to form fruit-bodies must not be overlooked. Oort (1930) found that in *Coprinus fimetarius*[1] two uninucleate mycelia, when they represent phases genetically alike for one fertility factor and heterozygous for the other, may intertwine and build a composite fruit-body. The basidia are of two kinds, both bispored. There is here no sexual fusion, but as clamps are formed, though sometimes incomplete or abnormal, there is obviously something more than mere mechanical mixing.

Occasionally bispored basidia have been described mixed with quadrispored ones in the hymenium. Basidia of various lengths are normal in many species, presumably as an adaptation to more effective spore-dispersal, but in two tropical species of *Hygrophorus* a dimorphism has been described where there are large basidia bearing four spores and small basidia bearing two much smaller spores. It is not known what relation the different types of spore bear to one another, but it is significant that in one of the species, *H. firmus*, Corner (1936) has described sixteen varieties, and regards their characters as clearly fixed and hereditary.

An additional spore-character is to hand when the wall is not smooth. Such markings have been found useful in distinguishing between some Discomycetes, and *Lycoperdon* spp., but recently Crawshay (1930) showed that markings on the spores of *Russula*, when examined under a high magnification, give a considerable certainty to identification in this difficult genus; it is likely to prove equally valuable in other genera. Well-marked spore-characters have also been used to suggest phylogenetic lines of development. Thus Malençan has connected up the subterranean Hydnangiaceae and *Russula-Lactarius* as Asterosporiales, and Romagnesi has joined *Rhodophyllus* with the subterranean *Richoniella* as Rhodogoniosporeae on account of the shape and colour of the spores.

The presence, situation, shape, size, and number of cystidia have been shown to be useful in distinguishing species.

---

[1] This is probably the same fungus as that which Hanna called *Coprinus lagopus*.

The internal gill-structure, arrangement of hyphae in the trama and subhymenial layer, the nature and structure of the pellicle of the pileus, the colour, width, and other characters of the mycelium—indeed anything that has a definite shape and size—is of value in making definitions more precise: but all characters are not necessarily diagnostic characters. It has to be borne in mind that, relatively speaking, as much variation is to be expected in microscopic structures as in macroscopic ones. Intensive study in this respect is usually necessary for distinguishing what we regard as species, and the criteria used are for grouping similar individuals and not for distinguishing them.

Following the use of sulphovanillin by Arnould and Goris (1907) as a test in *Lactarius*, there has been a tendency to place reliance on various chemical reactions. These are rarely specific. A well-known exception is the action of iron sulphate on *Russula xerampelina* (at least for the genus *Russula*). There is no reason for supposing that even all varieties of a single species have identical physiology, and consequently there is no *a priori* objection to assuming the existence of many similar specific reactions. It is illogical, however, in the present state of our knowledge to rely on such a test alone.

The form of the fruit-bodies of agarics varies a good deal according to the conditions of growth. It has been assumed that some forms, 'varieties', or even 'species' are only variants of a given species growing in association with the roots of different trees (Mycorrhiza); but usually the relation between the two is not so close as to be suspected of having such a disturbing effect on specific characters. Melzer and Zvara (1927) in their study of *Russula xerampelina* describe and illustrate the great range in the characters of this species, listing fifteen synonyms and four doubtful ones, and say, 'A cet égard *R. xerampelina* peut être le document classique de la révélation de l'origine des espèces attachées par la symbiose à certains arbres et nommées espèces biologiques'.

The several points touched upon in this summary are not necessarily restricted to the groups in which they have been treated, nor are they the only ones. There need be no concern in the minds of those interested in taxonomy about the lack of problems in mycology.

Summary

The points which seem of most general interest are:

1 Many fungi have one or more asexual stages in addition to the sexual stage.

2 Fungi may be heterothallic requiring two different strains for the formation of the sexual (perfect) stage.

3 A vast number of fungi have no known perfect stage.

4 When grown in culture many fungi show modifications (saltations) which may be morphological or physiological.

5 Recent work with Fungi Imperfecti has shown that some of the saltations may be due to the 'dual phenomenon', according to which each species is composed of two homotypes with a series of one or more intermediate heterotypes.

6 Most species of fungi comprise numerous strains which can be distinguished by cultural characteristics, biometrical methods, or by host differentiation. So far as is known these are independent of geographical range: possibly the fact that parasites have often been transported with their hosts might be a partial explanation of the non-occurrence of geographical races in those species where, if they occurred, they would be most likely to be observed.

7 Hybrids have been artificially produced in a few fungi. The problem is complicated by the absence of sex organs in most fungi and the question whether heterothallism replaces sexual fusions. Thus in some agarics and smuts there are four sexes, but in different individuals, often growing in proximity, there may be different sterility factors so that there is no limit to the number of sexes—all sexual stages of one fungus being compatible with all sexual stages of another.

REFERENCES

ARNOULD, J., and GORIS, A. (1907). 'Sur une réaction colorée chez les Russulas et les Lactaires — Application à la diagnose de certaines espèces.' *Bull. Soc. Myc. Fr.* **23**, 174–8.

BENSAUDE, M. (1918). *Recherches sur le cycle évolutif et la sexualité chez les Basidiomycètes.* Thèse (Paris), pp. 156.

BLAKESLEE, A. F. (1904). 'Sexual Reproduction in the Mucorineae.' *Proc. Am. Acad. Arts. Sc.* **40**, 205–319.

BURGEFF, H. (1914, 1915). 'Untersuchungen über Variabilität, Sexualität und Erblichkeit bei *Phycomyces nitens* Kunze.' *Flora,* **107**, 259–316; **108**, 353–448.

CORNER, E. J. H. (1936). 'Hygrophorus with dimorphous basidiospores.' Trans. Brit. Myc. Soc. 20, 157–84.

CRAWSHAY, R. (1930). The Spore Ornamentation of the Russulas, pp. 179.

DE BARY, A. (1879). 'Aecidium abietinum.' Bot. Zeit. 37, 800–11.

DIETEL, P. (1887). Beiträge zur Morphologie und Biologie der Uredineen. Inaug. Diss. Leipzig, pp. 25; also Bot. Zentralbl. 32.

DODGE, B. O. (1928). 'Production of Fertile Hybrids in the Ascomycete Neurospora.' J. Agric. Res. 36, 1–14.

ERIKSSON, J. (1894). 'Über die Specialisirung des Parasitismus bei den Getreiderostpilzen.' Ber. k. deutsch. bot. Ges. 12, 292–313.

FAYOD, V. (1889). 'Prodrome d'une histoire naturelle des Agaricinés.' Ann. Sci. Nat. Bot., 7 Ser., 9, 181–411.

FRIES, E. (1874). Hymenomycetes Europaei, pp. 755.

GÄUMANN, E. (1923). 'Beiträge zu einer Monographie der Gattung Peronospora.' Beitr. Krypt. Schweiz, 5 (4), 1–360.

HANNA, W. F. (1925). 'The Problem of Sex in Coprinus lagopus.' Ann. Bot. 39, 431–57.

—— (1928). 'Sexual Stability in Monosporous Mycelia of Coprinus lagopus.' Ann. Bot. 42, 379–89.

HANSEN, H. N. (1938). 'The Dual Phenomenon in Imperfect Fungi.' Mycologia, 30, 442–55.

—— and SMITH, R. E. (1935). 'The Origin of New Types of Imperfect Fungi from Interspecific Co-cultures.' Zentralbl. Bakt. II. 92, 272–9.

HOLTON, C. S. (1933). 'Inheritance of Chlamydospore Characteristics in Oat-smut Fungi.' Abs. in Phytopathology, 23, 16.

JACKSON, H. S. (1931). 'Present Evolutionary Tendencies and the Origin of Life Cycles in the Uredinales.' Mem. Torrey Bot. Club, 18, 1–108.

KLEBAHN, H. (1904). Die wirtswechselnden Rostpilze, p. 447.

KNIEP, H. (1919). 'Untersuchungen über den Antherenbrand (Ustilago violacea Pers.), ein Beitrag zum Sexualitätsproblem.' Zeits. Bot. 11, 257–84.

—— (1926). 'Über Artkreuzungen bei Brandpilzen.' Zeits. Pilzkunde, 10, 217–48.

LEONIAN, L. H. (1926). 'The Morphology and Pathogenicity of some Phytophthora Mutations.' Phytopathology, 16, 723–30.

MELZER, V., and ZVARA, J. (1927). 'Russula xerampelina Sch.' Bull. Soc. Myc. 43, 275–8.

OORT, A. J. P. (1930). 'Die Sexualität von Coprinus fimetarius.' Rec. trav. bot. néerl. 27, 85–148.

PATOUILLARD, N. (1900). Essai taxonomique sur les familles et les genres des Hyménomycètes. Thèse pharm., Paris, pp. 184.

SACCARDO, P. A. (1882–1931). Sylloge Fungorum.

SCHROETER, J. (1879). 'Entwicklungsgeschichte einiger Rostpilze.' Cohn, Beitr. Biol. Pflanzen, 3, 51–93.

STAKMAN, E. C. (1929). 'Physiologic Specialization in Plant Pathogenic Fungi.' Leopoldina, 4, 263–89.

3 K

STAKMAN, E. C., TYLER, L. J., and HAFSTAD, G. E. (1933). 'The Constancy of Cultural Characters and Pathogenicity in Variant Lines of *Ustilago zeae.' Bull. Torrey Bot. Club*, **60**, 565–72.

—— and LEVINE, M. N. (1922). 'The Determination of Biologic Forms of *Puccinia graminis* on *Triticum* spp.' *Univ. Minnesota Agric. Exper. Stat. Tech. Bull.* **8**, 3–10.

TRANZSCHEL, W. A. (1904). 'Über die Möglichkeit, die Biologie wirtswechselnder Rostpilze auf Grund morphologischer Merkmale vorauszusehen.' *Trav. Soc. Imp. Nat. St. Pétersbourg*, **35**, 286–97.

TYLER, L. J., and SHUMWAY, C. P. (1935). 'Hybridization between *Sphacelotheca sorghi* and *Sorosporium reilianum.' Phytopathology*, **25**, 375–6.

VAHEEDUDDIN, S. (1938). 'The Production of a New Physiologic Race of *Sphacelotheca sorghi.' Phytopathology*, **28**, 656–9.

VUILLEMIN, P. (1910). 'Les Conidiosporés.' *Bull. Soc. Sci. Nancy*, ser. III, **11**, 129–72.

WARD, H. M. (1902). 'On the Relations between Host and Parasite in the Bromes and their Brown Rust, *Puccinia dispersa* (Erikss.).' *Ann. Bot.* **16**, 233–315.

TAXONOMIC BOTANY, WITH SPECIAL REFERENCE TO THE ANGIOSPERMS

By T. A. SPRAGUE

TAXONOMY may be defined as scientific classification of the different kinds of living organisms according to their proved or inferred phylogenetic relationships. This definition excludes from taxonomy classifications which are not based on real or supposed phylogenetic relationship, such as ecological classifications and 'artificial' ones, made only for convenience of reference or identification. It covers only the so-called 'natural' classifications, whether the word 'natural' is used in a 'logical' sense or as equivalent to 'phylogenetic'.

The non-taxonomist is perhaps apt to set an unduly low value on taxonomic work because the reasons underlying particular pieces of classification are often omitted for the sake of space. The taxonomist on his side is apt to be indifferent to 'lay' (i.e. non-taxonomic) opinion, because he knows that his work will stand or fall by the test of time and the judgement of his fellow taxonomists.

It is possible to demonstrate experimentally the nature and origin of certain taxonomic 'groups', particularly such as are of lower rank than the species, and it may also be shown that there is a very high degree of probability that certain species had a particular origin. Most botanists would agree that such a strong case exists for regarding *Spartina townsendii* H. et J. Groves as a natural hybrid between *S. alterniflora* Loisel and *S. stricta* Roth that this origin may be accepted without hesitation.

Phylogeny mainly a Question of Probabilities

In groups above the rank of species, phylogeny becomes a matter of greater or less probability. It is therefore incumbent on the taxonomist to put his cards on the table. When he proposes a new or revised classification he should assess carefully the degree of probability attaching to each part of it. Failure to do so may give the impression that the particular arrangement adopted is a mere matter of opinion, and that taxonomy is not a branch of science, but a pleasant occupation demanding relatively little intelligence, an idea far from the truth.

Many of the hitherto generally accepted groups of Dicotyledoneae above the rank of family are clearly artificial. The sub-
class Metachlamydeae (Sympetalae, Gamopetalae), for example,
has long been regarded as polyphyletic (Warming, 1895; Wernham, 1912, p. 383), and has recently been broken up (Pulle,
1938) into five groups, four of which have been attached to
separate series of Archichlamydeae (Polypetalae and Apetalae).

Comparison of the classifications of dicotyledonous families
given by Warming (1895), Hutchinson (1926), and Diels (1936)
show what considerable differences of opinion exist. The two
latter works mention various evolutionary progressions considered probable by their authors, but neither of them states
the cases for the particular changes in classification made in it.
The non-taxonomist is accordingly left with the unfortunate
impression that such classifications are not based on an attempt
to secure maximum correlation of characters, but that they are
very largely subjective, being the resultant of taxonomic tradition and the author's experience and 'intuition'. While long
experience is invaluable in suggesting possible natural groupings, such suggestions need to be tested by thorough tabulation
and evaluation of characters before they can be accepted. To
do this adequately for the Dicotyledoneae alone would require
the life-work of a team of experienced taxonomists. It should be
clear that future progress in the classification of the groups of
higher rank will be by synthetic methods—not by attempting
to make a complete scheme embracing every family, but by
placing such families together as show maximum correlation
of characters, and by building up larger groups from them.

A natural classification built up in this way will for many
years be very incomplete, but it will have the supreme merit of
being based on established facts instead of on individual opinions.
All groups of doubtful position should either be omitted, or, if
they are inserted in the system, the doubt should be clearly indicated, and the cases for possible alternative positions stated.
Such a gradually growing natural classification must be kept
distinct from the practical classification adopted for working
purposes, although it should as far as possible form the basis or
framework of the latter. A claim that any *complete* classification
of angiospermous or even of dicotyledonous families is based on
probable phylogeny need not be taken seriously.

The order Polygonales (Polygoniflorae) may serve as an illustration of different treatment by each of four taxonomists. Warming included in it the three families Polygonaceae, Piperaceae (incl. Saururaceae), and Chloranthaceae and placed it before the Curvembryeae (Centrospermae); Hutchinson included the two families Polygonaceae and Illecebraceae (Caryophyllaceae, *pro parte*); Diels included the single family Polygonaceae. Rendle (1925, p. 80) had the following three consecutive orders: Polygonales (Polygonaceae), Piperales (Piperaceae, Saururaceae, Chloranthaceae), and Centrospermae. He regarded these orders as 'natural and well-defined groups which occupy at the present time a somewhat isolated position'. In this paper space will not permit of tabulation of characters. The following points may, however, be stated: (1) Each of the four authors places the Polygonales near the Centrospermae. (2) Warming and Rendle place the Polygonales (Polygonaceae) beside the Piperales, whereas Hutchinson appends the Piperales to the Ranales, Diels places the Piperales after the Verticillatae (Casuarinaceae), and Wettstein (1935, pp. 638, 1066) states that their systematic position is uncertain. It should be clear that the taxonomic position of the Piperales is at present a matter of opinion. (3) No reasons are given by Hutchinson for his transference of the Illecebraceae to Polygonales. Tabulation of characters would have shown that they have far more in common with the Caryophyllaceae, in which they are generally included. An extremely interesting transference—if it can be justified—is that of the Nyctaginaceae by Hutchinson from the Centrospermae to the Thymelaeales. Here again, no case is stated for the change. In its absence there seems to be no reason for questioning the view of Heimerl (1934), the monographer of Nyctaginaceae, that this family is undoubtedly most closely related to the Phytolaccaceae (Centrospermae).

On the other hand, certain major groups of Dicotyledoneae seem to be very natural. From the writer's personal experience the following may be named: Bicarpellatae (Contortae, Tubiflorae, Plantaginales, the position of the Plantaginales, however, being doubtful); Centrospermae (sensu Diels); Rhoeadales (sensu Diels); Malvales (Elaeocarpaceae, Tiliaceae, Malvaceae, Bombacaceae, Sterculiaceae); Myrtiflorae (sensu Bentham et Hooker); Ericales. It will be found that, in the main, these groups have been accepted, sometimes with additions, in recent classifications, e.g. those of Bentham and Hooker, Warming, Engler, Hutchinson,[1] and Wettstein, a fact which is in itself an indication that they are probably natural.

Wettstein's *Handbuch der systematischen Botanik* (ed. 4, 1935) is notable for stating cases for and against the positions assigned by him to various families (e.g. Cactaceae, Cucurbitaceae, Euphorbiaceae, Plumbaginaceae) and for indicating the degree of probability attaching to particular classifications (e.g. those of Leitneriaceae, Piperales, Hippuridaceae, Chlaenaceae, &c.). It is supplied with ample references to recent taxonomic research and takes an unusually wide range of characters into consideration. For these and other reasons it may be regarded as the best text-book on the taxonomy of the Angiosperms.

Nearly all the accepted *families* of Angiosperms appear to be 'natural' groups. It is a matter of opinion whether the Leguminosae, for example, should be treated as a single family or as an order, but no one would dispute that it is a 'natural' group. Among peculiarly 'natural' families, the Polygonaceae, Polygalaceae, and Cactaceae may be mentioned. On the other hand, there is some reason for considering the Loganiaceae (as defined in Bentham and Hooker's *Genera Plantarum*) as polyphyletic. The revised classification proposed by Solereder (1892, pp. 21–3) was based on anatomical research.

Where difference of opinion exists as to the family to which a particular genus should be referred, this is usually due to ignorance of essential data, frequently those concerning its anatomy. It has long been the practice at the Kew Herbarium to enlist the collaboration of anatomists in determining the correct taxonomic position of plants of uncertain relationships (cf. Stapf and Boodle, 1909; Sprague and Boodle, 1909, 1914; Sprague and Metcalfe, 1937). Where suitable material is available, the collaboration of cytologists would be very welcome.

In *genera*, the case is not so strong. Many appear to be very natural, but others are separated, as a matter of convenience, on what seem to be slender grounds, and may even be artificial groups. This applies to various recognized genera of such very natural families as Cyperaceae, Leguminosae, Rubiaceae,

[1] Hutchinson has separated the order Lythrales from Myrtales, and Loganiales and Apocynales from the rest of the Bicarpellatae.

and Compositae. Many subgenera and sections are unquestionably natural, but the precise arrangement of species in smaller groups seems in many cases to be a matter of opinion. It is accordingly desirable that taxonomists should state which part of their proposed classifications they regard as natural and which as artificial, giving reasons for their belief in each case.

As regards *species*, few would deny that we are dealing on the whole with natural groups, whatever the status that may be assigned to them. Some have argued that, owing to the operation of hybridization, the inter-relationships of plants have become so complicated that they may be compared to a network, and that phylogenetic classification is impossible owing to this mixed ancestry. Those who hold this view seem to have overlooked the fact that hybridization is commonly confined to species of the same genus and to subdivisions of species, and that, although bigeneric hybrids are known in cultivation, their occurrence in a wild state is very rare, and that there appears to be no evidence for wild bigeneric hybrids producing true-breeding offspring. The contrast between the comparatively easy classification of species into genera and sections, and the comparative difficulty met with in grouping species into smaller categories may perhaps be attributed to the operation of hybridization within the latter.

Natural and Artificial Classifications

Taxonomy progresses by 'trial and error'. The edifice of phylogenetic classification is subject to continual pulling down and rebuilding, but many foundation stones remain in position, and the permanent part of the structure continually increases.

Theophrastus (*b.* 370 B.C.) recognized certain taxonomic groups now accepted, such as Umbelliferae and Compositae—Liguliflorae, while Dioscorides (*fl.* A.D. 64) in his *Materia Medica* had a series of 20 consecutive Labiatae, and another of 35 Umbelliferae with which a few plants of other families were intermingled. Among the groups implicitly recognized by Kaspar Bauhin (1623) were Cruciferae, Solanaceae, Papaveraceae, Ranunculaceae—Anemoneae, Cucurbitaceae, and Papilionaceae, in addition to the above, and from his time onwards there has been a gradual increase in what may be termed the permanent part of the classification of Angiosperms. It is undeni-

able that there has been a vast improvement since the sixteenth
century in the classification of Angiosperms, which has become
increasingly more 'natural'. Asa Gray (1879, 331) expressed
the difference between 'natural' and 'artificial' classifications
as follows:

'A natural classification in botany aims to arrange all known plants
into groups in a series of grades according to their resemblances, and
their degrees of resemblance, in all respects, so that each species,
genus, tribe, order, &c., shall stand next to those which it most
resembles in all respects, or rather in the whole plan of structure.
For two plants may be very much alike in their external appearance,
yet very different in their principal structure. Artificial classifications single out one or more points of resemblance or difference and
arrange by those, convenience and simplicity being the controlling
principles.'

It is virtually impossible, however, to take all resemblances
into consideration. According to Moll (1934, p. 484), 'a complete pen-portrait of a higher plant will easily take a man's
work during a whole year'. The most that can be done is to
take into consideration such characters as experience has shown
to be useful in classification, particularly in the group concerned, together with any new ones that may suggest themselves. A further difficulty is: what are unit characters? Whereas
the shape of a leaf, e.g. ovate, lanceolate, obovate, oblanceo-
late, &c., is commonly treated in technical descriptions as if it
were a single character, a little consideration will show that it
is a complex of a number of characters including ratio of breadth
to length, position of maximum breadth, rates of tapering to base
and apex, &c. Unless agreement is reached as to the units, it
cannot be maintained that all characters have been considered.
Actually, then, even in the construction of 'natural' classifications only a small proportion of the total characters is examined,
and a still smaller proportion is utilized. Both in 'natural' and
in 'artificial' classification there is selection of characters, the
difference between the two lying in the method of selection.

The 'natural' system of classification of the Angiosperms has
been developed synthetically by grouping individuals into
species, species into genera, genera into families, &c. (Sprague,
1925, p. 9). Whereas synthetic methods may lead to natural
classifications, analytical methods almost inevitably lead to

artificial classifications, such as those proposed by Van Tieghem (Rendle, 1930, p. 25). It is recognized (Gilmour, 1937, p. 1041) that artificial classifications may be partly natural, but it is not always realized that such natural parts were often accepted previously, and may even have suggested the artificial classifications concerned. The usual 'didynamy' and 'tetradynamy' of the anciently recognized Labiatae and Cruciferae, the 'gynandry' of the Orchidaceae, the 'monandry' of most Scitamineae, and the 'hexandry' of most petaloid Monocotyledons, may well have suggested to Linnaeus his sexual system of classification. Although his higher groups (classes and orders) were mainly artificial, the lower ones (genera and species) were mainly natural, his sexual system constituting merely the framework of his classification.

To sum up: In making an artificial classification there is arbitrary selection of characters, no attempt being made to arrive at groups exhibiting a maximum correlation of characters. In attempting to build up a natural classification the units—individuals, species, genera, families, &c.—are arranged in various ways until such maximum correlation is obtained. In this process 'facies' (*vide infra*) is an invaluable guide, and experience suggests what categories of characters are likely to be significant.

Are 'Natural' Classifications Phylogenetic?

The view has been taken, more especially by botanists without wide taxonomic experience and intimate acquaintance with many natural groups, that a natural classification in biology is not necessarily phylogenetic, but is merely a particular example of natural classification in general (Gilmour, 1937). The experienced taxonomic botanist usually reaches the opposite conclusion, as the result of repeated tests of the 'natural' system. Suppose that certain associated groups of the same rank, A, B, C, &c., have been established on the basis of maximum correlation in the x characters taken into consideration. He examines the incidence of y additional characters, and retains, modifies, or rejects the old piece of classification in the light of the new data. If consideration of the $x+y$ characters as a whole extends correlations previously obtained, the particular classification stands. An even stronger case for its retention exists when the same result is obtained independently from consideration of the *y* characters alone.

I am indebted to Mr. C. E. Hubbard for the following remarkable example. The genera *Eragrostis*, *Diplachne*, and others, formerly placed in the tribe Festuceae, were removed by Stapf (1898, p. 316; 1917, p. 19) to a new tribe, Eragrosteae, mainly on account of their three-nerved lemmas and general facies. This new classification has been confirmed by the cytological data obtained by Avdulov (1931, pp. 199, 207, 232), and by the anatomical ones given by Prat (1936, i, pp. 498–506; ii, pp. 165–258). The Eragrosteae have *x*: the first leaf of the seedling *broad*, and 3-nerved lemmas; *y* (1): leaf-anatomy of the 'panicoid' type, two-celled hairs, and constricted siliceous cells; and *y* (2): small chromosomes, basic number 9 or 10. The Festuceae have *x*: the first leaf of the seedling *narrow*, and usually from 5- to many-nerved lemmas; *y* (1): leaf anatomy of the 'festucoid' type, no two-celled hairs, and siliceous cells not constricted; *y* (2) large chromosomes, basic number 7. Here the incidence of the *y* (1) and *y* (2) characters, previously unexamined, leads independently to the same classification as was obtained from the *x* characters.

If a natural classification in biology were merely 'a particular example of natural classification in general', why should characters previously unknown and unconsidered so frequently prove to be correlated in the same way? If, on the other hand, the 'natural' groups previously recognized are truly phylogenetic, there is every reason to expect such correlation. The fact that piece after piece of 'natural' classification has been strengthened by the discovery of additional correlated characters carries conviction to those most concerned. The taxonomist accordingly accepts the working hypothesis that the well-tested 'natural' groups in biology are phylogenetic, and this seems more scientific than to reject this hypothesis without offering any alternative explanation of the observed facts.

So-called phylogenetic systems and phylogenetic trees of the Angiospermous families belong, on the other hand, to the realm of speculation. The phylogenist is on relatively firm ground in maintaining that groups A and B form a phylogenetically natural group X, provided that he can show that they exhibit greater correlation of characters *inter se* than is found between either of them and an outside group, or groups. Let us suppose, however, that A possesses one or two primitive characters and represents an early stage in a recognized evolutionary progression, and that B has relatively advanced corresponding characters, and represents a later stage of the same progression. To assume, as is sometimes done, that B is therefore descended from A, or even from ancestors having more in common with A, is quite unjustifiable. Such an assumption ignores all the other characters, according to some of which B might represent an earlier stage than A in a different evolutionary progression. Furthermore, it seems probable that the common ancestors of two or more recent families of Angiospermae were of a much less specialized type than any of their recent descendants.

There are grounds for regarding two gamopetalous orders, Primulales and Plumbaginales, as more closely related to the Centrospermae (apetalous and polypetalous families) than to any other group. Hutchinson (1926, diagram facing p. 8, p. 26) and Wettstein (1935, p. 1068), however, go farther and give diagrams in which Primulales and Plumbaginales[1] are shown as actually derived from Centrospermae or from part of that group (Caryophyllales). Wettstein postulates a progression from apetaly through polypetaly to gamopetaly, Hutchinson two progressions from polypetaly, one to apetaly and the other to gamopetaly. Both authors construct this section of their phylogenetic trees according to the presence or absence of petals, and their free or united condition. Apparently the only reasons for deriving Primulales and Plumbaginales from Centrospermae, rather than vice versa, or both from a now extinct group, are that the recent Primulales and Plumbaginales are mostly gamopetalous and the Centrospermae polypetalous or apetalous, and that some of the latter have numerous stamens. The utility of such diagrams is doubtful, and if accepted uncritically they may be seriously misleading.

Evolutionary Progressions and Stages

Apart from the Caytoniales, which occupy an isolated position, the earliest Angiosperms recorded in the fossil state belong largely to recent families and genera, and afford no clues to the inter-relationships of the families. According to Scott (1924,

[1] Included by Hutchinson in Primulales.

p. 41), 'our present leading types of plants extend right back through the Tertiary Period to the Upper Cretaceous, and in a few cases even further down still.' 'The fossil history of the Flowering Plants shows no sign of a beginning, for, with few exceptions, all the specimens known can be referred to families still existing' (p. 42). If, however, we accept the premiss that the well-tested parts of the natural classification of Angiosperms are phylogenetic, it can be shown that there is a very high degree of probability that certain biological progressions have taken place independently in numerous lines of descent. For example, the hypothesis that there has been a general reduction in the flower of the Angiosperms (Čelakowský, 1894) is accepted almost as axiomatic by the taxonomists concerned, because it is the only one that seems to fit the facts. Other biological progressions in the Angiosperms generally accepted by taxonomists are those from the hermaphrodite flower to the unisexual one, from actinomorphy to zygomorphy and asymmetry, from free to united petals, and from a superior to an inferior ovary. By the application of such hypotheses there have been traced, in many parts of the system, general trends of morphological evolution, which seem probable in the light of our present knowledge. In so far as this results in improvements in classification (i.e. greater correlation of characters), the case for the acceptance of these hypotheses is strengthened. The stronger the case for the occurrence of a particular biological progression, the greater will be the number of independent lines of descent in which it has probably occurred, and the smaller will be the phylogenetic value of the character concerned. The widespread existence of a tendency to unisexuality in the Flowering Plants is axiomatic, and the classes Monoecia, Dioecia, and Polygamia accordingly contain the most miscellaneous assortment of genera found in any of the classes in the sexual system of Linnaeus. Such 'biological' (*vide infra*) characters, however, possess considerable phylogenetic significance in groups of lower rank, such as families, genera, and species. For example, although the Metachlamydeae (gamopetalous Dicotyledoneae) are admittedly polyphyletic, yet gamopetaly is a valuable family character in the Dicotyledoneae. So much is this so, that the existence of polypetalous members of various gamopetalous families (e.g. Ericaceae) comes as a surprise to the less experienced or well-read taxonomist. Similarly the existence of three genera of Rubiaceae (*Gaertnera*, &c.) with a superior ovary is an isolated exception in the large order of Rubiales, which is characterized *inter alia* by an inferior ovary. Consideration of the rarity of these and similar exceptions leads to the conclusion that in many cases the members of the same family have passed through the various stages of a biological progression more or less contemporaneously.

Constant Characters and Tendencies

For purposes of classification *constant* characters are obviously preferable to inconstant ones. In general, however, the smaller the group the larger the number of constant characters. Thus descriptions of species include many more such characters than do descriptions of genera, the length of the latter being largely due to the need of indicating the *range* of characters found in the constituent species. In families this state of affairs is even more accentuated, and it is desirable to include *tendencies* as well as constant characters. The occurrence of a relatively rare tendency in a group which, because of certain constant characters, is considered as phylogenetically natural, affords some measure of confirmation of that view. Thus the tendencies to trimery in the flowers of the Menispermaceae and Burseraceae, and to tetramery in the Onagraceae, confirm, as far as they go, the view that these families are phylogenetically natural. The co-existence in the Onagraceae of a second, much rarer tendency, namely, to tranverse septation of the anther-thecae, greatly enhances this probability. Such tendencies may be of value in larger groups: the tendency in Berberidaceae and Monimiaceae to valvular dehiscence of the anthers confirms the view, reached on other grounds, that these families are closely related to the Lauraceae and Gomortegaceae in which this character is constant.

Although constant characters are the most important, yet, paradoxically, unusual range in a character may itself be treated as a character of a group. Certain families, e.g. Umbelliferae (floral formula: $KCA_5 G_2$) have definitely homomeristic[1] flowers, while others, e.g. Crassulaceae ($KCAGn$, $n = 3$–30) and Gentianaceae ($KCAn G_2$, $n = 4$–12) are heteromeristic,[1]

[1] 'A homomeristic group is one in which all the subordinate groups have the

either in different genera, species, &c., or even on the same plant.

Different Categories of Characters and their Relative Values

A good deal of misapprehension exists among non-taxonomists as to the nature of the characters which are actually or should be used in classification. It cannot be emphasized too strongly that no category of characters,[1] whether morphological, anatomical, cytological, chemical, ecological, or physiological, should be neglected (Sprague, 1925, p. 10). In the Angiosperms the widest range of characters is usually found, however, in the external morphology. Anatomical characters generally come next in order of range and therefore of importance. One need only compare, for example, the number of characters of restricted incidence obtainable from the external morphology of a leaf with that obtainable from its anatomical structure, or the external characters of a flower and fruit with those drawn from the stem anatomy in order to see why a natural classification must in the main be based on external characters, simply on account of the much larger number of these and their much more restricted incidence. On the other hand, particular anatomical characters, on account of their occurrence in comparatively few groups, are of high taxonomic value, e.g. storied structure in wood, scalariform thickening of vessel walls (and, to a less extent, scalariform perforations), presence of latex cells or tubes, presence of internal phloem, and oil cells. For these examples I am indebted to Dr. C. R. Metcalfe.

For taxonomic purposes two primary categories of characters have been distinguished, the 'fortuitous' and the 'biological' (Wernham, 1912, p. 392). Fortuitous characters are defined as such as have 'no relation to the environment nor to any biological function', biological ones being 'such as are in direct relation to some vital function or advantage'. The term 'fortuitous' does not seem particularly happy, but refers apparently to the origin of such characters, not to their occurrence in a

same floral formula. . . . A heteromeristic group is one in which the subordinate groups have floral formulas which differ numerically' (Riley, 1922, p. 231).

[1] Geographical distribution is not here considered an intrinsic 'character' of a species or other group, though it often affords useful hints as to the delimitation of groups (Sprague, 1925, pp. 10–11). It is regarded rather as a spatial 'accident' of a population.

particular individual. Since the same 'biological' character
may have evolved independently, under similar environments,
in many different lines of descent, such characters are clearly
inferior, as phylogenetic criteria, to 'fortuitous' ones whose
presence appears to be due merely to inheritance.

Two corollaries have been drawn: that 'the occurrence of
several common fortuitous characters in a series of plant-forms
is valid evidence of their mutual affinity'; and that 'a group of
plants may share a number of biological characters in common
without being therefore closely related' (Wernham, l.c., pp. 393,
394). A possible objection to the acceptance of the two categories is that in many cases it may be a matter of opinion whether
a particular character is or is not connected with the general
mode of life of the plant or with some special function. On the
whole, however, there is not much difficulty in separating
characters which have no apparent connexion with function
from those which definitely have such a connexion; and experience has shown that classifications based mainly on the former
category exhibit greater correlation of characters than those
based mainly on the latter.

Diels (1921, p. 136) substituted the terms 'constitutive' and
'non-constitutive' for 'fortuitous' and 'biological' respectively.
He mentioned as examples of constitutive characters the mode
of phyllotaxy, the numerical relations and symmetry-relations
in the flower ('die Zahlen- und die Symmetrieverhältnisse in der
Blüte') and many peculiarities in anatomical structure. His
inclusion of 'symmetry relations in the flower' among constitutive characters seems strange, since zygomorphy of the corolla,
for example, is clearly a character connected with the process
of pollination. He subdivided his non-constitutive (biological)
group of characters into the following subordinate categories:

1. *Functional*—intimately connected with some special function, but uninfluenced by external conditions, e.g. the
   adaptations of flowers to particular insects, and of fruits
   for dispersal.
2. *Epharmonic*—apparently connected with the mode of life
   of the plant, but nevertheless remaining constant under
   varying external conditions, e.g. the microphylly of the
   Ericoideae, the succulent nature of the Crassulaceae,
   and the formation of bulbs in many species of *Oxalis*:

these may be regarded as adaptations which have become fixed.

3. *Adaptive*—varying according to the external conditions, e.g. the absolute size of members, and the degree of hairiness.

The use of the term 'adaptive' for subcategory 3 seems peculiarly unfortunate, since (1) functional and (2) epharmonic characters have surely more claim to be called adaptive in the usual sense of the word. A better term for subcategory 3 might be 'plastic' (modifiable with change of environment).

Generalizations regarding the relative values of characters are apt to be dangerous, since it is commonly found that a character which is extremely valuable taxonomically in groups A, B, C in one part of the natural system may prove to be of little or no taxonomic value in groups X, Y, Z in another part. Hence the importance of combining wide taxonomic study with monographs of special groups. The specialist whose entire working life is devoted to a small section of the Dicotyledoneae or Monocotyledoneae, for example, must almost inevitably suffer from a restricted outlook. It follows that a system of division of work in a great herbarium according to the different floras of the world rather than according to taxonomic groups has much to recommend it. On the other hand, for purposes of custodianship, it is preferable to divide the routine work of a herbarium according to taxonomic groups, in order to avoid inconsistencies of arrangement due to divided responsibility. Where there are two or more competing classifications of a group, it is clearly undesirable to have one classification used for the Asiatic material, for example, a second for Africa, and possibly even a third for America. The ideal policy is to combine general research according to floras, with custodianship according to taxonomic groups and monographic study of one or more large families as a whole.

Practical Methods and Examples

A taxonomic botanist beginning the study of a particular group, such as a genus, will, either before or after making himself acquainted with previous classifications, set out all his herbarium and other specimens together with the best available illustrations so that he may obtain a bird's-eye view of the whole. If he has a good 'eye' for detecting resemblances, he will gradually be able to sort out the material into a number of sets, some of which will correspond to species (as generally accepted) and others to groups of species. At the same time he will have the opportunity of noting any exceptions to the generally accepted generic characters, and any additional generic characters hitherto overlooked. The discovery of such exceptions may lead to the detection of actual errors in previous classifications, and the removal of the material concerned to another recognized genus, or to the segregation of new genera, or to the widening of the generic diagnosis.

In such preliminary work the faculty of appreciating what is called the 'facies' of a plant is invaluable. This faculty, while capable of cultivation, is possessed in very different degrees by different persons, and seems to be uncorrelated with general intellectual ability or intellectual training. On it depends to a large degree the rapid preliminary sorting of new collections of herbarium specimens. It follows that the economical performance of routine work in a great herbarium depends largely on the recruitment, as technical assistants, of individuals endowed with this faculty to perform the sorting, preliminary naming, and laying-in of material under the supervision of fully qualified taxonomic botanists.

It is difficult to define 'facies' precisely. It is a general effect produced on the eye by the sum total of all the visible external characters, many of which are not actually employed in modern technical descriptions owing to the difficulty of expressing them in precise terms. The increase of precision in modern technical descriptions so stressed and valued by trained taxonomists has been accompanied by a certain deterioration in the *art* of plant description. The better sixteenth-century descriptions of plants, such as those of Valerius Cordus, can be best understood by treating them as word-pictures designed to supply mental images of the plants. They are comparable in fact to good illustrations rather than to modern descriptions, and the species concerned may accordingly be identified most easily and certainly by comparison with the former. Sometimes the analysis of facies leads to the recognition of differences in anatomical structure, which in turn suggest or confirm changes in classification.

The glumes and lemmas of the Eragrosteae possess a firm 'skin-like' texture and a more or less glossy appearance, whereas in the Festuceae (proper) they are more fleshy and dull. These differences in facies are associated with, and due to certain anatomical differences. For example, in Eragrosteae the chloroplasts are restricted to layers of cells around the vascular bundles, whereas in Festuceae the chloroplasts occur in the tissue between the bundles.

The investigation of plants of unknown position is an important element in the education of the taxonomist. Where difficulty is experienced in assigning an Angiosperm to any known family, the usual reason is that the plant is 'anomalous', i.e. that it disagrees in one or more characters usually considered to be diagnostic of its family. The cases of *Anopyxis* and *Diclidanthera* illustrate this point. Herbarium material consisting of flowering shoots of a species of *Anopyxis* was received from West Africa at two important herbaria. The general structure of the flower, and in particular the presence of a tube formed by union of the filaments, suggested the Mahogany family, Meliaceae. Consequently at both institutions the species concerned was originally regarded as representing a new genus of Meliaceae. At one, it was described and published as a new genus and species of Meliaceae under the name *Pynaertia ealaënsis* De Wild. At the other institution, however, it was found out, before publication, that the species possessed a combination of characters unparalleled in Meliaceae, namely, whorled leaves, interpetiolar stipules, valvate aestivation of the calyx, and trifid petals. Anatomical examination of the stem and leaves suggested that it might be referable to the genus *Anopyxis* (Rhizophoraceae), of which the flowers were then unknown. Subsequent comparison of types confirmed this view, and the species was accordingly transferred to *Anopyxis* (Rhizophoraceae) as *A. ealaënsis* (De Wild.) Sprague (Sprague and Boodle, 1909, p. 309).

The case of *Anopyxis* revealed the existence of a valuable character hitherto neglected, concerned with the relative sizes of calyx and corolla in the bud. In certain families, e.g. Meliaceae and Vitaceae, the calyx is much shorter than the corolla in the bud stage, so that the flower-buds may be termed 'phaenopetalous', the aestivation of the calyx being 'open'. In others, such as Rhamnaceae, Malvaceae (and other Malvales), and Rhizophoraceae, the calyx encloses the corolla in the bud, so that the flower-buds are 'cryptopetalous', the aestivation of the calyx being 'closed'. This distinction had been recognized, in a vague way, in the Meliaceae and Vitaceae by the description of the calyx as 'small'. It is not always clear-cut, as a flower-bud frequently passes from the cryptopetalous to the phaenopetalous condition whilst enlarging prior to expansion, as in *Rosa*. Where it is well-marked, however, it forms a valuable additional character for phylogenetic purposes.

The history of the genus *Diclidanthera* affords an example of errors in classification due to taking too narrow a range of characters into consideration, to giving undue weight to one of them, and to neglect of data and suggestions supplied by previous workers. Originally assigned by Martius (1827, p. 139, tt. 196, 197) to the family Ebenaceae, it was transferred by Reichenbach (1828, p. 136) to the Styracaceae. Alphonse de Candolle (1844, p. 245) mentioned four characters in which *Diclidanthera* differed from the Styracaceae, and excluded it from that family. Miers (1852, p. 130) pointed out that the corolla of *Diclidanthera* was not truly gamopetalous, and transferred it to Hamamelidaceae as the type of a new tribe Diclidanthereae. Martius (1856, p. 16) suggested that both *Diclidanthera* and *Moutabea* should be referred to the Polygalaceae, on account of agreement in the general structure of the flower, especially the androecium. Lindley (1846, p. 378) had previously included *Moutabea* among the Polygalaceae, and it was retained in that family by Bentham and Hooker (1862, p. 136), who placed *Diclidanthera*, on the other hand, in the Styracaceae. Perkins (1907, p. 13) excluded *Diclidanthera* from Styracaceae, and Gilg (1924, p. 323) proposed a new family, Diclidantheraceae, for its reception, which he placed in the Metachlamydeae.

The discovery of *Barnhartia*, a new genus clearly related to *Diclidanthera*, offered the solution to the problem, though this was not realized by the describer. Additional material of the type species was collected by the Oxford University Expedition to British Guiana in 1929, and on naming the material it became apparent that *Barnhartia* was wrongly placed. A combination of certain unusual characters, combined with the purely racemose inflorescence, suggested the family Polygalaceae, namely,

crater-shaped nectaries on the bracts, and anthers dehiscing
by a single flap ('valve') breaking away from the two thecae.
Comparison of the external morphology of *Barnhartia* with
Chodat's summary of the characters of Polygalaceae (1896,
p. 323) showed no single point of disagreement, and the floral
diagram of *Barnhartia* was found to resemble closely that of
Polygala (Sprague and Sandwith, 1932, t. 3172). The case was
clinched by examination of the pollen, which was of the type
peculiar to Polygalaceae, and of the stem and leaf anatomy,
which agreed closely with that of the woody genera of that
family.

It will be observed that the correct taxonomic position of the
pseudogamopetalous *Diclidanthera* was established only after the
discovery of the polypetalous *Barnhartia*, which in this and other
respects exhibits closer agreement with the remaining Polygalaceae. Where such chains of related groups exist, phylogeny
is removed from the realm of the 'possible' to that of the 'highly
probable'.

It will be observed also that each of the three main characters
which led to the discovery of the real relationships of *Barnhartia*
may be regarded as 'fortuitous' (constitutive), namely, the purely
racemose inflorescence, the presence of a nectary of special shape
in a particular and unusual position, and the peculiar single flap
by the separation of which the pollen of both thecae is exposed.
For example, although the possession of nectaries is a definitely
'functional' character, their special shape and position on the
bracts seem unconnected with function and may accordingly
be regarded as 'fortuitous'. The families of Angiospermae are
and always will be defined largely by 'biological' characters.
The key to their inter-relationships, however, is often to be
sought by studying the sporadic incidence of 'fortuitous'
characters.

REFERENCES

AVDULOW, N. P. (1931). 'Karyo-systematische Untersuchung der Familie
    Gramineen' (*Bull. Applied Bot.*, Leningrad, Suppl. 44).
BAUHIN, KASPAR (1623). *Pinax Theatri botanici.* Basle.
BENTHAM, G., and HOOKER, J. D. (1862). *Genera Plantarum*, **1**, pars 1.
    London.
ČELAKOWSKÝ, L. J. (1894). *Das Reductionsgesetz der Blüthen* (Sitzb. K. Böhm.
    Ges. Wiss. 1894, Math.-Nat., No. 3).

CHODAT, R. (1896). 'Polygalaceae' (in Engler u. Prantl, *Die natürlichen Pflanzenfamilien*, Leipzig, **3**, 4).

DE CANDOLLE, ALPH. (1844). 'Styracaceae' (in De Candolle, *Prodromus systematis naturalis regni vegetabilis*, **8**. Paris).

DIELS, L. (1921). 'Die Methoden der Phytographie und der Systematik der Pflanzen' (Abderhalden, *Handbuch der biologischen Arbeitsmethoden*, Abt. **11**, Teil 1). Berlin and Vienna.

—— (1936). A. Engler's *Syllabus der Pflanzenfamilien*, ed. 11. Berlin.

GILG, E. (1924). 'Fam. Diclidantheraceae' (Engler, *Syllabus der Pflanzenfamilien*, ed. 9 and 10, p. 323. Berlin).

GILMOUR, J. S. L. (1937). 'A Taxonomic Problem' (*Nature*, **139**, 19 June 1937, pp. 1040–2).

GRAY, ASA (1879). 'Structural Botany' (*The Botanical Text-book*, ed. 6, part I). New York and Chicago.

HEIMERL, A. (1934). 'Nyctaginaceae' (Engler, *Die natürlichen Pflanzenfamilien*, ed. 2, **16c**, 86–134. Leipzig).

HUTCHINSON, J. (1926). *Families of Flowering Plants*: I. *Dicotyledons*. London.

LINDLEY, J. (1846). *The Vegetable Kingdom*. London.

MARTIUS, C. F. P. VON (1827). *Nova genera et species plantarum brasiliensium*, **2**, fasc. 2. Munich.

—— (1856). 'Genera aliquot . . . dubiae affinitatis' (Martius, *Flora Brasiliensis*, Munich and Leipzig, **7**, col. 11–17).

MIERS, J. (1852). 'On the affinities of the Olacaceae' (*Ann. Mag. Nat. Hist.*, ser. 2, **9**, 128–32).

MOLL, J. W. (1934). *Phytography as a Fine Art*. Leyden.

PERKINS, J. (1907). 'Styracaceae' (Engler, *Das Pflanzenreich*, **4**, 241. Leipzig).

PRAT, H. (1936). I. 'Contribution à l'étude systématique et histologique des Festucées' (*Bull. Soc. Bot. France*, **82**, 498–506).

—— (1936). II. 'La Systématique des Graminées' (*Ann. Sc. Nat., Bot.*, sér. x, **18**, 167–258).

PULLE, A. A. (1938). *Compendium van de Terminologie, Nomenclatuur en Systematiek der Zaadplanten*. Utrecht.

REICHENBACH, H. TH. L. (1828). *Conspectus regni vegetabilis*. Leipzig.

RENDLE, A. B. (1925). *The Classification of Flowering Plants*, II, *Dicotyledons*. Cambridge.

—— (1930). *The Classification of Flowering Plants*, I, *Gymnosperms and Monocotyledons*. Ed. 2. Cambridge.

RILEY, L. A. M. (1922). 'Meristic Floral Variation in Galieae' (*J. Bot., Brit. & Foreign*, **60**, 230–2).

SCOTT, D. H. (1924). *Extinct Plants and Problems of Evolution*. London.

SOLEREDER, H. (1892). 'Loganiaceae' (in Engler u. Prantl, *Die natürlichen Pflanzenfamilien*, Leipzig, **4**, Abt. 2).

SPRAGUE, T. A. (1925). 'The Classification of Dicotyledons' (*J. Bot., Brit. & Foreign*, **63**, 9–13, 105–13).

—— and BOODLE, L. A. (1909). 'Kokoti' (*Kew Bull.* 1909, pp. 309–12).

—— and METCALFE, C. R. (1937). 'The Taxonomic Position of Rhynchocalyx' (*Kew Bull.* 1937, pp. 392–4).

SPRAGUE, T. A., and SANDWITH, N. Y. (1932). 'Barnhartia floribunda' (Hooker's *Icones Plantarum*, London, **32**, t. 3172).

STAPF, O. (1898). 'Gramineae' (in Dyer, *Flora Capensis*, London, **7**, pt. 2).

—— (1917). 'Gramineae' (in Prain, *Flora of Tropical Africa*, **9**, pt. 1).

—— and BOODLE, L. A. (1909). 'Peglera and Nectaropetalum' (*Kew Bull.* 1909, pp. 188–91).

WARMING, E. (1895). *Handbook of systematic Botany* (transl. by M. C. Potter). London.

WERNHAM, H. F. (1912). 'Floral Evolution: IX' (*New Phytol.* **11**, No. 10).

WETTSTEIN, R. (1935). *Handbuch der systematischen Botanik*. Ed. 4. Leipzig and Vienna.

A MUSEUM ZOOLOGIST'S VIEW OF TAXONOMY

By W. T. CALMAN

THE zoologist whose work lies in one of the greater museums inevitably comes to see the problems of taxonomy somewhat differently from those of his colleagues who study animals in the field or in the laboratory. In the British Museum, for example, where the staff are, year after year, constantly unpacking and studying great collections from the uttermost parts of the earth and from the depths of the seven seas, one gets an impression, more vivid perhaps than can be gained anywhere else, of the unending diversity of animal form. Although the number of species already known is vast—the best estimates put it at something like three-quarters of a million—new species are brought to us almost every day. What is very remarkable and significant, however, in this constant influx of novelties, is the rarity of the unexpected. The diversity is indeed unending, but it runs in well-defined channels. Seldom, very seldom indeed, do we come across a species for which there is not a place waiting in the accepted classification. Not once in twenty years do we get a *Caenolestes*, a *Cephalodiscus*, an *Anaspides*, or a *Decolopoda*. As a result of this experience, we come to have a confidence in the Natural System of classification that is perhaps not always shared by our colleagues of the laboratory. The *Systema Naturae* becomes for us an objective reality, not merely a convenient filing device.

It is, of course, true that the kind of knowledge acquired by the museum systematist is superficial as compared with that resulting from the intensive studies of the geneticist, the experimentalist, and the ecologist. Nevertheless, it is reasonable to suppose that a broad, even if superficial, survey of the Animal Kingdom may tell us something that is worth adding to the knowledge acquired by more detailed study.

What, then, is this Natural System of classification in which we believe so firmly? How do we arrive at it, and how is it related, if at all, to the process by which existing animals have come to be?

We start with the empirical fact that the great majority of

animals can be sorted, with greater or less difficulty, into groups which we call species. What a species really is, and whether the groups that we call by that name are all equivalent, are questions that we may leave aside for the present, but of the existence of species there can be no doubt at all. It is true that we meet everywhere with what the systematist regards as 'difficult' groups. In almost every Class, Order, and family, even in many genera, by the side of well-marked and clearly definable species there is a residue in which the limits of species seem to become blurred. It often happens that closer study will enable us to define specific limits even in cases where they are not obvious on first inspection, and it is the constant hope of the systematist when dealing with a difficult group that he may light upon some character, previously unregarded, that will give him the necessary clue. It is a hope that is often, but not always, realized. And, as with species, so with groups of higher order. There are many instances where the limits of genera, families, and even Orders seem almost matters of individual opinion. It is possible, however, that the amount of study and discussion such cases demand and receive may lead us to overestimate their importance and to forget the much greater number that need no discussion. What is significant is the very general discontinuity of species and the readiness with which most of them fall, almost as it were of themselves, into definable genera and categories of higher order.

The practical question as to the method by which systematic categories are to be recognized and defined was answered by T. H. Huxley in the following words: 'The things classified are arranged according to the totality of their morphological resemblances, and the features which are taken as the marks of groups are those which have been ascertained by observation to be the indications of many likenesses or unlikenesses' (*Man. Anat. Invert.* 1877, p. 23), and he expressly disclaimed any attempt to base classification on phylogeny, although he agreed that the results of taxonomy 'readily adapt themselves' to the hypothesis of evolution.

It may be readily admitted that, as a matter of practice, systematic categories are, for the most part, based on an enumeration and evaluation of morphological resemblances, without explicit reference to phylogeny. Most zoologists nowa-

days, however, would find it difficult to divest themselves entirely of evolutionary preconceptions, and nearly all would agree that it is not only legitimate but necessary to be guided by ideas of probable phylogeny when the mere balancing of resemblances and differences leaves the position of an organism uncertain. For example, the structural similarities between the Rhizocephalan *Thompsonia* and a typical barnacle amount to very little indeed. Nevertheless, we are justified in appealing to the probable evolution of the parasite from a non-parasitic stock and to the 'chain of affinities' linking it with less modified forms to justify its inclusion in the Cirripedia.

The great majority of systematic zoologists in fact still believe, with Darwin, that 'the Natural System is founded on descent with modification' and that 'community of descent is the hidden bond which naturalists have been unconsciously seeking, and not some unknown plan of creation, or the enunciation of general propositions or the mere putting together and separating objects more or less alike' (*Origin*, chap. xiv).

It is perhaps worth while to comment here on what seems to be a somewhat common misconception as to what is meant by phylogeny. The units with which it deals are species, not individuals. In sexually reproducing organisms, as are the vast majority of animals, the ancestry of an individual cannot be represented by a 'tree' but only by a network. The analogy with the 'family trees' used to express human pedigrees is misleading since the latter are based on the arbitrary fiction of unilateral—mostly patrilineal—descent. It is only when the ancestral network becomes divided into 'bands of descent' by the cessation of interbreeding—due to interspecific sterility, geographical isolation, or other causes—that descent can be represented by a tree-like ramification and phylogeny can be said to begin. When we say that certain groups of animals have arisen from a 'common stock', we have in mind that, if we could carry the analysis far enough, we should ultimately come to a community of interbreeding individuals from which the various bands of descent have diverged. Of course it is never possible, in practice, to carry the analysis as far as this, and even the most complete of the palaeontologists' lineages stops far short of such an origin. It may be noted in passing that, as a general rule, the phylogenetic basis of classification is most obscure when we are deal-

3 N

ing with the highest and with the lowest taxonomic categories, and that it is the categories of intermediate grade that lend themselves most easily to phylogenetic grouping. It is unlikely. that we shall ever arrive at any degree of certainty regarding the origin of the great phyla, partly because palaeontology fails us and partly because their origin takes us back to organisms so widely different from any now living that speculation as to their structure and mode of life becomes unprofitable. On the other hand, the species within a genus, and often the genera within a family, are distinguished by characters so few in number and so trivial in morphological significance that any attempt to assign phylogenetic meaning to them is mere guesswork. We can be fairly confident about the origin of mammals, but not about the beginnings of vertebrates or the interrelations of the species of mice.

It is of interest to note that our botanical colleagues seem, on the whole, to be less confident than the zoologists in ascribing a phylogenetic meaning to their classification. This is no doubt due very largely to the fact that the morphology of plants is vastly simpler and less varied than that of all but the simplest animals. It may also be attributed, in some measure, to the fact that hybridization seems to have played a much greater part in the evolution of plants than it has done in that of animals, and the pattern of the phylogenetic tree is, in many places, hopelessly obscured by interosculation of the branches.

The museum zoologist is never allowed to forget the fundamental importance of the problems of geographical distribution. It is not only that he knows beforehand what the general aspect of the collection will be when he unpacks a box of mammals from South America, or of birds from the Himalayas, or of fish from the African lakes. There may be new species among them but they will, except in the rarest cases, fit in with what he already knows of the regional fauna. All this can be learned elsewhere than in the museum. What cannot be properly appreciated without museum study, however, is the amazingly precise correlation between geographical, or rather topographical, distribution and the 'infra-specific' categories, subspecies, local races, and so forth. Most zoologists must at times have felt impatient with the specialists who discriminate subspecies on all but imperceptible differences in colour or shape or size.

It is necessary to go to one of the larger museums, where scores or hundreds of specimens can be laid out side by side, before one can be convinced that these distinctions, trivial as they may seem, are really valid, and reflect with precision the degree to which the range of the species is interrupted by barriers of a topographical or climatic nature.

Finally, the museum zoologist is taught by experience that a natural or phylogenetic classification is of greater value in practical or economic work than one that is merely arbitrary or artificial. When the practical man comes to us for advice he wants information about the habits, life-history, or ecology of some species of animal that he has found to have a bearing, adverse or beneficial, on human affairs. As often as not we find that nothing is known under these heads of that particular species. What we can tell him, however, is that it will, in all probability, resemble most closely in these respects the species that come nearest to it in the natural classification. It is, of course, true that physiological or ecological categories sometimes cut across the divisions of our classification, but far oftener they will be found to coincide with them, at least approximately. Some species of Brachyurous Crustacea are hatched from the egg as miniature adults, creeping on the sea-floor, but if a crab is brought to us of which the development is unknown, we can tell our practical friend that he will have a 100-to-1 chance of being right if he assumes that it hatches as a zoea larva which swims freely in the plankton. A parrot may have the feeding habits of a hawk and a kingfisher may live in a waterless country and feed on lizards, but these exceptions must not obscure the fact that in defining the systematic groups of parrots and of kingfishers we are also defining, although somewhat less strictly, bionomic categories.

A distinguished zoologist once told the present writer that the search for a natural classification was no part of a museum curator's business. His job was identification, not classification, and he had only to devise some kind of key or card index that would enable one to sort animals quickly and easily into species. So far as the really scientific branches of zoology were concerned, an artificial classification was as good as, and might even be better than, any other. Few, if any, museum zoologists, however, would be satisfied with this limitation of their responsibilities.

TAXONOMY AND PHILOSOPHY

By J. S. L. GILMOUR

MOST systematic biologists would agree that there are a number of questions connected with the theoretical side of their work which are by no means satisfactorily settled and that these points of disagreement are frequently a hindrance to progress in taxonomic practice. An obvious example is the notorious difficulty in finding a generally accepted definition of a species, or, indeed, of any taxonomic category, with the resultant multiplicity of usages in practice. A related question, which is probably of greater practical importance than is usually admitted, is the frequently debated one of whether taxonomic groups are subjective or objective.

Another problem which has recently been discussed, for example, by Lam (1936, 1938), Gilmour (1937), and Dobzhansky (1937), is the significance of a natural classification and its relationship to phylogeny. During the past year this point has been exhaustively debated by the Taxonomic Principles Committee of the Association for the Study of Systematics in relation to General Biology, and a certain amount of agreement has been reached. There still exist, however, two schools of thought among its members, as among biologists in general. One school, consisting, in the committee, mainly of zoologists, maintains that a natural classification is one based on the phylogeny of the groups concerned. Their point of view may be fairly summarized in the words of Dendy (1924, p. 241): '. . . if only our knowledge of classification and phylogeny were so [complete]; we should then doubtless see at once that the taxonomic tree and the phylogenetic tree are, after all, one and the same thing, for we should arrange all organisms strictly in accordance with the course of their evolution.' The other school, however, feels doubtful whether a 'logical' classification (based on correlation or coherence of characters) is always and necessarily a phylogenetic one, and also whether, especially for existing flowering plants, data are yet available for a reconstruction of phylogeny. It is even doubtful whether the real significance of the term 'phylogenetic relationship' is yet fully understood. A resolution of these differences is surely one of the greatest needs of systematic biology.

Related to this problem is the question whether there exists a final, ideal classification towards which taxonomists are consciously or unconsciously striving. The first school pictures such a classification as a reconstruction of the phylogenetic tree, while the more sceptical second school wonders whether such a system is not, in fact, unattainable.

Lastly, during the past thirty years the problem of how to treat taxonomically the new data provided by cytological, genetical, and ecological research has become increasingly pressing. Should these data be incorporated into the existing taxonomic categories, or should new subsidiary categories be constructed to accommodate them?

In this chapter the view is put forward that no satisfactory solution to these problems is possible without first examining the fundamental principles which underlie the process of classification, and, further, that these principles cannot be adequately formulated without basing them on some epistemological theory of how scientists obtain their knowledge of the external world. Recent developments in experimental physics have induced physicists to examine the philosophical foundations of their work. It is suggested that biologists, and especially taxonomists, must follow their lead if the theoretical problems of taxonomy are to find solutions which will stand the test of time.

In recent years scientific epistemology, or 'the philosophy of science', has received a great deal of attention from philosophers, especially those grouped under or round the title of 'logical positivists'. The pages of such periodicals as *The Philosophy of Science*, *Erkenntnis*, and *Analysis* testify to the active interest in the subject, and recently a critical summary of current views has been published by Benjamin (1937). The most significant undertaking in this field, however, is the new *International Encyclopaedia of Unified Science*, part of volume i. of which has recently appeared (Neurath, O, 1938). This work was planned at successive International Congresses for the Unity of Science, the fourth of which was held at Cambridge in 1938, and seeks to elaborate a common basis for the logical, empirical, and pragmatic aspects of scientific activity. This movement for the unity of science is sponsored almost entirely by philosophers, physicists, and mathematicians. Biologists have fought shy of what is often called mere word-splitting or worse, and have left the philosophical foundations of their science to look after themselves, or rather to be pulled down and rebuilt by the philosophers. Woodger, who is one of the sponsors of the Unity of Science movement, and who has recently (1937) applied the methods of logical analysis to the data of biology, is an exception, but he stands nearly alone. The need seems clear for closer co-operation between philosophers and biologists in this very important task, and the present chapter is a preliminary and tentative attempt to bring the two viewpoints nearer together in the field of taxonomy.

What type of epistemological theory, then, may be used most fruitfully as a basis for an examination of the purpose and method of biological taxonomy, and hence towards a solution of the problems outlined at the beginning of the chapter? Recently Dingle (1938) has put forward, from the standpoint of a physicist, a scientific epistemology which seems to provide such a starting-point. Philosophically, Dingle's scheme, as he himself would certainly admit, does not contain any new features, but put forward as it is by a scientist, it is formulated in such a way as to appeal especially to scientific workers. It may be briefly outlined as follows: The primary division in the process which leads to the acquisition of knowledge is that between the *subject* 'I' and the *object*, which consists not only of those sense-impressions which go to form what we call the external world, but also of all the past and future states of the thinker (including feelings). Thus the primary duality is not one of mind as opposed to matter, but of the ever-present subject 'I', as opposed to the objects of thought of that subject, these objects including both 'mind' and 'matter'. This separation is automatically effected by the passage of time, the subject 'I' remaining always in the present, and the objects or thought either in the past or the future. The attributes and functions of the subject and object elements are radically different. The latter consists of a series of sense-impressions which are received through experience, and the former of the mental processes by which these sense-impressions are given order and coherence. 'Out of that chaos of past experience reason constructs myself, you, tables, chairs, stars and all the rest of the world, and tries to set them all in order' (Dingle, 1938, p. 150). (The question whether the sense-impressions are actually apprehended as separate data or in coherent groups is one for the psychologist, and does not affect the validity of Dingle's epistemological analysis.)

This account of the thought-process gives an entirely different picture of the acquisition of knowledge from that usually accepted by working scientists. In both there is a duality. The commonly accepted picture is that of mind, on the one hand, and the objects of the external world, on the other, the business of science being to bring to the knowledge of mind an ever greater number of these objects. Mind, in this picture, plays no active part in *creating* the objects of the external world, but merely records what already exists. In Dingle's picture, however, the duality is not one between a passive, receptive mind and a pre-existing external world, but between an active, subjective, reasoning agent, and the countless sense-data of experience out of which reason builds that logically coherent pattern which we call the external world. The 'objects' of this 'external world', therefore, consist of two distinct elements, one derived from sense-experience, the other supplied by the activity of the reasoning agent. For example, the object which we call a chair consists partly of a number of experienced sense-data such as colours, shapes, and other qualities, and partly of the concept *chair* which reason has constructed to 'clip' these data together. In any consideration of scientific method it is essential to distinguish between these 'clips' and the sense-data which they hold together. The latter are given, once and for all, and cannot be altered, whereas the former can be created and abolished at will so as the better to give a coherent picture of the ever-increasing range of sense-data experienced. For example, the phenomena of specific differentiation in Linnaeus's day were clipped together by the concept of special creation, which was later replaced by the concept of gradual evolutionary differentiation. As Dingle points out, a great many of the paradoxes of modern physics are due to a failure to distinguish between 'clips' and sense-data, the former being given the same objective, unalterable status as the latter. The same is equally true in the field of systematic biology.

Against this epistemological background, then, it is possible to outline the process of classification somewhat as follows. The classifier experiences a vast number of sense-data which he clips together into classes, each of which is definable in terms of certain specific data. Thus a class of blue things may be made for sense-data exhibiting a certain range of colour, and so on. Any given series of data can, of course, be clipped together in a number of different ways, depending on the *purpose* of the classifier, i.e. depending on which particular data he is interested in at the moment. Thus the range of data grouped under the class 'man' can be subdivided into nations, into professions, into age-groups, and so on. The important point to emphasize is that the construction of these classes is an activity of *reason*, and hence, provided they are based on experienced data, such classes can be manipulated at will to serve the purpose of the classifier. Classification, then, has always a pragmatic element as well as an empirical and a rational one. Broadly speaking, the purpose of all classification is to enable the classifier to make inductive generalizations concerning the sense-data he is classifying. Thus he constructs occupational and nationality classes among mankind, and by comparing the resulting groups he can make generalizations—e.g. that at the present time there is a greater proportion of clergymen in England than in the U.S.S.R. These generalizations are then used as guides to human action. In fact, the proper functioning of our daily lives, as has been neatly illustrated by Sayers (1926, p. 22), depends entirely on the use of inductive generalizations based on the classification of sense-data. As Hogben has said (1938, p. 125), 'The truths of science are recipes for human action. . . .'

Now the classification of animals and plants, though based on different data, is essentially similar in principle to the classification of inanimate objects. That is to say, it consists in clipping together the mass of sense-data collectively classed as 'living things' into a logically coherent pattern for the purpose of making inductive generalizations concerning those data. The primary 'clip' for living sense-data is the concept of the individual. As is well known, and as has been emphasized by J. S. Huxley (1911), and Hochreutiner (1937), this concept breaks down in a number of cases, but for general purposes, and especially in the higher animals and plants, the individual can be taken as a convenient unit of classification. It should never be forgotten, however, that the individual is a concept, a rational construction from sense-data, and that the latter are the real objective material of classification.

Living individuals are grouped together into a large number of different classes, based on the possession in common of certain sense-data or attributes. These classes are of two kinds, which are usually regarded as being quite distinct. On the one hand there are the taxonomic categories of species, genera, families, &c., and on the other the many other 'non-taxonomic' groups into which living individuals have been divided, such as succulents, annuals, calcicoles, marine animals, flying animals, &c. The former type, or at any rate species and categories of lower rank, are usually termed 'natural' groups, whereas the latter are regarded as artificial classes constructed by man. What is the essential difference between them? Apart from any possible phylogenetic significance, which will be discussed later, surely the fundamental difference is that natural groups class together individuals which have a large number of attributes in common, whereas in artificial groups the individuals concerned possess a much smaller number of common attributes. This was the view of the pre-evolutionary taxonomists (e.g. Lindley, 1846), of T. H. Huxley (1875), and of those philosophers and logicians who have studied the theoretical problems of classification (see especially Jevons, 1883).

Thus the essential difference between such a group as Ranunculaceae and one such as 'succulent plants' is that the individuals comprising the former have a greater number of attributes in common than those comprising the latter. By 'attributes' is here meant, of course, the whole range of sense-data including morphological, physiological, 'biological' (e.g. sterility and fertility), and distributional characters. This difference between natural and artificial groups, which is one of degree and not of kind, also has its pragmatic aspect. A natural group, being based on a large number of attributes, can be used for a wider range of inductive generalizations than can an artificial group, which is useful only in the particular sphere for which it was created. Thus many generalizations can be made regarding a natural family of plants (e.g. with reference to distribution, chemical properties, wood structure, &c.), whereas regarding an artificial group very few of such generalizations are possible.

It is often said that natural groups, especially of the rank of species and lower, have a 'biological reality' or an 'historical reality in the process of evolution' (see Timofeeff-Ressovsky's chapter, pp. 73–136), which is not possessed by 'artificial' groups. The use of the word 'reality' in this connexion is perhaps unfortunate, as it implies a qualitative difference between natural and artificial groups, and thus obscures the basic difference in number of correlated attributes. From the philosophical point of view a natural group is, of course, no more real than an artificial one; both are concepts based on experienced data. On analysis, the phrase 'biological reality' resolves itself into the possession of certain attributes which are usually the mark of a group which has reached subspecific or specific differentiation, namely a distinct geographical distribution and a certain degree of sexual isolation. These attributes are, of course, of particular importance in the evolutionary process and give a distinct biological character to the groups concerned, and it is, I think, in recognition of this 'biological objectivity' that the word 'reality' is used. Its use in this sense has, however, been extended so as to apply to the philosophic character of natural groups in general and has tended to give such groups a false appearance of 'metaphysical objectivity'. This is undoubtedly further emphasized by the binary system of nomenclature, which creates an impression of analogy between the Christian and surnames of individual humans and the specific and generic names of animals and plants. This analogy is quoted in some elementary text-books and even penetrates into higher spheres. For example, Swingle (1928) writes, 'There can be no doubt that people gave names to certain plants before they attempted to classify them', implying that names of species are given, not on account of the possession of certain characters by the individuals concerned, but in the same arbitrary way as the christening of a baby. It cannot be too strongly emphasized that all classes of living things, taxonomic and non-taxonomic, though differing in their biological importance, should be regarded as of the same philosophic character, namely as rational concepts constructed by the classifier to clip together certain sense-data experienced by him.

To sum up, starting from basic epistemological considerations, we are led to the view that a natural classification of living things is one which groups together individuals having a large number of attributes in common, whereas an artificial classification is composed of groups having only a small number of common attributes; further, that a natural classification can be used for a wide range of purposes, whereas an artificial classification is useful only for the limited purpose for which it was constructed; and lastly that both types are created by the classifier for the purpose of making inductive generalizations regarding living things.

The exact part assigned to the sense-data and the classifier respectively in the construction of a particular classification depends largely on the viewpoint adopted. It is true, of course, that some series of sense-data lend themselves more readily than others to a natural arrangement (Gilmour, 1937), and from this point of view it can be said that the data determine the classification. On the other hand, the choice of the actual arrangement adopted lies ultimately with the classifier, who may ignore the natural grouping and choose an artificial one based on a limited number of data if it suits his purpose.

With these considerations in mind, is it possible to solve the problem, mentioned at the beginning of the chapter, of the definition of a species and other taxonomic groups? The difference between categories of different ranks is one of *degree* of resemblance between the individuals comprising them, taking into account as many attributes as possible. For example, the individuals composing a species resemble each other more closely than do those composing a genus. Can any general agreement on these various degrees of resemblance be reached? If it were possible to define accurately a unit character, then resemblance and difference in a certain *number* of characters could be used as a basis for the definition of *degree* of resemblance and difference, and hence of the various taxonomic categories. The concept of a unit character, however, is a notoriously vague and relative one, and it would seem that taxonomic categories based on resemblance in the sum total of attributes can never be susceptible of precise definition. As a definition of a species, then, I would suggest something on the following lines, and analogous definitions could be constructed for other categories. 'A species is a group of individuals which, in the sum total of their attributes, resemble each other to a degree usually accepted as specific, the exact degree being ultimately determined by the more or less arbitrary judgment of taxonomists.'

Admittedly this definition, based as it is on resemblance in total attributes, is a very vague one, but any attempt to define a species more precisely in terms of particular attributes breaks down. It is true, of course, that certain types of attribute are particularly important at the specific level of differentiation, for instance interfertility and chromosome number, but it has proved impossible to use them as a basis for a generally accepted definition.

As stated above, since the acceptance of the theory of evolution a natural classification has generally been regarded as having some phylogenetic significance. Some who hold this view think that a natural classification is identical with a phylogenetic one, whereas others would say rather that a natural classification, especially for units of generic rank and higher, should be interpreted against a background of phylogeny. Whichever point of view is taken all must agree (1) that a definition of phylogenetic relationship is essential for clear thinking on the subject, and (2) the assessment of degree of phylogenetic relationship must be based on some criteria other than correlation of attributes or possession of a common plan. Even the most convinced phylogenetic taxonomist maintains, not that correlation of attributes *is the same thing* as phylogenetic relationship, but that such correlation *indicates* phylogenetic relationship, thereby implying that the latter is based on some other criterion. Let us examine then in what sense the term 'phylogenetic relationship' is actually used in practice.

The phylogenetic taxonomist working with living groups usually expresses his phylogenetic judgments in such terms as 'a group *A* is monophyletic if the groups composing it have originated from a single group' (i.e. presumably a group of equivalent rank to *A*, or of lower rank), or 'two groups are more closely related phylogenetically than two others if the former possess a more recent group ancestor than the latter'. This concept of phylogeny may be termed 'the group concept'.

The palaeobiologist, on the other hand, working with fossil material, expresses his phylogenetic judgments in terms of *lineages.* For example, Arkell and Moy Thomas, in another chapter of this book, describe parallel lineages in the evolution of the Ammonites in Devonian rocks. They find that genera occurring at different levels are composed of a number of such lineages, and they state that there is greater 'true affinity' between successive members of these lineages than between the horizontal groups. This may be termed 'the lineage concept of phylogeny'.

It is clear that we have here two quite different criteria of phylogenetic relationship. The first regards phylogenetic relationship between groups as *analogous* to the genealogical relationship existing between individuals. This concept leads naturally to the construction of phylogenetic trees analogous to the genealogical trees expressing individual relationship. The second, however, is dealing with *actual genealogical relationship* between the individuals concerned. Thus the 'true affinity' stated by Arkell and Moy Thomas to exist between members of the same lineage is an actual genealogical relationship of the individuals composing the groups, and not merely a group relationship analogous to it. Much of the confusion in phylogenetic discussion appears to be due to a failure to distinguish between these two concepts.

It must now be asked which of the two provides the criterion independent of correlation of attributes that we are seeking. Obviously the 'group concept' does not do so, for we must make our groups *before* constructing our phylogeny. This difficulty is very clearly pointed out by Bather (1927), who cites the case of the genus *Balanocrinus*, derived by a number of different lineages from the genus *Isocrinus*. If *Isocrinus* is regarded as a single genus, on the group concept *Balanocrinus* is monophyletic, having been derived from a single group of equivalent rank. If, however, the various species of *Isocrinus* forming the starting-points of the lineages are raised to generic rank, then *Balanocrinus* becomes polyphyletic, having been derived from a number of different groups of equivalent rank. Which view is taken thus depends on a *taxonomic* judgment, that is to say, on an assessment of the correlation of attributes. We are thus arguing in a circle.

The 'lineage concept', on the other hand, being based on the genealogy of individuals, is quite independent of taxonomic judgment. Thus the relationship between two cousins remains the same whatever may be their attributes.

It seems clear, then, that if the concept of phylogenetic relationship is to be based on independent criteria it must be confined to the lineage concept, as is in fact done by biologists who are studying actual evolutionary histories from fossil evidence. How does this view affect the relationship between phylogeny and a natural classification based on correlation of attributes?

In the first place, it means that while correlation of attributes may sometimes indicate closeness of phylogenetic relationship, it by no means always does so. Thus in the case of the Devonian Ammonites quoted by Arkell and Moy Thomas, a classification based on correlation of attributes would group the individuals horizontally, whereas a phylogenetic classification would group them vertically. Or again, among living forms, it is generally accepted that *Spartina townsendii* H. and J. Groves arose on the south coast of England by the hybridization of *S. alterniflora* Lois. and *S. stricta* Roth. A classification on the basis of lineages would group the south coast individuals of the two species with *S. townsendii*, whereas one based on correlation of attributes would group them with other individuals of the same two species in other parts of the world. From our knowledge of the methods of evolutionary change it seems highly probable that such change must very frequently take place along a number of parallel lineages and the resulting groups must be considered polyphyletic. Bather had this in mind when he wrote (1927, p. ci): 'The whole of our System, from the great Phyla to the very unit cells, is riddled through and through with polyphyly and convergence.' How is it, then, that the concept of group, as opposed to lineage, phylogeny has arisen? The chief reason seems to be that a false analogy has been drawn between taxonomic groups and individuals, in virtue of the objective existence which both were supposed to possess and which should rightly be confined to sense data. This analogy led to the belief that a relationship exists between groups analogous to the genealogical relationship between individuals. It is only when taxonomic groups are seen to be collections of individuals classed together because of the possession of certain attributes in common that the falseness of the tree analogy becomes clear.

What, then, in the light of foregoing considerations, is the relationship between 'natural' classifications, 'artificial' classifications, and phylogeny?

A natural classification is that grouping which endeavours to utilize *all* the attributes of the individuals under consideration, and is hence useful for a very wide range of purposes. This, in practice, is the procedure followed in what is sometimes called 'orthodox' taxonomy, and it would seem best to confine the use of the ordinary taxonomic categories of species, genus, family, &c., to a natural classification of this type. In so far as it is theoretically possible to envisage a classification on these lines, which does in fact embody all the attributes of the individuals being classified, it can be said that one final and ideal classification of living things is a goal to be aimed at. In practice, however, this aim would never be attained, owing both to the limitations of our knowledge and to the differences of opinion between taxonomists.

In addition, however, to this natural classification for general purposes, there must always be a large number of subsidiary— more or less 'artificial'—classifications which are based on a limited range of attributes and are therefore useful only for limited purposes. In one sense, any grouping of living things other than the main taxonomic grouping forms such a subsidiary classification; for example, the division into trees, shrubs, herbs, &c. In addition to these, however, a number of more systematized classifications in spheres of particular scientific interest have been constructed. This is true particularly of classifications based on the recently discovered data of genetics, cytology, and ecology. A good account of some of these new categories has been given by Du Rietz (1930).

In many cases, however, these new categories have not been clearly differentiated from those of 'orthodox' taxonomy, with a resulting confusion between them. For example, it is not clear whether Turesson's categories of ecotype, ecospecies, coenospecies, &c. (Turesson, 1922), which are based primarily on genetical and ecological criteria, are to be regarded as substitutes for or alternatives to the ordinary taxonomic categories. It would seem to be of great importance to keep the terminology of such subsidiary categories, based on a limited range of attributes, separate from that of orthodox taxonomy. Good examples of treatment on these lines are Danser's categories of comparium, commiscuum, and convivium (Danser, 1929), which are based on criteria of interfertility and intersterility (p. 524), Huxley's recently proposed 'cline' series (p. 31), and the 'deme' terminology suggested by Gilmour and Gregor (1939).

Another interesting example of such subsidiary classifications is the grouping of varieties of crop plants outlined by Vavilov in another chapter (p. 549). Vavilov's various 'geographical groups' are, in effect, the result of classifying his material on the limited attributes of geographical and ecological distribution for the special purpose of comparing those attributes with others in which he is interested from an agricultural point of view. The result is the establishing of a number of valuable generalizations regarding the attributes concerned.

The number and extent of such special classifications is, of course, a matter for testing by experience, discussion, and agreement. The point here emphasized is that they should be kept distinct in terminology from those used in the natural classification based on total attributes.

Lastly, what place is left for phylogeny? If the lineage concept of phylogenetic relationship is accepted, then a phylogenetic classification must be regarded as a subsidiary classification, useful for the special purpose of studying the relationship between genealogy and other attributes. For example, to quote again the case of *Balanocrinus* and *Isocrinus*, a phylogenetic classification on lineages, when compared with a 'natural' classification on correlation of attributes, discloses the fact that the 'natural' group *Balanocrinus* is composed of a number of distinct lineages which have run a parallel course, starting at different places and occurring at different times. Phylogeny, therefore, instead of providing the basis for the one, ideal natural classification, is seen to take its place among the other subsidiary classifications constructed for the purpose of special investigations. It may also be regarded as forming a sort of background to a natural classification, since, although natural groups are not primarily phylogenetic, they must, in most cases, be composed of closely related lineages.

The author realizes that the foregoing remarks on the relation between philosophy and taxonomy are tentative and fragmentary, but it is hoped that they may serve to bring the two subjects closer together and to stimulate an interest in an aspect of theoretical biology which certainly deserves further study.

REFERENCES

BATHER, F. A. (1927). 'Biological Classification, Past and Future.' *Quart. Journ. Geol. Soc.* **83**, p. lx.

BENJAMIN, A. C. (1937). *An Introduction to the Philosophy of Science.* The Macmillan Co.

DANSER, B. H. (1929). 'Ueber die Begriffe Komparium, Kommiskuum und Konvivium. . . .' *Genetica*, **11**, 399.

DENDY, A. (1924). *Outlines of Evolutionary Biology.* Constable & Co.

DINGLE, H. (1938). 'The Rational and Empirical Elements in Physics.' *Philosophy*, **13**, 148.

DOBZHANSKY, T. (1937). *Genetics and the Origin of Species.* Columbia University Press.

DU RIETZ, E. (1930). 'The Fundamental Units of Biological Taxonomy.' *Svensk. Bot. Tid.* **24**, 333.

GILMOUR, J. S. L. (1937). 'A Taxonomic Problem.' *Nature*, **139**, 1040.

—— and GREGOR, J. W. (1939). 'Demes: a suggested New Terminology.' *Nature*, **144**, 333.

HOCHREUTINER, B. P. G. (1937). 'La Valeur relative des groupes systématiques.' *Boissiera*, fasc. 2, 1.

HOGBEN, L. (1938). *Science for the Citizen.* George Allen and Unwin.

HUXLEY, J. S. (1911). *The Individual in the Animal Kingdom.* Cambridge.

HUXLEY, T. H. (1875). 'On the Classification of the Animal Kingdom.' *Nature*, **11**, 101.

JEVONS, W. S. (1883). *The Principles of Science.* Macmillan & Co.

LAM, H. J. (1936). 'Phylogenetic Symbols, Past and Present.' *Acta Biotheoretica*, ser. A, **2**, 154.

—— (1938). Over de Eenheid der Bijzondere Plantkunde.' *Vakblad voor Biologen*, no. **11**, 201.

LINDLEY, J. (1846). *The Vegetable Kingdom*, ed. I. Bradbury & Evans.

NEURATH, O., and others (1938). 'Encyclopedia and Unified Science.' *International Encyclopedia of Unified Science*, **1**, no. 1, 1. The University of Chicago Press.

SAYERS, W. C. B. (1926). *A Manual of Classification for Librarians and Bibliographers.* Grafton & Co.

SWINGLE, D. B. (1928). *A Textbook of Systematic Botany.* McGraw Hill Book Co.

TURESSON, G. (1922). 'The Genotypical response of the Plant Species to the Habitat.' *Hereditas*, **3**, 211.

WOODGER, J. H. (1937). *The Axiomatic Method in Biology.* Cambridge.

ENTOMOLOGICAL SYSTEMATICS EXAMINED AS A PRACTICAL PROBLEM

By JOHN SMART[1]

THEORETICALLY the work of the systematist is to build up a classification of living organisms that will show—assuming evolution to be a fact—their natural relationships and enable others to be fitted into the scheme when they are subsequently found. In practice his work may be divided into, firstly, the general work of identification, either for the purpose of building up systematic collections which are his principal tools or for economic and other purposes and, secondly, the prosecution of fundamental research in phylogeny and zoogeography.

These two sides of his work are directly dependent on each other, and also interdependent through their joint use of the systematic collections. There was a time when, owing to their numbers, ease of collection and preservation, apparent superficial distinctiveness and ease of macroscopic examination, insects were a favourite group for systematic work. At that time their taxonomy advanced rapidly and many important biological facts and generalizations emerged from their study. The application of more refined methods has, however, turned the above advantages to disadvantages, and taxonomic progress in the group as a whole has been seriously retarded.

Their numbers, combined with the greater specialization enforced by modern techniques, have led to a progressive reduction in the size of the group with which a worker is able to cope and to a general neglect of the broader aspects of entomological systematics. Ease of preservation, ease of collecting, and the numerical strength of insects, both with respect to species and individuals, have resulted in the accumulation of such immense collections as to impose exceedingly heavy curatorial duties upon systematists in charge of them. Their often deceptive distinctiveness has led to a great deal of confusion in the literature which, with the modern use of microscopic comparative

[1] The writer is much indebted to Mr. N. D. Riley and Mr. R. Washbourn, both of the Department of Entomology, British Museum (Natural History), for their kindly criticism and help in the preparation of this paper.

techniques, has made their study at the present time a laborious and elaborate procedure.

The systematic collection is the centre around which all entomological systematics revolve. Containing nowadays millions of specimens, they must be built up and continually expanded before identifications can be made or research carried out. Nor can the latter be done till the former have been made. Individual systematists may incline to, or excel at, one or other of the three aspects of the work—curatorial, identification, or research—but the burden as a whole must be borne by all alike; each aspect is dependent on the preceding one. An examination of the problem that is facing those responsible for the prosecution of insect taxonomy must proceed in the above order, though it is permissible and will save space if the first two are considered together as the natural routine work of the entomological systematist. It is only after the collections have been curated and the identifications made that research in phylogeny or zoogeography can be carried out.

The routine work position in entomology as compared with another branch of zoology can be most concisely shown by the tabulation of a few relevant figures. Mammals have been selected for this comparison, since this group is one in which systematics seem to have reached a fair state of advancement.

The figures given in the table refer to the position in the British Museum (Natural History), since the problem is being considered particularly as it presents itself in British entomology, and British systematic entomology centres around the Department of Entomology in the British Museum (Natural History).

The position of the entomological systematist as compared with the systematic mammalologist may be roughly stated as follows: the entomologist has to take cognizance of 20 times the number of species, and he must work with a collection that is, on the average, 40 per cent. less representative of the described species. Add to this the fact that he has to cope with 23 times the number of new species every year, 15 times the number of new specimens every year, and that his specimens are, compared with a skin or skull, relatively delicate objects which often have to be viewed under the microscope: we then have a picture of the work that the systematic entomologist has to do, before he is free to devote himself to fundamental research.

Table comparing the systematic field in Mammals and Insects

	Mammals	Insects	Ratio or difference
Total described species (1928) . .	3,750	625,000	× 160
Total specimens in B.M. (N.H.) . .	200,000	10,000,000	× 50
Per cent. described species in B.M. (N.H.)	90%	50%	40%
New species described per annum . .	50	10,000	× 200
Specimens added to collections per annum	2,000	250,000	× 125
Established scientific staff, B.M. (N.H.) .	2	17	
Described species per 1 staff . . .	1,825	36,765	× 20
Specimens per 1 staff	100,000	588,235	× 6
N. spp. per annum per 1 staff . .	25	588	× 23
No. specimens added per ann. per 1 staff	1,000	14,706	× 15

The figures for the number of species are from Metcalf and Flint (1928). The figures for the number of new species per annum are based on the *Zoological Record* for 1936; that for mammals on an actual count; that for insects on an estimate based on a page count. The other figures, apart from the number of staff in the B.M. (N.H.), are estimates made after consultation with various members of the B.M. (N.H.) staff and reference to the census made in 1931 by E. E. Austen (1931). The most unreliable figure is the 50 per cent. for the species representation of insects. In butterflies the representation is about 96 per cent., in Diptera 33 per cent., beetles, moths, &c., probably come between these two; 50 per cent. seems a reasonable mean. The osteological side of the mammal section of the B.M. (N.H.) has been excluded from the estimates, as have, as far as possible, all subspecific categories and fossil forms.

This enormous burden of routine work cannot be carried by any one else than the entomological systematic workers, but there should be ways and means of lightening it. The possibility of reducing the scope or bulk of the collections may be dismissed at once as unscientific. The lightening of the burden is mainly a question of financing and encouraging extra workers, not only as systematists but as clerical and technical assistants. These last two are wanted to work on the collections, under the supervision of the systematists, and to prepare and maintain the ancillary indices and records of information, without which accurate scientific work is almost impossible.

Catalogues are one of the greatest needs. There are comparatively recent published catalogues covering about a third of the insects,[1] but of course, these being printed works, they are automatically out of date as soon as published. Under present working conditions, lacking up-to-date catalogues or their equivalent,

[1] In this connexion it should, however, be noted that Coleoptera are, at the moment, particularly well catalogued, and that this order accounts for about two-fifths of the total number of described species of insects.

the entomological systematist is severely handicapped in carrying out his task of curating the collections and identifying material. That he manages to carry out this work at all is solely due to his persistence in following up clues and information furnished by his memory, at a cost in time quite incommensurate with the results.

There is, of course, no science that could not put forward a plea for financial aid to further its aims, but there is no group of skilled and trained scientists which prostitutes its knowledge and efforts to the extent that systematic entomologists must in the maintenance of their routine work. This could be checked at once and positively reduced in the future by the employment of sufficient numbers of technical assistants, cataloguers, bibliographers, and the like whose labour would be cheap compared with that of the trained systematists.

Having examined in merest outline the work of the entomological systematist in connexion with the collections that he has to look after and his work of identification, it will be well to turn to the actual output of the results of entomological systematics as seen in published work.

It appears that, as in all cases of systematic work, the output from entomological systematics falls into three main classes, namely, Systematics proper, Phylogenetic studies, and Zoogeographical studies. The so-called 'species problem', as far as it concerns the systematic worker, is covered by a combination of these subjects in varying proportions.

The first class of work, namely, systematics proper, is mainly a matter of naming, describing, and recording, and subsequent compilation, but it must not be belittled on these scores. Many systematists, entomological and otherwise, see in this work the main and only end of systematics. In its simplest form it consists of the mere description of species as, for instance, in F. Walker's volume on Diptera in the *Insecta Saundersiana*. In its more elaborate shape it consists in the publication of elaborate monographs and catalogues which may have to some extent a phylogenetic or a zoogeographical basis. However, such works, in that they do not propound and then prove or disprove theories, are not, strictly speaking, scientific research, and this, coupled with the fact that the labour involved in preparing them is of a kind that could be largely done by good clerical help, keeps down the output of such work since their preparation does not appeal to a mind that is speculatively inclined. This phase of the entomological systematist's work has behind it, as a driving force, all the pressure not only of the economic entomologist, but of the fact that the ultimate and more important phylogenetic and zoogeographical studies cannot proceed at any pace until such identificatory organization is relatively far advanced in the field in which the studies are to be carried out.

As an example of the way in which such pressure operates, the work done on mosquitoes is illuminating. Previous to the discovery at the end of the nineteenth century that mosquitoes were the active vectors of organisms pathogenic to man they received but little more attention than other groups that did not, like the butterflies and larger beetles, make an appeal to the aesthetic and acquisitive instincts of man. Then came the discovery of their importance from a medical point of view, and very soon the British Museum (Natural History) commissioned a special worker to take them up: he produced a two-volume monograph on them in 1901, following it with three supplementary volumes, the last of which appeared in 1910. This work aimed at aiding other workers in the accurate identification of species throughout the world, since this was what was required by the malariologists and others. Many of the groupings set up in it have proved artificial, and many characters selected for use in the separation of the groups and species have now been discarded as unsatisfactory criteria. In 1905 the same worker produced a volume in the *Genera Insectorum* series in which he set forth what he then considered to be a possible phylogenetic arrangement of the family, but this was soon rendered out of date by the later, supplementary, volumes of the monograph referred to above. The publication of the monograph was followed by thirty years of intensive systematic studies on mosquitoes throughout the world, mostly with reference to the fauna of particular geographic regions both political and natural. Then in 1932 there appeared, again in the *Genera Insectorum* series, a monumental volume, by the foremost mosquito systematist of the day, giving an arrangement of the genera and discussing their relationships, but making no attempt to aid in the actual identification of species beyond giving a catalogue and references to the literature. This was the natural climax to thirty years of probably the most intensive systematic study to which any group of organisms has ever been subjected. The first work (Theobald, 1901–10) was one of necessity, and as a contribution to fundamental knowledge its value was small. The second (Theobald, 1905) was really just a by-product of the labour of producing the first. The third (Edwards, 1932), following on a flood of papers occupying thirty years, is of much less value to the practical medical entomologist who merely wants to identify his species, but it is a major contribution to the fundamental systematics of insects.

The content of these three works may be profitably examined in tabular form.

Table of monographic works on Mosquitoes

Pages	Plates	Genera	Species	Treatment
Theobald, F. V. (1905). *Genera Insectorum, Culicidae.*				
50	2	62	450	Relationships
Theobald, F. V. (1901–10). *Monograph of the Culicidae.*				
2,459	82	142	1,050	Identification
Edwards, F. W. (1932). *Genera Insectorum, Culicidae.*				
258	5	30	1,400	Relationships

N.B. Theobald's *Genera Insectorum* volume really antedates the monograph as completed in the supplementary volumes.

The above is an example where there was a strong driving pressure behind the work, namely, the importance of mosquitoes as vectors of diseases affecting man. In other groups where there is less pressure a position of stalemate is very easily reached. This position arises where systematic workers, quite legitimately, perhaps, are disinclined to carry out the rather dull work of catalogue compilation and identification and then cannot, owing to lack of such works, engage in the more basic research work.

The two other classes of work, namely, phylogenetic and zoogeographical studies, blend into each other, since the one can seldom be considered without the other. They may therefore be considered together: in their final form they are usually monographs of one of two types. Firstly, monographs covering a large number of species or genera and endeavouring to show the relationships of these or their zoogeographical distribution, and, secondly, monographs on single genera or species in all their various subspecies, varieties, &c.

The task of producing monographs of the first type has, owing to the large number of species, become one of such magnitude that, in the large groups where they are most wanted, their appearance has become rare. There is also, in some cases, a suspicion that, owing to semi-mechanical means employed in their preparation, some of them are little better than elaborated catalogues, and, though valuable as catalogues, they may not, on critical examination, yield any genuine advance in knowledge such as they pretend. In many groups the vast amount of undescribed material and undiscovered forms militates against their production because they become rapidly out of date, though remaining valuable as a summary of the knowledge of a group at a certain date.

Excellent examples of this type of work are B. C. S. Warren's *Monograph of the Genus Erebia* (1936) and G. F. Ferris's *Contributions toward a Monograph of the Sucking Lice* (1919–35). This type of work is usually produced by a systematist who has been working generally on a group for a longish period of years. It must not be confused with a mere catalogue which requires a good bibliographical technique rather than an actual knowledge of the insects themselves.

The second type of research is that which results in a monograph of a single species in its various phases, races, geographical forms, &c. These researches give results which, if they are not actual contributions to the 'species problem' and zoogeographical theory, provide materials on which later workers may build. Unfortunately, in proportion to the number of entomological systematic workers, the output of this type of work is very low indeed and it is, perhaps, this disproportion between the apparent labours of the entomological systematist and the actual production of work of this type, that is creating a certain dissatisfaction amongst biologists in general, and a searching of hearts amongst the entomological workers themselves.

This type of work may best be illustrated by examining a recent example of it, entitled 'Die Rassen von *Papilio machaon* L.', by Dr. Karl Eller (1936). This paper appeared in 1936 and was the result of three and a half years' work; it consists of 95 pages of quarto text and 16 plates. Dr. Eller examined examples of *P. machaon* (the 'swallow-tail butterfly' found in England) in a large number of private collections and in many of the major museums which he visited personally for the purpose. He must have seen many thousands of examples of the butterfly which, in its various races, is a Holarctic species of wide distribution.

Dr. Eller studied his material biometrically as well as by the usual visual methods of the entomological systematist. The result of his investigations was that he was able to draw certain conclusions as to the relationships of the various Palearctic races of *P. machaon* to each other, and as to the routes along which these races had spread in the past from their point of common origin before their present distribution became established. His further studies on the Nearctic races have not yet been published. His conclusions represent a valid advance in knowledge. They have not yet given birth to any biological generalization, but they may be used at a later date by some other worker to make one.

A paper like this represents the type of research to which the methods of traditional entomological systematics lead. The tragedy is that such papers, like the comprehensive monographs, are few and far between. There are three reasons why this is so in general, and more particularly so in Britain. Firstly, the professional entomological systematists are prevented from undertaking this work by the pressure on them of curatorial and identificatory duties. Secondly, there is the fact that systematics are looked at askance by the scientific world in general and by academic circles, many of which do not recognize systematics as a science and so render systematics unremunerative to the biologist with academic attachments or aspirations. Thirdly, enormous as are our collections of insects, there are very few that have been collected on a scale similar to that on which *P. machaon* has been collected, and a series has to be of some length and from a wide range of localities before such studies can be carried out. *P. machaon* is probably one of the most collected butterflies in the world; there are certainly well over 1,000 specimens in the main series in the collection of the British Museum (Natural History). Of course, it is merely foolish to suggest that a great museum should aim at having 1,000 specimens of every described species—a simple calculation will show that to house such a collection the British Museum would require a department 62 times the size of the present one, employing at least 1,054 permanent scientific workers.[1] But there must already be many series in such institutions as the British Museum long enough to enable a study similar to that on *P. machaon* to be carried out, possibly with the aid of a few small expeditions to certain localities either unrepresented in the collections or which give some indication of being critical points in the zoo-geography of the species.

Apart from actual research in systematics, many important biological discoveries rest entirely on systematic studies. Thus the phase theory of locusts was based on the minute systematic study of large numbers of individuals as well as extensive field-work. Goldschmidt's important discoveries about intersexuality in insects had their basis in the observations of systematists made prior to his own experiments. Mimicry was first observed in the field by Bates (1862), but its most spectacular case (*Papilio dardanus* Fab.) was discovered by Trimen in 1870, who came on it by the study of pinned material in systematic collections; and he did this at a time when the available material of this butterfly was comparatively small. Seasonal dimorphism in tropical butterflies was another discovery made by Trimen, working on pinned material of *Precis octavia* Cram. and the dimorphic form *sesamus* Trim.

The study of phenomena, e.g. polymorphism, exhibited by organisms in various parts of the animal kingdom, is another form of work that may concern the entomological systematist. This work, however, involves systematics as a technique rather than as a science in itself, and it is a little doubtful if it has a real place in the work of a systematic institution as at present conducted. As an example of this type of work the studies of B. Rensch (1929) on what may be termed ecological variations may be cited. Such work cannot, of course, be carried out with-out the close co-operation of the systematic museums, and the possibility of having a department or small institute for such studies affiliated to the systematic museum might be explored. In some respects it may seem that this type of work is more suited to a biologist, not permanently attached to a museum, but using the museums as a technical tool. If this is the case, then the situation would be best dealt with by having research

[1] Based on the figures given in the table on page 477. *1,000 × No. of described species ÷ No. of specimens in B.M.Coll.*

scholarships, or grants in some form, that could be awarded to persons wishing to undertake the work. Either of these proposals would leave the systematists themselves free to continue the work that is at present considered their proper sphere.

The question of the possibility of bringing the newer biological sciences into the field to enlarge and improve the results of the traditional systematist must now be considered.

When this issue is brought up it is usually raised in rather a vague way, though some reference may be made to 'modern genetics', or the 'recent advances in the chemistry of specific proteins', and their bearing on the conception of a species. Systematists in general, and entomological systematists in particular, are fully aware of the fact that work is being done in such subjects as genetics, cytology, and biochemistry, which is of fundamental importance in connexion with the 'species problem' and evolution.

As collections expand it becomes more and more evident to those working on them that some groups of organisms consisting of what had appeared to be distinct species are but complicated and closely related groups of geographical races, subspecies, or other categories. When this happens, the systematist would be a very happy man if he knew something about the genetics and nuclear cytology of the various components of such a complex, and whether or not these, as interpreted by the geneticist and cytologist, bore out or contradicted his own findings and conclusions. Thus the purely morphological method has failed to elucidate completely the systematics of the obviously differing biological races of bed-bugs, lice, and mosquitoes. The final verdict in these cases will undoubtedly lie with the geneticist and others like him who are already studying them. Unfortunately the systematist himself cannot proceed to make the necessary investigations in such cases, and when he makes inquiries he usually finds that his genetical and cytological colleagues are already occupied with problems of their own.

The old conception of a species has to be retained for practical purposes in connexion with the systematist's function as an identifier. The term 'complex' may be conveniently applied to these groups of closely related organisms to which the ordinary categories of classification cannot be applied. The use of the word implies no more than a recognition, by the systematist, of the existence of such a group; it remains for further work on the part of the systematist, or the exponents of other branches of biology, to analyse the complex, explain its causation, and subsequently apply a definitive name to it. Nor is the complex by any means a universal phenomenon. There are very many groups of individuals of living insects to which the rigid conception of a species can be easily applied. The work of examining such complexes as become known to the systematist is bound, from its nature, to be slow. This being the case, it is better to stick to the old conception of the species since, owing to usage, it has a definite meaning and is identifiable if properly described, even though various systematists may differ in their subjective conception of it. One of the best examples of a complex that can be cited are the butterflies of the genus *Heliconius* from South America. Here the forms as they occur in nature grade into each other almost imperceptibly, and in order to distinguish them the lepidopterist has been forced to adopt quadrinomial names. Pending a full explanation of a given complex, the only way in which it can be treated, is for the systematist to apply an elaborate system of nomenclature to it. The forms exhibited over the range of the complex, be they aberrations, races, variations, mutations, or something else, must be given a description and a name to allow of their subsequent recognition. Given a name, even if, as in the extreme case mentioned above, this results in the use of quadrinomials, the specimen can be placed in the systematic collection, and, once there, it can be studied; it is one of the major misfortunes of the average systematist that pressure of work usually leads to the omission of this last step.

It took three and a half years to produce the paper mentioned above on the Palaearctic races of *P. machaon*; and the Nearctic forms remain to be dealt with. Undoubtedly a section on the nuclear cytology, genetics, and comparative serology of the various races of the butterfly would have been a highly desirable addition to the paper. To have carried this out would have necessitated several expeditions to some of the less accessible parts of the Holarctic region to obtain material in a condition that could be examined by these other specialists. In other words, the expense of carrying out such a project would have been, from a practical point of view, prohibitive. The fact that this is the case should not be allowed to prevent the systematist from doing what he can with the material available and coming to such conclusions as his observations warrant. The systematist will be quite prepared to withdraw his conclusions if and when his colleagues in other branches of biology produce satisfactory evidence that he is wrong.

In the above-quoted paper *P. machaon* was chosen for study from a systematic point of view for the same reason as the geneticist uses *Drosophila* or white rats. The organism appeared to be promising material to which a certain technique could be applied. The entomological systematist could indicate to an inquiring geneticist where genetical investigations would yield results that would have a bearing on systematic work; but the geneticist is not yet in a position to offer the systematist much advice as to where he, the systematist, should direct his labours. Let the biological investigator with the newer techniques consult the systematist before he commences work. The systematist will not only be able to indicate a variety of useful fields for the investigator to explore but, as a result of his experience, he may be able to help to overcome some of the initial difficulties in procuring and, when necessary, rearing material.

The geneticist and others like him will in the future make discoveries of the greatest importance to systematics; but they will never be able to study in detail the whole of the field that the systematist has to cover in his work. Unfortunately, but quite naturally, the geneticist and his ilk are inclined to choose their experimental material with a view to its availability and suitability to his technique rather than its systematic importance.

The field which the entomological systematist has to survey, in all but some of the most restricted areas of his work, is so large that it is impossible for any of the other biological sciences to attempt to cope with it on the same scale. To ask for a survey to supply the chromosome-numbers of all the insects in a certain family may not be asking the impossible, but it is asking the improbable, owing to the expense in time and money that would be involved. Is the systematist, then, to cease to attempt to take whole families within his purview because such a group is not capable of being subjected to the minute and detailed inquiries of the geneticist and others? No, the traditional methods cannot be jettisoned in a day, but till some newer conception than the species is demonstrated, that is capable of general application and of accurate definition, it will be necessary to retain the old conceptions and methods in order to support the enormous weight of economic work which is dependent on a stable taxonomy. The entomological systematist is as anxious as any one that his efforts should not be in vain, but at the moment his efforts are being almost smothered by the mass of work necessitated by the need to rectify the errors of past workers and in coping with the steady inflow of new species and specimens. In consequence of this, the results produced, measured in terms of real research, may be considered by some to be unworthy of the prodigious labourings of the entomological systematists. If, then, the trouble is really the small amount of fundamental research produced in proportion to the total numbers of entomological systematists at work, the problem is not one of grafting new ideas and conceptions upon traditional systematics, but of lightening the burden of non-productive work that the whole science of systematics has to carry before fundamental work can be undertaken. There is such fundamental research work to be done in systematics, and it has as much right to be carried out as any inquiry into genes, crystal structure, or cosmology. Can some way be found to lighten this burden that seems at times to be almost more than can be carried? It can.

Entomological systematics in this country centre around the Department of Entomology of the British Museum (Natural History). There is a smaller permanent centre at Oxford, namely the Hope Department, and the Liverpool School of Tropical Medicine has been the scene of much first-rate work on the systematics of Diptera of medical importance. Around these institutions are various individuals, mostly technically speaking 'amateurs', who are interested in systematics and are doing work on some particular group or other. The number of professional entomologists or biologists, outside the above-mentioned institutions, and such private institutions as the Tring Museum,[1] who are working at systematics, is remarkably few. The interests of the amateur are usually restricted to the British fauna or some particular family, with exceptions, of course; and, while in his restricted field he may easily be the peer of his

[1] Now merged in the British Museum (N.H.).

professional brethren, the portion of the general burden of the routine work of systematists which he carries is usually comparatively small. The same applies to the professional biologist working outside a systematic institution. The bulk of the burden falls on the professional systematist working in a systematic institution.

To suggest that the amassing of further collections and the sorting out of the present accumulations of unnamed material should stop, or be slowed down, or that certain parts of the collections should be marked out for special development or study, before some fact has emerged to indicate that such parts require special study is, as has been suggested above, an inadvisable if not scientifically unsound policy.

The solution to the problem of lightening the burden of routine on the entomological systematist, and possibly on systematists in general, is twofold. Firstly, every possible means must be taken to encourage the preparation of catalogues both of the species themselves and of all entomological information. Such catalogues will also prevent a great amount of duplication of work that goes on just now, especially when a highly specialized worker is suddenly withdrawn from the field. Secondly, steps must be taken to encourage more workers to take up systematics as a part-time subject. These may be considered separately.

With regard to catalogues. Printed and published catalogues are of great value; but no sooner are they published than they are out of date. What is wanted, looking at the matter from the point of view of the British systematist, is a complete card catalogue or index of all the available information, maintained up to date, and accessible to all bona-fide inquirers. Such a centralized information bureau is an urgent necessity. Its formation is a twofold task; first, the preparation of the index up to date; second, keeping it up to date after its formation.

The formation of the index up to date is a simple matter and there is only one way to do it. All that is required is that a team of a dozen or so typists, two or three of whom should have some experience of bibliographical work, be set to work under one or two systematists who have the formation of the index at heart. Details of actual methods and organization do not concern us here.

This is not a Utopian scheme, but a work of urgent necessity that, given the facilities, could be carried out. When completed, a search for information that at present may take a couple of days will be the work of as many minutes, and, moreover, the searcher will know that he has got all the known information, and has not overlooked any, as he often does at present. Although the cost of preparing such an information index would be large it would soon pay for itself on a cost-accounting basis. Every year that passes makes the task of obtaining information more and more complex; every year also makes the task of preparing the information index a heavier one. The objection can be raised that a proportion of the cards produced by such semi-mechanical methods would be inaccurate: it cannot be sustained. It would surely be better to have a reference that gives a lead in the right direction, rather than none at all; errors can be corrected when detected.

The keeping of such an information index up to date raises certain questions to which there are two possible answers. The simplest solution would be to have each year's Insecta section of the *Zoological Record*, which contains all the available systematic information of the year, 'carded', and the cards added to the main index. Information from other sources could be added as, and when, discovered. This method would keep the index automatically up to date with a time-lag of about two years.

The second solution, and in the absence of the *Zoological Record* it would be the only one, would be for every entomological paper to be searched and its contents 'carded', and the cards added to the index. To carry out this plan would involve the setting up of a language translation bureau, and the gradual building up of a library of translations which would be of enormous help to systematists, both saving time and preventing duplication of work in translating papers. Such a scheme might be organized, as is the *Zoological Record*, to serve both entomology and general zoology, since there is a considerable overlap in the literature of these two subjects. It would, of course, be foolish to set up such a library information, translation, and indexing bureau and for the present arrangements for the production of the *Zoological Record* to be continued side by side, as most of the work of either organization would be duplicated by the other. The greater part of the work of the preparation of all the sections of the *Zoological Record* is at present carried out in the British Museum, and, assuming that the information index would be located at that central institution, it would seem that the amicable arrangements between the two bodies might be extended so that, by co-operative effort, the work of recording and indexing could be reduced to a single operation fulfilling both needs.

The question of encouraging workers to take up entomological systematics is a larger and less concrete problem. Systematic work as a whole is hampered in Britain by the fact that the academic authorities, with one or two exceptions, are loath to recognize systematics as a scientific discipline. This is not the place to take up the question of the validity of the case that systematic workers could put up for the full recognition of their subject, but recognition is an objective that they should aim at.

In the U.S.A. and on the Continent academic recognition is given, and higher degrees are awarded, for systematic work. In the U.S.A. systematic work will qualify for the Ph.D. of many of the most distinguished universities, and, as a result of this, many persons, who in later life pass out of the field of active professional systematic entomology, come into contact with the subject during post-graduate university work, and carry on their interest later, on a part-time basis, or as a semi-professional hobby. Such workers, whether they are professional biologists or not, may devote their attention to a restricted group and very often become world authorities on it. In the U.S.A. the burden of the identification work of entomological systematics is thus spread over a very large number of individuals, very few of whom are full-time professional systematic entomologists. Complementary to the recognition by the universities of systematics as a discipline, arrangements would have to be made for it to be possible for the scientific staff of the British Museum (Natural History) to be recognized as teachers of London University for the purpose of supervising post-graduate research. This would be necessary because, even with the most lenient terms for the loan of specimens to other institutions, students doing systematic research would have to come to the Museum for some part of their work. The time given by the professional systematists in the employ of the Museum to teaching and supervising would be amply repaid by the increased output of systematic work and in the work that such students would carry out on the collections themselves.

To sum up. The present dissatisfaction with entomological systematics in Britain is due to the enormous weight of curatorial and identificatory routine work that falls on the shoulders of those engaged in the professional study of insect systematics, and leads to a very low output of basic research by them. The time is not ripe, even in the light of the newer biological knowledge, to give up the traditional methods of systematics; but there are obvious lines along which co-operation with the other branches of biology could be arranged with mutual benefit. The present state of affairs will continue, and probably get worse, until systematists apply scientific methods to their problem, and take proper steps to co-ordinate and record their information. The present chaos would yield to order if steps were taken to enforce order on it. The first step in enforcing this order, and the principal step, is to reduce the bulk of the burden of curatorial and identificatory routine work that at present falls on the professional systematist, and, apart from the need for additional workers, this can be done by the formation of a properly organized information index catalogue at, perhaps, considerable initial expense, but resulting in an enormous saving in the long run. Steps should be taken to prove the worthiness of systematics for recognition as a discipline by the academic world. The present objection to recognition would, possibly, be largely removed if systematists showed genuine signs of adopting real rational and scientific methods for the co-ordination and recording of their information, and the prosecution of their work. It is possible that these findings may have an application to a wider field than Entomological Systematics alone.

REFERENCES

Austen, E. E. (1931). 'The Present State of the National Collection of Insects.' *The Entomologist*, **64**, 241–2.

Bates, H. W. (1862). 'Contributions to an Insect Fauna of the Amazon Valley.' *Trans. Linn. Soc. Lond.* **23**, 495–566.

Edwards, F. W. (1932). Culicidae. *Genera Insectorum*. Belgium: Wytsman, Terveuren.

Eller, K. (1936). 'Die Rassen von *Papilio machaon* L.' *Abh. Bayer. Akad. Wiss.*, N.F., **36**, 1–96.

FERRIS, G. F. (1919–35). *Contributions toward a Monograph of the Sucking Lice.* Stanford: Univ. Press.

METCALF and FLINT (1928). *Destructive and Useful Insects.* New York: McGraw-Hill.

RENSCH, B. (1929). *Das Prinzip geographischer Rassenkreise und das Problem der Artbildung.* Berlin: Borntraeger.

THEOBALD, F. V. (1901–10). *A Monograph of the Culicidae.* London: Brit. Mus. (N.H.).

—— (1905). Culicidae. *Genera Insectorum.* Belgium: Wytsman, Terveuren.

TRIMEN, R. (1870). 'On some remarkable Mimetic Analogies among African Butterflies.' *Trans. Linn. Soc. Lond.* **26**, 497–522.

WALKER, F. (1850–6). *Insecta Saundersiana. Diptera.* London: Voorst.

WARREN, B. C. S. (1936). *Monograph of the Genus Erebia.* London: Brit. Mus. (N.H.).

POLYMORPHISM AND TAXONOMY

By E. B. FORD

IN the past, the term polymorphism has often been loosely
applied so as to cover the existence of any sharply marked
variations of a species occurring within the same habitat. For
this, however, the term *polyphasy* is preferable. It is important
that a more exact definition should be substituted for this vague
usage. Now genetic variability is divisible into four types:
(1) disadvantageous varieties eliminated by selection and
maintained at a low level by recurrent mutation of the genes
controlling them; (2) variations due to the effects of genes
approximately neutral as regards survival value; (3) those
dependent upon genes maintained by a balance of selective
agencies; and (4) advantageous varieties controlled by genes
spreading through the population and displacing their allelomorphs. Of these, the first is responsible for much of the
variability normally encountered in organisms (excluding that
important component which is environmental). Though such
genes must be rare at any one locus, their total effect is great
owing to the very large number of loci available. The second
type contributes relatively little to the variability of organisms
as a whole; for it has been shown by Fisher (1930c) that for a
gene to be effectively neutral, the balance of advantage between it and its allelomorph must be extraordinarily exact.
The third and fourth types constitute polymorphism. Here
two or more well-marked forms, capable of appearing among
the offspring of a single female, occur with frequencies high
enough to exclude the maintenance of the rarest of them by
recurrent mutation.

It will be appreciated that two distinct conditions are thus
combined as polymorphic, and we must briefly consider them.
In one, two or more forms of the same species are maintained
in optimum proportions, a departure from which, in either
direction, constitutes a disadvantage. A *balanced polymorphism*
of this nature is therefore permanent, apart from changes in
the conditions controlling the balance. It may be controlled
either by genetic or environmental means. In the other, no

such stability is attained. This *transient polymorphism* may be said to continue until the gene determining an advantageous variety has so far displaced its allelomorph that the latter is preserved only by recurrent mutation. Such an advantage will usually be due to a previously disadvantageous gene becoming of use owing to a change in environment. For practical reasons only, it is convenient to include this condition with the true balanced polymorphism, owing to the difficulty of distinguishing between the two situations in nature. Often this cannot be done until the species involved has been observed for several generations.

A good instance of transient polymorphism is provided by industrial melanism. For example, the normal pale form of the Geometrid moth *Biston betularia* Linn. was the only one known in the industrial areas of northern England up to 1850. To-day it has been almost completely superseded in these districts by the black variety *carbonaria* Jord. Thirty or so years ago the pale and the dark forms were to be found there in approximately equal numbers; but this was not a permanent condition, it merely represented the replacement of the one by the other.

We can now turn to the consideration of balanced polymorphism in more detail. Diver (1929) has demonstrated in a striking manner that in its presence the ratio of the different classes may remain unaltered for long periods of time. He studied the proportions of various forms of the snails *Cepaea nemoralis* (Linn.) and *C. hortensis* (Müller) in shells of Pleistocene age, and found them practically unaltered in colonies living to-day. Naturally such long-range comparisons can rarely be obtained. However, other data exist which demonstrate a similar constancy over periods of several generations, and in this respect they may reveal a striking contrast to other types of variation. For instance, Dobzhansky (1937) examined a number of colonies of the European ladybird *Sospita viginti-guttata* Linn. near Kiev. The majority of them contained forms with black or yellow elytra respectively, in approximately equal numbers; but in one colony only the black, and in another only the yellow, type was found. These conditions persisted for a period of at least three years. We may well contrast this condition with that detected in wild populations of *Drosophila melanogaster* Mg. by Dubinin and others

(1934), chiefly in the Caucasus. Not only did they demonstrate that rare 'mutant' genes were present in a large proportion of the individuals composing them, but showed that their frequency was subject to very marked variations in successive years. More extended data bearing upon this subject would be easy to obtain and are much to be desired. We shall return to consider other aspects of it when we have discussed the attri-butes of polymorphism more fully.

Now it has been pointed out by Fisher (1927) that the various forms of a species[1] cannot coexist in stable proportions in the absence of opposing selective agencies. The reason for this is easily appreciated. It can be shown that the number of indi-viduals in a population which possess a gene of approximately neutral survival value cannot greatly exceed the number of generations since its occurrence, if it be derived from a single mutation (Fisher, 1930 b). Furthermore, with particulate in-heritance, the rate of mutation is so slow that its recurrent nature cannot considerably accelerate the spread of such genes. Consequently, when we find that any form (controlled, in the simplest instance, on a uni-factorial basis) occupies even as much as a few per cent. of a fairly numerous population, its increase must necessarily have been hastened by selection. But this cannot of itself lead to a permanent polymorphism. An unopposed selective advantage will merely cause a given gene to spread gradually through the whole population. This must lead to greater variability until it and its allelomorph are present in equal numbers. Its subsequent advance will, however, pro-gressively restore uniformity. Only when the advantage which it possesses wanes, is extinguished, and is finally converted into a disadvantage, can stability in the gene-ratios be attained and diversity permanently established.

The source of variation utilized in this system is usually genetic. It may, however, be environmental, as in the social Hymenoptera, where it depends upon modifying the food sup-plied to the larvae. The component tending to check varia-bility may also have a genetic basis, or it may be of an ecological kind. We must briefly consider the ways in which it operates.

It is apparent that polymorphism will arise when a hetero-zygote is at a greater advantage than either of its homozygous

[1] We are not here concerned with rare variation, for which see pp. 502–3.

types. This may evidently be due to a difference in the effects of a gene when in single or double dose, or it may result from its linkage with a recessive lethal. Rather curiously, the latter situation seems not infrequently to constitute the check imposed upon an otherwise advantageous form. Thus the Nymphaline butterfly *Argynnis paphia* Linn. possesses two forms of female. In one (*paphia*) the ground-colour of the wings is golden-brown resembling that of the male, though somewhat darker, while in the other (*valezina* Esper) it is olive-green. This is much the rarer in the western part of the Palaearctic Region, occurring only here and there, and then constituting but a small proportion of the females (from 5 to 10 per cent.). Goldschmidt and Fischer (1922) showed that it is determined by a single gene. This is a sex-controlled dominant in expression, autosomally transmitted and linked with a lethal. They therefore obtained a 2:1 ratio of *valezina* to *paphia* in their crosses, where one of 3:1 was expected; but the linkage broke down during their experiments, and the F_2 segregation which they subsequently obtained was of a normal kind. In eastern China, however, nearly all the females are of the *valezina* form, and here it is presumably free from its lethal association.

A similar condition is common in Pieridae of the genus *Colias*. In many of these butterflies the males are yellow, while the females may either be yellow or whitish. The latter is nearly always the rarer form, and it has been proved uni-factorial and dominant in a number of the species (for a summary of the genetics of this genus, see Ford, 1937). The extensive experiments of Gerould (1923) demonstrate that the gene controlling the rarer white form (*alba*) of the North American *Colias philodice* Godart is linked with a recessive lethal in a similar manner to that determining the *valezina* females of *A. paphia*. He too obtained individuals in which crossing-over had freed the gene from the lethal, though this was always brought back when he crossed his stocks with wild specimens. It is said that the white females are the commoner in a restricted area in New England, and the lethal may be absent there.

We may quote one more example of this kind. It is provided by another North American Pierine, *Anthocaris cethura* (Felder). In this species the yellow patch near the tips of the fore-wings, constantly present in the males, is absent in about 5 per cent. of the females, though in a single small valley the frequency of the latter form approaches 50 per cent. (Dobzhansky, 1937). The genetics are here unknown, but the parallel with the two preceding instances is obvious.

It is worth while to reflect briefly upon these examples. Evidently the rarer and dominant form possesses some advantage in all of them. We do not know its nature, but it may well be of a physiological kind. That it exists, and that it must be a very considerable one, is clear; otherwise the forms concerned could not have attained 5 per cent. or more of a large population in the face of so great a handicap as homozygous lethality. The same thing is indicated by their success in some localities, where we may reasonably suppose that the check imposed upon them elsewhere is removed. That this takes the form of a linked lethal has been proved in two of the examples, but here we are confronted with an unsolved problem. As we have seen, the beneficial gene and the lethal have more than once been separated during the course of breeding experiments. The linkage between them cannot therefore be very close, and crossing-over must part them in nature also. The resulting condition should have a considerable advantage and should spread: why, therefore, does it not do so? In the absence of relevant experimental work, any discussion of this problem can be conjectural only. However, it is probable that in certain environments the gene producing the recessive lethal effects may be of advantage in other directions, so tending to its own preservation and, consequently, to that of the polymorphism. One striking fact supports this suggestion. Gerould found the lethal quite common in the *Colias philodice* population in nature: when eradicated in his stocks, his crosses with wild males always brought it in again. This is inconsistent with the view that it is purely disadvantageous and maintained only by recurrent mutation. In fact, the situation may involve a rather complex balance of advantages, reaching equilibrium at different positions in different environments.

We may now consider another genetic mechanism of a somewhat specialized kind which is sometimes responsible for checking the spread of genes having advantageous effects, and so establishing a balanced polymorphism. It is to be found in those instances in which polymorphism is associated with close linkage, and with the existence of a relatively common 'universal recessive'. They may occur in widely distinct groups, such as the grouse locusts *Apotettix* and *Paratettix*, in land snails such as *Cepaea hortensis* and *C. nemoralis*, and in the fish *Lebistes reticulatus* (Peters). Haldane (1930) has pointed out that the association of these phenomena may best be accounted for by the occurrence of sectional translocations, together with duplications of such translocated sections.

That the universal recessive, though the commonest form, is at a disadvantage compared with the others is indicated by the fact that the latter are completely dominant to it. They do not, however, show dominance between one another: a fact in harmony with the concept of dominance modification by selection (Fisher, 1931). It has been suggested by Fisher (1930 a) that the advantage of these less common dominants is probably opposed by a reduction in viability associated with the homozygous duplication: he has indeed been able to demonstrate a significant deficiency of homozygous dominants in Nabour's extensive data on the genetics of grouse locusts.

The fundamental feature determining this type of polymorphism seems to be found in the close linkage which exists between the genes controlling the different forms, since this reduces the number of combinations available for genetic improvement. In these circumstances the genes no longer compete independently with their allelomorphs; rather, systems of linked genes come into competition as if they belonged to a multiple allelomorph series. Hence numerous genetic improvements cannot take place simultaneously, but one at a time—the lesser always making way for the greater. Thus, as stressed by Fisher (1930 a), such genes, if involving only a small selective advantage, may be debarred from establishing themselves in ordinary circumstances. However, a duplication, though lethal when homozygous, may provide them with a tract of chromatin in which as heterozygotes they may be improved by the selection of modifiers. At the same time they are sheltered from the competition of the gene-complex associated with the universal recessive, and maintained as polymorphic forms.

We have so far considered a few instances in which the component which tends to check the spread of advantageous variation has a genetic basis. On the other hand, it may, as already mentioned, be an outcome of the particular ecological situation involved. The best-known examples of this kind are provided by the mimicry of a more protected by a less protected form. This situation occurs both in plants and animals and is, particularly, important in insects. It has received special attention in the Lepidoptera, but is perhaps equally striking in other groups.

Relative immunity to the attacks of predators may be attained by the possession of stings, of nauseous taste or odour, or other protective qualities. It is well known that species with such attributes are frequently copied by others not so fortunately endowed. Such a resemblance will be of use while the form possessing it is relatively rare. As its numbers increase owing to the protection so afforded, the advantage due to its mimicry will be progressively reduced, and finally converted into a disadvantage, when a particular pattern comes to be associated more often by predators with something palatable than repellent. It is easy to see, therefore, that there must be an optimum proportion of mimics to models in any particular set of circumstances. This places a severe limitation upon the spread of a mimic when monomorphic. If, however, the species is a polymorphic one, some or all of whose forms are adapted to copy different models, a greater increase can be attained. Evidently it should be to the advantage of Batesian mimics to become polymorphic and the majority of them have done so. The proportions in which the forms of such species exist then reach stability at their optimum levels, when each receives equal protection. The loss in usefulness as any one of them increases relatively to its particular model now acts as the check upon its spread.

The attainment of an effective mimicry generally requires the modification of a number of very distinct characters. These may include shape, colour, pattern, and habit. Any or all of them may be altered simultaneously in the different forms of a polymorphic species in order to bring about a convincing likeness to a number of often widely dissimilar models. Yet such forms are controlled genetically on a simple basis, which can act as a switch in determining the development of one or the other of them, and so maintain clear-cut distinctions between them. Thus, two forms of the Nymphaline butterfly *Hypolimnas dubius* de Beauvais exist in East Africa. These are known as *mima* and *wahlbergi*. The former copies *Amauris albimaculata* Butler and the closely allied *A. echeria* Stoll, and the latter *Amauris niavius dominicanus* Trimen. Genetically they are under uni-factorial control, but they differ from one another in colour, in pattern, and in their habits. Jacobson (1909) and de Meijere (1910) have studied the genetics of three forms of *Papilio memnon* Linn. in Java. These are *laomedon*, *isarcha*, and *achates*. The latter is mimetic, while the two former seem not to be so. Thus it appears that polymorphism, controlled presumably by genetic means, tends to occur in this species, and that *some* of the forms so maintained have been utilized as a basis for mimicry: a conclusion which receives definite support in analogous conditions in other mimetic butterflies (p. 502). A single gene (*A*), dominant in its effects, converts *laomedon* into *isarcha*. A second gene (*B*) has no detectable action on the *laomedon* constitution (*aa*). It interacts, however, with *A* to produce *achates*. This differs from *isarcha* not only in colour and pattern but also in shape: for it possesses a tail, in mimicry of *Papilio coon* Fab., while the other two forms are tailless.

The multiplicity of adaptation illustrated by the foregoing examples is a phenomenon of very general occurrence in mimicry. In view of the simple nature of the genetic control involved, it is one of much interest. Theoretically, it can be accounted for in three possible ways. First, selection has had in each instance to wait for a mutation producing the requisite adaptive effects in all their perfection. Considering that complex mimicry is under uni-factorial control in numerous species, the chances against such an interpretation seem to me quite incredibly great. Secondly, it has been suggested that parallel mutation in model and mimic are responsible for a similar series of effects: in the same way that the mutant characters, white coat-colour and pink eyes, are almost certainly due to the same gene in a number of species of Rodents. Among the numerous objections to such a view, we may here mention the apparently overwhelming one that mimetic resemblances are generally purely superficial, such as deceive the eye and no more. The similar colours may be produced by chemically different pigments (Ford, 1937), or by pigments and structural effects respectively, while resemblances in shape and pattern are often attained by means fundamentally distinct (Carpenter and Ford, 1933). In my view, the facts can only be interpreted on the assumption, due originally to Fisher (1927), that selection acting upon the gene-complex has gradually modified the effects of particular genes, improving any chance resemblance to a protected form for which they might have been originally responsible. This contention derives strong support from the occurrence from time to time of genetic variation in mimetic characters which are yet under uni-factorial control (Carpenter and Ford, 1933). I have discussed this view more fully elsewhere (Ford, 1937), and it need not be elaborated further here. Suffice it to stress that such selection of the gene-complex provides an important mechanism for evolutionary advance within the somewhat rigid framework of a genetically controlled polymorphism.

It is possible to imagine other ecological situations which may check the spread of variation when it reaches a given level. One which may be of importance is of a psychological kind. Fraser Darling (1938) has provided data which show that in some species of birds the stimulus provided both to copulation and to gonad maturation by display is not confined to that of the display of the single potential or actual mate, but is cumulative as between all members of a group. This would account for the numerous instances in which display is confined to special areas, and thus becomes social. It is possible that this may also provide a clue to the puzzling polymorphism of the male Ruff (*Philomachus pugnax* Linn.). This affects the ruff round the neck and the crests, used by the male in display but absent in the female, also the general colour of the males in the breeding season. The variation both in the colour and marking of these structures is very considerable, but it falls into a number of classes the distinctions between which are tolerably clear-cut. The explanation of this condition has long seemed obscure, but it may well be that the diversity of display going on around the females on the common courting-ground is a factor contributing to the stimulus necessary for copulation. If this indeed be so, selection would favour the genes concerned up to the point at which they promote maximum variability. The same psychological factor would, however, hinder the extension of any one of them beyond this optimum and prevent its further spread from leading back to uniformity.

In the foregoing account we have drawn a sharp distinction

between those types of polymorphism in which variation is checked respectively by genetic and ecological means. This has been a convenience for explanation but, in reality, the two are not always so easily separable, for in certain situations they may coexist. It has already been pointed out that mimicry of itself provides a complete basis for the maintenance of polymorphism. Yet it may in addition be associated with a reduction in the viability of the homozygous dominant class compared with the heterozygotes; and this, as already mentioned, attains the same end. Thus Fisher (1927) has pointed out that such a condition supplies the most probable interpretation of the numerous sterile unions encountered by Fryer (1913) during his extensive breeding experiments on the Oriental butterfly *Papilio polytes* Linn. The genetic situation in this species resembles that found in *Papilio memnon* already described. Here, too, the male is monomorphic, and three forms of female are controlled by two pairs of allelomorphs, involving a simple type of factor-interaction. A non-mimetic male-like form *cyrus* is converted into the dominant *polytes*, which copies *Papilio aristolchiae* Fab., by a gene *A*. Another gene *B*, dominant in effect, interacts with *A* to produce a third form *romulus*, mimicking *P. hector* Linn., but it is inactive in the *cyrus* constitution. In a similar way, I find that the two female forms of the African Nymphaline *Hypolimnas misippus* Linn. segregate in a ratio approximating to 2 : 1, where one of 3 : 1 is expected. These are *misippus* the dominant, and *inaria* the recessive: they copy respectively *Danaus chrysippus* Linn. and its form *dorippus*. In such instances as these, it seems that those mutations capable of producing a convincing copy of suitably protected species were initially defective in homozygous viability: indeed, mutations naturally tend to disturb the genic balance and to impair normal vigour, rather than to maintain or improve it.

It will now be apparent that stability in the ratios of the different forms constitutes the essential feature of a permanent polymorphism. There is, however, one qualification to be added here, and this is provided for in our definition of it: the stability must be attained by a balance of selective agencies. This serves to distinguish the condition from that of the vast majority of rare varieties, which are subject to adverse selection and maintained at a low level in the population by recurrent mutation. The rate of the latter process appears to be constant. The counter-selective pressure to which they are exposed will also be uniform in an unchanging environment. Since organisms endeavour to live in optimum, and therefore constant, conditions, the check imposed upon such varieties will in the long run also tend to uniformity. They will therefore exist in a stable, though small, proportion of the species: but subject, no doubt, to very considerable minor fluctuations (p. 494). However, the large store of rare varieties which all organisms normally possess falls outside the definition of polymorphism, since the component tending to promote their increase does not consist in a selective advantage but in recurrent mutation.

Having discussed the chief characteristics of polymorphism, we must consider a few minor qualifications to which they may be subject. In the first place, though polymorphic forms are to be distinguished from geographical variation, they may be a function of it. Not infrequently, species are polymorphic in one region but not in another: or different polymorphic forms may be characteristic of different parts of their range. This will be particularly clear in the mimetic instances, in which the forms are dependent upon the distribution of the species which they copy. *Papilio polytes*, a mimetic butterfly already mentioned, is able to maintain itself outside the range of its models. However, only the non-mimetic and male-like form *cyrus* is found in such regions. Thus the species is monomorphic in northern India. Where both models occur, as in Ceylon, all three female forms of *polytes* are found. At Hong Kong, however, where *Papilio hector* Linn. is rare or absent, so also is the *romulus* form of *polytes* which resembles it.

We may conveniently illustrate this point further by reference to the African butterfly *Papilio dardanus* Brown, well known for the extreme complexity of its mimicry. Here, too, the male is non-mimetic. The female form which preponderates in South Africa, and up the East Coast to the neighbourhood of Delagoa Bay, is known as *cenea*. It is absent on the West Coast, for there the species which it copies (*Amauris echeria* and *albimaculata*) do not occur. *Papilio dardanus* is divided into a number of geographical races, and we may compare the polymorphism of two of them: the race (as opposed to the form) *cenea*, inhabiting

South Africa and the south-eastern coast-line, and the 'transitional race' found in Uganda and Tanganyika Territory (data from Ford, 1936).

Forms of Papilio dardanus	'Transitional race'	Cenea race
hippocoon (or hippocoonides)* .	60 per cent.	9 per cent.
planemoides	21·5 ,,	none
cenea	7 ,,	85 per cent.
niobe	7 ,,	none
trophonissa (or trophonius)* . .	4·5 ,,	4 per cent.
leighi	none	2 ,,

* The western forms *hippocoon* and *trophonissa*, which occur in the Transitional race, become slightly modified in East Africa (where the *cenea* race is found), resembling the eastern races of their models, and are known as *hippocoonides* and *trophonius* respectively.

It will be observed that, apart from those characters (relating to the male) used by Jordan (1905) in separating the various races, they differ both in the nature and in the proportions of their polymorphic forms.

We have already seen that similar variations in frequency may occur in different parts of the range of non-mimetic species also. The examples drawn from *Argynnis, Colias,* and *Anthocharis* already quoted (pp. 496–7) illustrate this fact. Furthermore, Dobzhansky (1933) in his study of lady-beetles (belonging to a number of genera) found that in some species the proportions of the different forms varied in different localities. In others, however, he proved them constant over the total range of the species, which covered a large area. That such widespread similarities in frequency can exist in certain circumstances must be regarded as providing further evidence for the stability of the ratios attained in balanced polymorphism.

It is evident, however, that this stability must be relative rather than absolute. Since it is due to opposing selective agencies, changes in environment may affect it and ensure an equipoise at a different value—in time, just as we have seen that they do in space. For example, the proportions of the different forms of a mimic will be affected by changes in the abundance of their models, stability being attained at each new level. So too, alterations in the absolute numbers of a polymorphic species affect its ecological adjustment, and may therefore influence the distribution of the classes of which it is composed.

Elton (1927) has demonstrated that many animal and plant populations are subject to *periodic* fluctuations in numbers of an extreme kind. We may conjecture, therefore, that when such species are polymorphic, the proportions of their forms will undergo cyclical modification.

In view of the nature of the check imposed upon the spread of advantageous varieties in balanced polymorphism, we should expect that any reduction in the pressure of counter-selection will lead to increased variability. This anticipation is realized. A single instance will suffice to illustrate this effect. I have studied a large random collection of *Papilio dardanus* made at Entebbe, a locality where its models are common, and compared it with one from the mountainous region near Nairobi, where they are scarce (Ford, 1936). In the former locality, selection in favour of the mimetic pattern eliminates variation in the different forms, which are—as is usual—remarkably constant. In the latter it seems that the models are too rare to provide effective protection, and variations, leading to imperfections in mimicry, are here quite common. It should be emphasized that in several instances the development of one or the other of these particular mimetic forms is none the less under the control of a single pair of alleles (Ford, op. cit.). The actual data show that at Nairobi the models are seventy times rarer relative to their mimics, and the imperfectly developed forms of the mimics are eight times commoner, than they are at Entebbe:

	Models (*Totals*)	Mimics*	
		Totals	% *imperfect*
Entebbe . . .	1,949	111	4
Nairobi . . .	32	133	32

* Females only are included in the totals of mimics, the males of *Papilio dardanus* being monomorphic and non-mimetic.

It is important to distinguish true polymorphism, as already defined (p. 493), from the existence of multiple phases attained at different stages of development, so thoroughly analysed by Huxley (1932). Thus Smith (1906) studying the crab *Inachus mauritanicus* Lucas at Naples found three forms of the male: those of small size with *relatively* small but male-type chelae, those of large size with *relatively* large male-type chelae, and those of intermediate size with very small chelae of female type. These prove merely to represent different developmental stages: males in their first and second breeding-seasons respectively, separated by a non-breeding phase during which their secondary sexual characters regress to the neuter (and female-like) state. The difference in relative chela size of the breeding individuals being due, as shown by Huxley, to the operation of simple allometry.

When combined with the special type of moulting which takes place in the Arthropoda and with holometabolism, the existence of such constant differential growth-rates may give rise to developmental phases. Thus in the insect *Forficula* there exists a diphasic condition of the male forceps, but not of the female forceps nor of the body-size in either sex. Huxley (1927) finds that when the data on forceps-length in this species collected by Djakanov (1925) are tabulated by body-size, mean forceps-length against mean body-length gives a fairly constant value of α in the allometry formula.[1] When, however, he plotted curves for forceps-length for each body-size class separately, he found that those for both the smallest and the largest groups were uni-modal, containing only individuals with relatively short or long forceps respectively, while those for the intermediate sizes were bimodal. Among the latter, the number possessing relatively small forceps diminished as the body-size increased. This he interprets in terms of moulting-frequency. It seems likely that the processes determining male allometry begin at a relatively constant period in late larval life. They cannot, however, be expressed until the adult phase, which may be reached after either one or two more moults. This allows them either a shorter or a longer period for action, resulting in the two phases actually encountered; variation in the time of moulting will bring about the observed overlap between them.

An admirable summary of this type of problem, together with a number of further instances, may be obtained from Huxley (1932), who himself stresses the completely distinct nature of such phenomena of growth from true polymorphism. He remarks that they 'are dimorphisms of developmental origin,

[1] $y = bx^\alpha$, where $y =$ the size of a given organ, $x =$ the size of the body minus that organ, and b and α are constants.

and have nothing in common with genetic dimorphisms like those of "diphasic" mammals or birds, such as arctic fox, certain squirrels, herons, owls, &c., or the genetic polymorphism of the females of various mimetic butterflies.'

In the course of systematic work many instances are encountered in which the data do not enable us to decide whether the existence of two or more forms of a species are or are not dependent upon polymorphism. They may in fact be due to this cause, or to various other agencies. Among the latter we may mention: a transient outburst of variation due, perhaps, to a temporary mitigation in selection, developmental phenomena of the kind just discussed, or environmental effects. Furthermore, where the records are very imperfect, even geographical variation, or the existence of rare forms having no selective advantage, may be attributed to polymorphism. In addition, it is necessary to separate polymorphism of the balanced and transient types. It is a matter of much importance to collect data in such a way as may distinguish between these various situations. In order to do so it is evident that, where possible, the proportions of the different forms should be estimated over a period of several generations. During this time information should be obtained upon the occurrence or otherwise of fluctuations in the total number of the population under study. Any changes in environment should also be carefully recorded, and analysed as far as possible to show if they can be related to alterations in the proportions of the different forms, should these prove to take place. We will select a few examples to illustrate the foregoing situations.

Black specimens are occasionally encountered in most species of Pocket Gophers of the genus *Thomomys* in California. *T. niger* Merriam, however, is always black: probably it is homozygous for *a*, the well-known non-agouti gene of the Rodents. Yet about 10 per cent. of the population of another species, *T. townsendii* (Bachman), are black in the neighbourhood of Nampa, Idaho, though elsewhere no blacks are to be seen (Storer and Gregory, 1934). This suggests the spread of a gene owing to changes in environment, perhaps of a local kind. Further data collected at the present time might settle the question.

Alexander (1928) states that two forms of the Herald Petrel (*Pterodroma heraldica* Salvin) exist. The upper parts are always dark brown, but the under-surface may either be dark brown also or white (intermediates sometimes occur). The former is almost confined to Henderson Island, where 99 per cent. of the breeding birds possess this plumage. The same form is known among breeding colonies on Ducie Island and Uapu in the Marquesas where, however, it constitutes less than 1 per cent. of the population. Elsewhere no dark-breasted birds are known. This may merely represent an instance of geographical variation, for the occurrence of a very small proportion of the dark form in two populations might be the result of migration. However, further data collected after an interval of some years are required in order to exclude other possibilities.

Some species are normally extremely variable, even when subject to no exceptional conditions involving a reduced selection pressure. From a very large number of examples we may select the Geometrid moth *Cidaria furcata* Thunb., in which a great diversity of forms, some tolerably distinct, others merging into one another, may be found year after year in the same localities. Some of them may be environmental in origin, others may depend upon genetic recombination perhaps involving numerous genes, while analysis might show that two or three of the phases are indeed maintained as a balanced polymorphism.

Melanism in the Lepidoptera is often under uni-factorial control (Ford, 1937). In many species melanic forms have, during the last fifty years or less, almost completely replaced those of normal coloration in industrial districts. They have, however, usually failed to do so in unpolluted country. Consequently a zone surrounds such areas in which melanic and non-melanic forms coexist, the proportion of the former decreasing outwards. In any one locality situated in such a zone a balance of rather a special type exists, depending upon the flow of a particular gene from a region where it is maintained as an advantage to one where it is eliminated by selection.

The larvae of a number of species of Lepidoptera may assume one of two colour-phases, dark brown or bright green. In some the former, and in others the latter, is the commoner; or the two may occur with approximately equal frequency. They are to be found together in the same localities and among the members of a single brood, intermediates between the two conditions being extremely rare. Moreover, the phenomenon is of somewhat wide occurrence in the order; for example, it is well known both in the Sphingidae (e.g. *Chaerocampa*) and in the Geometridae. In fact, it clearly suggests a balanced polymorphism for which, without further study, it would undoubtedly be accepted: but this is deceptive. The presence of these two larval colour-phases is a striking feature of the Geometrid genus *Cosymbia* (*Ephyra*), and in my own rather extensive breeding experiments (unpublished), which involved five of the six British species, I found that broods of wholly brown larvae might result both from the cross brown × brown and from the cross green × green (as well as from green × brown in either direction). The condition in reality appears to be determined environmentally, probably by temperature acting over a short critical phase passed through at different times by the larvae—which grow at somewhat different rates. It seems that the brown colour is produced by higher, and green by lower, temperatures.

Instances such as these serve to show that an apparent polymorphism may require careful study before its true nature can be determined: they have often been described as polymorphic on insufficient evidence. Yet it must not be supposed that the condition, as more strictly defined, is a rare one. Indeed, we are constantly faced by it in the most universal of all dimorphisms, that of sex. Here the development of the male or female phase is determined by a simple mechanism, and the one is balanced against the other in optimum proportions in the same environment: a perfect example of the situation which we have been analysing.

Further instances which suggest polymorphism are widespread among organisms. It will now be clear that many of these require critical study before they can be accepted as such, and some of them will prove to be of a different nature. However, others can reasonably be regarded as polymorphic in advance of further evidence. As an appropriate example we may mention the Eastern Reef-heron (*Demiegretta sacra* Gmelin). This bird is common along the coasts, and on suitable islands, on both sides of the Malay Peninsula; but it extends from the Andaman Islands to Australia, and as far north as the Philippines. It exists in two colour-phases, blackish-grey or white, which as Robinson and Chasen (1936) remark, 'seem to be independent of sex, age, or season; white and grey birds may be seen feeding together on the same coral reef'.

Even where the existence of polymorphism is clear, it may not always be possible to determine immediately whether it is of a permanent or a transient kind. It should however, be stressed that the stability of the ratios encountered in the former should suffice ultimately to distinguish between these two types. We may cite two relevant instances. 'Taste-blindness' in man is a recessive condition in which it is impossible to taste the organic compound phenol-thio-urea, and some of its chemical allies. These substances are intensely bitter to those who can detect them. However, in western Europe at any rate, about one-quarter of the population is unable to do so. The particular interest of this condition lies in the extremely high proportion in which the gene controlling it occurs. It seems clear that it must have some unknown and advantageous effect, in addition to that already observed, otherwise it could not have spread so widely. Predictions in biology should be made with caution, but we may anticipate that such an effect certainly exists and that this, when found, unlike the one at present discovered, will not be recessive in expression. It may be remarked that somewhat similar problems are presented by the existence of the various blood-groups. Zimmerman (1935) has studied the distribution of a particular form of the third upper molar, the 'simplex' pattern, in the field-vole *Microtus arvensis* Schinz. He finds that this character is possessed by 80 to 90 per cent. of these animals, in Schleswig-Holstein and Mecklenberg. From here it spreads with decreasing frequency to the east, south, and south-west, but it is not found in those of the upland country of central Germany. It is at present uncertain whether the polymorphism encountered in these instances is, or is not, in stable equilibrium, but the collection of further data in the future should decide the point.

It is worth considering very briefly whether balanced polymorphism can be regarded as an agent in species formation. At the outset, it is clear that in normal circumstances such a condition promotes a free flow of genes between the forms which it involves, and so ensures that these shall remain within the same species. On the other hand, it has already been explained that the switch mechanism which controls them is consistent with their evolution along divergent lines. Indeed, they may come to differ from one another so widely that no systematist would hesitate to regard them as specifically distinct, were they not proved to segregate in the same families. Now, should any tendency arise for the individuals to mate with their own form rather than any other, the ecological isolation so introduced would increase the diversity between them. For the free flow of genes from the one to the other would then be impeded: consequently evolutionary change would reduce the stock of genes which they hold in common leading, sooner or later, to infertility on crossing and to specific distinction.

Though I am aware of no clear instance in which the operation of this type of species formation can be traced, it would be well to watch for any sign of it in appropriate circumstances. Changes in mating-habits, comparable to that postulated here, are known to result even from a single factor difference. For example, that producing recessive melanism in the moth *Zygaena trifolii* Esp. affects also the choice of a mate by the individuals concerned (Grosvenor, 1926–7). In this instance, normal males tend to pair with black, rather than normal, females, and the reverse. We may, furthermore, anticipate the initiation of selective mating among polymorphic forms where these differ from one another in habit: a condition by no means unknown, and exemplified by the *mima* and *wahlbergi* forms of the butterfly *Hypolimnas dubius* de Beauvais (Platt, 1914). These are under uni-factorial control (Carpenter and Ford, 1933), and differ also in colour and marking. Here then we have a situation in which the individuals of a species, already strikingly dimorphic, are actually led in natural conditions to a closer association with their own than with the alternative form. The possibility of cleavage in such circumstances cannot be ignored. It is evident that this will be greater in those instances in which polymorphism is not associated with a reduction in viability of the homozygous dominants. However, this might be overcome should selection favour the existence of this class, as it might do when the species is splitting into two, instead of tending to maintain the state of polymorphism.

Summarizing a few of the most fundamental features of balanced polymorphism, it may be emphasized that this condition (defined on p. 493) can only be maintained by opposing selective agencies. On the one hand, a source of advantageous variation tends to spread certain forms through a given population; on the other, a distinct component tends to check this spread. Both the agent serving to increase, and that serving to diminish, the frequency of a given form may be either genetic or environmental, or the two methods may be combined.

The genetic mechanism which acts as a switch in controlling the appearance of the different types must of necessity operate upon a simple basis. It does not, however, prevent the evolutionary modification of any one of them, although they may be determined even by uni-factorial means. Any reduction in the degree of counter-selection should increase the frequency of one form, when operating upon this alone: when operating over the whole range of forms in the population, it should, however, result in their greater variability. It is possible also that polymorphism may act as an agent in species-formation.

Finally, it should be stressed that instances of apparent polymorphism may require careful analysis before their true nature can be determined. They have been accepted too uncritically as such in the past.

I am much indebted to Dr. J. S. Huxley in the preparation of this account. His advice and criticism have been of the greatest value to me. I should like to express my thanks to Prof. E. S. Goodrich for his kind help.

REFERENCES

ALEXANDER, W. B. (1928). *Birds of the Ocean.* New York.

CARPENTER, G. D. H., and FORD, E. B. (1933). *Mimicry.* London.

DARLING, F. FRASER (1938). *Bird Flocks and the Breeding Cycle.* Cambridge.

DIVER, C. (1929). 'Fossil Records of Mendelian Mutants.' *Nature,* **124,** 183.

DJAKANOV, D. M. (1925). 'Experimental and Biometrical Investigations on Dimorphic Variability of *Forficula.*' *J. Genet.* **15,** 201–32.

DOBZHANSKY, TH. (1933). 'Geographical Variation in Lady-beetles.' *Amer. Nat.* **67,** 97–126.

—— (1937). *Genetics and the Origin of Species.* New York.

DUBININ, N. P., *et al.* (1934). 'Experimentelle Analyse von Ecogenotypen von *Drosophila melanogaster.*' *Biol. Zh. Mosk.* **3,** 166–216.

ELTON, C. S. (1927). *Animal Ecology,* London.

FISHER, R. A. (1927). 'On Some Objections to Mimicry Theory: Statistical and Genetic.' *Trans. roy. ent. Soc. Lond.* **75,** 269–78.

FISHER, R. A. (1930*a*). 'The Evolution of Dominance in certain Polymorphic Species. *Amer. Nat.* **64**, 385–406.

—— (1930*b*). *The Genetical Theory of Natural Selection.* Oxford.

—— (1930*c*). 'The Distribution of Gene Ratios for Rare Mutations.' *Proc. roy. Soc. Edinb.* **50**, 204–19.

—— (1931). 'The Evolution of Dominance.' *Biol. Rev.* **6**, 345–68.

FORD, E. B. (1936). 'The Genetics of *Papilio dardanus* Brown (Lep.).' *Trans. roy. ent. Soc. Lond.* **85**, 435–66.

—— (1937). 'Problems of Hereditary in the Lepidoptera.' *Biol. Rev.* **12**, 461–503.

FRYER, J. C. F. (1913). 'An Investigation by Pedigree Breeding into the Polymorphism of *Papilio polytes*, Linn.' *Philos. Trans. (B)*, **204**, 227–54.

GEROULD, J. H. (1923). 'Inheritance of White Wing Color, a sex-limited (sex-controlled) variation in Yellow Pierid Butterflies.' *Genetics*, **8**, 495–551.

GOLDSCHMIDT, R., und FISCHER, E. (1922). '*Argynnis paphia-valesina*, ein Fall geschlechtskontrollierter Vererbung bei Schmetterlingen.' *Genetica*, **4**, 247–78.

GROSVENOR, T. H. L. (1926–7). *Proc. S. Lond. ent. nat. Hist. Soc.*, pp. 95–6.

HALDANE, J. B. S. (1930). 'A Note on Fisher's Theory of the Origin of Dominance, and on a Correlation between Dominance and Linkage.' *Amer. Nat.* **64**, 87–90.

HUXLEY, J. S. (1927). 'Discontinuous Variation and Heterogony in *Forficula*.' *J. Genet.* **17**, 309–27.

—— (1932). *Problems of Relative Growth*, London.

JACOBSON, E. (1909). 'Beobachtungen über den Polymorphismus von *Papilio memnon* L.' *Tijdschr. Ent.* **52**, 125–57.

JORDAN, K. (1905). 'Der Gegensatz zwischen geographischer und nichtgeographischer Variation.' *Z. wiss. Zool.* **83**, 187–210.

MEIJERE, J. C. H. DE (1910). 'Über Jacobsons Züchtungsversuche bezüglich des Polymorphismus von *Papilio memnon* L. O und über die Vererbung sekundärer Geschlechtsmerkmale.' *Z. indukt. Abstamm.- u. Vererb.lehre.* **3**, 161–81.

PLATT, E. E. (1914, publ. 1915). 'A Large Family of *Hypolimnas* (*Euralia*) *mima*, Trim., and *wahlbergi*, Wallgr., bred from known parents of the *wahlbergi* form at Durban.' *Proc. ent. Soc. Lond.* **70–4**.

ROBINSON, H. C., and CHASEN, F. N. (1936). *The Birds of the Malay Peninsula*, **3**, London.

SMITH, G. W. (1906). 'High and Low Dimorphism.' *Mitt. Zool. Stat. Neapel.* **17**, 312–40.

STORER, T. I., and GREGORY, P. W. (1934). 'Color Aberrations in the Pocket Gopher and their probable Genetic Explanation.' *J. Mamm.* **15**, 300–12.

STRESEMANN, E. (1923). *Accipiter leucosomus* (Sharpe): eine leucistische Mutante von *accipiter etorques* (Salvadori).' *Orn. Mber.* **31**, 127–31.

ZIMMERMANN, K. (1935). 'Zur Rassenanalyse der mitteleuropäischen Feldmäuse.' *Arch. Naturgesch.* N.F. **4**, 258–73.

NATURAL HYBRIDIZATION IN RELATION TO TAXONOMY

By H. H. ALLAN

Et quid curae nobis de generibus et speciebus?

NO matter what Thomas à Kempis may have felt about it, the taxonomists have always tried to define their kinds and sorts. They have lumped and split to their hearts' content, and quarrelled enormously. No one is satisfied with the definitions of the other, yet many accept a 'species' as a reality of nature, whether it be the elementary species of a Jordan, or the larger group we loosely call 'Linnean'. *Capsella bursa-pastoris* Medic. travels the world over, may drop certain forms here and there, but does not change into something else. *Hypericum androsaemum* L. finds the climate of New Zealand congenial, but does not [*pace* Atkinson (1928), followed by Ridley (1930)] become more succulent-fruited, or more favoured by birds. The searching analyses of the geneticists begin to assume impressive proportions, but have revealed a great danger. Important and necessary as the delimitation of the microspecies may be, we must hold fast to the broader concept of species if we are not to miss the forest by getting lost among the trees. There are also many, many groups that will long await genetic analysis, but which must be considered in our floras and in botanical work generally. For the numerous still largely unexplored floras the broad way must long remain the only safe way. A vague admission of 'variability' is gradually being replaced by an analysis of the kinds of diversity, and as Bailey (1929) said, 'A new approach to the whole subject of variables is now the greatest desideratum in systematic botany.' In this approach we should not be unduly pessimistic, even if we fully agree with De Wildeman (1929): 'Nous ne constituons rien de définitif, nos études amènent journellement des faits nouveaux, nous en recherchons l'explication et essayons par la synthèse à nous rapprocher de plus en plus de la vérité, que nous n'atteindrons probablement jamais.' The view that taxonomy should be based on phylogeny is very popular and is *ex cathedra* imposing. But the argument is too apt to be circular, and the 'phylogenetic' charts are generally based on taxonomic findings into which we read phylogeny, rather than deduced from any true knowledge of descent. Our phylogenies are invented to account for our taxonomic facts or theories.

It has become a commonplace that all branches of biological research should be utilized for taxonomic purposes—the geneticist, the anatomist, the cytologist, the physiologist, all have their contributions to make. But actual co-ordination of effort is no easy matter, and will not be completely effected in our day. The 'new' systematics must proceed with caution, and keep in mind what the 'old' has of good. Pioneering attempts are not wanting, e.g. those of Babcock and his co-workers on *Crepis*, of Melderis on *Erythraea* (*Centaurium*), and the contributions of Brainerd, Clausen, Gersky, Zamelis, and others on *Viola*. We need many more monographic efforts on these lines, whether of local groups or studies of world-wide scope, such as that of Shull on *Capsella*. The time certainly seems ripe for a general review of the situation so that carefully planned attacks on selected groups may be made by combined forces. It has become clear that in these attacks the results of crossing between species in the wild state must receive attention. Darlington (1937) may be correct in stating that systematists have generally been content to use the term 'hybrid as a label for misfits', but there is much work, both old and recent, that cannot be so summarily dismissed, whether or not we agree with Darlington's 'the one vigorous and unequivocal definition: a hybrid is a zygote produced by the union of dissimilar gametes (or which by mutation has the character of such a zygote)'. Lotsy would have rejoiced at the parenthesis! 'The method of observation', Darlington continues, 'is cytology and the method of analysis is genetics.' But surely the method of field observation can, at the lowest, supply useful data, and point to profitable groups for investigation.

Some defence for the statement that the study of wild hybrids is an essential aspect of taxonomic work still seems necessary. 'The variables lure us into the swamps of hybridity,' says Bailey (1929). No doubt it may be tempting to *assume* hybridity as an easy way out of our taxonomic difficulties, just as it has been so easy in the past to assume a 'variability' of species *sine causa*, or even to speak of 'mutations' without evidence. If the study of the systematics of variables is to progress, if we are to learn to avoid the quicksands and the bogs as well as the marshes, the facts of hybridity cannot be neglected. Bailey adds: 'Hybridity is not a taxologic or descriptive concept; it is more correctly used by the horticulturists and geneticists.' But Nature is something of a horticulturist and a geneticist! She has hybridized, and sometimes freely, to the discomfiture of the old taxonomy, and by the amphidiploid way has, with little remaining doubt, used hybridization in the production of new species.

Whatever methods the systematic botanist uses to deal with wild hybrids, he cannot ignore them. By purely observational methods a great deal can be and has been done as a preliminary to more intensive work. I have discussed these matters rather fully in earlier papers (1931, 1937) and with Cockayne (1927) from an ecological standpoint. Bailey refers to *Rubus* colonies that 'belong to nothing', and recommends that we 'give them name and diagnosis; this puts them on record; the origin is another question, for a different kind of study'. I have very rarely come across colonies that after any adequate study in the field persist in 'belonging to nothing'. But I know of colonies of *Hebe* that present a multitude of forms none of which can at present be separated out as belonging to a 'good' species, and so with *Alseuosmia*. To give names is as easy as to assume that we have in front of us a mass of hybrids with the species 'swamped'. But what shall we name? The whole heterogeneous group? A casually selected specimen, as has sometimes been done? Or shall we attempt to name the hundreds of forms we can distinguish? The *Index Kewensis* would soon assume truly noble proportions! And when one considers diagnoses one's mind goes back to the remark of Focke (1881): 'Genaue Beschreibungen von solchen Bastarden können sich nur auf locale und individuelle Formen beziehen, sind daher nicht allein für die Systematik völlig unbrauchbar, sondern selbst in physiologischer Beziehung ziemlich werthlos.' It seems best to record the existence of such complicated populations and to pass on, meantime, to more resolvable groups.

The New Zealand flora is not very extensive, and in a very broad general way may be said to be fairly well known. But the work of recent years has shaken our complacence, and revealed how complex the situation really is, and what a great amount of taxonomic work awaits the doing. A glance at a few genera—say *Cassinia, Danthonia, Pimelea;* I choose almost at random—in any well-stocked herbarium will reveal this.

It has been demonstrated that wild hybridism accounts for a great deal of this complexity. Cockayne and Allan (1934) record 491 hybrid groups, and others are being brought to light. It is true that some of these records are doubtful, and were mentioned only as an incitement to further investigation, but the number of well-attested cases is so great as to put beyond doubt the importance of hybrid studies in the taxonomic revision of any genus of more than one species. On the other hand, this very investigation of hybridism has revealed that many 'variable' or 'polymorphic' species contain a number of true-breeding units, and that polymorphy in itself is not too lightly to be taken as evidence of hybridism. As an example, *Hebe salicifolia* Pennell, is a polymorphic group containing several clearly demarcated true-breeding units (varieties), with fairly clearly defined geographical bounds, some being known to hybridize where they meet. *Hebe elliptica* Pennell is as distinct from any form of *H. salicifolia* as the most inveterate lumper could wish, and has fewer subsidiary units. Field-work demonstrated that the two species hybridize freely, and produce progeny with some degree of fertility. Garden tests, coupled with genetic and cytological work, have substantiated the views derived from field observation. *H. amabilis* Andersen, *H. blanda* Pennell, and *H. divergens* Cockayne (at least in part) of the older taxonomy are now known to belong to this hybrid group. Taking the 111 species of *Hebe* treated by Cheeseman (1925)—I include certain species placed by him in *Eu-veronica* that are quite definitely *Hebe* in capsule-dehiscence—71 are fairly clearly differentiated (splitters would segregate certain 'varieties', lumpers would unite certain 'species'), 5 are definitely known to be hybrids. No fewer than 27 (and here is an important lesson for taxonomy) are based on odd specimens taken from polymorphic populations the status of individuals of which is quite uncertain, and 8 are cultispecies of still more doubtful origin. Cultispecies with *nomina nuda* there are in shoals in our gardens and trade catalogues. The Hebes of the Chatham Islands are still awaiting any detailed study; the 'species' at present included in floras are only the result of a casual examination.

No one knows how many species of *Alseuosmia* occur; whether we accept the eight of Allan Cunningham or the four of Cheeseman, we are only guessing. What we do know is that in the northern part of North Island, N.Z., there is an extraordinary multiplicity of forms, and that as we come south the complexity diminishes, till in the southern part of North Island we are left with one, there easily recognized, species. The multitudinous sheets in our herbaria serve at present only as a source of wonder and humility. Fortunately no one has as yet ventured to provide names and diagnoses to fit the herbarium material. *Alseuosmia* must be studied *de novo*. *Clematis* looks in the New Zealand floras a fairly simple genus, but a monographer would soon find himself in deep waters. There is good evidence in both these genera that hybridism is in large part responsible for the confusing polymorphy.

New Zealand is both unfortunate and fortunate in its considerable assemblage of introduced species, mainly from Old World sources, often forming distinct communities. The thoroughly naturalized introduced flora may be put roughly at 500 species. In these hybridism is low, in striking contrast with the conditions in the indigenous flora, although opportunities for crossing, so far as proximity of species is concerned, are common enough. A list (Allan, 1929) of thirty-seven supposed species-hybrids has been published. Further studies show a number of these to be very doubtful, and only nineteen of them can be said to be definitely known, including hybrids between three indigenous species of *Acaena* and the Australian *A. ovina* A. Cunn. Nearly all these hybrids are infrequent, and the evidence is all in support of the view that they are highly sterile. Such studies as I have been able to make of *Rumex*, for instance, support the views of Danser (1925) for this genus. The reasons for this contrast between the two floras cannot be insignificant, and surely affect the taxonomist. A comparative study of *Agrostis* in different countries should be illuminating.

An interesting contrast, in the other direction, is afforded by *Rubus*. The New Zealand species are pretty clearly defined, tnough several have more than one variety. Recognized hybrids are few, of apparently rare occurrence in the field (actually only one or two individual plants are known), and of a very high degree of sterility. An artificial cross made by me has a like sterility, having flowered very sparingly only once during fourteen years of vigorous vegetative growth. In Europe, however, and the like appears true for America, *Rubus* presents an even more complicated problem than does *Hebe* in New Zealand.

The criteria for the recognition of wild hybrids in the field have received attention from numerous workers and need not be elaborated here. That hybrids between species do occur, and that they are sometimes fertile, is now conceded on all hands. Certainly field evidence is circumstantial only, but it is often so overwhelming as to leave no doubt in an unprejudiced mind. Huskins (1929) reminds us that there is no *one* satisfactory and final criterion, and the work of Heribert Nilsson (1930) on *Salix* shows how careful we must be in interpreting the field evidence. But the argument is still sometimes repeated that incapability of crossing outside its group is *the* test of a 'good' species, despite the fact that we have definite knowledge of incompatibility within a species group, and of the possibility of species widely separated taxonomically crossing and even producing fertile offspring. Surely no one would treat *Nothofagus cliffortioides* Oerst, and *N. fusca* Oerst, as belonging to one species because they cross freely, or unite *Cordyline australis* Hook f., with *C. pumilio* Hook f., because hybrids occasionally occur between them. The grassland herb *Senecio southlandicus* Cockayne, and the forest-margin shrub *S. hectori* J. Buck, are widely separated in growth-form, habitat requirements, and geographical distribution, yet brought together in a garden they have produced spontaneous hybrids, flowering freely, but apparently quite sterile. Generic crosses are not unknown! When we find Karpechenko (1928) crossing radishes and cabbages, and Venkatraman (1938) successfully raising bamboo-sugar-cane hybrids we begin to wonder *where* the limits of crossability will finally be drawn.

Field studies can go a very long way in determining the status of individuals and groups. In *Rubus* it is now known that the 'variety' *pauperatus* T. Kirk of *R. squarrosus* Fritsch is an inconstant habitat modification, while the 'variety' *subpauperatus* (Cockayne) Cheeseman is a true-breeding unit allied to *R. schmidelioides* A. Cunningham, and quite distinct from the species it is placed under. On the other hand, *R. barkeri* Cockayne is equally definitely a hybrid. A first taxonomic task resulting from field study is the correction of such mistakes in status. Anderson (1928) has argued that undue importance has been placed on the criterion of true-breeding as a delimiting mark of subordinate units: 'with more genetical or horticultural experience they would have realized that coming true from seed (homozygosity) is a mere corollary of the amount of inbreeding which has taken place and that it is of minor taxonomic and phylogenetic significance.' He also argues that in cross-pollinating groups no constant jordanons will persist. There is a good deal of truth in this as regards true-breeding units within a 'Linnean' species, but the argument hardly applies to species-crosses, and pays too little attention to the facts of geographical distribution. *Coprosma propinqua* A. Cunn. crosses very freely with *C. robusta* Raoul and the hybrids are fertile, as experiments have shown, up to the third generation at least, while back-crossing also takes place. Certain populations contain no pure forms, but there are many localities in which either one or the other species is found predominant or alone. Certain populations of *Hebe* and *Leptospermum* elude analysis in the field, and possibly the jordanons have been completely swamped. But these have never been seriously tackled, and may not be so impossible of elucidation as now appears. Work on *Festuca novae-zelandiae* Cockayne is showing that geographically limited jordanons occur, and only merge into one another by crossing at their boundaries. Field studies on these lines yield important evidence, though no one denies that they must be followed up as far as possible by experimental studies—genetic, transplant, and so on. The incidence of hybridism and jordanons in *Myrtus*, in New Zealand, with the species largely separated geographically, can be determined with comparative ease; similar work with *Alseuosmia* will be extremely difficult. Decisions must wait on full field-study. Du Rietz (1930) noted populations where the hybrids between *Senecio lyallii* Hook. f. and *S. scorzoneroides* Hook. f. outnumbered the pure species, and suggested that it was as 'equally probable that the "species" are segregates of the hybrid as that the hybrid was formed by the meeting of two species originally isolated'. But this ignores the fact that both species, especially *S. lyallii*, occur in numerous localities in pure or practically pure populations. Taxonomically they are 'good' species. We can only push on field studies as far as they can be made to yield useful results. It has become recognized that purely herbarium studies may be utterly misleading. In pioneering field-work little advance on older methods may be possible, but for more detailed studies herbarium material must be gathered in much greater quantity than has been usually attempted, with much more attention to field data. Field studies will suggest where the experimental garden or genetic and cytologic examination will be likely to prove most profitable. Here, perhaps, is its most useful contribution to the new taxonomy. *Coprosma* has proved most difficult cytologically. *Bulbinella* may be much more amenable, in these the very early days of genetic and cytological work with the indigenes of New Zealand. It has also the advantage of comprising fewer species.

Work has not advanced far enough in any country for a thoroughgoing classification of wild hybrids. There appear to be significant differences in the extent to which hybridism prevails in the different floras and in the comparative degree of fertility in the hybrids found. In New Zealand it has been found useful to distinguish hybrid groups as *pauciform* or *multiform*. Most *Celmisia* hybrids are pauciform, e.g. × *C. pseudo-lyallii* Cockayne (*C. lyallii* Hook. f. × *spectabilis* Hook. f.). The individuals closely resemble one another and usually occur sporadically. These pauciform hybrids appear to be sterile first-generation crosses, though the possibility of parthenogenesis has also to be investigated. Multiform hybrids, the individuals showing great diversity and often occurring in populations or 'swarms', are frequent in many genera. There is evidence of a considerable degree of fertility, and back-crossing is probably not uncommon. All intergeneric hybrids so far noted in New Zealand are pauciform and rather rarely met with. They are not often found in flower, and no evidence of fertility is to hand. The genera concerned differ in floral characters only in small details, e.g. certain very closely allied composite genera are linked by hybridism as follows:

Ewartia—Helichrysum—Gnaphalium

Raoulia—Leucogenes

The taxonomic importance of intergeneric hybrids is in the evidence they afford of relationships, e.g. *Triodia*, as understood in New Zealand, appeared to be closely related to *Danthonia*, and 'intergeneric' crosses are known. Recent research at Kew has shown that the former genus has to be sunk in the latter. Some hybrid forms have not escaped being treated as species, e.g. *Raoulia gibbsii* Cheeseman includes specimens of *Leucogenes grandiceps* Beauv. × *Raoulia bryoides* Hook. f., as does *Helichrysum pauciflorum* Kirk.

A feature of interest is the occurrence of what I have called 'mimics'. *Celmisia argentea* T. Kirk and *C. sessiliflora* Hook. f. are two short-leaved species very similar in life-form and habitat requirements. *Celmisia longifolia* Hook. f., with long, narrow, flaccid leaves, is a species of wide range, made up of several distinct jordanons. When one of these meets either of the former, species-hybrids are frequently met with. These are apparently sterile and mimic a species remarkably well, and have received the name *C. linearis* Armstrong. Closely similar forms have been noted as the result of crossing between *C. sessiliflora* and *C. insignis* Martin, a species with long, narrow, stiff leaves. Hardly distinguishable is *C. compacta* Cheesem., based on a few specimens only, and probably also a cross between *C. sessiliflora* and some other species.

The New Zealand forms of *Coriaria* show a remarkable series of gradations from the small-tree *C. arborea* Lindsay to the tiny creeping *C. parvifolia*. That hybridism is frequent is abundantly clear from studies in a number of localities. Certain of the hybrid forms closely mimic constant forms in areas geographically separated. This genus stands much in need of a combined attack. Long ago Colenso described his *C. kingiana*, a striking feature of which is the undulate leaf-margins. Name and description were lost sight of. Petrie much later distributed specimens of a similar form under the manuscript name of *C. thymifolia* Humb. and Bonpl. var. *undulata*. Since then '*undulata*' forms of the '*thymifolia*' group have been found in the *ruscifolia* group and in *C. parvifolia*. The undulate leaf-margin also occurs in hybrids between *C. arborea* and '*thymifolia*'. The whole genus is thus at present in a most unsatisfactory taxonomic state. We have hardly advanced on the treatment of Lindsay (1868), who remarked, after an examination of all available herbarium specimens and studies in the field, 'it appeared impossible to define or limit them by any permanent characters of sufficient value'. The forms can be arranged to exhibit a closed chain. How far our *'ruscifolia'* and *'thymifolia'* assemblages are conspecific with South American species we do not know, no full comparisons having been made. It is clear from field studies that the *'thymifolia'* group contains several jordanons. Here is an excellent field for concerted effort on a genus of phytogeographical importance.

In regard to more minute differences, Du Rietz (1930) has pointed out that 'in the genus *Celmisia* brown and yellow hairs showed a remarkable frequency in the northern part of South Island, being found there in species widely differing in other respects'. Whether it be, as Du Rietz suggests, that 'certain genes had been generally distributed only in certain districts, but in those districts had "infected" the whole population' or not, such facts of distribution and transference of characters are not lacking in taxonomic importance.

How far the ecotype hypothesis of Turesson (1930) and the views of Danser (1929)[1] on comparia, commiscua, and convivia are likely to be of service in practical taxonomy is debatable, but it is beyond my immediate purpose to contribute much towards the debate. The following species of *Hebe*, and possibly others, form a comparium, and as far as the evidence available goes, also in large part a coenospecies: *angustifolia, cookiana, elliptica, laevis, leiophylla, macrocarpa, macroura, obtusata, parviflora, pubescens, salicifolia, speciosa, subalpina*. In *Hebe* we certainly seem to have some *convivia sumptuosiora*. Two further comparia, the lines indicating hybrid linkages, are diagrammed below (p. 527). To prevent misunderstanding, may I add that I regard the work of Turesson and Danser as of great importance to students of wild hybridism in general. Studies on wild hybrids should throw

---

[1] Danser's terms are defined by him, in German, in his paper 'Ueber die Begriffe Komparium, Kommiskuum und Konvivium und ueber die Entstehungsweise der Konvivien' in *Genetica*, **11**, 399 (1929). The following brief English definitions are based on the original German ones: A comparium is the whole of the individuals which can be combined directly or indirectly by crossing. A commiscuum is the whole of the individuals which can be combined directly or indirectly by mixture, i.e. by crossing which results in the production of fertile hybrids. A convivium is, within a commiscuum, a group of individuals which can be distinguished from other groups by more or less sharp characters and which is maintained by conditions of some kind in regard to its propagation (isolation).

light on the views of Turesson as to the origin of the ecotypes we find in nature.

As a further indication of the importance of wild hybridism in taxonomic treatment I give the two following tables (p. 526), based on the work of Burtt and Hill (1935) on *Gaultheria* and *Pernettya*, and that of Oliver (1929) on *Dracophyllum* subgenus *Oreothamnus*. It will be noted that Oliver finds only one hybrid group *within* his smaller taxonomic groups, and it should be mentioned that certain species not known to hybridize have a very restricted range. No definitely established hybrids had been recorded in the subgenus *Eudracophyllum* (eight New Zealand species), but there is now good evidence that *D. traversii* Hook. f. (*Eudracophyllum*, flowers panicled) crosses with *D. longifolium* R. Br. (*Oreothamnus*, flowers racemose).

Possibly at the present stage the fewer nomenclatorial rules concerning hybrids the better. Comparative studies on diverse floras are still too few for the drawing up of rules likely to be acceptable to a majority of the actual workers in this field. Yet the rules regarding hybrids in the 1935 'International Rules' show but little advance on those of 1867, being based on all too little consideration of the phenomena. A major weakness is the lack of any definite recognition of the status to be given hybrids in nomenclatorial procedure. A further source of confusion is the lack of any reference to historical considerations. Long enough ago Focke (1881) drew attention to these matters, and his sections on 'wildwachsende Bastarde' and 'Nomenclatur der Mischlinge' still deserve our earnest attention. 'Je mehr sich die Erkenntnis der wildwachsenden Bastardpflanzen ausbreitete, umso zahlreichere Streitigkeiten entspannen sich über die Bedeutung der alten Namen.' This, however, is not the place to enter into discussion of a very technical problem. A short paper, under the title 'The Nomenclature of Hybrids' has been sent for publication to *Chronica Botanica* and readers are referred to this publication for the author's suggestions.

REFERENCES

ALLAN, H. H. (1929). 'A List of Supposed Wild Hybrids among the Naturalized Plants of New Zealand.' *N. Z. J. Sci. & Techn.* **11**, 255–61.
—— (1931). 'The Significance of Hybridism in the New Zealand Flora.' *Rep. 20th Meeting Austral. & N. Z. Ass. Adv. Sci.* **20**, 429–77.

TABLE I

Hybrid linkages in Gaultheria *and* Pernettya (p. 525)

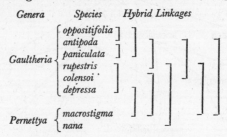

Genera	Species	Hybrid Linkages
Gaultheria	oppositifolia	
	antipoda	
	paniculata	
	rupestris	
	colensoi	
	depressa	
Pernettya	macrostigma	
	nana	

TABLE II

Hybrid linkages in Dracophyllum *subgenus* Oreothamnus (p. 525)

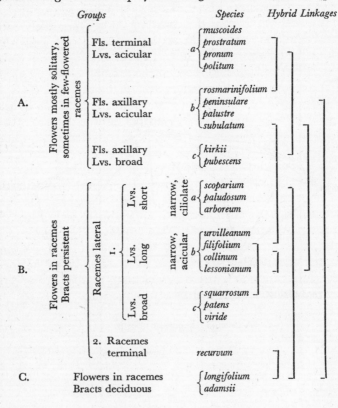

Groups				Species	Hybrid Linkages
A.	Flowers mostly solitary, sometimes in few-flowered racemes	Fls. terminal Lvs. acicular	a	muscoides prostratum pronum politum	
		Fls. axillary Lvs. acicular	b	rosmarinifolium peninsulare palustre subulatum	
		Fls. axillary Lvs. broad	c	kirkii pubescens	
B.	Flowers in racemes Bracts persistent	1. Racemes lateral — Lvs. short	narrow, ciliolate a	scoparium paludosum arboreum	
		Lvs. long	narrow, acicular b	urvilleanum filifolium collinum lessonianum	
		Lvs. broad	c	squarrosum patens viride	
		2. Racemes terminal		recurvum	
C.	Flowers in racemes Bracts deciduous			longifolium adamsii	

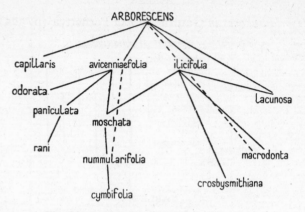

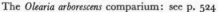

The *Olearia arborescens* comparium: see p. 524

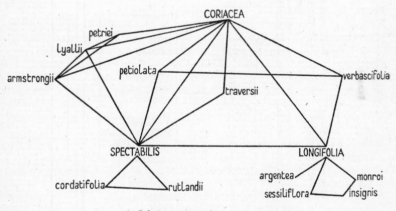

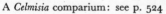

A *Celmisia* comparium: see p. 524

ALLAN, H. H. (1937). 'Wild species-hybrids in the Phanerogams.' *Bot. Rev.* **3**, 593–615.

ANDERSON, E. (1928). 'The Problem of Species in the Northern Blue Flags, *Iris versicolor* L. and *Iris virginica* L.' *Ann. Miss. Bot. Gard.* **15**, 241–332.

ATKINSON, E. (1928). 'Weeds and their Identification. Tutsan (*Hypericum androsaemum* L.).' *N. Z. J. Agric.* **37**, 408–10.

BAILEY, L. H. (1929). 'Statement on the Systematic Study of Variables.' *Proc. Internat. Congr. Plant Sciences*, **2**, 1427–33.

BURTT, B. L., and HILL, A. W. (1935). 'The Genera *Gaultheria* and *Pernettya* in New Zealand, Tasmania, and Australia.' *J. Linn. Soc. Bot.* **49**, 611–44.

CHEESEMAN, T. F. (1925). *Manual of the New Zealand Flora*, ed. 2. Wellington, N.Z.

COCKAYNE, L., and ALLAN, H. H. (1927). 'The Bearing of Ecological Studies in New Zealand on Botanical Taxonomic Conceptions and Procedure.' *J. Ecol.* **15**, 234–77.

—— —— (1934). 'An Annotated List of Groups of Wild Hybrids in the New Zealand Flora.' *Ann. Bot.* **48**, 1–55.

DANSER, B. H. (1925). 'Beitrag zur Kenntnis der Gattung Rumex.' *Nederl. Kruidk. Arch., Jaarg.* **1925**, 414–84.

—— (1929). 'Ueber die Begriffe Komparium, Kommiscuum und Konvivium und über die Entstehungsweise der Konvivien.' *Genetica*, **11**, 399–450.

DARLINGTON, C. D. (1937). 'What is a Hybrid?' *J. Hered.* **28**, 308.

DE WILDEMAN, É. (1929). 'A propos de l'espèce en botanique.' *Proc. Internat. Congr. Plant Sciences*, **2**, 1413–21.

DU RIETZ, G. E. (1930). 'The Fundamental Units of Biological Taxonomy.' *Svensk. Bot. Tidskr.* **24**, 333–428.

FOCKE, W. O. (1881). *Die Pflanzen-Mischlinge*. Berlin.

HUSKINS, C. L. (1929). 'Criteria of Hybridity.' *Science*, **69**, 399–400.

KARPECHENKO, G. D. (1928). 'Polyploid hybrids of *Raphanus sativus* L. × *Brassica oleracea* L.' *Z. indukt. Abstamm.- u. Vererb.lehre*, **48**, 1–85.

KIRK, T. (1899). *The Student's Flora of New Zealand*. Wellington, N.Z.

LINDSAY, W. L. (1868). *Contributions to New Zealand Botany*. London.

NILSSON, N. H. (1930). 'Synthetische Bastardierungsversuche in der Gattung *Salix*.' *Lunds Univ. Årsskrift*, N.F., Avd. 2, Bd. **27**, Nn. 4. Lund.

OLIVER, W. R. B. (1929). 'A Revision of the Genus *Dracophyllum*.' *Trans. N. Z. Inst.* **59**, 678–714.

RIDLEY, H. N. (1930). *The Dispersal of Plants throughout the World*. Ashford, England.

TURESSON, G. (1930). 'Genecological Units and their Classificatory Value.' *Svensk. Bot. Tidskr.* Bd. **24**, H. 4: 511–18.

VENKATRAMAN, T. S. (1938). 'Hybridization in and with the Genus *Saccharum* (its Scientific and Economic Aspects).' *25th Ind. Sci. Congr.*, Pres. Addr. (Sect. Agric.), 1–18. Calcutta.

THE ORIGIN AND BEHAVIOUR OF CULTIVATED PLANTS

By M. B. CRANE

THE taxonomist has generally regarded the study of cultivated plants with suspicion. He has tended, possibly on
account of a false philosophical distinction between natural and
artificial conditions, to ignore all cultivated plants as outside his
discipline or as forming a secondary applied branch of it, namely,
economic botany. The geneticist, on the other hand, following
Darwin's example, has found convenient and useful material in
cultivated plants and domestic animals, with their wealth of
analysable varieties and frequent high fecundity in crosses. This
is no doubt one of the reasons why taxonomy and genetics have
had so little fertile intercourse.

The trend of modern investigation, however, is to show that
the laws of inheritance and variation in cultivated plants and
domesticated animals are essentially the same as those in wild
species, and that generalizations of importance to the systematist
may be made from the study of cultivated plants. This is indeed
now being recognized, as witness the work of many enlightened
systematists; by the cultivation of wild plants and the analysis of
their characters they are adopting the geneticist's method of
investigation.

Our cultivated races of plants, like all living organisms, owe
their individuality to the materials received from their parents.
The transmission of these materials from one generation to
another depends normally upon the production of specialized
germ-cells, and it is by the union of these cells, one from each
parent, that the genes which determine the character of the
plant are transmitted to the offspring. It is therefore evident
that the constitution of a plant and way in which it has originated will be reflected in the variation of its offspring and in
the mode of inheritance of its characters.

Genetical and cytological studies have shown that from an
evolutionary point of view we can arrange our races of cultivated
plants conveniently in four classes according to their mode of

origin, although the classes overlap. These classes originate as
follows:

1. By selection from gene-mutations within a single species.
2. By simple auto-polyploidy, such as results from the functioning of unreduced germ-cells or from somatic duplication without hybridization.
3. By selection from products of interspecific hybridization
   unaccompanied by chromosome duplication or aberration.
4. By interspecific hybridization accompanied by chromosome doubling (allo-polyploidy) or other nuclear aberrations.

These different methods by which new kinds of cultivated plants
have originated are, we believe, the principal causes of variation
in nature and the processes by which evolution continues. They
occur both in nature and under cultivation and give rise to new
species and races, and are therefore fundamentally involved
with problems of taxonomy.

Gene-mutations

The part which gene-mutations have played in the origin of
new plants is evident from the many new varieties and forms
which have appeared even within living memory. For example
the sweet pea, *Lathyrus odoratus* L., was widely cultivated fifty years
ago, and at that time no great range of varieties existed. Since
then not only has the range of colour been greatly extended, but
a large number of varieties have appeared involving marked
differences in habit of growth, structure of leaves, pollen, and
flowers. Indeed, the Spencer form of flower with large erect
waved petals has completely ousted the typical hooded form
from cultivation. The same applies to the Chinese primrose,
Primula sinensis Sabine, the tomato, the raspberry, the peach, and
a great many other plants which could be cited. Such variations have resulted spontaneously from gene-mutation. They
are not directly due to hybridization. Nor are they due to the
direct effects of cultivation, although indirectly cultivation has
important effects, first on account of the close inbreeding involved, which reveals mutations latent in the stock, and secondly
on account of selection and vegetative reproduction, which
maintain these mutations as distinct strains. In general the new
forms which have originated as a result of gene-mutations have

been recognized as varieties, although they occasionally give rise to variations which, as judged by morphology, approach specific, or at least subspecific, rank. For example the distinctive dwarf campanula, *Campanula nitida* Ait., is a simple segregate from *C. persicifolia*, L., and *Urtica dodartii* L. from *U. pilulifera* L. In both cases they are recessive forms and the result of a single gene-difference. Similarly, *Rubus idaeus* L. *obtusifolius* Willd. is a segregate from *R. idaeus*. Although first discovered in nature, it also occurs under cultivation, and many cultivated raspberries such as Superlative, Norwich Wonder, and Pyne's Royal are heterozygous for the character of the sub-species *obtusifolius*.

The two Linnean species of peas, *Pisum arvense* L. and *P. sativum* L., can hardly be regarded as specifically different from a genetic point of view. They form a fertile hybrid whose breeding behaviour shows that only a limited number of gene differences are involved. In the genus *Ulmus* such a distinct character as opposite and alternate leaves appears to be governed by a single gene (see Henry, 1910).

Most plants are genetically the same all through. Consequently when they are propagated asexually, it does not matter which tissue—stem, root, tuber, &c.—is used to make the new individual, or whether the tissue comes from the inside or the outside: the resulting offspring are always the same. A surprisingly large number of plants, however, are known which do not possess this uniformity or individuality, and when they are vegetatively propagated, different tissues give rise to different types of offspring. Such plants, which are composed of two or more genetically distinct tissues, are known as chimaeras, and they can be classified according to the way in which the different tissues are arranged. A common type is the so-called periclinal chimaera, in which one genetic type completely surrounds another, just as a glove covers a hand. For example, investigation has shown that the Bouvardia 'Bridesmaid' with pink flowers has a central core of the red-flowered variety 'Hogarth', and the potato 'Golden Wonder' with thick brown russet skins to the tubers has a core of the variety 'Langworthy' with thin, white, smooth-skinned tubers. Autogenous chimaeras such as these arise spontaneously in different ways, but many are due to gene-mutations occurring in somatic tissues. They are commonly thought to be fantasies peculiar to cultivation, but they are also found in nature. For example, the American blackberry 'Cory's Thornless' was first found in nature growing on a mountain pass in California; externally it has no prickles, but propagated asexually from internal tissues, i.e. from root cuttings, or sexually from seeds, the plants are all thorned. The breeding behaviour of the crested-leaf form of the common wood-sage, *Teucrium scorodonia* L. *crispum* Stansf., in giving all non-crested offspring, is likewise explicable on the assumption that it is a periclinal chimaera.

Auto-polyploids

The second way in which new cultivated forms have arisen is by simple auto-polyploidy, i.e. the duplication of the chromosome complement without hybridization; for example, as a result of unreduced germ-cells functioning, or by somatic duplication. There are, for example, tetraploid forms of raspberries which from their general characteristics appear to be auto-polyploids. They include such varieties as Belle de Fontenay, Merveille Rouge, Hailshamberry, and Everbearing. Raspberries fall into two classes, the (ordinary) summer-fruiting varieties and the autumn-fruiting ones. The latter bear fruits on the current season's growth, whereas the summer-fruiting varieties bear on the previous season's wood. All the tetraploid varieties (with 28 somatic chromosomes) are in the autumn-fruiting class, whilst with rare exceptions the diploids (14 chromosomes) are in the summer-fruiting class. The tetraploids also have morphological differences which separate them from the diploids. The tetraploids have arisen from the diploids during the last eighty years.

There are two races of *Primula sinensis*, the diploids with 24 and the tetraploids with 48 chromosomes. The latter are giant auto-polyploids and arose from the diploids spontaneously at the beginning of the present century. In grapes the varieties Muscat and Sultanina have 38 chromosomes, the respective giant forms *Muscat gigas* and *Sultanina gigas* have 76.

The above are examples of auto-polyploids arising from a complete duplication of the chromosome complement. Many new forms, however, have arisen from unilateral duplication. For example, some of the finest varieties of tulip such as Keizerskroon, Pink Beauty, and Massenet are triploid; they presumably arose from the fusion of an unreduced diploid egg with a reduced haploid pollen-grain. The earliest of these triploid varieties, Zomerschoon, arose in the sixteenth century. Many hyacinths are also triploids of similar origin.[1] The first to appear was Grand Maître in 1870. Other triploid varieties are General de Wet, King of the Blues, Lord Balfour, and Lord Derby. These giant forms are widely grown and have largely displaced the old diploids in cultivation. Many varieties of the Japanese cherry and the triploid varieties of apples and pears appear to have arisen in the same way. Triploid and other auto-polyploid forms also occur in nature, e.g. *Pyrus minima* Aug. Ley, *Tulipa praecox* Ten., *T. saxatilis* Sieber ex Spreng., *T. lanata* Regal, *Nasturtium officinale* L., &c. Triploids commonly arise from crossing diploids with tetraploids, but it seems probable that many of the triploids found in nature, such as the *Tulipa* species, are auto-polyploids.

Interspecific Hybrids

The third process of change has been by interspecific hybridization unaccompanied by chromosome duplication or other major cytological aberrations. This has occurred from hybridization both between diploid and between polyploid species. Three species of *Ribes* appear to have entered into the constitution of the garden red currant, namely *R. vulgare* Lam., *R. rubrum* L., and *R. petraeum* Sm. Some cultivated varieties are predominantly *vulgare*, others *rubrum*, and others *petraeum*. Some again combine the characters of one or another pair of these species. All the species and varieties appear to be diploid. They have sixteen chromosomes, two sets of eight.

An example of the origin of a new race of plants from hybridization between polyploid species is provided by the large-fruiting garden strawberry. The cultivation of the strawberry in Europe goes back to the fourteenth century. At that time only the wild wood strawberry, *Fragaria vesca* L., was grown under cultivation. *F. elatior* Ehrh., found sporadically in the woods on the continent of Europe, and *F. virginiana* Duchesne, the woodland and hedgerow strawberry of eastern North America, were brought into cultivation in the sixteenth and

---

[1] De Mol (1923) states that the triploid hyacinths probably arose from the fertilization of haploid egg-cells by duplicated sperm-nuclei.

seventeenth century respectively. The fruits of all three species are comparatively small, and at this time no appreciable increase in the size of the fruit had occurred under cultivation. Early in the eighteenth century a fourth species, *F. chiloensis* Duchesne, with large flowers and fruits, was introduced into Europe from South America, and from all accounts it is clear that the introduction of this species provided the first opportunity of raising the large-sized fruits characteristic of our modern race. The first varieties of this type, combining the large size of *F. chiloensis* with the aromatic qualities of *F. virginiana*, appeared in Europe towards the end of the eighteenth century.

In recent years the genus *Fragaria* has been cytologically studied; the basic chromosome number is seven, and the figures as shown below make the story clear.

Species	Chromosome no. (somatic)		Time of introduction into cultivation in Europe
Fragaria vesca	2x	14	14th century
F. elatior	6x	42	16th ,,
F. virginiana	8x	56	17th ,,
F. chiloensis	8x	56	18th ,,
Garden strawberry . .	8x	56	19th ,,

On the genetical side, experiments have shown that diploid forms, including *F. vesca*, hybridize freely and give fertile offspring. Similarly, crosses between octoploids result in fertile offspring, but crosses between the species with different chromosome numbers, such as *F. vesca* × *F. elatior* or *F. virginiana*, and *F. elatior* with *F. virginiana* or *F. chiloensis*, are abortive or result in sterile hybrids. These facts throw direct light on the development of the strawberry subsequent to the introduction into Europe and hybridization of the two octoploid species *F. virginiana* and *F. chiloensis*, which until then had been geographically isolated; when the history, genetics, and cytology of the genus are considered there can be little doubt that the garden strawberry arose from hybridization between the two octoploid species.

Amongst the many other genera in which species-hybridization, without chromosome doubling, has given rise to new races of cultivated plants may be mentioned *Dianthus*, *Streptocarpus*,

Rubus, Rhododendron, and *Vitis.* In the genus *Iris, I. chamaeiris* Bertol., *I. mandshurica* Meissn., *I. olbiensis* Henon, *I. reichenbachii* Heuffel, and *I. sub-biflora* Brot. have 40 chromosomes and *I. mesopotamica* and *I. trojana* have 48. Other species such as *I. albicans* Lange, *I. germanica* L., and *I. kochii* A. Kern. ex Ṣtapf have 44 chromosomes, and Randolph (1935) suggests that it is probable that the species with 44 chromosomes arose from hybridization between species with 48 and 40 chromosomes.

Hybrid Polyploids

The fourth and most important way in which new forms arise is by interspecific hybridization in which unreduced germ-cells take part or where somatic duplication of the chromosome complement subsequently occurs. As a result, sometimes we have complete duplication of the complement, and sometimes unilateral duplication, i.e. non-reduction of the gamete in one parental species only. Many of our cultivated species and races of plants have originated in this way, either in nature or under cultivation. Details are given below of a few examples.

Dahlia variabilis Desf. From combined genetical, cytological, and chemical investigations, Lawrence (1929) and Lawrence and Scott-Moncrieff (1935) have shown that with the exception of *D. variabilis* and *D. merckii* Lehm, all the species of *Dahlia* examined have 32 chromosomes and that they may be divided into two groups for flower-colour, (1) with magenta (2) with scarlet or orange flowers, as follows:

Group 1. Magenta flowers	Group 2. Scarlet or orange flowers
D. dissecta	*D. coccinea* ($2n = 32$)
D. excelsa	*D. coronata* ($2n = 32$)
D. imperialis ($2n = 32$)	*D. gracilis*
D. lehmanni	*D. tenuis*
D. maximiliana ($2n = 32$)	
D. maxoni ($2n = 32$)	
D. merckii ($2n = 36$)	
D. platylepis	
D. pubescens	
D. scapigera	

The anthocyanins in group 1 are cyanidin types. In group 2 the anthocyanins are pelargonidin types. Variation within these species is limited; the magenta species may give ivory-white varieties and the scarlet species yellow varieties.

Dahlia variabilis, the garden dahlia, combines the pigments of the two groups, and it also has twice as many chromosomes, $2n = 64$. Experiments have convincingly led to the conclusion that *D. variabilis*, with its wide range of colour and form, arose in nature from hybridization between species in group 1 and species in group 2, followed by chromosome duplication. *D. variabilis* was introduced into Europe from Mexico in 1789.

Prunus domestica L. Our European plums may have arisen on many different occasions in prehistoric and historic times from the hybridization of diploid and tetraploid species, followed by chromosome doubling, to give the fertile hexaploid *Prunus domestica*. Indeed, the results of breeding work with species and varieties of *Prunus* have led to the conclusion that the diploid species *P. divaricata* Ledeb. and the tetraploid species *P. spinosa* L. are involved in the origin of *P. domestica* (Crane and Lawrence 1934).

Such a view is also supported by a consideration of the variation which occurs within these species. For example, in *P. divaricata* the ground colour of the fruits is yellow and the anthocyanin red, in *P. spinosa* the ground colour is green and the anthocyanin blue, and the range of variation in both species is limited. In *P. domestica*, however, both red and blue colours and also yellow and green grounds occur, and from their various recombinations an infinitely wider range of variation results. The increase in size and wider variation in the form and flavour of the fruits of *P. domestica* are also in agreement with the above view. The hypothesis also receives support from recent investigations by Dr. V. Rybin (1936) in Russia. In correspondence Dr. Rybin informs me that he has raised seedlings from crosses between *P. spinosa* L. × *P. divaricata* Led. (= *P. cerasifera* Ehrl.). One of these seedlings is a hexaploid; it is large and more robust than the normal triploids of the same origin. Rybin also states:

'In the forests of the Maikop district, North Caucasus, the species *P. spinosa* and *P. divaricata* hybridise rather freely. I found many wild-growing hybrids which showed 24 chromosomes in the root-tips; they flowered abundantly but were highly sterile. One of these trees bore only six fruits, and another seven. The characters of the leaves, branches, flowers, fruits, stones, the colour of the bark and other characters of the hybrid trees showed clearly their close relationship to both parental species. All these facts I think may be regarded as giving strong support to your idea that the European plum *P. domestica* arose by means of hybridisation which took place between the two Asiatic species *P. spinosa* and *P. divaricata*.'

Aesculus carnea Wats. (pink chestnut). Nothing seems to be known as to when or where this tree originated. In Edwards's *Botanical Register* for 1827 a specimen is described which was then a full-sized tree, so it probably dates from the eighteenth century. It is generally agreed that the pink chestnut is a hybrid between two species belonging to distinct sections of the genus, namely the common horse chestnut *A. hippocastanum* L. of Europe and Asia, which makes a tree up to 100 feet in height, and *A. pavia* L. from North America, a small shrubby species which rarely attains a height of over 12 feet. Apart from stature several well-marked characters separate *A. hippocastanum* from *A. pavia*. In the former the fruits are very spiny and the flowers usually have five petals, with a patch of colour confined to the base. In *A. pavia* the fruits are smooth and the flowers only have four petals, which in contrast to those of *A. hippocastanum* are richly coloured and glandular at the margins. These widely contrasting characters were formerly regarded as constituting a generic difference between *Aesculus* and *Pavia*.

A. carnea is intermediate between the above two species; it makes a tree 50 to 70 feet high and its fruits are slightly spiny. In habit of growth and foliage it resembles *A. hippocastanum*, whilst in the colour of its flowers and the glandular-edged petals it approaches *A. pavia*. Although generally accepted as a hybrid, *A. carnea* is usually propagated by sexual means, and it has aroused considerable interest both among horticulturists and biologists, first by its fertility and secondly by its behaviour in breeding approximately true from seed. In hybrids from widely distinct parents we are perhaps more familiar with the occurrence of sterility than fertility, and when hybrids are fertile considerable diversity in the progeny and some approach to the parental forms is a common expectation. But during the last decade genetical and cytological research has shown that to expect a distant hybrid always to be infertile, and to assume that its parental types will inevitably reappear in the second generation, is taking too simple a view of the potentialities of interspecific hybridization. In this connexion cytological studies of *A. carnea* and its parental species are of interest. Hoar (1927) found that both *A. pavia* and *A. hippocastanum* had 20 pairs of chromosomes, whilst *A. carnea* had 40 pairs. The chromosomes of *A. carnea* have therefore doubled, and given rise to a constant true-breeding new species in which the characters of the two sections of the genus are combined. Thus taxonomic, genetic, and cytological studies all confirm the hybrid origin of the species.

Rubus loganobaccus L. H. Bailey. The loganberry, $2n = 42$, which appeared in America about 1881 and was originally said to be a cross between *R. vitifolius* Cham. and Schlecht $2n = 56$, and a raspberry, $2n = 14$. This origin has been frequently disputed. Experimental results, however, tend to confirm the putative origin, in which true hybridization and unilateral chromosome duplication were involved, i.e. non-reduction in the raspberry parent.

Delphinium 'ruysii'. This species arose from hybridization between *D. nudicaule* Torr. and Gray ($2n = 16$) and *D. elatum* L. ($2n = 32$). *D. ruysii* also has $2n = 32$ and arose from unilateral duplication, i.e. non-reduction on the female side only (Lawrence, 1936).

Brassica napocampestris Frandsen and Winge. From crosses between the turnip *Brassica campestris* L., $2n = 20$, and the swede, *Brassica napus* L., $2n = 36$, Frandsen and Winge (1931) obtained a fertile form. The hybrid *Brassica napocampestris*, $2n = 56$, is in general intermediate between its parents.

Digitalis mertonensis Buxton and Darlington. From a cross between *Digitalis ambigua* Murr., $2n = 56$, and *Digitalis purpurea* L., $2n = 56$, the new species *D. mertonensis*, $2n = 112$, was obtained (Buxton and Newton, 1928; Buxton and Darlington, 1932).

Saxifraga potternensis Marsden-Jones and Turrill. Marsden-Jones and Turrill (1930-4) crossed *Saxifraga rosacea* Moench, $2n = 64$, with *S. granulata* L., $2n = 48$, and in F_2 they obtained a plant $2n = 80$. This plant bred approximately true and was named *S. potternensis*. Philip (1934) from cytological studies concluded that *S. granulata* is hexaploid, *S. rosacea* octoploid, and *S. potternensis* decaploid; and that the latter arose from unilateral failure of reduction, i.e. non-reduction of its male parent *S. granulata*.

Veitchberry. This hybrid was raised from crossing the raspberry November Abundance with the hedgerow blackberry *Rubus rusticanus* E. Merc. The chromosome complement of the raspberry November Abundance may have been $2n = 14$ or 28. *R. rusticanus* is diploid, $2n = 14$. The veitchberry has 28 chromosomes and is therefore a tetraploid which has arisen from hybridization and chromosome doubling, either of one or of both parents. The leaves of the raspberry are pinnate and those of the blackberry palmate, whilst the fully developed leaves of the veitchberry are partly pinnate and partly palmate. The offspring of the veitchberry vary only in minor respects; upon selfing there is no approach to either of the parental forms, and upon crossing with other species the behaviour of the veitchberry is typically that of a species. Breeding experiments indicate that the veitchberry arose from fusion of unreduced germ-cells. Such cells are of not infrequent occurrence in the genus *Rubus*, e.g. the Mahdi, Laxton, and John Innes berries arose from interspecific hybridization accompanied by the functioning of unreduced germ-cells (Crane and Darlington, 1928).

We are often unable to say how a particular polyploid arose, but it is clear that the functioning of unreduced germ-cells is a frequent method and that in conjunction with hybridization it has played an important part, both in nature and in cultivation, in the origin of new forms and species. But the possibility of cells of aposporic origin being fertilized and giving rise to polyploid forms must also be considered. For example, in the genus *Rubus*, apomixis, resulting in $2n$ purely maternal offspring, appears to be frequent. In this genus many cases of new polyploid forms have also been recorded, and the question arises as to whether the new polyploids always result from unreduced germ-cells, or whether they may not also arise from the union of male germ-cells with $2n$ maternal aposporic cells.

Thus in breeding experiments in progress at Merton, from crossing a female plant of *Rubus vitifolius* ($2n = 56$) with a hermaphrodite raspberry ($2n = 28$), approximately one-half of the seedlings have either male or female flowers and 56 chromosomes. They also have simple three-lobed leaves like their female parent *R. vitifolius*. The majority of the remainder have 42 chromosomes, hermaphrodite flowers, and like their raspberry parent pinnate leaves with five leaflets. Again in a family from *R. nitidioides* crossed *R. thyrsiger* Banning and Focke the majority of the seedlings are in all respects identical with *R. nitidioides*.

Primula kewensis W. Wats. Somatic doubling of the chromosomes also occurs, and the origin of the tetraploid *P. kewensis* provides a good example. As reported by Digby (1912) and later by Newton and Pellew (1929) the sterile diploid hybrid between *P. floribunda* Wall., $2n = 18$, and *P. verticillata* Forsk., $2n = 18$, produced a branch with fertile flowers. From this branch were obtained tetraploid offspring, $2n = 36$, which bred approximately true.

Nicotiana digluta Clausen, $2n = 72$. This species arose from *N. glutinosa* L., $2n = 24$, crossed *N. tabacum* L., $2n = 48$, and is believed to have doubled its chromosome number after fertilization (Clausen and Goodspeed, 1925).

Raphanus-Brassica. Even crosses between genera may give fertile hybrids, e.g. *Raphanus sativus* L. ($2n = 18$) crossed *Brassica oleracea* L. ($2n = 18$) gave the fertile *Raphanus-Brassica* hybrids ($2n = 36$) (Karpechenko, 1928).

Galeopsis tetrahit L. This species has $2n = 32$. Müntzing (1930–2) crossed *G. pubescens* Bess., $2n = 16$, with *G. speciosa* Mill., $2n = 16$. In the F_2 a triploid plant appeared which to some extent resembled the species *G. tetrahit*. This triploid was crossed with *G. pubescens* and gave one seedling, a tetraploid $2n = 32$. The tetraploid was fertile and in all respects similar to *G. tetrahit*. The artificially produced *G. tetrahit* crosses readily with the natural *G. tetrahit* and gives fertile offspring.

Spartina townsendii H. and J. Groves. The history of this species goes back to 1870, when a specimen was collected at the edge of Southampton Water. It appears to have arisen in nature as a hybrid between *S. stricta* Roth, a European species, and *S. alterniflora* Loisel., an American species. The latter species was first reported in Europe at Bayonne in 1803 and near Southampton in 1829. Its introduction was attributed by De Candolle (1855) to shipping from America. Since it was first noticed in 1870 *S. townsendii*, which shows the vigour so common in hybrid polyploids, has spread all round the coasts of Britain and has very largely displaced its parents.

Huskins (1930) found the somatic chromosome numbers to be *S. alterniflora* 70, *S. stricta* 56, *S. townsendii* 126. *S. townsendii* is fertile and breeds practically true.

In this account of the origin of cultivated plants examples have been taken from horticulture rather than from agriculture, and comparatively few examples, chosen to illustrate different methods of origin, have been described. Many more could be cited. In tropical crops and agricultural plants polyploids commonly occur, and their methods of origin appear to be the same as those described for the plants of our gardens. In the cereals the principal crop plant, the bread wheat, is hexaploid. Reference to the origin of *Prunus domestica* and, *Dahlia variabilis* and to the synthesis of *Galeopsis tetrahit* directly shows that the same process takes place in nature, and the way in which the European species *Spartina stricta* and the American species *S. alterniflora* were brought together to give rise to *S. townsendii* is analogous to the way geographical barriers are overcome in cultivation.

It is clear from the foregoing account that no sharp line can be drawn between new hybrid species which are the result of cultivation and new species which have arisen spontaneously in the wild. We can indeed discriminate four groups according to the part cultivation and experiment has played:

(1) New species which have arisen in nature and which on genetical and cytological grounds are believed to be of hybrid origin (*Dahlia variabilis*, *Spartina townsendii*).

(2) Species which have arisen in nature without any human interference, but which are known to be of hybrid origin because they have since been synthesized (*Galeopsis tetrahit*, *Prunus domestica*).

(3) New species from spontaneous crossing of parents which have been brought together in cultivation from distinct habitats, but not otherwise interfered with (*Aesculus carnea*, *Rubus loganobaccus*).

(4) New species raised by deliberate experiment or arising spontaneously after deliberate crossing (*Primula kewensis*, *Digitalis mertonensis*).

Sterility

Sterility has long been known to occur when species are intercrossed. Often it is the result of unbalance in the whole chromosome complement. Numerical differences, too great a dissimilarity, or even too great a similarity in the chromosome complement may lead to reduced fertility or to sterility. In general diploids, tetraploids, hexaploids, &c., which have an even number of chromosome sets are more fertile than triploids, pentaploids, &c., which have an odd number. Apart from other considerations it is obvious that at germ-cell formation an odd number cannot divide evenly, and so irregularities and sterility will inevitably follow. Vegetative and apomictic reproduction, however, sometimes enable such forms and species to maintain and perpetuate themselves.

Among plants derived from the inter-crossing of species all degrees of sterility occur. Such interspecific sterility may occur whether or not the chromosome numbers of the species are equal. The degree of sterility varies from complete failure to obtain seeds from interspecific pollinations to the other extreme where interspecific hybrids are as fertile as the parental species themselves. Complete fertility in such hybrids is, however, exceptional, and following interspecific hybridization some degree of sterility is almost the rule. When complete fertility does occur it often results from an unusual form of reproduction; in other cases the validity of the taxonomic distinction may come under suspicion. Although many related species fail to cross, experience has shown that initial failures cannot be too readily accepted as indicating complete inter-sterility. Many species hybrids, though vigorous and healthy, are completely sterile. In such cases the two sets of chromosomes derived from the respective parents work in harmony throughout the somatic life of the hybrid, but are unable to pass successfully through the more intricate processes of germ-cell formation.

Many sterile plants have by doubling of the chromosome complement given rise to fertile forms, for example *Primula kewensis* and the *Raphanus-Brassica* hybrids of Karpechenko (1928). On the other hand, reduced fertility sometimes results from chromosome doubling. For example, the tomato, *Solanum lycopersicum* L., is a highly fertile diploid plant with 24 chromosomes. By the simple process of decapitation, adventitious shoots may be induced to arise which have 48 chromosomes, and their fertility is greatly reduced. Similarly, in the auto-tetraploid forms of *Primula sinensis* and *Rubus idaeus* fertility is lower than in the diploid forms.

From very considerable evidence it appears possible to predict that the doubling of the chromosomes of sterile hybrids will lead to increased fertility, but in fertile forms will lead to a reduction of fertility. The reason for this apparent contradiction becomes clear when we consider the nature of the chromosome complement in the two kinds of polyploid. An autopolyploid may be represented as *AAAA*, derived from doubling in a fertile diploid *AA*; an allopolyploid as *AABB*, derived from doubling in a more or less sterile diploid *AB*, itself the result of the cross *AA* × *BB*. In the former case the change from two to four identical groups will set up mechanical difficulties in pairing, owing to excess of choice. In the allopolyploid the doubling of *AB* to *AABB* will allow the identical sets *AA* and *BB* to pair, giving gametes all *AB* and identical. The plant will behave as a diploid and fertility will be restored (see Darlington, 1928).

In this account, examples have been given which demonstrate how the sterility barrier between species may be broken down by chromosome duplication. In such cases constant and virtually true-breeding hybrids arise as a result of the pairing within themselves of the two parental chromosome sets. Many new and important races and species of plants have originated in this way, both in nature and under cultivation, and often they have arisen at a single step.

Variation within the Species

Genetics may be defined, at least from one aspect, as the study of uniformity and variation, of resemblances and differences and the frequency with which the characters constituting these resemblances and differences appear from generation to generation. Genetics is thus an intimate and exact study of variation and the variability of variation, not only in morphological characters but also in the chemical and physiological processes of plants. It is upon their hereditary behaviour and phenotypical interactions that genetical conclusions are based, and in conjunction with cytology they often provide reliable means for the determination of taxonomic relationships, and in some cases direct knowledge of the origin of plants.

The consequences of the different methods of origin and of chromosome constitution in plants are seen in various ways, and when we compare the studies of the systematist, the geneticist, and the cytologist a striking parallelism is often found in their results and conclusions. Thus sexual incompatibility, both in inheritance and in its phenotypical behaviour, is a comparatively simple phenomenon in the diploid cherry, *Prunus avium* L.; it is more complex in the hexaploid plum, *Prunus domestica*, while in the more involved secondary polyploid apple it is again more complex than in the plum. There is, that is to say, a direct correlation between the behaviour and frequency of incompatibility and the chromosome number and complexity. Again, the systematist long ago found that he could satisfactorily classify the variation within *Prunus persica* Stokes according to whether individuals had smooth or hairy fruits, eglandular or glandular leaves, and so on. The geneticist found that the mode of inheritance of these characters conformed to the comparatively simple Mendelian rules; and the cytologist found *Prunus persica* to be a simple diploid plant with two sets of eight chromosomes. At the other extreme, attempts to provide a satisfactory classification of apples, *Pyrus malus* L., have been numerous, but systematists continue to find such a classification an involved and difficult task. The geneticist finds their characters difficult to analyse; and finally the cytologist has found them to be secondary polyploids with a complex nuclear constitution.

Although exceptions occur, it is a commonplace to find a more complex and wider range of variation in polyploid species, and especially in high polyploids, than in diploids; compare for example the variation within the diploid *Prunus divaricata* and the tetraploid *P. spinosa* with that of the hexaploid *P. domestica*, also the variation within the tetraploid species of *Dahlia* with that of the octoploid *D. variabilis*. Again variation is commonly sharply discontinuous in diploid species, but in polyploid species it tends to be more of a continuous nature, owing to the presence and action of a greater number of gene-differences. Where two or more genes govern the expression of the same character, as is common in polyploids, their effect is often cumulative and consequently a given character may intergrade from one extreme to the other. Although new species which arise from interspecific hybridization breed true to a new and distinctive type, great variation may occur subsequently as a result of the action and interaction of the many genes brought together.

Vavilov (1926–30) from his researches and wide experience has concluded that the origin of a cultivated plant must be sought in the region where the maximum number of varieties are to be found in a wild state. Such a diversity itself may be evidence of the adaptation of the species-group to that habitat. It may be the meeting area of two or more species; then by hybridization a variable complex, and eventually new races and species, may arise.

In cultivation geographical and ecological barriers are commonly overcome; species distantly separated in nature are brought together and opportunities provided for hybridization, which as in the case of *Aesculus carnea* and the garden strawberry may lead to important results. Is there not good reason to believe that such barriers are broken down from time to time by changes in nature and with similar consequences?

I have confined this account almost entirely to plants which have arisen in a natural or spontaneous way. However, the more direct experimental side of genetical and cytological research, such as the acceleration of mutation and the deliberate induction of polyploidy by the use of chemicals, extremes of temperature, wounding, and X-rays and other radiations, is of great practical and theoretical importance and is likely to lead to far-reaching taxonomic and biological results.

In conclusion, it is clear that the precise results which have been obtained from the study of cultivated plants cannot be neglected by the student of wild species, many of which bear the same relation to one another that cultivated plants bear to their wild ancestors.

REFERENCES

BUNYARD, A. E. (1917). 'The History and Development of the Red Currant.' *J.R.H.S.* **42**, 260–70.

BUXTON, B. H., and DARLINGTON, C. D. (1931). 'Behaviour of a new species *Digitalis mertonensis.' Nature,* **127**, 94.

—— and NEWTON, W.C.F. (1928). 'Hybrids of *Digitalis ambigua and Digitalis purpurea,* their Fertility and Cytology.' *J. Genet.* **19**, 269–79.

CLAUSEN, R. E., and GOODSPEED, T. H. (1925). 'Interspecific Hybridisation in Nicotiana, II. A Tetraploid Glutinosa-Tabacum Hybrid, an Experimental Verification of Winge's Hypothesis.' *Genetics,* **10**, 279–84.

CRANE, M. B. (1921). 'Experiments in breeding Plums.' *J. Pomol.* **2**, 137–59.

—— (1935). 'The Origin of the Pink-flowered Chestnut, *Aesculus carnea.' J.R.H.S.* **60**, 171–6.

CRANE, M. B., and DARLINGTON, C. D. (1927). 'The Origin of New Forms of Rubus.' *Genetica*, **9**, 241–78.

—— and LAWRENCE, W. J. C. (1929). 'Genetical and Cytological Aspects of Incompatibility and Sterility in Cultivated Fruits.' *J. Pomol.* **7**, 276–301.

—— —— (1938). *The Genetics of Garden Plants.* 2nd Ed. London: Macmillan.

DARLINGTON, C. D. (1928). 'Studies in *Prunus* I and II.' *J. Genet.* **19**, 213–56.

—— and MOFFETT, A. A. (1930). 'Primary and Secondary Chromosome Balance in *Pyrus*.' *J. Genet.* **22**, 151.

DE MOL, W. E. (1923). 'Duplication of Generative Nuclei by means of Physiological Stimuli and its Significance.' *Genetica*, **5**, 225–72.

DIGBY, L. (1912). 'The Cytology of *Primula kewensis* and other Related Hybrids.' *Ann. Bot.* **26**, 357–86.

FRANDSEN, H. N., and WINGE, O. (1931). '*Brassica napocampestris*, a New Constant Amphidiploid Species Hybrid.' *Hereditas*, **16**, 212–18.

HENRY, A. (1910). 'On Elm-seedlings showing Mendelian results.' *J. Linn. Soc. (Bot.)*, **39**, 290–300.

HOAR, C. S. (1927). 'Chromosome Studies in Aesculus.' *Bot. Gaz.* **84**, 156–70.

HUSKINS, C. L. (1931). 'The Origin of *Spartina Townsendii*.' *Genetica*, **12**, 531–38.

ICHIJIMA, K. (1926). 'Cytological and Genetic Studies in Fragaria.' *Genetics*, **11**, 590–604.

KARPECHENKO, G. D. (1928). 'Polyploid Hybrids of *Raphanus sativus* L. × *Brassica oleracea* L.' *Zeitschr. indukt. Abstamm.- u. Vererb-Lehre*, **48**, 1–85.

LAWRENCE, W. J. C. (1929). 'The Genetics and Cytology of *Dahlia* Species.' *J. Genet.* **21**, 125–59.

—— (1936). 'On the Origin of New Forms in Delphinium.' *Genetica*, **18**, 109–15.

—— and SCOTT-MONCRIEFF, R. (1935). 'The Genetics and Chemistry of Flower Colour in Dahlia; a New Theory of Specific Pigmentation.' *J. Genet.* **30**, 155–226.

LONGLEY, A. E. (1926). 'Chromosomes and their significance in Strawberry Classification.' *J. agr. Res.* **32**, 559–68.

MARSDEN-JONES, E. M., and TURRILL, W. B. (1930). 'The History of a Tetraploid *Saxifraga*.' *J. Genet.* **23**, 83–92.

—— —— (1934). 'Further Breeding Experiments with *Saxifraga*.' *J. Genet.* **29**, 245–68.

MOFFETT, A. A. (1931). 'The Chromosome Constitution of the Pomoideae.' *Proc. roy. Soc. B*, **108**, 423–46.

MÜNTZING, A. (1932). 'Cyto-genetic Investigations on Synthetic *Galeopsis Tetrahit*.' *Hereditas*, **16**, 105–54.

NEBEL, B. (1929). 'Zur Zytologie von Malus und Vitis.' *Gartenbauwiss.* **1**, 549–92.

NEWTON, W. C. F., and PELLEW, C. (1929). '*Primula kewensis* and its Derivatives.' *J. Genet.* **20**, 405–67.

PHILIP, J. (1934). 'Note on the Cytology of *Saxifraga granulata* L., *S. rosacea* Moench and their Hybrids.' *J. Genet.* **29**, 197–201.

RANDOLPH, L. F. (1935). 'Iris Breeding.' *Cornell Univ. Expt. Sta. Bull.* **324**, 40–51.

RYBIN, V. A. (1936). 'Spontane und experimentell erzeugte Bastarde zwischen Schwarzdorn und Kirschpflaume und das Abstammungsproblem der Kulturpflaume.' *Planta*, **25**, 22–58.

VAVILOV, N. I. (1926). 'Studies on the Origin of Cultivated Plants.' *Bull. appl. Bot. Select.* **16**, 1–248.

—— (1930). 'The Wild Progenitors of the Fruit Trees of Turkistan and the Caucasus.' *Proc. 9th Int. Hort. Cong. London*, 271–86.

THE NEW SYSTEMATICS OF CULTIVATED PLANTS

By N. I. VAVILOV

THE study of cultivated plants in relation to plant-breeding, as well as to a better understanding of the problems of evolution, requires differential systematics. For cultivated plants classification into various Linnean species is only the first step. The plant-breeder, the agronomist, must distinguish not only species but varieties. For this purpose morphological characters represent only the first approach to knowledge. The agronomist is more interested in biological and physiological characters, in the relation of varieties to different diseases, in their behaviour with respect to drought, cold, &c.

It is quite impossible to say how many varieties of soft wheat (*Triticum vulgare* Vill.) exist in the world. There are at least 400 different characters which distinguish the different varieties, and if we take into account that most of these characters may be combined in various ways, we can get some notion of the number of hereditary forms existing in the world (Vavilov, 1936). The same holds true for barley, oats, beans, potatoes, &c.

Practical needs have obliged the systematist of cultivated plants and closely allied wild species to give, in addition to the ordinary key to botanical types and varieties, a scheme of the variation of characters and of the geographical distribution of these characters. The history of the systematics of cultivated plants is very instructive. It shows how step by step the investigator was obliged to differentiate his concept of a species. We have definitely entered the age of the physiological and bio-chemical classification of varieties.

Cultivated species, as well as their closely allied wild relatives, in their evolution, during the course of their distribution from the primary centres of species-formation, have been differentiated into definite ecological and geographical groups. From differential systematics we are coming to differential geography. After many years of collective studies of the most important cultivated plants, with the aid of cytologists, geneticists, physiologists, anatomists, and immunologists, we are coming to *the concept of a Linnean species as a definite, discrete, dynamic system differentiated into geographical and ecological types and comprising sometimes an enormous number of varieties.*

The new classification of cultivated plants constitutes a very extensively branched system. At the same time, and to some extent in opposition to the views of some systematists, our concrete studies have convinced us that the species concept corresponds to reality, that it is necessary not only for the sake of convenience but for a real comprehension of the evolutionary process. Evolution may proceed uninterrupted on its fundamental course, but it has knots in its chain, which are the species, constituting discrete systems of hereditary forms.

In our study of cultivated plants we have advanced step by step. Some twenty years ago, coming to the study of cereals, we soon found that the previously existing classification into botanical varieties based on a few easily determined spike and kernel characters—which was elaborated by the German taxonomist, Friedrich Körnicke, and has been accepted by most investigators, including Professor John Percival in his monograph on the wheat plant (1921)—was not adequate. We found it necessary to elaborate a new, more detailed morphological and physiological system based on a study of the evolution of plants from their primary regions, which are usually characterized by the presence of a great diversity of botanical varieties. As a result of the establishment of the law of homologous series in variation (Vavilov, 1922), according to which closely allied species and genera to a great extent repeat one another in their differentiation, we came to the discovery of a huge number of varieties unknown before. Many expeditions to the various primary regions of the origin of cultivated plants and thorough and many-sided studies (in sowings) of the collected material were conducted by the Institute of Plant Industry of the U.S.S.R. The evolutionary and geographical principle was taken as the chief basis of our studies of the species systems. We have tried as far as possible to follow in detail the steps of evolution from the primary regions where the differentiation into Linnean species took place. Fortunately, the location of these regions may be established on the basis of historical, archaeological, and, particularly, botanical data. Looking backward, we see that we took the correct course. It led to the discovery, even in the case of the most important crops, of an enormous diversity of species and varieties formerly unknown. It suffices to mention that for wheat alone a dozen or so of good new Linnean species have been discovered and hundreds of botanical varieties in the old botanical sense, each of which includes many hereditary forms. From the 191 botanical varieties known to the best monographer of wheat, Professor John Percival, Soviet expeditions have increased the total to over 800. Formerly there was known but one Linnean species of potatoes (*Solanum tuberosum* L.), but during the past decade Soviet expeditions have discovered, with the aid of cytologists, physiologists, and botanists, eighteen new species of cultivated potatoes and dozens of species of wild potatoes, some of them comprising many varieties (Bukasov, 1933). A new world of diversity has been disclosed.

The *Flora of Cultivated Plants of the U.S.S.R.*, which we have started to publish,[1] is a first attempt at a critical survey of the diversity of varieties of important crops on a world scale. Wheat and potatoes give us a good example of how complicated evolution is. From Friedrich Körnicke's very simple scheme of classification of cereals—published in 1885 in his *Handbuch des Getreidebaues*—we are proceeding farther and farther with the opening up of new continents of varieties. Recent detailed studies of Chinese wheats have led us to the necessity of establishing new complex Linnean species, differentiated into a great number of botanical varieties unknown in other parts of the world, although of secondary origin. By crossing different types within the same morphological species genetical differences have been established. Hybrids between different durum wheat types proved to be sterile. Cyclic crosses[2] showed definitely the appearance of many lethals in crosses between Indian and European types of soft wheat.

Plant breeding requires for its purposes not only a knowledge

---

[1] Published to date: Vol. I (Wheat); Vol. II (Rye, Barley, Oats); Vol. IV (Grain Leguminosae); Vol. XVI (Small Fruits); Vol. XVII (Nuts).

[2] By the term 'cyclic crosses' we understand crosses between one definite ecological and geographical type and all other types belonging to the same botanical species. For instance, flax is differentiated into twenty different ecological and geographical types, and by cyclic crossing we mean the crossing of one of these types with all the others.

of morphological botanical varieties but also a knowledge of their differentiation into ecological and physiological groups. What interest plant breeders more than morphological characters are differences in resistance to drought, to cold, to various fungi, bacteria, viruses, and insects, and also biochemical differences between varieties. The needs of practical plant-breeding have brought us to the elaboration of a new, agro-ecological classification of intraspecific diversity—on a world scale, as far as this has been possible for us. This work could only be accomplished with the aid of what we call 'geographical sowings' in different regions, studying the same varieties (collected from all parts of the world) under different conditions, examining their reaction to different parasites, to various environmental conditions.

The 'ecological passport' is based, as a rule, on the following characters:

1. Differences in the vegetative period.
2. Differences in the length of the various developmental phases; also in the rhythm of phasic development.
3. Economic characters, such as the size of fruit and seeds and other quantitative characters.
4. Vegetative characters.
5. Resistance to different kinds of drought.
6. Resistance to cold.
7. Specific characters of flowering: open or closed flowering, &c.
8. Resistance to various fungi: different species of rust, mildew, smut, bunt, &c.
9. Resistance to different bacteria and viruses.
10. Resistance to infestation by various insects.
11. Ecological type of plant: xerophytic, hydrophytic, mesophytic, &c.

It may seem to a biologist that this work is quite endless, taking into account the great diversity of varieties. But this diversity is not without some limit and regularity. In our study of the evolution and systematics of cultivated plants we have established many parallelisms which are especially clear for plants which belong to the same general group (say, annual, herbaceous), are characterized by the same area of distribution, and have followed geographically the same route in their evolution. The comparative study, under various environmental conditions, of the agro-ecological groups of the most important annual crop plants of the Old World, which has recently been conducted by us and our collaborators, has made it possible to establish regularities in the differentiation of species during their evolution.

If we take, for instance, such cereals as wheat (in its diversity of Linnean species), barley, rye, and oats, such grain Leguminosae as peas, lentils, chick-peas, grass-peas (*Lathyrus sativus* L.), vetch (*Vicia sativa* L.), and horse-beans, and such a plant as flax, both seed and fibre forms, all of which originated and started their evolution chiefly in anterior Asia, we may establish their differentiation into definite ecological and geographical groups, showing many similar characters for all of these plants.

Let us briefly describe the chief agro-ecological and geographical groups for these plants:

1. *Syrian Group*. Located chiefly in the foot-hills of Syria, Palestine, and Transjordania, a territory characterized by mild winters and very dry summers, the rains occurring in the late autumn and early spring. To this agricultural territory belongs a definite agro-ecological group of durum and soft wheats, barley, oats, flax, peas, lentils, beans, vetch, chick-peas, and grass-peas. Some of these plants are represented here chiefly by a great number of wild species. Here we find a great diversity of wild wheat, barley, oats, peas, lentils, grass-peas, and chick-peas, side by side with unique cultivated forms closely related to the wild types. All varieties of the above-mentioned plants are characterized by: comparatively small size; resistance to summer drought; earliness; small leaves, fruits, and flowers; thin, stiff stems; non-shattering spikes or pods; need of high temperature when maturing. Both the first stage of development (the vernalization stage) and the second stage are short.

2. *Anatolian Group*. This primary region of distribution of the above-mentioned plants comprises the mountainous part of Turkey, a region characterized by a dry climate and an adequate amount of warmth in the summer-time. The specific characters of varieties of the plants under study are: medium size; thin, stiff stems; seeds, fruits, and spikes medium-sized; short stages of development; plants resistant to drought and

4 B

requiring considerable warmth during the last phases of development. Here are found many wild relatives of these plants.

3. *Armenian Xerophytic Mountain Group.* Occupies the region of arid, mountainous steppes of Soviet and Turkish Armenia. Here, in the specific conditions of the habitat, are concentrated in great diversity a large number of wild relatives of wheat, endemic forms of wild rye (*Secale vavilovii* Gross.), and unique types of weed vetch. Cultivated types of wheat are represented here by peculiar species, some of which show a high degree of xerophily, as, for example, *Triticum vavilovianum* Jakubz., which is extremely resistant to shattering, the grains being firmly enclosed by the chaff, and which at the same time is comparatively winter-resistant. Recently we found here unique types of early, dwarf, small-seeded, xerophytic chick-peas. As a whole, this entire group is characterized by earliness, marked xerophily, small, narrow leaves, and small seeds.

4. *Caucasian Mesophytic High-Mountain Group.* Occupies a large territory of high plateaux in mountainous Daghestan and Georgia, including also the northern part of Armenia, where drought conditions are less severe than in the regions occupied by the preceding group. Here, under the specific conditions of mountainous steppes, were elaborated original ecotypes of soft wheats, prototypes of European steppe winter and spring soft wheats. Here we discovered a new, unique species of 28-chromosome wheat, called by us *Triticum persicum* Var., and a very specific group of barleys with narrow leaves and equal, candelabra development of the stems. The entire group is characterized by small or medium-sized seeds, thin stems, comparatively smooth awns, and a short or medium vegetative period. Here are found in great quantity xerophytic and mesophytic types of wild mountain rye, *Secale montanum* Guss., and also weed rye (*Secale cereale* L.), which frequently infests fields of winter wheat and is represented by a great diversity of red- and brown-coloured forms.

5. *Daghestan-Azerbaijan Foot-hill Group.* The primary region of this group is the coast region of Daghestan and Azerbaijan. Winters here are comparatively mild. Winter sowings of wheat and barley predominate. Here there have developed giant forms of soft and durum wheat, barley, rye, peas, and vetch. The specific characters of this group are: tallness, leafiness,

large seeds, thick stems, long vegetative period, comparative resistance to leaf rust. Here are found winter types of durum wheat unknown in other regions of the world. As a whole, this group is mesophytic. Under favourable conditions it is extremely productive.

6. *Transcaucasian Humid Subtropical Group.* The territory occupied by this group includes primarily the regions of western Georgia and the Black Sea coast, humid regions of Turkey, humid southern regions of Azerbaijan (Lenkoran), and northern regions of Persia. These regions are characterized by excessive humidity and mild winters. They are not far from the primary centre of origin of wheat species. Here there have developed several original, endemic species of wheat, such as *Triticum macha* De kapr. and Men. and *T. timopheevi* Zhuk., and special Georgian types of emmer (*T. dicoccum georgicum* De kapr. and Men.) and of *T. monococcum* L. All the chromosome types of wheat have existed here from times immemorial. Here is the primary centre of late types of prostrate fibre flax with the candelabra form of bush. These varieties of flax are sown in the autumn. Cereals are here chiefly represented by winter, semi-winter, or very late spring varieties. The specific characters of this group are: hydrophily, lateness, tallness, leafiness, and comparatively high resistance to different European fungus diseases.

7. *Iran-Turkestan Group.* Located in irrigated and non-irrigated regions of Iran, Afghanistan, and Soviet Central Asia (Uzbekistan, Tadjikistan, and Turkmenistan). As a whole, this group is characterized by medium or low height, weak stems subject to lodging, slow growth during the early stages of development, drought-resistance during the later stages, need of high temperature at the time of maturing, resistance to shattering, rough spikes, and extreme susceptibility to all European fungus diseases when sown in steppe or wooded-steppe regions of Europe.

To this large group belong also two sub-groups: the Khiva and the Kashgar. The former is located near the mouth of the Amu-Darya river, and is characterized by late varieties of wheat, barley, flax, and peas. The Kashgar group occupies high plateaux near the Pamirs, and includes extremely cold-resistant varieties of soft wheat and comparatively late varieties of unique flax, frequently with white flowers and seeds. The general characteristics of these sub-groups are the same as those given above for the entire Iran-Turkestan group.

8. *Pamir-Badakhshan Group.* Located in Soviet and Afghan Badakhshan, in the Pamir agricultural districts, and also in Chitral and northern Kafiristan, at very high altitudes, reaching 3,000 metres and over above sea-level. On account of the arid conditions irrigation is universally practised. This group also includes types of the Upper Himalayas and Tibet.

Here there has developed a specific group of cultivated plants characterized by a short vegetative period, mesophytic type, medium height, broad leaves, and extreme susceptibility to all European fungus diseases. Here we discovered a gigantic form of spring rye, with large anthers and pollen, large grain, and large spikes. Here also we found unique, recessive types of liguleless soft and club wheat, and recessive forms of rye and peas. Here there is cultivated on a large scale broad-leaved, naked, six-rowed barley. Small-seeded varieties of early peas, beans, and grass-peas are found here.

9. *Indian Group.* Northern India is characterized by very specific types of the crop plants above mentioned. Notwithstanding the diversity of conditions, the Indian group as a whole is comparatively uniform. Here are grown chiefly spring varieties of barley and wheat. In general, all spring varieties of cereals, as well as flax and grain Leguminosae, in India are distinguished by: earliness; non-bushy habit; small, narrow leaves; thin, stiff stems; short stages and rapid rhythm of development; resistance to drought; need of high temperature, especially during the last stages of development; rapid filling out of seeds; and small seeds. The spikes of wheat and barley are not rough; the grain is non-shattering. Some Indian varieties are comparatively susceptible to European fungus diseases.

In Kashmir there is found a distinct sub-group. Kashmir soft wheats are characterized by long, narrow leaves, medium height, thin stems, winter habit, small kernels, comparatively smooth awns, and less susceptibility to leaf-rust than those of the Iran-Turkestan group.

10. *Arabian Mountain Group.* Here in Yemen (Arabia Felix), under conditions of high-mountain agriculture subjected to the influence of the surrounding deserts, there has been elaborated a specific, very early, spring group of annual plants, character-

ized by dwarfism (nanism), extremely rapid growth, narrow leaves, thin, stiff stems, and comparatively large seeds.

11. *Abyssinian Group*. Agriculture is carried on here, as in Eritrea, chiefly at an altitude of 1,800–3,000 metres. In general, this region is characterized by a comparatively humid climate during the period of vegetation. Here are cultivated only spring varieties of cereals. Agriculture is non-irrigated. In Abyssinia we distinguish two ecological sub-groups. One embraces varieties which are sown at the beginning of the main rainy season; the other varieties sown at the close of the rainy season. The first group is represented by hydrophytic, cosmopolitan types of tall, large-seeded varieties of barley and peas. Abyssinian wheats, though not so cosmopolitan, may also be classed in this sub-group. The second group, which includes flax, chick-peas, lentils, beans, and grass-peas, as well as a specific Arabian type of pea, is represented by early, low, small-leaved, small-seeded, xerophytic types. This latter group of plants is very likely linked in its origin with India and mountainous Arabia. The first group is more specific for Abyssinia, and is extremely diverse botanically.

12. *Chinese-Japanese Group*. This group, as a whole, is distinguished by great diversity as regards vegetative period—from very early spring and winter types to late spring and semi-winter types. Very likely the original material was brought several millennia ago from anterior Asia by way of India, but very important new characters have been elaborated. The entire group is characterized by low or medium height, short stages of development, extremely small seeds, and rapid filling out of the grain. In China many varieties of wheat have proved to be resistant to brown and yellow rust. A special physiological property of Chinese barleys and wheats is the rapid filling out of the grain, which is correlated with small kernels and short awns or the absence of awns. Although this peculiar group is doubtless secondary, which is proved by the complete absence in China of closely allied wild types and the limited number of Linnean species of wheat, yet there have developed here during several millennia of cultivation unique types of wheat characterized by rapid filling out of the kernels and by beardless, many-flowered spikelets. In the southern and central regions of China there are many types of wheat immune to leaf rust.

13. *Mediterranean Group.* Occupies the coast regions of the Mediterranean, characterized by mild winters and the concentration of rain chiefly in the late autumn and early spring. Although cereals are sown here, as a rule, in late autumn, spring varieties predominate. The specific characters of this group are: comparative tallness, large seeds, large spikes, long awns, straw usually solid. The first stage of development is of medium length, the second short. All annual Mediterranean species are characterized by rapid development at the beginning of vegetation. They show comparatively little resistance to cold. The entire group is resistant to atmospheric drought during the last phases of development and requires comparatively much warmth during maturation. *A special feature of this group is the presence of a great many varieties resistant to fungus diseases, such as leaf-rust, smut, and bunt, and to other parasitic diseases.* As a whole, this group is very productive under good conditions of growth. Plants are usually bushy and are directly the opposite of the Indian group as far as size of fruits and seeds are concerned. The Mediterranean group is characterized by a predominance of light-coloured seeds.

14. *Egyptian Group.* Egyptian forms of barley and durum wheat, grown chiefly on irrigated fields, are characterized by low, stiff stems, short duration of the first and second stages of development, and medium-sized spikes. Similar types are found on the island of Cyprus.

15. *South-European Group.* Occupies the territory of southern France, northern Italy, part of Jugoslavia, and the coast regions of Bulgaria. The climate is comparatively mild. The chief characteristics of this group are tallness and large leaves, fruit, and grain. Here are concentrated very productive types, the result of many years of cultivation and selection, such as the extremely productive *Triticum turgidum* L., with large spikes, long awns, and large grain. Even the soft wheats of this group are characterized by large spikes and grain. In Lombardy we found very large-grained forms of soft wheat, approaching *T. polonicum* L. in length of grain. Here are also found giant forms of oats, chick-peas, and horse beans.

16. *European Steppe Group.* Occupies the extensive territory of the European steppes from Tyrol to the Urals. Here is located a unique group of spring and winter xerophytic types

of cereals and grain Leguminosae, the winter types being characterized by winter resistance and the spring types by drought resistance. The seeds are comparatively small, the straw not very stiff and subject to lodging, the leaves narrow, and the plants drought-resistant. Here are found in abundance winter types of soft wheat (bearded Banat type) and also beardless spring soft wheat (Poltavka type). Rye is represented here by extremely winter-resistant forms with light-coloured spikes. Steppe oats, as, for instance, the varieties 'Kherson' and 'Rykhlik', and steppe barleys are distinguished by their drought-resistance. Here medium-sized forms of seed flax are cultivated on a large scale.

This group was later transferred to North America, and is now widely cultivated in Canada and the United States, being concentrated chiefly in steppe and wooded-steppe regions. This steppe group may be divided into two ecological subgroups: the arid steppe and the humid steppe.

17. *West European Group*. Located in the lowlands of western Europe, including England, southern Finland, southern Sweden, a great part of northern Germany, northern France, Belgium, and Holland. This group is represented chiefly by typical hydrophytes, tall plants with large, broad leaves, thick, stiff stems, large, dense, productive spikes, and large or medium-sized grain. Almost all varieties are late. Here are located chiefly very productive varieties requiring good cultivation and plenty of fertilizer, such as squarehead wheats, brewing barleys, &c.

This group may be divided into two sub-groups. The first comprises local, primary types, characterized by lax spikes, tallness, and comparative earliness. The second sub-group comprises newly selected forms, such as squarehead wheats, dense-eared brewing barleys, Petkus type of rye, &c. It is characterized by dense spikes, high productivity, and late maturity.

18. *Central European Group*. Located chiefly in the forest and wooded-steppe regions of Europe. This group is mesophytic in type. Here are found typical long-fibre flax, European productive types of peas, and beardless winter varieties of soft wheat. As a whole, this group is comparatively productive.

19. *Northern (Boreal) Group*. Occupies the northern part of the

U.S.S.R., Siberia, and northern Scandinavia. This entire group is characterized by comparative earliness and medium size. The plants do not require much heat. The whole group is meso-hydrophytic in type. The first stage of development is short, the second long in accord with the long, northern summer day. The specific characters of this group are: low requirements as regards temperature, compaative cold-resistance, long second stage of development. In this group we found self-fertile rye and very early types of forage barley.

Some of the above-enumerated groups are so sharply defined that if, not knowing the evolutionary stages, one were to compare the extreme representatives of different groups, one might think that they belonged to different botanical species.

If we compare the behaviour of different species and genera in their differentiation into agro-ecological and geographical groups, we cannot but note many parallelisms not only in morphological characters but also in physiological and biological properties. This has led us to the establishment of the regions where definite types with definite physiological and morphological characters are located. Now we know in which regions of the world we must look for definite genotypes. We know where productive, large-seeded forms are located, where to look for plants with solid straw, for varieties resistant to definite fungus diseases.

Eastern Asiatic agricultural regions, including China and Japan, are characterized by the development of beardless or semi-bearded, small-seeded, dwarf types of barley, wheat, and rye. Here, and only here, were elaborated during the course of evolution beardless varieties of barley and small-seeded varieties of wheat with many florets per spikelet. In the Mediterranean region we established an enormous accumulation of forms immune to different fungus diseases. Central Asiatic varieties of barley, soft wheat, rye, oats, peas, and flax are, on the other hand, extremely susceptible to European fungi .

We have mentioned here only the chief agro-ecological groups of the world for wheat, barley, rye, oats, grain Leguminosae, and flax. In regions where the conditions present intermediate characteristics we find intermediate ecotypes, but usually all the above-enumerated ecotypes are very sharply defined. During recent centuries the crops mentioned were introduced into America and Australia, but even here under the new conditions it is still possible to follow all the main agro-ecological groups of the Old World. Only during the past few decades has the hybridization of different ecological groups been accorded some attention.

It is clear enough that physiological and immunological studies of varieties require much time and work. The very methods of such studies need further elaboration, but by these complex methods we are beginning to understand anew the whole process of differentiation and evolution of cultivated plants. Differential systematics sheds a new light on this process. We are beginning to understand the role of natural and artificial selection and the role of the environment in the formation of definite ecological types.

The whole system of differentiation of Linnean species is represented by the following series. First of all, the species is divided into various ecological and geographical types, which correspond to the *proles* of systematists. Then these geographical types (proles) may be divided for convenience into botanical varieties, according to a few easily defined morphological characters. Lastly, the botanical varieties ('varietas' of the old systematics of cultivated plants) are divided into forms, which correspond to the commercial varieties of plant-breeders.

The practical plant-breeder uses this material as bricks with which he must construct new forms. He now knows where to find definite construction material. The modern systematist, armed with physiology, cytology, genetics, and immunology, provides the practical plant-breeder with a new scientific foundation. The whole study of the initial material in plant-breeding is now quite different from what it was a few years ago. Modern differential systematics is elaborating a new chapter in plant-breeding, the knowledge of the initial material. On the basis of the differential study of the evolution and geography of species, it gives to the plant-breeder all his necessary constructional materials.

The next step, after establishing the definite agro-ecological groups elaborated during the evolutionary process, is to determine the best combinations for hybridization. This may be achieved by cyclic crossing of different ecological types. Phenotypes are not genotypes, and by cyclic crossing it is possible to determine the best combinations. We shall give here only one example.

For a long time it was considered impossible to improve the local fibre flaxes of northern Russia, which are regarded as the best types of fibre flax and are the result of a long process of natural selection. Crosses with different ecological types of north Russian seed flax resulted in diminishing the length of the fibre. Many crosses made resulted in a decrease in the height of the flax plant and in a deterioration in the quality of the fibre. Most flax breeders came to the conclusion that crossing northern fibre types with other ecological and geographical groups could only result in spoiling the qualities of the fibre types. The capsules and seeds might be bigger as a result of such crosses, but the stems were always shorter. However, at last, as a result of cyclic crossing of different ecological types, it has been found that, by crossing north Russian fibre flax with the prostrate winter type from humid Transcaucasian regions, which is characterized by the candelabra type of bush with comparatively many and short stems, a great increase in size is obtained. The hybrids are one-third taller than even the best fibre types. At the same time, many of these hybrids have the candelabra type of bush, i.e. they have many long, equal stems, instead of a single stem as is characteristic of ordinary northern fibre flax. Thus, by a careful study of all the evolutionary types of flax and by utilizing them in cyclic crosses, new possibilities for increasing the production of fibre flax have been revealed.

We could give many examples of analogous cases for wheat, barley, rye, maize, and grain Leguminosae.

Such detailed studies have brought us to the elaboration of a new geography of cultivated plants, to the establishment and localization of definite steps in the evolutionary process. The evolution of cultivated plants is connected in time and space with the role of man in the selection and remoulding of plants. The enormous varietal diversity which is now available for plant-breeders may be comprehended and systematized only in the light of the theory of evolution. The evolutionary steps may be followed in much greater detail than they could before these recent investigations. For many important cultivated plants of the Old World the initial steps of the process of differentiation into Linnean species may be followed in the Caucasus and in south-eastern and south-western Asia. The mountainous regions of southern Mexico, Central America, and the South American Andes show very clearly the evolutionary steps of differentiation for many New World crop plants. Here one may actually observe the links which connect wild and cultivated types. The study of closely allied wild species has proved to be of extreme importance, since very frequently important characters, such as immunity to diseases and resistance to cold and drought, are peculiar to these wild species. The very limits between cultivated and wild forms are in many cases not sharply expressed during the first evolutionary steps.

In the Kopet-Dagh mountains of Soviet Central Asia (Turkmenistan) it is possible even now to observe all intermediate forms between wild and cultivated types in the case of such crops as almonds, figs, pistachios, walnuts, and grapes. In eastern Transcaucasia it is possible to follow in detail the whole evolutionary series, from typical, small-fruited, sour and bitter, wild pomegranates and quinces to extremely large, sweet, cultivated forms. The same may be observed in the Caucasus and other regions with respect to other plants, such as wheat, rye, oats, and hemp. Our differential taxonomic studies bring us to an understanding of the different evolutionary steps. Even for such crops as wheat, barley, maize, and flax, where the divergence between wild and cultivated types is very sharp, detailed geographical and taxonomic studies have revealed new links, which enable us to understand the successive stages in the differentiation of species and their relation to wild types. For many European plants anterior Asia, including Transcaucasia, has proved to be of extreme importance in this respect. Here are concentrated plant riches of species and even of genera; here may be followed the initial steps in the species-formation of many cultivated plants. Here, there have already been discovered many new wild and cultivated species of wheat and rye and an enormous number of new varieties and characters. The geographical and climatological differentiation of these mountainous regions has facilitated the differentiation of plants into definite agro-ecological types. Here, on a comparatively small territory, are found not only morphological differences but also great physiological differences.

The whole problem of the origin and evolution of cultivated plants now appears in a new light. We are beginning to acquire a definite understanding of the differences between primary and secondary regions. The mutation process and the genesis of new forms are going on everywhere, but the rate differs in different places. Primary regions are at present characterized, as a rule, by the presence of many different species (in the sense of Linnaeus). They reveal practically the entire systems of genera. Transcaucasia, for instance, as regards wheat, rye, flax, peas, lentils, vetch, and chick-peas, is characterized by the presence of a great diversity of Linnean species and closely allied wild genera. Here, among wild and cultivated species of wheat, we have found all the basic chromosome sets ($2n = 14$, 28, 42). Here we have found many endemic species. Here we may trace all the links between wild and cultivated types. Here, in the great diversity of conditions specific for mountainous Caucasus as regards humidity, temperature, &c., we have established the presence of a great ecological and physiological diversity of species and varieties of wheat. The same applies to all the other investigated crops.

Secondary regions, as well as primary regions, may be of great importance for practical plant-breeding. Chinese wheats and barleys, which no doubt are of secondary origin but which have been elaborated during the last four or five thousand years, show many original characters, which have made their appearance as a result of mutation and selection under the specific conditions of intensive cultivation and particularly of the monsoon climate, which favoured the natural selection of early maturing, small-seeded, beardless, or short-bearded types.

Systematics, in our understanding, is the basis of knowledge of the plant and animal kingdoms. It was not by mere chance that the greatest evolutionist, Charles Darwin, started his work from systematics.

Some biologists are of the opinion that the age of classical systematics is at an end. From our personal experience we have come to the conclusion that even for cultivated plants, such as wheat, potatoes, and fruits, this is not quite so. For there are vast areas in South America, Central America, and southern Asia with enormously rich floras, which have not yet been studied even superficially. If we say this from our experience with cultivated plants, it is still more applicable to wild floras. Thousands and thousands of new species are yet to be discovered. And the lack of even such superficial knowledge is a great hindrance to our general understanding of the flora and fauna of the world. The basic biological work, which must embrace a knowledge of the entire flora and fauna of the world, is not yet finished, even in its first approach, i.e. in the Linnean understanding of species. But from what we have already said here it is sufficiently clear that we regard classical systematics, which works only with Linnean species, as merely a first step in biological knowledge and quite superficial for the purposes of practical plant and animal breeding. Nor does it satisfy the requirements of a thorough study of species from an evolutionary point of view.

We are now entering an epoch of differential, ecological, physiological, and genetic classification. It is an immense work. The ocean of knowledge is practically untouched by biologists. It requires the joint labours of many different specialists—physiologists, cytologists, geneticists, systematists, and biochemists. It requires the international spirit, the co-operative work of investigators throughout the whole world. The most remarkable regions of the world, the cradles of primitive civilizations—the mountainous regions of southern Asia, Central and South America—are still in need of investigation even as to their resources of cultivated plants and domestic animals.

We do not doubt that the new systematics will bring us to a new and better understanding of evolution, to a great increase in the possibilities of governing the processes of evolution, and to great improvement in our cultivated plants and domestic breeds of animals. It will bring us logically to the next step: integration and synthesis.

REFERENCES

BUKASOV, S. M. (1933). 'The Potatoes of South America and their Breeding Possibilities.' *Bull. Appl. Bot., Gen., and Plantbr.*, Suppl. **58**, 192 pp. (In Russian; English summary, pp. 154–92.) Leningrad.

Flora of Cultivated Plants of the U.S.S.R. (1935–   ). Vols. I, II, IV, XVI, and XVII published to date. (In Russian.) Leningrad.

KÖRNICKE, F., and WERNER, H. (1885). *Handbuch des Getreidebaues.* Vol. I. *Die Arten und Varietäten des Getreides.* Berlin.

PERCIVAL, J. (1921). *The Wheat Plant; a Monograph.* London.

VAVILOV, N. I. (1922). 'The Law of Homologous Series in Variation.' *J. Genet.* **12**, 47.

—— (1936). *Scientific Bases of Wheat Breeding.* (In Russian.) Leningrad.

INDEX OF NAMES

4 D

INDEX OF SUBJECTS